The arts applied
Catalogue 29

B. Weinreb Architectural Books Ltd

93 Great Russell Street London WC1B 3QL

telephone: 01-636 4895
cables: wedou London

The arts applied

A CATALOGUE OF BOOKS

edited by Denise Chafer

*furniture · interior design · murals · mosaics · ceilings
exhibitions · ceramics
metalwork · jewelry · textiles · vases · ornament*

some original drawings

B. Weinreb Architectural Books Ltd

Published by B. Weinreb Architectural Books Ltd 1975
Copyright © B. Weinreb Architectural Books Ltd

Catalogued and annotated by
Denise Chafer & Hugh Pagan

Photographs by Joe Greenbury and Joe Hajnal
Printed by Robert Stockwell Ltd
Baden Place London SE1

Contents

Furniture, woodwork, carving, marquetry — *page* 7

Interior design, decoration, painting, plasterwork, panelling, chimneypieces — 49

Murals, mosaics, ceilings, floors, decorative wall paintings — 93

Design and exhibitions, industrial design, Arts & Crafts — 111

Metalwork — 129

Gold, silver and jewelry, pewter, engraved and antique stones — 145

Ceramics — 163

Glass, stained and painted glass, bottles, drinking glasses — 187

Fabrics and textiles, tapestries, carpets, papers, lace, needlework, embroidery — 199

Ornament and applied decoration — 211

Vases — 247

'Frustum'
  General — 257
  Sales catalogues and special collections — 265
  Collectable objects — 269
  Clocks, watches and precision instruments — 272

Original drawings and watercolours — 277

References

The following standard works are those most frequently referred to in the item descriptions.

Abbey Life: Life in England in aquatint and lithography 1770-1860 ... from the library of J. R. Abbey. A bibliographical catalogue. London 1953

Abbey Scenery: Scenery of Great Britain and Ireland in aquatint and lithography 1770-1860 from the library of J. R. Abbey. A bibliographical catalogue. London 1952

Berlin Cat: Katalog der Ornamentstisch-Sammlung der Staatlichen Kunstbibliothek Berlin. Berlin 1939

Destailleur Notices: H. Destailleur. Notices sur quelques artists français, architects, dessinateurs, graveurs du XVIe au XVIIIe siècle. Paris 1863

Destailleurs Cat 1895: Catalogue de livres et estampes relatifs aux beaux-arts provenant de la bibliotheque de feu M. Hippolyte Destailleur. Paris 1895

Cicognara: Catalogo ragionato dei libri d'arte e d'antichità posseduti dal Conte Cicognara. Pisa 1821

Fairfax Murray: Catalogue of a collection of early French books in the library of C. Fairfax Murray. London 1910

Fowler: The Fowler Architectural Collection of The Johns Hopkins University. Baltimore 1961

Guilmard: Les maîtres ornementistes ... par D. Guilmard. Paris 1880

Harvard Cat: Harvard College Library Department of Printing and Graphic Arts. Catalogue of books and manuscripts. Part I: French 16th century books. Cambridge Massachusetts 1964

McLean: R. McLean. Victorian book design and colour printing. London 1963

Nagler Mon: G. K. Nagler. Die Monogrammisten ... Munich 1835-52

We can supply copies of most of these books.

In-print books

For the sake of completeness we have included in the catalogue a range of in-print books at their published price at the time of going to press. Since increases in the prices of these books are not directly within our control we regret that in some cases we will have to charge the price current at the time of supply.

Furniture

1a

1 **Diderot, D. & J. L. d'Alembert** (Encyclopédie) Recueil de planches sur les sciences, les arts libéraux, les arts méchaniques, avec leurs explications *Paris, Briasson, David, Le Breton & Durand 1762-72; Livorno 1772-1779*

Although complete sets of the 'Encyclopédie' (see also item 1701) are difficult to find incomplete volumes turn up from time to time of both the original plates and those of the third edition. For the Livorno edition the plates were redrawn copying the original illustrations and are frequently of a higher quality of execution than those of the first edition. From odd volumes of both editions we have been able to select series of suites appropriate to the subjects in this catalogue. They all show, in varying detail, a workshop scene, tools of the trade and related machinery and processes, and are particularly suitable for display or exhibition purposes. The extracts below comprise complete sections on the various occupations related to furniture and fittings. The detailed engravings are accompanied by letterpress sheets of explanatory text. Each section listed is folio and the plates, whose sizes average 360 × 225mm, are preserved in a paper wallet.

a **Menuisier en meubles** (Cabinet-maker)
A vivid picture of a cabinet-maker's workshop showing the processes of sawing planks, cutting out the pieces, planing the wood and roughing out the frames. Other plates include detailed illustrations of the construction of chairs, benches, armchairs, chaise-longues, beds, cupboards and tables, with the tools in current use and even various types of caning for chair seats. *20 engraved plates with 594 illustrations, and 5 + (1 blank) pp text.* **Illustration above.** £40

b **Ebénisterie-marqueterie** (Cabinet-maker & veneerer)
Beginning with another lively workshop scene, figures 2-60 show designs for commodes, chest of drawers, tables, cupboards, screens, desks, bookcases, gaming tables, dressing tables, chess and backgammon boards, music stands, pedestals and

clockcases. Then follows a plate of designs for inlaid floors and wall panelling, a plate of inlay metal designs (copper, pewter, tin etc with shell, ivory and wood), a plate of work benches and vices and a final plate of tools (much the same as those in use today). *11 plates with 118 illustrations, and 2pp of text.* £35

c **Menuisier en voitures** (Coach-frame maker)
Not exactly the makers of interior furniture pieces but included in this group since the technical practices form part of the furniture-maker's trade. The carriage workshop view has carpenters busy at four benches and the frames of different types of carriages standing around. The plates show the various types of carriage: Berlin, a barouche, an English stage-coach, a two-wheeled carriage, a post-chaise, a gig, a four-seater garden coach, a vis-à-vis and a sedan chair, and include details of the various parts of the frame, profiles and mouldings and end with plates of bores, planes, templates and other tools. *30 engraved plates with over 600 illustrations, and 5+(1 blank)pp.* £45

d **Sellier-carrossier** (Coach-builder)
This section provides a continuation to the previous suite devoted as it is to the coach maker and shows the coaches and carriages listed above finished and fitted out with all their exterior parts richly ornamented. 14 larger double-page plates show beautiful drawings of the completed vehicles surrounded by details of their decorative parts and a plan of the chassis. *25 engraved plates of which 14 double-page, and 4pp text.* £70

e **Tapissier** (Upholsterer)
Aspects of the upholstery and soft furnishing trade with a splendid large double-plate workshop view showing finished pieces, rolled mattresses, bales of cloth, workers sewing hangings and curtains, the master examining an upholstered chair and a glimpse inside the front shop. The illustrations include diagrams of the different seams and stitches employed, complete designs for beds, chairs, settees, stools, screens and draperies, with examples of appliquéd motifs and various stages in the upholstering of a chair, together with the tools employed. *14 engraved plates of which 4 double-page with 63 illustrations and 2pp text.* £55

2 Ackermann, R(ichard) The upholsterer's and cabinetmaker's repository: consisting of seventy-six designs of modern and fashionable furniture ... drawn, by various artists, from real furniture London, R. Ackermann (c 1815)
A separate issue of a selection of the furniture plates from Ackermann's 'The Repository of Fine Arts', the magazine which disseminated current ideas and taste in the arts, dress, decoration and architecture during the Regency period. The majority of its 240 parts contained one plate devoted to furniture or interior decoration. These featured the designs of individual cabinet-makers and craftsmen such as George Smith (see items 196, 197) who was responsible for many of the early plates, George Bullock, a friend of Walter Scott, who designed many of the interiors at Abbotsford, John Taylor who produced furniture pattern books of his own, and included early Gothic interiors by Augustus Pugin. Large commercial firms were also represented, often in a number of successive plates: one of the most important was Morgan & Sanders who provided the furniture for Trafalgar House and appeared often in the early issues, later were featured Snell of Albemarle Street who specialized in French furniture, and the pieces of Morell & Hughes who provided the furniture for Syon House, while John Stafford, an upholsterer from Bath, provided a series of fashionable window draperies between 1812 and 1814.
The reissue of the furniture plates as a separate work with its own title-page seems to have occurred about 1815, some time after the completion of the first series and was originally devoted to the plates of those first 84 parts. Later the same title-page appears to have been issued with a selection of plates from all the parts as in the Abbey copy (see Abbey: Life in England, No 1).
This present copy contains the plates from the First Series, 1809-1815. Quarto. *Letterpress title and 76 etched and aquatinted plates in contemporary hand colouring. Average size of plates 150 × 235mm. Some plates remargined to give a uniform outer size. Preserved in quarter morocco drop-backed box.* £385

3 (Adam, Robert) **Harris Eileen** The furniture of Robert Adam London, Tiranti 1963
The first full scale examination and assessment of Adam's furniture style which gives an account of the origin, development and character of Adam furniture with an inventory of the designs and evaluation of their place in English and French neo-classical furniture. Octavo. *viii+122pp with 5 text illustrations, and 156 photographic illustrations on 124 plates. Publisher's cloth.* £4

4 **Adams, Maurice** Modern Furniture *(London 1931)*
Trade catalogue of Adams' own firm, illustrating his range of furniture designs in a modern idiom–'purpose beautifully and truthfully expressed without needless or useless ornament'. *Quarto. 16pp with many photo illustrations. Original printed wrappers.*
£20

5 **Andrews, Edward Deming & Faith** Shaker furniture. The craftsmanship of an American communal sect *New York, Dover 1950*
Quarto. xii+134pp and 48 photographic plates. Original wrappers. £1.65

6 **Aslin, Elizabeth** Nineteenth century English furniture *London, Faber 1962*
Brief but convenient work of reference covering the main designers and design trends. *Octavo. 96pp with 4 colour plates and 96pp of photographic illustrations. Original cloth.*
£5.50

7 **(Baillie Scott, M. H.)** Furniture made at the Pyghtle Works Bedford by John P. White. Designed by M. H. Baillie Scott *(Bedford 1901)*
A range of 82 items of furniture executed in Baillie Scott's best Arts and Crafts manner, with a no nonsense introduction asserting that 'there are at least some who are equally dissatisfied with the old ugliness or the new vulgarity posing as Art, and who wish merely for furniture which shall be simply and reasonably constructed'. *Quarto. 8pp text and 46pp of plates with 82 illustrations of which 8 coloured. Original decorated wrappers, preserved in cloth folder.*
£95

8 **Bemrose, William** Manual of wood carving with practical instructions for learners of the art, and original and selected designs ... with an introduction by Llewellynn Jewitt. Twenty-first edition *London, Bemrose (c 1905)*
A manual first published in 1862. Bemrose (1831-1908), head of the Derby firm of printers, was the author of a number of publications intended for the amateur woodcarver and for the collector of porcelain. *Quarto. 72+(8)pp including 20 plates. Original decorated cloth.*
£12

9 **Bemrose, William** Fret cutting and perforated carving with practical instructions. Sixth edition *London, Bemrose (c 1870)*
Bemrose followed up the success of his 'Manual of Wood Carving' with this book on a type of carving not covered in the 'Manual'. It has attractive lithograph plates of fretwork. *Quarto. 14pp and 53 illustrations on 64pp of litho plates. Quarter calf. Ex library copy, some foxing.*
£12

10 **Berain, J(ean)** (Commodes et lustres.) Suite A *(Paris, the author c 1680)*
These furniture designs are some of Berain's most interesting work. They show 'commodes-tombeaux', a new article of furniture invented by Boulle and derived from the form of antique sarcophagi. They are accompanied by designs for several smaller pieces including chandeliers using Berain's favourite motifs: unicorns, winged griffons, winged masks, etc. First issue. In the later collected edition of the works a further plate was added to this suite. Berlin Cat 343. Guilmard p90. *Untitled suite of 4 engraved plates, average size 330 × 285mm, with large margins. In paper wallet.* £65

11 **Bergeron, L. E.** Manuel du tournier ... ouvrage dans lequel on enseigne aux amateurs la manière d'exécuter ... tout ce que l'art peut produire d'utile et d'agréable; précédé de notions élémentaires sur la connoissance des bois, la menuiserie (etc.). Seconde édition revue, corrigée, et considérablement augmentée par P. Hamelin-Bergeron *Paris, Hamelin-Bergeron 1816*
A substantial work on turning, interesting for its information on technique and for its illustrations of tools and 72 different cabinet woods (each handcoloured). *Quarto. 3 volumes. xxxii+509+(1)pp; xi+(1)+542pp; engraved title and 39 engraved plates (8 handcoloured and 21 folding), printed part title and 57 engraved plates (36 folding). Half brown morocco, marbled paper boards, untrimmed. Signature of Hamelin-Bergeron on verso of half title of vol 1.*
£185

12 **Berlage, H. P.** Over stijl in bouw- en meubelkunst *Amsterdam, Soep (1904)*
First edition. A history of furniture styles and their relation to social, political and cultural events by the leader of the 'Amsterdam School' of architecture. *Octavo. 130pp with 38 text illustrations by the author. Original decorated cloth.* £25

13 **Berlage, H. P.** Over stijl in bouw- en meubelkunst. Tweede geheel verbeterde druk *Rotterdam, Brusse 1908*
Second edition with the text illustrations from different blocks and the text reset, though the contents are unchanged. *Octavo. 131+(5)pp with 38 text illustrations. Original decorated cloth.* £18

14 **Boucher, (Juste-François)** (Cahiers d'ameublement et décoration) *Paris, Le Pere & Avaulez (c 1775)*
The appearance of the engraved designs of the younger Boucher, son of the painter, marked the complete attainment of the Louis XVI style. His inventions covered a wide range of objects and those conceived in the purely classical style he labelled 'à la moderne' thus designating neo-classical forms the latest fashion, as opposed to the outmoded extravagances of the rococo. The following are the parts of his complete works which are devoted to furniture pieces and are made up from the original edition. Guilmard p230. Berlin Cat 1267. (See also item 330).

a **1er Cahier. Lits**
Beds of various types with low boards and baldaquins. *Six plates, average size 325 × 200mm. In paper wallet.* **Illustration below.** £48

b **2e Cahier. Lits**
Includes a wide variety of alcove beds. *Six plates, average size 330 × 200mm. In paper wallet.* £48

14a

c **4e Cahier. Sièges**
Chairs, stools and upholstered benches. *Six plates, average size 210 × 320mm. In paper wallet.* £42

d **7e Cahier. Commodes**
Commodes with drawers, supported on short legs, and all except one design in the rectilinear style. *Six plates, average size 210 × 320mm. In paper wallet.* £42

e **8e Cahier. Commodes**
Commodes with drawers in designs of both curved and rectilinear form. *Six plates, average size 220 × 325mm. In paper wallet.* £42

f **9e Cahier. Sécretaires et demies commodes**
Drop-fronted writing desks and small chests of drawers. *Six plates, average size 195 × 320mm. In paper wallet.* £42

g **11e Cahier. Bureaux plats**
Very neo-classical tables ornamented with swags masks and rosettes. *Six engraved plates, average size 195 × 320mm. In paper wallet.* £36

h **12e Cahier. Cippes, gaines, piédestaux**
A variety of stands for supporting busts, urns, etc. Very good garden ornament designs. *Six engraved plates, average size 215 × 320mm. In paper wallet.* £18

i **14e Cahier. Gaines et piédestaux**
Eighteen designs for pedestals and supports. *Six plates, average size 205 × 330mm. In paper wallet* £18

k **16e Cahier. Demies commodes, petites bibliothèques**
Narrow, low cupboards and corner cabinets. *Six plates, average size 205 × 330mm. In paper wallet.* £36

l **17e Cahier. Petites chiffonières, tables, vides-poches**
Bedside tables and small cabinets with doors, fall fronts, or small series of drawers. *Six plates, average size 200 × 330mm. In paper wallet.* £24

m **18e Cahier. Sécretaires, serre-papiers**
Cylindrical and fall-front desks, writing tables with pigeon hole cabinets, and small jewellery cabinets. *Six plates, average size 200 × 235mm. In paper wallet.* £42

n **19e Cahier. Consoles**
Console tables of strictly neo-classical form. *Six engraved plates, average size 200 × 330mm. In paper wallet.* £30

o **20e Cahier. Consoles**
Console tables with a wider variety of form and decoration including leaf and garland hanging swags. *Six engraved plates, average size 325 × 200mm. Two plates trimmed into plate mark on right with loss of between 10 and 15mm, but not affecting illustration. In paper wallet.* £22

p **28e Cahier. Armoires, encoignures, petites bibliothèques**
Corner cupboards, small bookcases, and the tiers of shelves which usually surmount such pieces. *Six engraved plates, average size 200 × 325mm. In paper wallet.* £36

15 **Bowers, R. S.** (and others) Furniture making. Designs, working drawings, and complete details of 170 pieces of furniture, with practical information on their construction. By R. S. Bowers, John Bovingdon and other designer-craftsmen *London, Cassell 1920*
These designs, 'suitable for cultured homes', first appeared in 'Work', 'the Weekly Journal of Handicrafts', and were re-drawn for this book. *Octavo. viii + 408pp with 1082 text illustrations. Original cloth.* £4

16 **Brackett, Oliver** (editor) An encyclopaedia of British furniture. A pictorial review of English furniture from Gothic times to the mid-nineteenth century *London, Benn 1927*
Quarto. vii + (1) + 14pp and 310pp of plates. Original cloth, rebacked. £12

17 **Bridgens, R(ichard)** Furniture with candelabra and interior decoration *London, William Pickering 1838*
A special interleaved copy with fine hand colouring of a very influential early Victorian book containing furniture and decoration in Gothic, Grecian and Elizabethan styles. Although Bridgens was more at home in the Grecian style of the Regency period, 27 of the plates are devoted to Elizabethan or Jacobean designs putting Bridgens in the forefront of fashion. Few of the drawings in this section are his own invention; instead they show original examples of which a large number were taken from pieces in Aston

Hall, Warwickshire, a Jacobean mansion of 1618-1635. These archaeological drawings were probably due to the influence of Bridgens's friend and colleague, Henry Shaw, who etched and aquatinted the plates. *Quarto. Coloured engraved title, letterpress contents leaf, and 58 plates of which 12 aquatinted, the remainder etched (numbered 1-60 including title and a double-page plate numbered 53-4). Large paper copy from the library of Elton Hall with a bookplate dated 1894. Full red morocco, gilt, gilt revers; binding by Zaehnsdorf.* £340

18 **Bridgens, R(ichard)** Furniture with candelabra and interior decoration *London, William Pickering 1838*

A standard coloured copy of the previous item. *Quarto. Engraved title, contents leaf and 58 hand coloured etched or aquatinted plates numbered 1-60 to include title and a double page plate numbered 53-4. Contemporary oiled-paper boards, cloth spine.* £200

19 **Brown, Richard** The rudiments of drawing cabinet and upholstery furniture: . . . proportioned upon architectural principles, after the manner of the antique, on twenty five plates . . . Second edition, improved. To which is subjoined an Elucidation of the principles of drawing ornaments *London, J. Taylor 1822*

An arrogant little work placing emphasis on perspective drawing and concerned with making furniture designs intelligible rather than considering the inherent structural problems. Brown, a painter and architectural draughtsman, criticises the drawing of Chippendale and Sheraton and dismisses their designs as 'trivial compositions'. His own pieces show the Empire style and neo-Greek fashion becoming more flowing and relaxed with an increase in turned work and heavier supporting members. A most important section is the 'Elucidation' which preaches the need for classical purity and emphasises the importance of decorative symbolism, illustrating Grecian motifs and outlining the rules for drawing them. Here the corinthian capital is first revived after the sway of the more austere orders. *Quarto. 14 (numbered to xvi but lacking pp vii-viii) 87+(1)pp and 25 etched and aquatinted plates of which 16 hand coloured, 7 etched plates. Half calf, gilt.* £210

20 **Bury, (J. B. M.)** Modèles de menuiserie accompagnés de détails et de développements qui doivent en faciliter l'exécution. Suivis d'un abrégé de l'art du menuisier et d'un traité des escaliers *Paris, Librairie Centrale d'Architecture (1850s)*

Engravings of carved woodwork of buildings in Paris, much of it ecclesiastical. Cafés and wooden shop fronts are also illustrated, and there is a group of plates illustrating carpentry techniques. (See also item 810). *Folio. (4)+8pp, engraved title and 73 engraved plates. Cloth.* £60

21 **The Cabinet Maker and Art Furnisher** *London, Cabinet Makers Exchange 1883-8*

Monthly illustrated magazine about furniture and the contemporary furniture trade, with new designs by Owen Davis, Henry Pringuer, Valentyne Aspen and others. Edited by J. Williams Benn (Mr Wedgwood Benn's grandfather). *Folio. 5 vols. Volumes 3-8 (nos 37-96). Original cloth.* £15 each

21a **Carlsson, Daniel** Svenska möbel ritningar *Stockholm, R. Blaedel 1892*

Excellent examples of high quality commercial furniture to be found in Scandinavia at the turn of the century. The pieces are in either a neo-renaissance style or have simple forms richly carved with intricate decoration. Increasing mechanisation never quite reduced the high standard of craftsmanship in Scandinavian furniture as it did elsewhere. These pieces retain an essentially peasant flavour influenced by traditional vernacular design and look to ancient Nordic art for their motifs, producing the style which was known as 'Fornordisk' (Old Norse). The work was issued in parts but we have never seen the final part, and we believe it was never published. *Folio. 4 of 5 parts. 6 litho plates in each part numbered consecutively 1-24. Original printed wrappers, as issued. In card envelope.* £25

22 **Cescinsky, Herbert & Ernest R. Gribble** English furniture & woodwork *London, Routledge 1922*
History of English furniture and associated woodwork from the 15th century to 1700, based on wide knowledge of the material and well illustrated. *Quarto. 2 vols. (4) + xvi + 382pp with 401 illustrations; vii + (1) + 386 + (2)pp with 527 illustrations. Original full gilt panelled morocco.* £65

23 **Cescinsky, Herbert** Chinese furniture. A series of examples from collections in France *London, Benn, 1922*
Illustrations of Chinese lacquer furniture, with an explanatory preface. *Quarto. 20 + (2)pp with 10 text illustrations and 54 collotype plates. Original cloth.* £35

24 **Cescinsky, Herbert** The old-world house its furniture and decoration *London, Black, 1924*
Extensive collectors' guide to furniture of the 17th and 18th centuries and its history and function. *Octavo. 2 vols. ix + (3) + 307 + (1)pp; (4) + 371 + (1)pp. Each vol has frontispiece and there are 664 illustrations in all. Original morocco, gilt spines.* £35

25 **Cescinsky, Herbert** The gentle art of faking furniture *London, Eyre & Spottiswoode 1969*
Reissue of Cescinsky's charming and very necessary study, first published in 1931. *Octavo. x + 167 + (7)pp with 292 illustrations. Original cloth.* £10

26 **Chalk, L. & B. J. Rendle** British hardwoods their structure and identification *London, HMSO for DSIR 1929*
Quarto. vi + 54pp with 45 illustrations. Original cloth. £9

27 **Chambers, William** Designs of Chinese buildings, furniture, dresses, machines, and utensils. Engraved by the best hands, from the originals drawn in China by Mr Chambers, architect, ... to which is annexed, a description of their temples, houses, gardens *London, for the author 1757*
Chambers started his career as a merchant in the Swedish East India Company and spent nearly nine months in its service at Canton. When subsequently he became an architect he used his knowledge of China to produce this fine series of engraved plates with an explanatory text and an essay on landscape gardening in China. Subjects illustrated range from buildings and furniture to porcelain, boats, costume and calligraphy. *Large folio. (10) + 19 + (1)pp and 21 engraved plates by Fourdrinier, Fougeron, Rooker, P. Sandby and Grignion. Quarter calf, original marbled paper boards.*
Illustration below. £310

28 **Chambers, William** Designs of Chinese buildings, furniture, dresses, machines and utensils *London 1757 (Gregg reprint 1969)*
Quarto. 30pp and 21 plates. Original cloth.   £10

29 **Chambers, William** Designs of Chinese buildings, furniture, dresses, machines and utensils *London 1757 (Blom reprint 1969)*
A better production than the Gregg reprint but on a reduced scale to the original. *Folio. 24pp and 21 plates. Original cloth.*   £12

30 **Charles, R.** The Compiler. Furniture & decorations. Choice & select designs from the best authors *London, the author 1879*
A collection of designs for furniture and decoration taken from the works of Sheraton, Thomas, Pergolesi, Pain, Gibbs, Swan, Ince & Mayhew, Shearer, Robert and James Adam, Carter and others; a pattern book for the reproduction furniture trade. The first volume (probably all published). *Quarto. Title, index leaf, 240 plates. Quarter calf, marbled paper boards.*   £35

31 **Chenavard, (Claude-Aimé)** Recueil des dessins de tapis, tapisseries et autres objets d'ameublement exécuté dans la manufacture de M. M. Chenavard à Paris *(Paris, the author c 1828)*
A lesser-known publication of Aimé Chenavard, one of the promoters of the nineteenth century eclectic style in decoration. The book shows small furniture pieces and furnishings designed in a mixture of styles as well as schemes for complete interiors in Egyptian, Chinese or Turkish fashion. The designs were primarily for objects executed in the workshop of Chenavard's brother, Henri, but they also include a design carried out at the Manufacture Royale de Sèvres where the author was employed as consultant designer. *Large folio. 30 numbered plates including decorative etched and aquatinted title printed on india-paper and mounted, and 29 outline engraved plates numbered 2-30, which 1 plate partly hand coloured. Decorative embossed-paper boards; some foxing. (See also item 1910).*   £75

32 **Chenavard, A(imé)** Album de l'ornemantiste recueil d'ornements dans tous les genres et dans tous les styles *Paris, Lenoir 1845*
A collection of designs for all manner of furniture and furnishing objects including examples of historical pieces and illustrations of eastern ornament as well as Chenavard's own designs for objects made at the Manufacture de porcelaine de Sèvres and the Beauvais and Gobelin carpet works. Chenavard was one of the earliest artists in France to try to link art and industry promoting ideas in the family factory as well as at the Beauvais tapesty works where he was made director in 1829 and later joint advisor to the Imprimerie Royale and Sèvres. He began publication of the present work in parts in 1832 completing it when 12 parts had appeared. This collected edition is a reissue of these parts. See also items 31 & 1910. *Folio. (12)pp and 72 zinc engraved plates. Half morocco portfolio.*   £60

33 **Child, Peter** The craftsman woodturner *London, Bell 1974*
Guide to the techniques of wood turning. *Octavo. 238pp with 125 illustrations. Original cloth.*   £5

34 **Chippendale, Thomas** The gentleman and cabinet-maker's director. Being a large collection of the most elegant and useful designs of household furniture in the Gothic, Chinese and modern taste (etc) *London, for the author 1754*
First edition of the first and most important collection of furniture designs to be published in England. Indeed, its comprehensive scope and its intended function as a trade catalogue out-distanced anything comparable published in Europe at this date. It found 310 subscribers (140 of them joiners, carvers and cabinet-makers) and was so immediate a success that an unchanged second edition was required by the following year. A third edition appeared in instalments between 1759 and 1763. With its wide and prolonged circulation, the Director enjoyed considerable influence particularly in the introduction and establishment of the Rococo style of furniture, and Chippendale's reputation rose by it to colossal heights, overshadowing such skilled craftsmen as Vile and Lock. *Folio. (2)+x+27+(1)pp, engraved dedication leaf, 161 engraved plates (numbered 1-160 and 25A). Last plate defective. Quarter calf, gilt tooled spine, marbled paper boards.*   £485

35 **Chippendale, Thomas** The gentleman and cabinet-maker's director: being a large collection of the most elegant and useful designs of household furniture, in the most fashionable taste. The third edition *London, the author 1762, (Berlin, Wasmuth reprint c 1905)*
Full scale facsimile reprint. *Folio. xxviiipp and 212 plates. Original quarter cloth, marbled boards.* £45

36 (Chippendale, Thomas) **Coleridge, Anthony** Chippendale furniture. The work of Thomas Chippendale and his contemporaries in the rococo taste Vile, Cobb, Langlois, Channon, Hallett, Ince and Mayhew, Lock, Johnson, and others circa 1745-1765 *London, Faber 1968*
The most recent and best documented study of Chippendale and his immediate competitors. *Quarto. 229+(1)pp and 193pp of plates, 3 colour plates. Original cloth.* £15

37 (Chippendale, Thomas) **Symonds, R. W.** Chippendale furniture designs from the Gentleman and Cabinet-Makers' Director 1962 *London, Tiranti 1950*
A selection of the most interesting of the furniture plates together with Chippendale's own descriptive notes and a short biography and assessment, both printed in English and French. *Royal octavo. 24pp and 80 photolitho plates. Publisher's cloth.* £1.50

38 **Clouston, R. S.** English furniture and furniture makers of the 18th century *London, Hurst & Blackett 1906*
Critical study of cabinet-makers from Chippendale to Sheraton, candid in its judgments and no respecter of persons. *Octavo. xii+362+(2)pp with many illustrations. Original cloth.* £9

39 **Committee of Master Carpenters** Measured prices for carpenters' & joiners' work, including labour and materials: with the addition of a supplement for finding the value of several articles, according to the variation of prices and materials *London, Cox & Baylis (for the Committee), 1814*
Up-dated edition of the work first published in 1811 now taking into account the fluctuation in the costs of materials. *Octavo. 86+(2)pp interleaved with blanks throughout. Full contemporary calf, rebacked.* £42

40 **Cotchett, Lucretia Eddy** The evolution of furniture *London, Batsford 1938*
Trends in European furniture design from the 12th century to the 1930s. *Octavo. vii+(2)+118pp, frontispiece and 94pp of photo plates. Original cloth.* £9

41 **Crallan, Franklyn A.** Details of Gothic wood-carving. Being a series of drawings from original work chiefly of the fourteenth and fifteenth centuries with explanatory notes *London, Batsford 1896*
Folio. xx pp and 34 plates of measured drawings. Original cloth. £14

42 **Darty, Peter** Chairs, a guide to choosing, buying and collecting *London, Barrie & Jenkins 1972*
The evolution of the chair and an examination of the influences which have dictated its form together with advice on choosing and buying selected pieces, copiously illustrated with many examples in each style. *Small quarto. (10)+118pp with 204 text illustrations, and 14 colour illustrations on 6 plates. Publisher's cloth.* £5

43 **Deville, J.** Dictionnaire du tapissier: critique & historique de l'ameublement Français depuis les temps anciens jusqu'à nos jours *Liège, Claesen (c 1870)*
Illustrations of upholstered furniture, arranged by period. *Octavo. Title and 124 plates (printed in colour with some hand tinting). Original printed portfolio, cloth spine.* £20

44 **Dohme, Robert** Moebel aus den koeniglichen Schloessern zu Berlin und Potsdam *Berlin, Wasmuth 1889*
The fine 18th century furniture made for Frederick the Great by J. A. Nahl, J. M. Kambly and others. *Folio. (8)pp and 50 photo plates Original printed-paper portfolio, repaired.* £18

45 **Eastlake, Charles L.** Hints on household taste in furniture, upholstery and other details *London, Longman 1868*
First edition. The most important treatise on home furnishings of the Victorian period. Eastlake seems to have been the first to apply the term 'art furniture' to distinguish between artist-designed and purely commercial products. His own furniture was simple in form and decoration, with certain affinities to Gothic and Early English models, and was especially successful in America. *Octavo. xiv+269+(1)pp and 33 plates (including 4 coloured of tile designs and 8 of coloured wallpaper designs), other text illustrations. Original decorated cloth.* £30

46 **Eastlake, Charles L.** Hints on household taste . . . third edition (revised) *London, Longman 1872*
Octavo. xviii+306pp with text illustrations, and 32 plates. Original decorated cloth. £25

47 **Eastlake, Charles L.** Hints on household taste in furniture *London 1872 (Blom reprint 1971)*
Octavo. 318pp with many illustrations. Original cloth. £4

48 **Ecke, Gustav** Chinese domestic furniture *Rutland, Vermont, Tuttle 1963*
Important study, published in Peking in 1944 on the basis of much material not now accessible, and here reissued in facsimile. *Folio. (12)+49+(1)pp and 161+(1)pp of plates. Original cloth.* £15

49 **Edwards, Ralph & Margaret Jourdain** Georgian cabinet-makers *London, Country Life 1944*
Short biographies of 90 cabinet-makers, joiners and carvers of the 18th century, with illustrations of their furniture. *Quarto. xiv+80+(2)pp and 102pp of plates numbered 83-183. Original cloth.* £15

50 **Edwards, Ralph & Margaret Jourdain** Georgian cabinet-makers c 1700-1800. New and revised edition *London, Country Life 1955*
Quarto. 248pp including 120pp of illustrations. Original cloth. £35

51 **Edwards, Ralph** The dictionary of English furniture from the middle ages to the late Georgian period. By Percy Macquoid and Ralph Edwards. Revised and enlarged by Ralph Edwards *London, Country Life 1954*
The most complete and most extensively illustrated history of English furniture. This is the second edition, which entirely superseded the first edition of 1927 in which Edwards collaborated with Macquoid; it has not itself been superseded and has become very scarce in the book trade. *Folio. 3 vols. viii+350pp; viii+384pp; viii+376pp. Each volume has a colour frontispiece, colour plates and hundreds of photo text illustrations. Original cloth.* £275

51a **Edwards, Ralph** The shorter dictionary of English furniture from the Middle Ages to the late Georgian period *London, Country Life 1964*
Condensed but still very substantial version of Edwards' great 'Dictionary of English Furniture' published in its second edition in 1954 and long out of print. Even the shorter version is the most complete and extensively illustrated publication on English furniture available. *Folio. 684pp with 1900 illustrations, colour frontispiece. Original cloth.* £20

52 **Examples of French furniture** From Louis XIII, XIV, XV, XVI, and Empire periods *London 1899*
Trade catalogue, advertizing a large stock of reproduction French furniture. It gives no indication of the firm who issued it, but the initials 'E.K.L.' are printed on the front cover and they may be relevant. Oblong quarto. 36+(5)ff, and several hundred illustrations. Original printed boards.   £17

53 **Fastnedge, Ralph** English furniture styles from 1500 to 1830 *Harmondsworth, Penguin 1970*
Octavo. xxii+(2)+322pp with 101 text figures, and 64pp of plates. Original wrappers.
     £1

54 **Fawkes, F. A.** Architects' joinery and its ornamentation. Revised and enlarged edition *London, Batsford 1896*
Trade catalogue for Fawkes' joinery firm, based in Chelmsford, illustrating over 200 overmantels, friezes, panels, etc, with price lists. *Folio. 8pp text and 82pp of plates. Original printed paper boards.*   £36

55 **Feulner, Adolf** Kunstgeschichte des mobels seit dem Altertum *Berlin, Propylaen-Verlag 1927*
A comparative study of European furniture from the Middle Ages to the end of the 19th century. A scholarly study, unsurpassed in its day, well illustrated and indexed.
Octavo. 656pp including 494 illustrations. Original quarter morocco.   £40

56 **Foley, Edwin** The book of decorative furniture. Its form, colour, and history *London, Jack (c 1910)*
'There are pieces of furniture so fine as to convey a sense of almost human personality. Some remind one of Haydn's simple melodies ... the austere formal beauty of fugues or church music seems to emanate from others'; the lavish prose matches the lavish illustrations and production, and this is authentic stockbroker-belt literature. *Folio. 2 vols. (4)+xv+(1)+427+(1)pp with (50) colour plates; xii+420pp and (100) colour plates. Original decorated cloth.*   £25

57 **J. Foot & Sons Ltd** Foot's adjustable chairs and couches *London 1910*
Rather pleasing trade catalogue; the furniture is scarcely fashionable (and brand names like 'Osborne' emphasize its Victorian quality), but its comfort is illustrated by pictures of a cigar-toting late Victorian reclining or otherwise positioned on the firm's products. *Oblong quarto. 44pp with illustrations. Original printed wrappers.*   £15

58 **Frey, Gilbert** The modern chair: 1850 to today *Teufen, Niggli 1970*
History of chair design from 1850, in three languages, with short biographical notes on designers. *Oblong quarto. 188pp including many text illustrations. Original cloth.*   £9

59 **Furniture and decoration and The furniture gazette** Collection of plates & Supplement parts *London (c 1880-5), 1887, 1894*
A collection of plates from two of the most important trade journals of the end of the century which eventually merged. The illustrations show a wide range of furniture pieces and interiors including features such as doors and chimneys, in the 'art furniture' and 'bracket and overmantel' styles which were commercially popular at that period. The collection was part of a designer's reference and comes with 5 parts of the Furniture gazette Supplement. *60 litho plates mounted on card; 5 magazine parts. In portfolio.*   £40

60 **The Furniture History Society** Furniture history. The journal of the Furniture History Society *(Leeds) 1966, 1968-70*
Quarto. 5 vols. Vols II, III-VI. Printed wrappers.   £15

61 **The Furniture trades organiser and hardware expert journal**
London 1921-30
Shows conventional designs of the post first-war period, but interesting for highlighting the demand for art deco. *Quarto. Vols 2-21. Publisher's cloth.* £120

62 **Le Garde-Meuble** A collection of plates of curtains, furniture and chairs *Paris (late 1860s)*
Plates for the use of designers—and this set of them comes from the workshops of Waring & Gillow. *Folio. 76 litho plates erratically numbered. Cloth, with studio stamp of Waring & Gillow.* £75

63 **Gibberd, Frederick** Built-in furniture in Great Britain *London Tiranti 1948*
Brief but evocative sketch of interior fittings of the 1940s. Furniture illustrated is by Coates, Fry, Gibberd, Goldfinger, the Russells—and Symonds and Yorke from an older school. *Octavo. viii+44pp and 48pp of illustrations. Original cloth.* £8

64 **(Gimson, Ernest)** Ernest Gimson his life and work *Stratford, Shakespeare Head Press 1924*
Limited edition of 500 copies. A memorial volume with contributions from Lethaby, A. H. Powell and F. L. Griggs. Gimson, the central figure in a design partnership with the brothers Ernest and Sidney Barnsley, devoted himself to the production of furniture, metalwork and plasterwork in a modern idiom but with the use of traditional country materials and skills; his work thus has a solidity and a technical competence that distinguishes it from much Arts and Crafts production. *Quarto. vii+(1)+47+(1)+v+(1)pp, 60 collotype plates and 8 text illustrations. Contemporary full green morocco, gilt panelled, uncut. Binding signed 'E.T.'.* £225

65 **Gloag, John** British furniture makers *London, Collins 1946*
Octavo. 48pp including 25 illustrations, and 8pp colour plates. Cloth. £4

66 **Gloag, John** The Englishman's chair. Origins, design, and social history of seat furniture in England *London, Allen & Unwin 1964*
The fullest history of the English chair. *Octavo. xviii+307+(1)pp and 64pp of plates, colour frontispiece, text illustrations. Original cloth.* £3.75

67 **Gloag, John** A short dictionary of furniture (revised and enlarged edition) *London, Allen & Unwin 1974*
Admirable, compact dictionary, first published in 1952. This revised edition contains over 2600 entries (900 more than in 1952), covering American as well as English furniture; there are additionally lists of furniture makers, a bibliography, etc. *Octavo. 813+(3)pp, with over 1000 text illustrations. Original cloth.* £8.40

68 **Gloag, John** Guide to furniture styles: English and French 1450 to 1850 *London, Black 1972*
Relates the development of English and French furniture design; a general survey. *Octavo. 232pp with many text illustrations. Original cloth.* £4.50

69 **Goldfinger, Ernö** British furniture to-day *London, Tiranti 1951*
A survey of the designs of the immediate post-war period (the most interesting are Goldfinger's own examples) with a short note on the aims of modern designers. *Octavo. 20pp and 98 photographic illustrations. Publisher's cloth.* £2

70 **E. Gomme Ltd** Furniture catalogues *(London c 1935)*
A run of furniture catalogues from Gommes' 'Silent Salesman Series', including catalogues of bedroom and dining room furniture and of easy chairs and settees. Very good illustration of late 'art deco'. *Oblong folio. 5 vols bound in 1. Approx 250pp of furniture illustrations in all. Original cloth folder.* £40

71 **Goodman, W. L.** The history of woodworking tools *London, G. Bell 1971*
The first comprehensive history of tools. Each of the most important tools is treated separately and its evolution traced to present times. *Quarto. 208pp including 200 text illustrations. Publisher's cloth.* £5

72 **Goodman, W. L.** British plane makers from 1700 *London, G. Bell 1971*
Names, addresses, dates and marks of all the known makers. *Quarto. 133pp including 12 photoplates. Publisher's cloth.* £5

73 **Grandjean, Serge** Empire furniture 1800 to 1825 *London, Faber 1966*
Furniture in the manner of Percier and Fontaine (items 450-3), executed by Jacob-Desmalter, Biennais and others. *Octavo. 120pp, 4 colour plates and 96pp of plates. Original cloth.* £8

74 **Guilmard, D.** Album du menuisier Parisien. Recueil de pièces de menuiserie dans le goût le plus moderne *Paris, Le Garde-Meuble c 1860*
Designs for bookcases, screens, doors, pulpits, stalls and an altar. Parts 1-10 only of 12 issued. *Small folio. Lithotitle and 39 (of 48) litho plates. Contemporary quarter calf, gilt tooled spine.* **Illustration below.** £4

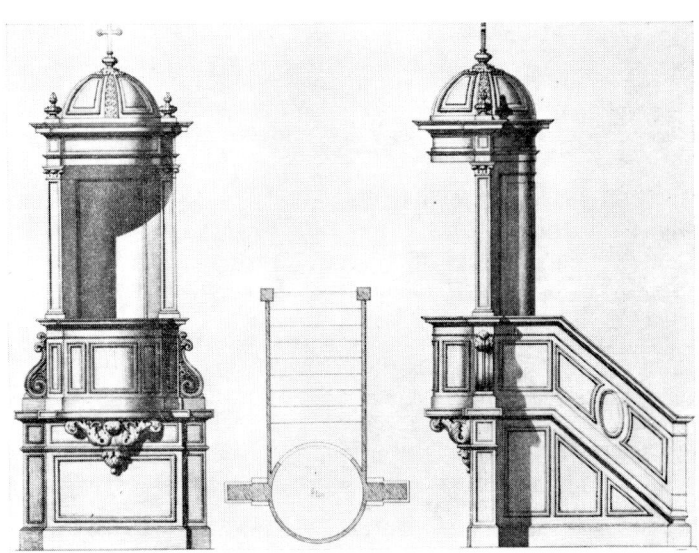

74

75 **Hahm, Konrad** Deutsche Bauernmobel *Jena, Diederichs 1939*
Good pictorial study of German folk and peasant furniture. *Octavo. 33+(3)pp and 88pp of photo plates, 11 mounted colour plates. Original decorated cloth.* £6

76 **Harris, John** Regency furniture designs from contemporary source books 1803-1826 *London, Tiranti 1961*
Reproduces illustrations from Sheraton, Hope, Ackermann, Nicholson and Smith. *Quarto. vi+26pp and 108pp of plates. Original cloth.* £4

77 **M. Harris & Sons** The English chair. Its history and evolution *London 1937*
Octavo. 182pp, including 96pp of plates and text illustrations. Original boards, cloth spine. £15

78 **Hasluck, Paul N.** Cabinetwork and joinery *London, Cassell 1909*
Designs for furniture originally printed in 'Work' or 'Building World'. *Octavo. 568pp with 12 colour plates and 2021 text illustrations. Original decorated cloth. Covers faded.*
£9

79 **Hayward, Helena** (editor) World furniture. An illustrated history *London, Hamlyn 1965*
Ranges from the furniture of Pharaonic Egypt to that of the 20th century (more akin to each other than much of what intervenes). Contributors include Hugh Honour, Hans Huth, T. Lunsingh Scheurleer, E. T. Joy, Clifford Musgrave, Charles Handley-Read and Herwin Schaefer. *Folio. 320pp with 1177 text illustrations, colour frontispiece and 30pp of colour plates. Original cloth.*
£5

80 **Heal, Sir Ambrose** The London furniture makers from the Restoration to the Victorian era 1660-1840 . . . with a chapter by R. W. Symonds *London, Batsford 1953*
Lists all London cabinet-makers with their addresses, dates of activity and other relevant information. An important book. *Quarto. xx+276+(2)pp including many illustrations. Original cloth.*
£55

81 **Heaton, John Aldam** (editor) Furniture and decoration in England during the eighteenth century. Facsimile reproductions of the choicest examples from the works of Chippendale, Adam, Richardson, Hepplewhite, Sheraton, Pergolesi, and others *London, Bumpus 1889*
Plates of chairs, tables, cabinets, mirrors, chimneypieces, friezes and carvings reproduced from the originals, often on a larger scale. Almost the first facsimiles of English furniture pattern books and an instance of a dealer–for Aldam Heaton had his own firm (see items 376-7)–increasing public interest in his stock by a scholarly publication on it. *Large folio. 2 vols. 22pp and 100 plates; viiipp, and 100 plates. Contemporary quarter morocco.*
£36

82 **Hefner-Altenek, J. H. von** Ornamente der Holzsculptur von 1450 bis 1820 aus dem Bayerischen National-Museum *Frankfurt, Keller 1881*
Photographic plates of examples of carved woodwork in the Bavarian Museum at Munich. *Folio. (8)pp and 40 photographic plates. Cloth portfolio.*
£20

83 **A. Hepplewhite & Co** The cabinet-maker and upholsterer's guide; or, repository of designs for every article of household furniture, in the newest and most approved taste . . . the third edition, improved *London, I. & J. Taylor 1794*
Hepplewhite's Adamesque designs, first published in 1788 and reissued in 1789 and 1794, were not the height of fashion when they appeared–Hepplewhite had died in 1786–and were dismissed by Sheraton in 1793 as having 'already caught the decline, and perhaps in a little time, will suddenly die in the disorder', but attracted a large readership. Their success must be credited to the fact that they were eminently suitable for the ordinary household–sober, plain, useful, elegant. George Hepplewhite (the A. Hepplewhite of the title reflects the fact that after his death the business was run by his widow Alice) was a cabinet-maker in London who seems to have made his living by supplying designs to other firms, since no furniture survives that is connected with him by positive documentation. His influence on English furniture is difficult to measure but the fact remains that as a result of the 'Guide' the name Hepplewhite has become indissolubly linked with a mass of anonymous neo-classical furniture. *Folio. (6)+24pp and 127 engraved plates numbered 1-125, with numbers 124-5 relating to a double-page plate, two plates numbered 9 and additional plates 40* and 78*. Plate 82 neatly repaired at lower margin. Contemporary full calf, rebacked.*
£510

84 **A. Hepplewhite & Co** The cabinet-maker and upholsterer's guide *London, Taylor 1794 (Batsford reprint 1897)*
Full-scale facsimile reprint. Folio. (6)+24pp and 128 plates. Original cloth.
£45

85 **(Hepplewhite, George)** Hepplewhite furniture designs from the

Cabinet-Maker and Upholsterer's Guide 1794. With a preface by Ralph Edwards *London, Tiranti 1965*
Octavo. 12pp and 80pp plates. Original cloth. £1.95

86 **Hertel, G(eorge) L(eopold)** Sofas *A(ugsburg), J. G. Hertel (c 1750)*
Rococo canapés of rather exaggerated but delicately pretty form with a suggestion of Chinese influence. Eight designs on four plates. The complete suite. Berlin Cat 1191. Guilmard p. 456. *4 engraved plates. No 21 from Hertel's collection. Average size 240 × 190mm. Preserved in paper wallet.* **Illustration below.** £60

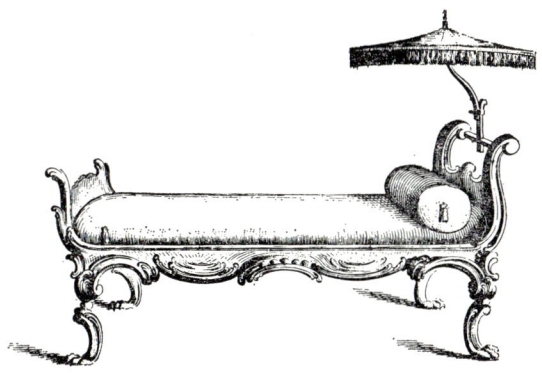

86

87 **Hettwig, Carl** Journal für Tapezierer und Decorateure. Original-Zeichnungen moderner Zimmer-Decorationen, Polstermoebel etc. Zweite Auflage *Berlin, Grieben (c 1880)*
Complete run of this series of litho plates of designs for draperies and upholstered furniture. Each part includes a view of a room furnished as recommended and the whole production conveys an air of the comfort and opulence of the 1880s. *Folio. 8 vols. Each vol with 18 litho plates. Original boards, cloth spines, with original printed labels on front covers.* £260

88 **Himmelheber, Georg** Biedermeier furniture ... translated and edited by Simon Jervis *London, Faber 1974*
The furniture made in Germany and Austria between 1815 and 1830; Himmelheber's study of it features the work of the Viennese cabinetmaker Josef Danhauser and furniture made in Berlin from designs by Schinkel. *Quarto. 115+(blank)pp and 3+115 monochrome photoplates on 44ff, 4 colour plates. Original cloth.* £12

89 **Hinckley, F. Lewis** Directory of the historic cabinet woods *New York, Bonanza 1960*
Details of 118 woods employed in cabinet making, with illustrations of 17th-19th century furniture showing the different appearance of each wood. *Quarto. (6)+186pp including 172 illustrations. Original cloth.* £1.45

90 **Hindley & Wilkinson Ltd** Architectural decorators designers upholsterers & manufacturers of high-class furniture *London (c 1910)*
Trade catalogue of a Bond Street firm of furnishers, specializing in reproduction French furniture. *Folio. 114pp including 27 plates and many illustrations. Original cloth.* £22

91 **H. L.** Furniture designs. Dessins d'ameublement *London 1912*
Trade catalogue with text in French and English, advertising a very extensive range of furniture, partly in reproduction styles and partly from original designs; the whole stock is calculated to appeal to a general suburban taste, whether English or French. *Oblong quarto. 512pp, with approximately 2000 illustrations. Original decorated boards, cloth spine.* £45

92 **Holbourne Ltd** Catalogue of furniture *London (c 1920)*
Illustrates furniture, lamp fittings, etc. *Quarto. 98pp with 453 illustrations. Original wrappers.* £15

93 **Honour, Hugh** Cabinet makers and furniture designers *London, Spring Books 1972*
Studies of fifty of the greatest furniture designers and craftsmen (Du Cerceau, Vredeman de Vries, Boulle, Chippendale, Roentgen, Sheraton, Pugin, Mackintosh, Aalto, Breuer, Eames, etc.). *Quarto. 320pp with many illustrations some coloured. Original cloth.* £5

94 **Hope, Thomas** Household furniture and decoration *London, Longman, Hurst, Rees & Orme 1807*
A misleadingly prosaic title for a work which shows not the run-of-the-mill pieces of the period but illustrates the furniture and interiors of Thomas Hope's luxurious Duchess Street mansion in London (acquired in 1799). The book is a lavish and uncompromising publication with plates (in the outline technique developed by Flaxman) prepared by Edmund Aikin and George Dawe from the drawings of Hope himself. Originating from a Scottish-Dutch family of bankers from Amsterdam, Thomas Hope had settled in England in 1795 and proceeded to set himself up as a maecenas of the arts and the arbiter of English taste. As well as commemorating the remodelling of his town house, and announcing the plans for Deepdene, the country house he had acquired in 1806, Hope intended the purpose of the book to be an attempt to bring some cultural education in household decoration to London society, and he hoped to steer English taste towards a purified imitation of the various forms of antiquity. The austere Egyptian, Greek, Roman, Indian and Moorish interiors of Duchess Street are characterized by what Hope believed to be a scholarly accuracy and refinement in design. In the series of rooms a painstaking effort was made to ensure connection between the objects displayed and their setting. The all-embracing idea was to present a coherent antique vision of the interiors of successive civilizations. The illustrations of furniture in the book are all pieces which were actually made and we know from those still in existence that the plates are of the greatest accuracy. Berlin Cat. 1236. *Folio. Decorated engraved title. (4) + 53 + (1)pp and 60 outline engraved plates (of which 1 remargined). Original decorated printed-paper boards, quarter straight-grained morocco, rebacked and cornered. Preserved in matching slip-case. Large uncut copy.* £360

95 **Hopkinson, James** Victorian cabinet maker. The memoirs of James Hopkinson 1819-1894. Edited by Jocelyne Baty Goodman *London, Routledge 1968*
Autobiography of a cabinet maker who was in business successively in Nottingham, Preston, Liverpool and Loughborough. *Octavo. xiv + 138pp and 20pp of plates. Original cloth.* £4

96 **Hoppenhaupt, (Johann Michael, the elder)** Clock cases *A(ugsburg), J. G. Hertel (c 1745)*
Pendulum clockcases in rococo style with candelabra; the asymmetrical decoration includes putti with foliage. Hoppenhaupt worked under Knobelsdorff in the decoration of the new state rooms of the German royal residences and helped to evolve the 'Frederican Rococo' which relied on boldly contrasting curves. Guilmard p 448 lists only 3 plates. Suite 90 from Hertel's collection. *Four numbered plates, average size 160 × 290mm. Preserved in paper wallet.* £48

97 **Huber, A.** Gothische Bautischlerarbeiten. Thüren, Wandverkleidungen, Plafonds, Erker, Geländer und alle sonstigen Holzarbeiten des inneren Ausbaues *Berlin, Hessling (c 1890)*
First series. *Folio. Title and 30 litho plates. Original printed portfolio.* £15

98 **Hulme, F. Edward** Examples for fret-cutting and wood-carving *London, Marcus Ward 1877*
A pattern book of floral and foliage designs which illustrates the range and character of Hulme's decorative work. (See also items 1454-5). *Folio. 32pp with 24 coloured litho plates. Original decorated boards, cloth spine.* £20

99 **Hurrell, John Weymouth** Measured drawings of old oak English furniture. Also of some remains of architectural woodwork, plasterwork, metalwork, glazing, etc *London, Batsford 1902*
'My object has been to represent... the true spirit of the work in exhaustive detailed analysis of its construction and design, with the mouldings and ornamentation drawn full size wherever practicable'. *Folio. (8)pp and 110 plates of measured drawings. Original cloth. Author's presentation copy, ex library.* £16

100 **Ince & Mayhew** The universal system of household furniture... a complete reprint with a preface by Ralph Edwards *London, Tiranti reprint 1960*
A collection of designs published c1762 by the London cabinet-makers William Ince and John Mayhew; they included notes in French as well as in English to attract continental orders and the range of designs is wider than in Chippendale's rival 'Director'. The reprint has prefaces by Edwards in English and French also. *Quarto. (32)pp and 95+(1)pp of plates. Original cloth.* £4

101 **Jack, George** Wood carving: design and workmanship.. with drawings by the author and other illustrations *London, John Hogg 1903*
Has preface by Lethaby. *Octavo. 318pp including 16 plates and 77 text figs. Original boards, cloth spine.* £5

102 **Jackson, F. Hamilton** Intarsia and marquetry *London, Sands 1903*
Historical survey with a long section on Italian work of the early Renaissance. *Octavo. xx+152pp and 54 photo plates. Original cloth.* £8

103 **Jervis, Simon** Printed furniture designs before 1650 *(Leeds) Furniture History Society 1974*
A selection from the furniture designs of Du Cerceau, Vredeman de Vries, de Passe, Du Breuil, Ebelmann, Krammer and others, backed up by a scholarly introduction and bibliographical references. A long-needed study of a neglected aspect of furniture history. *Octavo. x+54pp and 449 illustrations on 372pp of plates. Original cloth.* £9.50

104 **Joel, David** Furniture design set free. The British furniture revolution from 1851 to the present day *London, Dent 1969*
A survey of the development of British furniture from the late nineteenth century to the late sixties, heavily weighted to describe the author's own endeavors in the furniture business as a founder of Betty Joel Ltd, David Joel Ltd, and Le Grest & Co. The book upholds the distinctive quality of traditional British design and affirms the British furniture industry as a source of original design and high quality. The work is a new edition of 'The adventure of British furniture' originally published in 1953, here brought up to date with many amendments and new material. Useful appendices deal with the influence of royalty, and give biographical notes on important 20th century figures. *Large quarto. 108pp and 198 photographic illustrations. Publisher's cloth.* £7

105 **Jones, Barbara** English furniture at a glance *London, Architectural Press 1971*
'Crisp, clear and witty... altogether an excellent book'. *Octavo. 100pp with text illustrations. Original wrappers.* £0.65

106 (Jones, John). **Brackett, Oliver** Victoria and Albert Museum. Catalogue of the Jones collection. Part I. Furniture *London, Board of Education 1930*
Mainly 18th century French furniture. The collection was formed by John Jones (1800-82), a London tailor and army clothier. *Quarto. viii+36pp and 48pp of plates. Original cloth.* £6

107 **Jonquet, A.** Original sketches for art furniture, in the Jacobean, Queen Anne, Adams, and other styles *London, Batsford 1879*
Furniture suitable for houses designed by architects of the Nesfield–Norman Shaw variety. *Folio. (4)pp and 60 plates of furniture designs. Original cloth.* £50

108 (Jourdain, Margaret) **Lenygon, Francis (pseud.)** Furniture in England from 1660 to 1760 *London, Batsford 1914*
The companion volume to Jourdain's 'Decoration in England 1660-1760' (item 396), and like that published pseudonymously. *Folio. x+300pp with 447 illustrations. Original decorated cloth.*
£25

109 **Jourdain, Margaret** Regency furniture 1795-1830 ... revised and enlarged by Ralph Fastnedge *London, Country Life 1965*
A pioneer study first published in 1934 and expanded in this edition to cover the decade 1820-1830. *Folio. 116pp with 4 colour plates and 249 text illustrations. Original cloth.*
£16

110 **Jourdain, Margaret & F. Rose** English furniture: the Georgian period (1750-1830) *London, Batsford 1953*
Intended as a companion volume to Miss Jourdain's 'English interior decoration, 1500-1830' (see item 399), the project was incomplete on her death in 1951 and the volume was published posthumously from the preparatory writings edited and completed by F. Rose who added a fresh section of illustrations. In the writer's usual accurate and learned manner it surveys the leading designers and cabinet makers–including previously neglected names–charts the influence of taste on the development of style and gives technical accounts of woods and constructional methods. *Large quarto. 210pp with 172 photographic illustrations. Publisher's cloth.*
£25

111 **Jupe, Robert The original patent** under the Great Seal granted to Robert Jupe, of Jupe Johnstone & Co, cabinet makers and upholsterers, of 67 New Bond Street, London, for 'improvements in ornamental dessert flower and other stands' for 14 years from 9 October 1835
Original patents of this date are not often found. *Parchment sheet measuring approximately 750 × 580mm, inscribed in red and black ink and with an ornamental border which includes portraits of King William IV and Queen Adelaide, and the royal coat of arms; wax impression of Great Seal attached (repaired for crack).*
£85

112 **Jupe, Robert The original patent** granted to Robert Jupe for 'improvements in apparatus applicable to book & other shelves' for 14 years from 22 September 1836
Parchment sheet as last but royal arms have contemporary hand colouring.
£50

113 **Kindts, E. Julien** Le mobilier moderne. Recueil de meubles variés de forme et de style dans le gout de l'art Français du XVe au XVIIIe siècle *Liège, Claesen (1891)*
Designs and working drawings for furniture based on historical precedents but not merely a collection of reproductions; the largest number of designs are in a renaissance manner. *Folio. 3ff text and 48 plates. Lacks plates F3 and F4 called for in printed list, but has additional plates F9 and F10 not called for and is likely to be complete. Original portfolio, printed paper covers.*
£35

114 **Der klein Möbel-Tischler, enthaltend:** Abbildungen von Möbels nach dem neuesten Geschmacke *Leipzig, Gebhardt und Reisland (c 1850)*
A tiny pocket-book showing German cabinet designs of the mid-nineteenth century which includes illustrations of beds, bookcases, commodes, sideboards, small cupboards and shelf units and a wide variety of tables. The continuing dominance throughout the continent of French furniture is still apparent in the captions and scale rules which are given in French. *Duodecimo. (2)ff letterpress and 31 hand coloured litho plates. Original paper boards, publisher's printed label, decorated and hand coloured. Library stamp on title-page.*
£40

115 **Krauth, Theodor** Die gesamte Bauschreinerei einschliesslich der Holztreppen, der Gläserarbeiten und der Beschlage ... zweite durchgesehene und vermehrte Auflage *Leipzig, Seemann 1891*
Quarto. 2 vols. viii+193+(1)pp; title leaf and 75 plates of detailed working drawings. Original decorated cloth.
£24

116 **Krauth, Theodor & Franz Sales Meyer** Die gesamte Möbelschreinerei mit besonderer Berucksichtigung der kunstgewerblichen Form. Vierte durchgesehene und vermehrte Auflage *Leipzig, Seemann 1902*
Two-volume guide to furniture and furniture manufacture, with many measured drawings of furniture in the plate volume and a group of plates at the end illustrating recent work by H. Michael, Van de Velde, Pankok, Riemerschmid, Hoffmann and Ashbee. For Meyer see also item 853. *Quarto. 2 vols. (6)+290+(2)pp with 276 text illustrations; (4)pp and 136 plates. Original decorated cloth.* £48

117 **Laking, Guy Francis** The furniture of Windsor Castle *London, Bradbury Agnew 1905*
The Royal collection at Windsor which Laking describes includes a number of very fine pieces acquired by Charles II and William III, but is essentially the creation of George IV; Edward VII's contribution of the fire screen from the Hôtel de Russie at Frankfurt-am-Main adds a bizarre touch. *Quarto. xx+200pp and 47 plates. Original quarter morocco, cloth sides.* £45

118 **Lalonde, (Richard)–Salembier, (Henri)** Cahiers du livre d'ameublemens par Lalonde Ier (-VIIIe).–Premier (-quatrième) cahier de meuble d'ebenisteries dessiné par Lalonde.–Oeuvres diverses de Lalonde ... XIIIe (-XVIIIe) cahier;–Cahier de frises ... (d'arabesques) composé et gravé par Salembier *Paris, Chereau (c 1780-85)*
A fine collection of French late 18th century furniture and decorative designs. Lalonde– a prolific designer who was obviously influenced by the ebenistes Roentgen and Riesen–produced designs thoroughly representative of the fashion in the latter part of the 18th century. In the drawings for ceiling mouldings, cornices, rosettes and brackets, Lalonde shows a preference for simple classical forms. This is carried over to some of his furniture designs to produce an 'Empire style' effect which is evident in the suites of bureaux, writing desks, commodes, cupboards and bookcases. Some of his later designs, however,–represented here with the beds, sofas, chairs, wall clocks and fire-dogs–show the characteristic features of the final two decades of the century which favoured over-elaborate effects such as the use of free-cut festoons, superfluous ornament and swagged drapery. Unlike most of the furniture designs which had been published in France Lalonde gives measured drawings showing the framework construction and all the details of the joinery and ornament.
The two suites by Salembier are for distinctive friezes and panel decoration in the Louis XVI style with delicately attenuated scrollwork mixed with nymphs and putti,

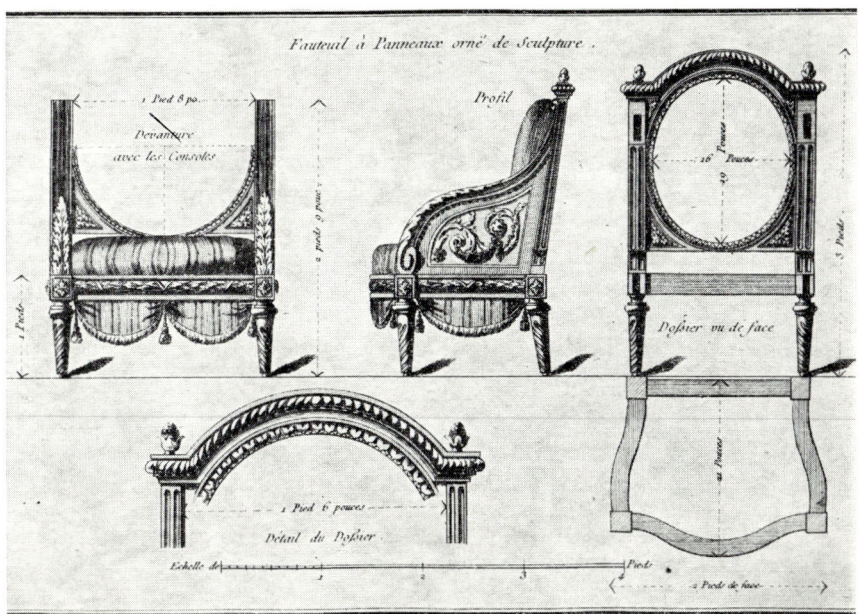

118

and vertical panels of renaissance arabesques transmuted by Salembier's swirling and looping lines. Berlin Cat 1270, 1271, 1269, 491. Guilmard pp241-4. *Folio. 4 works in one. 20 parts. In all 108 engraved plates consisting of: 18 suites lettered A-H, A-D, N-R and one unlettered, each with 6 numbered plates; 2 suites each of 6 plates, one unlettered, one lettered B. Full contemporary calf, gilt spine.* **Illustration previous page.**
£620

119 Le Pautre, J(ean) Les cabinets *(Paris) le Blond (c 1650)*

Richly carved cabinets with panelled doors, flanked by figures, caryatids or putti, and surmounted by figure groups, busts or vases. The cabinets are supported on stands exuberantly carved in high relief with sea horses, terms, griffons or elaborate consoles. These are lively baroque designs showing a strong italian influence. One of Le Pautre's few suites of furniture designs. (Oeuvres suite 63). Destailleur Notices p92. Guilmard p72. *Six unnumbered engraved plates, average size 215 × 146mm, with good margins. In paper wallet.* **Illustration below.**
£50

120 **Litchfield & Co** Furniture and interiors of the 16th, 17th & 18th centuries *London (c 1910)*
Catalogue of the firm's stock of antique furniture, panelling, mantelpieces—they also did reproductions. *Folio. 56pp, mostly of illustrations. Original cloth.* £14

121 **Litchfield, Frederick** Illustrated history of furniture from the earliest to the present time *London, Truslove 1903*
Octavo. xviii+272pp, coloured frontispiece, with many illustrations. Original cloth. £10

122 **Liversidge, Joan** Furniture in Roman Britain *London, Tiranti 1955*
'The materials for this study are ... scattered and varied. But from their collection ... it is possible to paint a clear and consistent picture of some, at least, of the principal contents of a typical living-room in Britain in the Roman period'. *Octavo. viii+72pp and 48pp of plates. Original wrappers.* £1.25

123 **London Cabinet Makers** Designs of ornaments; for cabinet furniture, with prices. *London, for the London Cabinet Makers;* **and sold at the Plough, Museum Street, Bloomsbury,** 1826
The price book for nearly one hundred and fifty different applied ornamental shapes sold by the inch. Interesting to see what kind of trade went on at our local pub a century and a half ago. *Quarto. 4pp and 11 steel engraved plates (dated 1st Dec 1811). Quarter morocco.* £60

124 **London Cabinet Maker's Union** The London Cabinet Makers' Union Book of prices. By a Committee of masters and journeymen.— The London Cabinet Makers' Book of prices, for the most improved extensible dining tables, with illustrative engravings. By a Committee *London, Richard F. Benbow for the Committee 1866*
The third edition of the price book which superseded that originally issued in 1788 (item 181). By now the designs of Shearer, Casement and Hepplewhite are well out of fashion and the plates have been replaced by far less elegant designs with more concentration on the carving and detailing. In the first work the unsigned plates show cornices, mouldings, pilasters, feet and stretchers, table tops, panelling and a few complete designs for items such as dining tables and dressing tables, music stands, and writing tables. The second work concentrates on a piece which was becoming increasingly popular—the extending dining table. An interesting piece of ephemera is included with this item—a letter from the Committee asking members to thank the Union for the wages increase which they have managed to obtain. *Quarto. 2 works in one. Decorative engraved title, (8)+xi+(1 balnk)+474+(2)pp and 8 engraved plates; (6)+27+(1 blank)pp and 9 engraved plates. Quarter morocco.* £115

125 **Loudon, J. C.** An encyclopaedia of cottage, farm, and villa architecture and furniture; containing numerous designs for dwellings, from the villa to the cottage and the farm including farm houses, farmeries, and other agricultural buildings: country inns, public houses, and parochial schools: with the requisite fittings-up, fixtures, and furniture; and appropriate offices, gardens, and garden scenery ... A new edition, edited by Mrs Loudon *London, Frederick Warne and Co 1869*
Loudon's monumental work, first published in 1833, exerted a considerable influence on small builders, craftsmen and furniture designers of the Victorian period continuing in circulation as a pattern book up until the end of the century. The relevant sections illustrate the interior finishing of, and furniture for, cottages, farmhouses, country inns and villas, and the contributors to these sections included Charles Barry, Henry Shaw, Edward Lamb, Dalziel the upholsterer as well as Robert and William Mallet on parts relevant to ironwork. The many illustrations of furniture range in style from debased versions of Regency to the opening phase of the style which developed in the 1840s: Victorian vernacular. The majority of the designs were reproduced from the catalogues of the principal manufacturers of the day but among them can be found some experimental suggestions by new designers which were innovating in their suggestions

for fresh solutions to old problems and unusual combinations of the materials they specified. This final edition, which was edited by Jane Loudon, is generally considered to be the best and contains a Supplement of an extra 200 pages. *Octavo. xxiv + 317 + (1)pp including 2342 text illustrations. Publisher's cloth boards, rebacked.* £60

126 **(Loudon, J. C.)** Loudon furniture designs from the Encyclopaedia of cottage, farmhouse and villa architecture and furniture 1839. With an introduction by Christopher Gilbert *Wakefield, S. R. Publishers and The Connoisseur 1970*
A facsimile of the three sections of Loudon's influential encyclopædia which deal with furniture prepared from the 1839 revised edition. *Octavo. viii + 135 + (1)pp including numerous text illustrations. Original cloth.* £2.10

127 (Mackintosh, Charles Rennie) **Alison, Filippo** Charles Rennie Mackintosh as a designer of chairs *London, Warehouse Publications 1974*
An illustrated study with information on Mackintosh's visit to Italy in 1891 and on his exhibits at the Turin Exhibition of 1902. *Oblong octavo. 106pp with many illustrations (some coloured). Original wrappers.* £3.95

128 **Macquoid, Percy** A history of English furniture *London, Lawrence and Bullen 1904-08*
English furniture from 1500 to 1820, in four extensively illustrated volumes with the titles 'Age of Oak', 'Age of Walnut', 'Age of Mahogany' and 'Age of Satinwood'. A substantial publication which set the standard for subsequent writers. *Folio. 4 vols. viii + 244pp with 215 illustrations; (4) + 248pp with 223 illustrations; (4) + 272pp with 254 illustrations; (4) + 266pp with 243 illustrations. Each volume has additionally 15 colour plates. Original cloth.* £95

129 **Macquoid, Percy** A history of English furniture *London 1904-08 (Dover reprint 1972)*
Reprint, demonstrating the vitality of Macquoid's book–and there is in fact no other narrative history of English furniture on this scale. *Folio. 4 volumes. Original wrappers in cloth case.* £8

130 **Mallett, W. E.** An introduction to old English furniture *London, Newnes (c 1905)*
Brief historical guide based on Mallett and Son's stock, with drawings by H. M. Brock. *Octavo. 143 + (1)pp with 168 text illustrations. Original decorated boards, cloth spine.* £8

131 **Manufacturers' brochures** A collection of 24 manufacturers' brochures and pamphlets relating to the furniture and decoration 1906-51 *(but chiefly of the 1920s)*
Firms represented include Waring & Gillow (6 items), Hamptons (4 items), Goochs (2 items), Midland Furnishing, William Spriggs, Frederick Lawrence, Civil Service Supply Association and The United Lumber and Veneer Co. 24 items. *Original wrappers.* £25

132 **Manwaring, Roger** The cabinet and chair-maker's real friend & companion or the whole system of chair-making made plain and easy *London, Webley 1765, (Tiranti reprint 1970)*
Manwaring provides designs in rococo, Gothick, Chinese and rustic styles, 'calculated for all people in different stations of life'. *Octavo. (14)pp and 38pp of plates. Original cloth.* £0.90

133 **Maple & Co Ltd** Inexpensive furniture for modern homes *London (c 1920)*
Trade catalogue of very upper middle class furniture. *Quarto. 136pp with many illustrations. Original wrappers.* £16

134 **Maple & Co Ltd** Illustrations of furniture *London (c 1930)*
A complete illustrated catalogue of Maple's furniture, eminently suitable for 'embassies, clubs and officers' messes' and also supplied to royalty, nobility and the average middle class home. A price list is attached. *Oblong folio. (24)+384+(4)pp with illustrations throughout and a 16pp price list inserted. Original quarter cloth.* £25

135 **McGaw & Co** Catalogue of wooden mouldings *London (c 1865)*
Mouldings for skirting boards, dados, doors, window frames. The firm was established in 1857 and is described in its catalogue as the only firm in England which 'exclusively confine themselves to the manufacture & supply of wood mouldings'; the catalogue is not dated but must pre-date 1873 when the firm was trading under the name of Smith & McGaw at a different address. *Oblong folio. (1)+19pp of lithographic plates after drawings by J. McGaw. Original blue printed wrappers, in folder.* £18

136 **Meubles et objets de goût** *Paris (Bureau du Journal des Dames) Ans 9 & 10 (i.e. 1801)*
First part of the series of furniture designs which appeared until 1833 as an offshoot of the 'Journal des Dames et des Modes'. The series was to provide an admirable reflection of the current trends in furniture fashion. These plates show 17 highly decorative illustrations of a variety of pieces in the Etruscan style popular at the turn of the century. Berlin Cat 1274. *Five engraved plates numbered 1-5, hand coloured. Average size 195 × 305mm. Stitched in original blue sprinkled-paper wrappers.* £70

137 **Moffatt, H. C.** Illustrated description of some of the furniture at Goodrich Court, Herefordshire and Hamptworth Lodge, Wiltshire *Oxford, privately printed 1928*
A catalogue of the author's fine private collection of English furniture, chiefly oak. 117 items are illustrated in collotype and the text describes and dates them and gives details of their provenance. *Quarto. (6)+90pp, with 117 illustrations on 86pp of plates. Original half vellum.* £45

138 **Morrell, J. B.** Woodwork in York *London, Batsford 1949*
A record of interior and exterior woodwork in York, with extracts from the records of the local Guild of Carpenters and Joiners. *Quarto. 192pp including 211 illustrations. Original cloth.* £10

139 **Musgrave, Clifford** Adam and Hepplewhite and other neo-classical furniture *London, Faber 1966*
Octavo. 224pp, 4 colour plates and 96pp of plates. Original cloth. £7

140 **Musgrave, Clifford** Regency furniture 1800 to 1830 *London, Faber 1970*
Furniture by Hope, Holland, Sheraton and Smith; a thorough survey, taking account of recent research. *Octavo. 158pp and 96pp of plates, 4 colour plates. Original cloth.* £5.50

141 **Nicholson, Peter** Practical carpentry, joinery, and cabinet-making *London, Thomas Kelly 1840*
Nicholson devotes a whole book to his 124 numbered principles of furniture design, construction and decoration, laying down the rules for styles and types appropriate to various parts of the house and supplying information on veneering, inlaying, carving, and ornamental moulding, together with hints on the care and upkeep of furniture and the best methods of cleaning, staining, polishing and varnishing. His second book on joinery deals with interior finishes and details, and would make an excellent addition to the handyman's library, particularly for its useful section on the hanging of doors on which subject Nicholson was the first to write. The continuing practicality of the work, first published in 1826, is demonstrated by the fact that it was reprinted several times, by the same printer, without any change, until as late as 1857. Even the 1845 and later editions, pretending to be revised by Tredgold, are still straight reprints. *Quarto. viii+140+36pp, and 84+6 numbered engraved plates including title. Full contemporary calf, gilt; rebacked.* £38

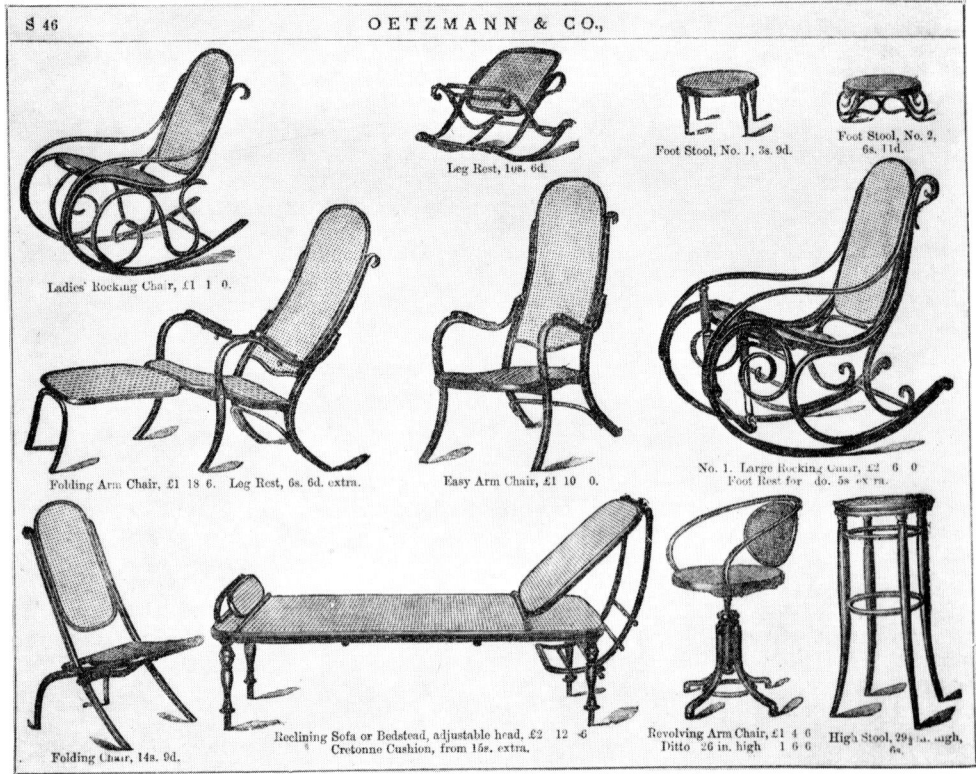

142 **Nicholson, Peter & Michael Angelo** The practical cabinet-maker, upholsterer, and complete decorator *London, H. Fisher, Son & Co 1826 (-1827)*

This comprehensive collection of designs was (unlike the majority of furniture books to this period) not intended as a pattern book but was one of the series of practical handbooks which Peter Nicholson,–a one-time cabinet-maker and carpenter, later practising architect, expert mathematician, and prolific author–issued. In this instance he enlisted the aid of his son–a talented architectural draughtsman–to draw the plates and possibly contribute to the designs. The pieces illustrated are elegant, well-proportioned, and richly detailed with a profusion of leaf decoration and an inclination to carved ornament. At a time when fine design in furniture was on the wane their popularity with more conservative craftsmen and patrons is underlined by the continual reissue of the work at varying intervals up until at least 1846. *Quarto. 152+(12)pp, engraved title and 103 engraved plates of which 35 hand coloured. Full calf, gilt; rebacked.*
£220

143 **Nicholson, Peter & Michael Angelo** The practical cabinet-maker. With a new introduction by Christopher Gilbert *Wakefield, E. P. Publishing Ltd 1973*

A facsimile reprint of the 1826 edition omitting pp11-152 which deal with geometry and adding two plates from the 1843 edition. *Quarto. x+(8)+12pp and 80 photolitho plates. Original cloth.*
£3.50

144 **Oetzmann & Co** A guide to house furnishing. Supplement *London (c 1881)*

A shorter, but not at all short, version of their general catalogue of house furnishings. Oetzmanns, founded in 1848, did a large business in furnishings, specializing in mail order and export trade. Their stock included furniture, bedding, carpets, ironmongery, china and glass, and most of it must be listed and illustrated in this volume; in addition, there are interesting interior views of the firm's showrooms. *Octavo. 290pp (3 leaves defective) with many woodcut ills (some full-page). Original printed wrappers.* **Illustration above.**
£40

145 **Oetzmann & Co.** A collection of 27 catalogues, brochures, etc., relating to their furniture and furnishing business *London (c 1900-1933)*
Catalogues of clearance sales at special reduced prices c1900 (2), 1904, 1907, 1910, 1911, 1912, 1915; catalogues of 'inexpensive furnishings for cottage or flat' of 1906 and 1910; a catalogue of the stock of Cleret & Co., acquired by Oetzmanns c1907 and offered by them at half price; several pamphlets 1910-33 advertising cottages and bungalows specially designed for Oetzmanns and sold by them completely furnished; and a group of brochures from the 1920s with such titles as 'Vogue in the Home' and 'The Charm of the Fireside' which mark Oetzmanns first ventures in modern advertising techniques. An interesting group of sales literature, much of it issued without printed dates and dated in a contemporary hand. *27 items. Original wrappers.* £35

146 **Osmont** Die elegante Welte. Meubles und Verzierungen im modernsten Geschmäcke. Erste Sammlung. Erstes ... Drittes ... Viertes Heft. (Le beau monde. Meubles et décorations de gout. Premier collection. Premier ... deuxième ... troisième cahier) *Augsburg & Paris, Math. Rieger 1840*
German issue of a little known furniture periodical in the style of 'Meubles et objets de gout' (see item 136) but beginning almost at the time when that periodical ceased to issue its designs. The pieces illustrated here show the Empire style turning into the heavy solid pieces of the mid century influenced by exhibition work. *Oblong quarto. Three parts: 1, 3 & 4. 24 zinc engraved plates, hand coloured and numbered I-VIII; XIII, XIX-XXIV; XXV-XXXII. Original printed-paper wrappers with titles in French and German. Contemporary stipple-paper covers, printed labels. Preserved in cloth wallet. Ex libris with library stamp on verso of plates.* £160

147 **Packer, Charles** Paris furniture by the master ébénistes *Monmouth, Ceramic Book Co 1956*
Based mainly on pieces in American collections the work gives a commentary on the styles and techniques of 17th and 18th century furniture makers, a list of the masters from Boulle to Jacob, and a useful pictorial review of pieces arranged in chronological order. An appendix lists artists and craftsmen who influenced furniture design and gives brief notes concerning them. *Quarto. xxvi+(2)+104pp and 72ff with 237 photographic illustrations. Publisher's cloth. Limited edition of 1000 copies.* £12

148 **Passe, Crispin de (junior)** Oficina arcularia in qua sunt ad spectantis diversa eximia exempla ex varijs autoribus collecta. Boutique menuserie ... Schriner laden ... Schrinwerckers Winckel ... *Amsterdam, the author 1642*
Second edition of one of the most important contemporary records of northern European renaissance furniture, and a most lasting furniture pattern book which not

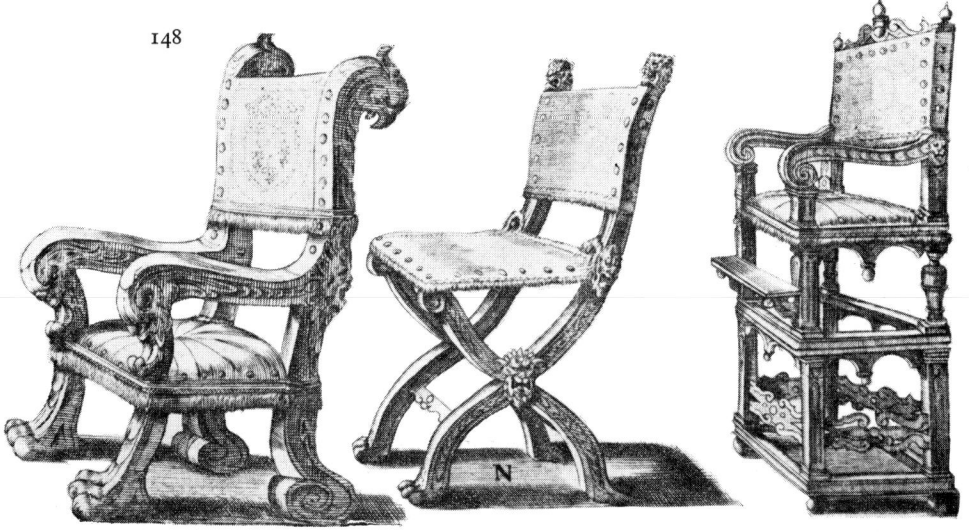

only influenced English cabinet makers but set the format for later works of the type. Crispin de Passe was a prolific and versatile engraver not a furniture craftsman so his illustrations probably record pieces which actually existed rather than his own projected designs (the half pulpit drawing on plate O is said to be the design for that in the Westerkirk, Amsterdam, the author's local church). The book begins by treating briefly of the orders in 2 plates and follows with examples of overdoors, beds, buffets, chests of drawers, cupboards, cabinets, mirror frames, tables and chairs, shields and cartouches, and applied decorative motifs for carving and stucco. Most of the plates show the application of the orders to cabinet pieces, and are decorated with intricate carving or rich inlaid work. The work was originally published in Utrecht in 1621 by the elder de Passe with a title and 14 plates. This edition reproduces all but two of those plates and adds 8 more. It was reprinted again in 1651 (see Berlin Cat 1223). The present copy lacks 2 plates, plate T of shields and a duplicate plate O of cartouches. Guilmard p 493. *Folio. Engraved title and 18 engraved plates lettered A-S; sizes varying from 337 × 238mm to 211 × 157mm. Loose plates in board folder.* **Illustration on previous page.** £180

149 **Patents for Inventions** Abridgements of Specifications. Class 52 (i), (ii), (iii), (iv) and (v). Furniture and upholstery. 1909-15, 1916-20, 1921-5, 1926-30 *London, HMSO 1921-33*
Run for 1909-30 of specifications for furniture (which includes sub-categories for chairs, tables, window & stair furniture, and so on). Not much art furniture but plenty of ingenious ideas for the internal fittings of motor cars, railway carriages and aeroplanes. *Octavo. 20 parts bound in 4. Contemporary quarter morocco.* £40

150 **Payson, William Farquhar** (editor) Mahogany antique and modern. A study of its history and use in the decorative arts *New York, Dutton 1926*
Folio. xxii + 154pp, frontispiece and 232 photo illustrations. Original cloth. £36

151 **Portefeuille des arts décoratifs** *Paris (c 1900)*
Phototype illustrations of furniture and woodwork of Louis XV and Louis XVI date. *Folio. 200 photo plates carrying numbers between 5 and 671. Contemporary quarter morocco. Ex Waring & Gillow studio copy.* £15

152 **Prignot, (Eugène) and others** L'ameublement moderne. Par MM. Prignot, Liénard, Coignet et plusieurs autres artistes spéciaux *Liège, Claesen (c 1880)*
Large collection of furniture designs, mostly in French renaissance and Louis XIV-XV-XVI styles, but including examples of 'genre Gothique anglais'. A source of precedents for the reproduction furniture trade. Litho plates by Creuset. *Folio. 2 vols. (2)pp, litho title and 72 unnumbered litho plates, of which 24 are double-page and the other 48 tinted; (2)pp, litho title and 72 litho plates of which 6 are double-page and 66 tinted. Contemporary quarter morocco, marbled paper boards.* £140

153 **Pugin, A.** Gothic furniture consisting of twenty-seven coloured engravings, from designs by A. Pugin *London, R. Ackermann (c 1828)*
Reissue of the gothic designs from Ackermann's 'Repository' (item 1). Credit for these designs was, for a long time, given to the elder Pugin but they are now largely believed to have been by A. W. Pugin although when the first plates in this copy was originally published he could have been no more than thirteen years old. However, it is recorded that the father passed on much of the work for the Windsor Castle furniture designs to his son and the younger man was working on these in 1827. Certainly the designs do seem to have that profusion of medieval ornament which the younger Pugin was later to complain about on furniture and to confess to having perpetrated himself in his designs for Windsor Castle. Although the title claims the prints to be coloured only some copies were issued fully coloured as in the original impressions, the standard copy had only one coloured plate. Abbey: Life in England 51. *Quarto. iv + (28)pp and 26 etched and aquatinted plates including title, of which 2 coloured. Original blue patterned wrapper, publisher's printed label on front cover.* £65

154 **Pugin, A.** Pugin's gothic furniture *London, R. Ackermann (c 1835)*
Litho reprint of the previous item. *Quarto. 27 litho plates including title. Original decorated boards, cloth spine.* £24

155 **Pugin, A. Welby** Gothic furniture in the style of the 15th century *London, Ackermann 1835*
Suite of designs dated 1 April 1835 on each plate, more mature and more convincingly mediaeval than those of 1827; it was through this and Pugin's other published designs of these years that his reputation as a decorative designer spread. *Quarto. Coloured title and 24 etched plates. Original cloth, printed paper label on front cover.* £25

156 **Pugin, A. Welby** A series of ornamental timber gables, from existing examples in England and France, of the sixteenth century. Drawn on stone by B. Ferrey, under the direction of A. Pugin, architect; with descriptive letter press, by E. J. Willson, architect. Second edition, improved *London, Bohn 1854*
Quarto. 16pp, lithotitle and 30 litho plates. Original quarter morocco, gilt stamped. (Binding after a design by Pugin). £25

157 **Raynal, G.** Le meuble au XXeme siècle *Paris, Librairies-Imprimeries Réunies (c 1910)*
Very pretty plates produced to resemble watercolours, showing art nouveau furniture set against harmonizing wall schemes. *Folio. Printed title, contents leaf and 30 numbered chromolitho plates. In portfolio.* £125

158 **Ricci, Seymour de** Le style Louis XVI. Mobilier et décoration *Paris, Hachette 1913*
One of the earliest works to produce a photographic survey, mainly from sales catalogues, of the less sumptuous but more typical pieces of the period. *Quarto. xviii+(2 blank)+260pp with 456 photographic illustrations. Publisher's cloth. A used copy.* £20

159 **Rocher, G(eorge) M(ichel)** (Schränke nebst kleineren Möbeln und Details) *Aug(sburg), Joh. Georg Hertel (c 1750)*
Each plate contains one large central design for a bureau cabinet and smaller designs for chairs, frame corners and tops, clocks, tables and plinths; all in asymmetrical rococo style. The complete suite. Berlin Cat 1196(2). Guilmard p 449. Suite 100 of Hertel's collection. *Four numbered engraved plates, average size 200 × 305mm. Preserved in paper wallet.* £45

160 **Roe, Fred** A history of oak furniture *London, Connoisseur 1920*
Primarily about English oak of pre-1700 date, with chapters on French, Dutch and Tyrolese furniture of the same period. *Quarto. (8)+44pp with 8 plates and 68pp of photo illustrations. Original cloth.* £9

161 **Roe, Fred** Ancient church chests and chairs in the Home Counties round Greater London *London, Batsford 1929*
Quarto. xii+130pp including 95 text illustrations. Original cloth. £6

162 (Roentgen, Abraham & David) **Hüth, Hans** Abraham und David Roentgen und ihre Neuwieder Möbelwerkstatt *Berlin, Deutscher Verein für Kunstwissenschaft 1928*
The authoritative study of the Roentgens, their followers and their furniture. *Quarto. (8)+77+(1)pp with colour frontispiece and (8)+112pp of plates. Original cloth.* £40

162a (Roentgen, A. & D.) **Hüth, Hans** Roentgen furniture. Abraham and David Roentgen: European cabinet-makers *London & New York, Sotheby Parke Bernet 1974*
A new edition, the first in English, incorporating later research, biographies of the Roentgens, a history of the firm and details of the followers and workmen with biographical notes and source material. *Quarto. viii+108pp (including 3 colour plates and text illustrations) and 15+273 photographic plates. Original cloth.* £21

163 **Rogers, J. C.** Modern English furniture *London & New York, Country Life and Scribner's (c 1935)*
The pieces of 42 designers including the Barnsleys, Gimson, Lutyens, Seeley, Symonds, Waals, Ambrose Heal and Gordon Russell. The illustrations are grouped according to function of the pieces with sections showing furniture in the different rooms of the house. *Quarto. (6) + 208pp including 190pp of photographic illustrations. Publisher's cloth.*
£30

164 **Rogers, John C.** English furniture . . . revised and enlarged by Margaret Jourdain *London, Spring Books 1973*
Rogers's study, published as long ago as 1923 and revised by Margaret Jourdain in 1949, owes its successive reprints to the emphasis it lays on details of construction and the clarity of its text and illustrations. Still useful as a guide to the development of furniture making techniques since the 16th century. *Octavo. 244pp, including 201 illustrations. Original cloth.*
£2

165 **Roscher, G(eorge) M(ichel)** (Uhregehäuse, Rahmen und kleinere Möbel) *Aug(sburg), John George Hertel (c 1750)*
Rococo decoration. Each plate contains a large design for the case of a wall clock placed in the centre and around this smaller designs for cartouches, frame corners, occasional tables, candelabra etc. The complete suite. Berlin Cat 1196(1) Guilmard p499. Suite 99 from Hertel's Collection. *Four engraved plates, average size 197 × 296mm. Preserved in paper wallet.*
£45

166 (Rothschild Collection). **Bellargue, Geoffrey de** The James A. de Rothschild Collection at Waddesdon Manor. Furniture, clocks and gilt bronzes *London & Fribourg, Office du Livre for The National Trust 1974*
A fully researched and detailed catalogue of one of the three most important collections of French 18th century furniture and decorative pieces in England. The introductory essays and full catalogue descriptions are followed by biographical notes on the craftsmen. *Large quarto. 2 volumes with continuous pagination: 904pp including 48 colour plates, 560 black and white plates, 133 marks and signatures, 30 diagrams. Original cloth.*
£58

167 **Roubo, M.** (Description des arts et metiers). L'art du menuisier *Paris, Académie Royale des Sciences 1769-75*
The 'Description des Arts et Metiers', the Académie's famous account of contemporary crafts and trades, was published in 113 separate parts between 1761 and the outbreak of the French Revolution, and Roubo's work on joinery accounts for 6 of them. By itself it runs to 1300 pages and over 380 full page engraved plates and it is the most comprehensive French publication of the 18th century on woodwork and furniture. Roubo was a working joiner who had entered the trade at the age of 11 as an apprentice to his father, and he began the writing of his book with a background of eighteen years' practical experience and five years of attendance at the drawing classes held by the architect J. F. Blondel. He begins by discussing joinery generally, the woods and tools used, and the construction of doors, floors, panelling, cupboards, bookcases and church woodwork (stalls, organ cases and pulpits). He then proceeds to coach building–a section illustrated by handsome engravings of Berlins, diligences, sedan chairs, etc–; cabinet making; other types of furniture; and treillage. The final part of the work contains essays on costing and on trade practices, the latter offering the fruits of Roubo's own business experience. Very few sets survive. Berlin Cat 1263. *Folio. 6 vols (lacking the text to accompany plates of Vol 3 but otherwise complete). (4) + 151 (misnumbered to 155) + (1)pp and 50 engraved plates; (4) + 300 (numbered 153-452)pp and 120 engraved plates (nos 51-170) of which 26 folding; (2) + 146pp (nos 453-598) and 52 engraved plates (nos 171-221, 176) of which 13 folding; 55 engraved plates (nos 222-276) of which 2 folding; (2) + 274pp (nos 763-1036) and 61 engraved plates (nos 277-337); (2) + iv + 276pp (nos 1037-1312) and 46 engraved plates (no 107 bis, 338-382) of which 3 folding. Contemporary full calf, rebacked. Bookplate of Marquess of Donegal.* **Illustration opposite.**
£850

168 **Rowe, Eleanor** (editor) French woodcarvings from the national museums *London, Batsford 1897*
Collotype illustrations of 15th-18th century French woodwork in British museums, intended for the student of art woodcarving. *Folio. 3 parts in 1. (10) + 8 + (6) + 8 + (6) + 10pp with 54 collotype plates. Original quarter calf.*
£20

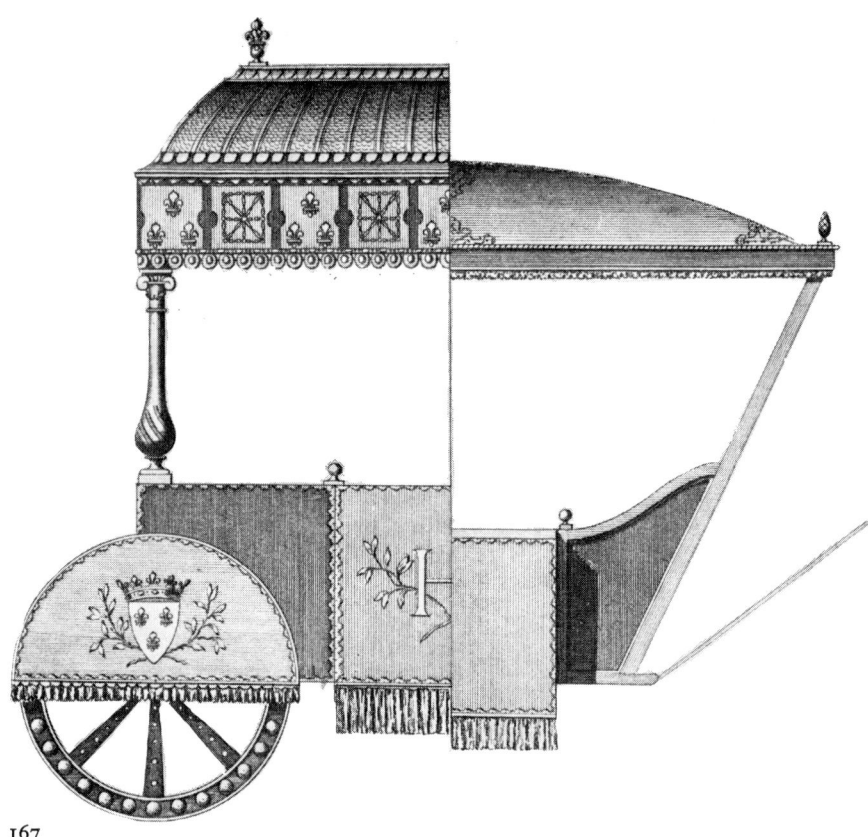

167

169 Russell, Gordon Designer's trade *London, Allen & Unwin 1968*
The autobiography of one of Britain's best known designers of furniture and former director of the Council of Industrial Design. *Octavo. 328pp, colour frontispiece, 22pp of illustrations. Original cloth.*
£8

170 Fredk Sage & Co Ltd A souvenir of the Sage contribution to the new House of Commons *London (c 1950)*
The Sage firm supplied the decorative woodwork and panelling for much of the interior of the House of Commons when rebuilt after the 1939-45 war. *Oblong folio. (28)pp of illustrations. Original wrappers.*
£9

171 Salda Societa anonima lavori di ammobigliamento. Meda *Milan, Torriani (1900s)*
Trade catalogue, with five thousand illustrations of chairs, tables, cupboards, etc,—but principally chairs. *Folio. 278pp with up to 20 photo illustrations of furniture per page. Original decorated cloth.*
£150

172 Salverte, François de Les ébénistes du XVIIIe siècle. Leurs oeuvres et leurs marques. Nouvelle édition *Paris, Vanoest 1927*
A catalogue of 18th century cabinet-makers with biographical notes, records of extant furniture and marks, and full bibliographical references. *Quarto. xxi+(1)+374pp, with frontispiece and 66 plates. Original wrappers.*
£48

173 Sanders, William Bliss Examples of carved oak woodwork in the houses and furniture of the 16th & 17th centuries *London, Quaritch 1883*
Accurate drawings of oak furniture with information on pieces' history and use. Two illustrations at the end are of the author's own designs for furniture–one of

which is for Messrs Gillow. *Folio. (48)pp and 25 photolitho plates. Original decorated cloth.* £20

174 Fritz Schachinger Special-Katalog über feine Holzwaren, Metallplastik, Samtbrand, Holzbrand-Apparate, Schnitzkasten etc. *Munich (1914)*
Trade catalogue of a large stock of small decorative boxes, signboards, wall brackets, photo frames, etc. in metal and wood. *Large octavo. Approximately 270 pp, illustrated throughout. Original printed wrappers.* £42

175 F. Schönthaler & Söhne Ledersofas. Clubfauteuils *Vienna (c 1900)*
Substantial leather upholstered chairs and sofas, suitable for clubs or Viennese psychiatrists' waiting rooms. *Oblong folio. 40ff of illustrations. Original wrappers.* £25

176 Schottmüller, Frida Furniture and interior decoration of the Italian renaissance. Second, revised edition *Stuttgart, Hoffmann (1928)*
Pictorial review of Italian renaissance furniture, with emphasis on decorative detail. *Octavo. xxxvi + 250pp, including 585 illustrations. Original cloth.* £15

177 Schübler, Johann Jacob Werck *Augsburg, Jeremias Wolff (1715-1738)*
Schübler, a German mathematician (who is often described as an architect) published several books on perspective, carpentry and architectural theory but never seems to have practised. The 'Werck' is his most famous publication and includes designs for all types of furniture, garden buildings and church furnishings. The suites on household furniture and interiors were very popular even though his designs, based on complicated mathematical calculations, were often obscured by the overwhelming detailing and a drawing style which produces a particular atmosphere that can only be described as 'high gothic baroque'. The individual pieces also reveal a genius for gadgetry that mark him out more as an inventor than a practical furniture designer (see also items 476-9).

a **Neu-inventiert sehr curieusen frantzösischen Betten.** (1720).
Part One of the 'Werck'. Highly elegant canopied beds in richly detailed settings. Two plates illustrate Schübler's inventive genius by showing an interesting device by which a sort of magic lantern projects a clock-face onto the opposite wall while another has the clock dial reflected on the floor. Berlin Cat 98. *Letterpress title and 6 engraved plates, average size 300 × 192mm. With large margins. In paper wallet.* **Illustration.** £52

b **Neu inventirte französchen Betten mit dem angehörigen Holtzwerck.** (c 1738).
Supplement to Part One of the 'Werck' giving much more formalized designs showing canopied beds with details of the construction of the framework, the hangings and the particulars of the ribbon pattern on the draperies. *Letterpress title, 1ff text and 6 copperplate engravings, average size 280 × 190mm, with large margins, untrimmed. In paper wallet.* £50

c **Neu-inventirte Schreib-Tische wohl-façonirte Frauen-Zimmer Toilette-Tische, wie auch zierliche moderne Medailles- und Commod-Schräncke.** (c1723).
Part Four of the 'Werck'. Writing desks, dressing tables and medal cabinets of intricate and bulky form with cantilevered corners, serpentine curves and applied volutes. One design was lifted direct by Batty Langley and used in his 'City and country builder's and workman's treasury' of 1745. Berlin Cat 98. *Letterpress title and 6 numbered engraved plates, average size 300 × 195mm, with wide margins, untrimmed. In paper wallet.* £48

d **Neu-inventirte Verkleidungen zu modernen Geographischen und Astronomischen Perpendicul-Uhren.** (c1724).
Part Five of the 'Werck'. These clock-cases besides showing the wide range of decorative ideas fully illustrate the inventive and mechanical bent of Schübler's mind. The designs are specified to include not just the hours and minutes, and the day, month and year, but have a number of other refinements which include naming the Saints' days, built-in globes showing the time zones of the world, and astrological globes with signs of the zodiac. In the background additional details include various sundials, one of which works by means of a translucent sheet over part of a window. *Letterpress title and 6 engraved plates, average size 300 × 193mm, with wide margins, untrimmed. In paper wallet.* £50

177a

e **Neu-façonirte Commod- und Schlass-Sessel vornehmer Herren geheime Speiss-Tische sirlichte geschnittene und verguldete Parade-Tische.** (c1725). Part Six of the 'Werck' with designs for tables and chairs. They include fascinating ideas for comfort and ease in a reclining chair with an adjustable back (unheard of elsewhere) and a dining-table containing a dumb-waiter and a fountain, this latter design was for those who desired privacy while eating. Berlin Cat 98. *Letterpress title and 6 numbered engraved plates, average size 300 × 190mm, with wide margins, untrimmed.*

£42

178 **Scott, William Bell** Antiquarian gleanings in the north of England, being examples of antique furniture, plate, church decorations, objects of historical interest, etc *London, Bell (1851)*
A publication by the author of 'The Ornamentist' (item 1531). The plates illustrate examples of furniture, metalwork, stone and ivory, tiles and bookbinding, chiefly medieval and renaissance, taken from collections in the northern counties of England. *Quarto. 18pp and 38 plates of which 17 aquatint, 2 printed in sepia, the rest line. Original embossed cloth.* £28

179 (Seymour, John & Thomas). **Stoneman, Vernon C.** John and Thomas Seymour cabinetmakers in Boston *1794-1816 Boston, Special Publications 1959*
First book on the Seymours and the Boston-Salem school of furniture makers, the most important in early post-Colonial America. *Quarto. 393+(3)pp including 291 illustrations (8 coloured). Original cloth.* £20

180 **Shaw, Henry** Specimens of ancient furniture drawn from existing authorities by Henry Shaw FSA with descriptions by Sir Samuel Meyrick *London, William Pickering 1836*
The first book treating furniture as antiques and notable for showing accurate illustrations of early pieces with surviving examples from medieval times to the late seventeenth century in private collections, churches and colleges, and including plate and decorative objects. The work is a primary source for the Elizabethan and Jacobean revival of the 1830s and '40s. Except for a few plates drawn by J. C. Buckler, William Twopenny and others, the plates were executed by Shaw, a skilled draughtsman and antiquarian who devoted a great part of his life to the publication of illustrated books on the visual arts of the medieval and Elizabethan periods. Abbey: Life in England 70. *Quarto. Engraved title, letterpress title (in red and black), (2)+57+(1)pp and 74 engraved plates (1 double-p) of which 25 printed in sepia. Paper boards, quarter green morocco, rebacked.* £40

181 **(Shearer, Thomas)** London Society of Cabinet Makers. The cabinet-makers' London book of prices, and designs of cabinet-work, calculated for the convenience of cabinet makers in general: whereby the price of executing any piece of work may be easily found. Illustrated with twenty-nine copper-plates, containing above two hundred various designs, intended as a guide towards the prices ... The second edition with additions *London, W. Brown & A. O'Neil for the Society 1793*
A new, enlarged edition issued in 1000 copies, of the price list of over 200 standard items of cabinet furniture first published in 1788 and compiled by the London Society of Cabinet-makers. The list itemizes in the minutest detail all the variations of parts or features which might be involved in any particular work. The book contains the same 20 plates as the original edition, of which 17 are by Thomas Shearer who may also have acted as general editor. It is upon these designs that Shearer's reputation as a furniture craftsman rests and which place him alongside Hepplewhite and Sheraton as one of the great names of the late 18th century in furniture design. This 1793 edition with its corrected and clarified text also contains 9 plates additional to the first edition–three by William Casement, a little-known cabinet-maker, and six by Hepplewhite (obviously not George who died in 1786, but probably someone connected with the firm of Alice Hepplewhite & Co). The book enjoyed a rapid sale and a third edition appeared in 1803. It continued in use until 1811 when it was superseded by a new work 'The London Cabinet Makers' Union book of prices' (item 124). *Large octavo. Engraved frontispiece, xvi+266pp (including 26 tables) and 29 engraved plates. Old marble-paper boards, quarter calf, rebacked.* £250

182 **(Shearer, Thomas)** Shearer furniture designs from the Cabinet-Makers' London Book of Prices 1788. With a preface and descriptive notes by Ralph Fastnedge *London, Tiranti 1962*
Shearer's designs for the working cabinet maker, first published in 1788 and reissued in 1793 and 1803, are here reproduced in facsimile. *Octavo. (6)+22pp and 17 plates of furniture. Original cloth.* £3

183 **(Sheraton, Thomas)** The cabinet-maker and upholsterer's drawing-book in three parts.—Appendix to the cabinet maker and upholsterer's drawing-book ... An accompaniment to ... *London, T. Bensley for the author 1791-3, 1793, (1794)*
First edition of the most celebrated monument of Regency taste and a summary of fashions in furniture during the last decade of the 18th century. Sheraton, a journeyman cabinet-maker, prolific designer of furniture, gifted draughtsman, and teacher of 'perspective, architecture and ornament' issued the main part of this most important publication in 49 separate numbers between 1791 and 1793. The first two parts of the Drawing Book are devoted to geometry, perspective, architecture and drawing, subjects to which Sheraton attached great importance as the back bones of design, and which he expounded in a complicated dissertation. The first, and to us the most valuable part, together with the Appendix and Accompaniment, show how Sheraton interpreted the neo-classical furniture fashions in his own elegant manner. However, the book's influence among fellow-craftsmen was due to its copious and full descriptive notes which gave more useful information about methods of executing and finishing designs than could be found in any other publication of the period and for that reason is still of particular value to us today. Berlin Cat 1234. *Quarto. Five parts in one. xxxii+(8)+446+(2)pp, engraved frontispiece and 66 engraved plates numbered 1-61, & 25, 29, (30), 54, 56 bis, including 5 folding; 54+(2)pp and 33 engraved plates numbered 1-32, 30 bis, of which 4 folding; 27+(1 blank+1+1 blank)pp and 14 numbered engraved plates of which 8 folding. Plate 1 of the main work has only the blank part of the leaf (as it is frequently found) and the engraved plate is here reproduced in photostat. The plates are somewhat soiled as is often the case with this work and a number have been repaired. Full calf rebacked.* £280

184 **Sheraton, Thomas** The cabinet-maker and upholsterer's drawing-book.—Appendix to ... An accompaniment to ... *London, for the author by T. Bensley 1794*
The first edition of the Drawing-Book, with its list of over 700 subscribers, was so successful that this second edition was issued later in the same year with 9 additional plates. This edition has an added section 'To the Reader' replying to Malton's criticism of the work. All the first part is reset in smaller type so that it makes up only 125 instead of 176 pages. Further parts either used old sheets or were reset line by line in the same type as the earlier edition, and kept the old pagination. In order to bridge the gap, a final quire (after page 120) of the first part was given the signature 'Q-Z' and the pages numbered 121, 172-176, and made up with a new, unnumbered, title leaf. This first part has also one additional plate, lettered A, which shows the diagrams for mitering the corners of boxes which are not right angles. The other extra plates, dated between 21st April and 24th September 1794, are found in Part III and show more furniture designs including a sideboard, a turkey sofa, chairbacks, a bookcase, a writing drawer, a lady's secretary & cabinet, a commode, and bed steps. This copy contains two more plates than is usually catalogued for this edition. Berlin Cat 1234. *Quarto. Five parts in one. xxxii+(8)+396pp (numbered to 121, 173-446, plus errata leaf, see notes above), engraved frontispiece and 74 engraved plates (with miscellaneous numbering); 54+(2)pp and 33 engraved plates numbered 1-32, 30 bis; 27+(1 blank+1+1 blank+2)pp and 14 numbered engraved plates. This also includes a 1794 title page to accompany the work if it was to be bound in two volumes. Quarter red morocco, marbled-paper boards. Some foxing but a fine untrimmed copy, partly uncut.* £625

185 **Sheraton, Thomas** The cabinet-maker and upholsterer's drawing-book. The third edition, revised *London, 1802 (reprint c 1900)*
Quarto. 440pp with 122 plates. Original cloth. £40

186 (Sheraton, Thomas) **Edwards, Ralph** Sheraton furniture designs from the Cabinet-Maker's and Upholsterer's Drawing-Book 1791-94 *London, Tiranti 1970*
A reproduction of all the furniture and ornamental designs from the 'Drawing Book' with extracts from Sheraton's original notes and a brief introduction. *Duodecimo. 12pp and 80 photolitho plates. Original stiff printed wrappers.* £1.25

187 (Sheraton, Thomas) **Fastnedge, Ralph** Sheraton furniture *London, Faber 1962*

A study of the influence of Sheraton's designs, the 'Drawing Book' and its readership, and general trends in furniture design in the last decade of the 19th century. *Quarto. 126pp, 4 colour plates and 96pp of plates. Original cloth.* £10

188 **Siddons, G. A.** The cabinet-maker's guide; or, rules and instructions in the art of varnishing (etc). Fifth edition, considerably augmented by the addition of several new articles, receipts, etc *London, Sherwood Gilbert & Piper 1830*

'A complete pocket companion for the Cabinet Maker, as well as a necessary and useful addition to his tool-chest'. *Octavo. xvi + 223 + (1)pp, frontispiece and 4 plates. 36pp of publisher's adverts bound in at end. Original boards, cloth spine.* £18

189 **Simon, Constance** English furniture designers of the eighteenth century *London, Batsford 1907*

Prints basic documentation on Chippendale not known to earlier writers. *Octavo. xvii + (1) + 216pp, frontispiece and 61 plates. Original cloth.* £15

190 **Singleton, Esther** The furniture of our forefathers ... with critical descriptions of plates by Russel Sturgis *London, Batsford 1901*

A well-documented and extensively illustrated history of American furniture in the colonial and early Republican periods. Sturgis contributes detailed descriptions of the pieces of furniture illustrated. *Large octavo. 2 vols. xii + 312pp, many photo plates and text illustrations; xvi + 664pp, many plates and illustrations. Original decorated cloth, top edge gilt, otherwise uncut.* £28

191 **Singleton, Esther** The furniture of our forefathers *London 1901 (Blom reprint 1969)*

Large octavo. 700pp including many full-page plates and line drawings in text. Original cloth. £10

192 **Small, John W.** Ancient & modern furniture *Edinburgh, for the author 1883. Limited edition 500 copies*

Sketches and details of 16th-17th century Scots woodwork together with the author's own furniture designs in the same idiom. Small's furniture was designed for clients in Dundee, Hamilton, Beith and Newcastle. Pleasant lithograph plates 'drawn for the stone' by the author himself. *Folio. (60)pp with 50 litho plates. Original printed paper boards, cloth spine.* £40

193 **Small, Tunstall & Christopher Woodbridge** Mouldings of the Tudor period. A portfolio of full size sections *London, Architectural Press (1930)*

Sections of windows, panels, staircases and beams. *Quarto. ivpp and 20 plates. Original portfolio.* £5

194 **Small, Tunstall & Christopher Woodbridge** Architectural turned woodwork of the 16th, 17th & 18th centuries. A portfolio of full-size details *London, Architectural Press (1930)*

Quarto. ivpp and 20 plates. Original portfolio. £5

195 **Small, Tunstall & Christopher Woodbridge** Mouldings of the Wren & Georgian periods. A portfolio of full-size sections *London, Architectural Press (1928)*

Sections of 257 skirtings, panel moulds, fireplace surrounds, handrails, architraves, sash bars. *Quarto. xvipp and 20 plates. Original portfolio.* £5

196 **Smith, George** A collection of designs for household furniture and interior decoration, in the most approved and elegant taste; ... with various designs for rooms ... showing the decorations, adjustment of the furniture, &c. also some general observations and a description of each plate. Engraved on 158 plates from original drawings *London, J. Taylor 1808*

196

The most ambitious and comprehensive furniture book of the period illustrating a wide range of eclectic designs in Greek, Roman, Egyptian, Chinese and Gothic styles. The work is not only remarkable for the variety of its styles but also for the number of different articles which it shows extending through the whole domestic household to include both richly adorned and special pieces as well as the simple and the ordinary, and includes whole room schemes with the decoration and the arrangement of the furniture as well as individual pieces. Smith was a practising cabinet-maker (calling himself 'upholder' and cabinet-maker to the Prince of Wales) so his designs were commercially motivated and as a result had a sound basis of practicality making the work useful to other cabinet-makers as a pattern book. Today it is of value to designers and craftsmen restoring or reproducing interiors and furniture. This publication which illustrates the Regency style in full bloom is now one of the rarest of the great furniture books. Abbey Life 71. Berlin Cat 1237. *Large quarto. xiv + 33 + (1 blank)pp and 158 etched and aquatinted plates, all hand coloured. Contemporary brown morocco with blind tooled decoration of anthemion and palmettes, gilt fillets and dentel corners, spine gilt; rebacked using original pieces. Plate 45 remargined, otherwise a very good copy with wide margins.* **Illustration above.** £950

197 **Smith, George** The cabinet-maker and upholsterer's guide: being a complete drawing book; in which will be comprised treatises on geometry and perspective ... numerous engravings. To which is added, a complete series of new and original designs for household furniture and interior decoration ... *London, Jones & Co 1826*

A swan song of the Regency style, forecasting in its text as well as in its plates the early Victorian decline in taste by showing indications of grossness in the design and hints of the corpulence of the shapes to come. It is also Smith's last publication and as such an aptly ambitious testimonial of his forty years of experience as a successful cabinet-maker and upholsterer. In addition to his designs for all sorts of furniture and decoration (primarily in Greek but also in the Egyptian, Etruscan, Roman and French styles) Smith provided an interesting 'historical view of the origin of the art in this country' (of cabinet-making and upholstery), long treatises on perspective and geometry, and an important essay on ornamental drawing: a subject in which he was particularly well versed being principal of the Drawing Academy at Brewer Street, Golden Square, Soho. Although dated 1826 on both the engraved and printed title pages, the work cannot have been issued completely until 1828. It was probably issued in parts at the times of the dates given on the plates which are between 3 April 1826 and 19 April 1828. Abbey Life: 73, Berlin Cat 1826. *Quarto. Engraved title, viii + 219 + (1)pp with several woodcut diagrams in text, and 153 plates of which 26 aquatints, the rest line engravings, 38 plates hand coloured. Full contemporary calf, rebacked. Some damp staining.* £240

198 **Stalker, John & George Parker** A treatise of japanning and varnishing *Oxford 1688 (Academy Editions reprint, London 1971)*
Reprint of one of the earliest English works to consider the subject. *Quarto. xvi + 84pp and 24pp of plates. Original wrappers.* **Illustration above.** £3

199 **Stanley-Barrett, H.** The A.B.C. history of antique English furniture . . . third edition *London, Old-World Galleries (1923)*
Pictorial handbook illustrated from the stock of the author's firm, Old-World Galleries Ltd, which supplied 'most of the furniture for the English film producing companies'. *Octavo. 200pp, over 420 photo illustrations. Original cloth. Author's presentation copy.* £9

200 **Stokes, J.** The complete cabinet-maker, and upholsterer's guide: comprising, the rudiments and principles of cabinet-making and upholstery . . . the art of drawing . . . and a number of receipts . . . embellished with explanatory and illustrative engravings, by J. Stokes. Fourth edition *London, Dean & Munday 1841*
Practical manual on cabinet-making and the associated processes (staining, lacquering, gilding, varnishing). Intended for the craftsman. *Duodecimo. 167 + (1)pp and 5 engraved plates misnumbered 2-6. Original cloth.* £20

201 **Symonds, R. W.** English furniture from Charles II to George II. A full account of the design, material and quality of workmanship of walnut and mahogany furniture of this period; and of how spurious specimens are made *London, The Connoisseur 1929*
Specially valuable for its excellent illustrations (taken from furniture in a private collection) and for its discussion of the techniques of 17th - early 18th century cabinet-making. *Folio. xviii + 322pp with 259 illustrations. Limited edition. Original cloth.* £48

202 **Talbert, Bruce** Gothic forms applied to furniture, metal-work and decoration for domestic purposes *Birmingham & London, S. Birbeck and the author (1868)*
The original and influential drawings in this book marked Talbert as an innovator in furniture design and showed him to be the first to provide consistant and progressive alternatives to High Victorian Gothic furniture. Both text and drawings reveal a firm grasp of the principles of construction and it was this, coupled with his flair for evolving attractive details that led to his success. The designs include some pieces displayed at the Paris Exhibition of 1867 and show the weight, mass and exhibition scale of some of Talbert's work. It was the decorative ideas, however, which probably had their origins in the work of Webb, Burges, Seddon and Shaw, that the book helped to popularise. *Folio. (12)pp including decorative litho title, and 30 litho plates. Publisher's gilt-decorated cloth.* £140

203 **Talbert, Bruce** Gothic forms applied to furniture.—Examples of ancient and modern furniture *London 1867, 1876 (Gregg reprint 1971)*
Slightly reduced from originals. *Quarto. 2 works in 1. 22pp and 51 plates. Original cloth.*
£6

204 **Talbert, Bruce** Examples of ancient & modern furniture metalwork tapestries decoration etc. *London, Rickatson 1876*
A supplement to Talbert's book of 1868, reprinting Talbert's introduction of that date with some supplementary notes (with comments on the revival of 'the so-called Queen Anne style'), and providing further furniture designs numbered to follow on

from the earlier work. Some copies of the book are found with the Rickatson imprint, others with the Batsford imprint, with the date 1876. *Folio. (4) +6+(6)pp and 21 plates numbered 31-51. Original gilt and blind stamped cloth.* £120

205 **Tanner, Henry** English interior woodwork of the XVI, XVII, & XVIIIth centuries. A series of the best and most characteristic examples of chimney-pieces, panelling, staircases, doors, screens, etc. *London, Batsford 1902*
Measured drawings of chimney-pieces, panelling, staircases, doors and screens in major English buildings (Hardwick, Haddon, Knole, Hatfield, Hampton Court, Chelsea Hospital, Oxford and Cambridge colleges). *Folio. viii + 10pp and 50 litho plates. Original cloth.* £10

206 **Theunissen, André** Meubles et sièges du XVIIIe siècle. Menuisiers, ébénistes, marques, plans et ornementation de leurs oeuvres *Paris, Éditions 'Le Document' 1934*
A standard work on French furniture makers and their marks with descriptions of the pieces studied including their form, dimensions, material and ornament. Includes an alphabetical and chronological table of makers, a classification of marbles with a list of their origins and indices of the collections. *Large quarto. (8) + 196 + (18)pp with many text illustrations including 13 full-page, and 50 plates outside the text of which 1 coloured, 2 large folding tables. Publisher's cloth with original printed labels. Limited edition of 1050 copies. Copy numbered 519.* £45

207 **Thiollet, F. & H. Roux** Nouveau recueil de menuiserie et de décorations intérieures et extérieures ... contenant en outre un choix de grosse menuiserie et de charpentrie légère combinées avec le fer (etc) *Paris, Bance Aîné 1837*
A companion volume to Thiollet's 'Serrurerie' (item 876), illustrating examples of woodwork. Since the publication of a previous collection of woodwork designs the authors had detected a tendency for designs to become 'plus sveltes, plus coquettes ... plus riches' and they illustrate their point by examples taken from ordinary bourgeois houses and shops. Berlin Cat 1282. *Folio. (2) +iv+ 12pp and 72 engraved plates. Contemporary quarter calf, marbled paper boards. (This copy has two additional suites of 4 plates each bound in, with the titles 'Modèles de balcons').* £225

208 **(Thomson, P.)** The cabinet-maker's assistant: a series of original designs for modern furniture, with descriptions and details of construction. Preceded by practical observations on the materials and manufacture of cabinet-work and instructions in drawing adapted to the trade *Glasgow, Blackie 1853*
A vast collection of furniture designs issued without the author's name on the title page but shown by the signatures to the plates to be by Thomson (see following item). The plates illustrate hall, dining-room, parlour, drawing-room, bedroom and 'miscellaneous' furniture–the latter category including such exotic pieces as 'fret rails and clock for steamboat cabins'. The publication was aimed at the trade and its value lay in its accurately measured designs and the detailed working instructions that accompanied them. *Folio. Engraved title. viii+lxxx+60+63+(1)pp and 101 steel engraved plates. Quarter morocco, marbled paper boards.* £140

209 **Thomson, P.** The cabinet-maker's sketchbook. A series of original details, for modern furniture *Glasgow, Mackenzie (c 1860)*
Essays on perspective, geometry and the orders, 'hints for young tradesmen', and many plates of furniture designs with an emphasis on ornamental detail. A solid mid-Victorian publication in the instructional vein of Batty Langley and the Nicholsons. *Folio. 45+(1)pp, litho title and dedication leaves and 98 litho plates, 1 large folding table. Contemporary quarter calf, rebacked.* £160

210 **Tipping, H. Avray** Old English furniture its true value and function *London, Country Life for Waring & Gillow 1928*
Quarto. viii+24pp, frontispiece and 30pp of plates. Original boards, cloth spine. £4

211 **Toller, Jane** Country furniture *Newton Abbot, David & Charles 1973*
Furniture made by local English craftsmen between 1690 and 1840. Octavo. *176pp with 11 text figures, and 16pp of photo plates. Original cloth.*
£2.95

212

212 **Toms, W.** Thirty six new, original and practical designs for chairs adapted for the drawing and dining room, parlour and hall *Bath, W. Evans (c 1835)*
A varied collection of chairs designed with curved back legs, turned and carved front legs, plain and upholstered seats, balloon and carved backs at times complete with buttoned upholstery. Toms seems to have had little success with these outline designs for the stock of this now rare book was bought as a remainder by the bookseller and publisher W. Evans who issued them with his own label. It is not clear whether the designer, who describes himself as 'carver in general', had any connection with the firm of Toms & Luscombe of New Bond Street who were active as producers of French styled furniture from 1850 to 1880. *Quarto. Title and 36 litho plates. Original printed boards, cloth spine.* **Illustration above.**
£85

213 **Ungewitter, G. G.** Plans and designs of Gothic furniture *London, Trubner 1858*
Extraordinarily uncomfortable-looking furniture in very correct Gothic styles. The techniques of the cabinet maker have no appeal whatever to the author, and he is strong on the point that ornament should emphasize, rather than conceal the

constructional features of furniture. Ungewitter's designs were originally published for a German readership and their character is less unexpected in that context. *Folio. 10pp with litho title and 48 litho plates. Quarter morocco.* £65

214 **Unwin, William Cawthorne** Exercises in wood-working for handicraft classes in elementary and technical schools *London, Longman 1887*
Folio. 8pp and 28 plates of drawings. Original portfolio. £5

215 **Verchère, J.** L'art du mobilier. Traité graphique d'ameublements des styles renaissance, Louis XIII, Louis XIV, Louis XV & Louis XVI avec coupes & plans de construction . . . accompagnés de tous les éléments d'ornementation et motifs d'architecture pour servir à la composition ou à la décoration du meuble *Paris, the author (1878 or later)*
Verchère's own copy of this scarce pattern book for the furniture trade. It is heavily corrected in pencil and red chalk, presumably with a view to the publication of a second edition. *Folio. Half title, title, 58 plates engraved on copper. Original gilt and blind stamped cloth.* £110

216 **Verlet, Pierre** French furniture and interior decoration of the 18th century *London, Barrie & Rockliff 1967*
Study in depth of the furniture and the furnishings of the great houses of 18th century France, by the Conservateur-en-Chef at the Louvre. A section at the end is devoted to inventories of the contents of three representative mansions. *Quarto. viii + 291 + (1)pp including 228 illustrations. Original cloth.* £12.50

217 **Victoria & Albert Museum** Department of Woodwork. The panelled rooms *London, HMSO 1914-24*
Rooms from Bromley, Clifford's Inn, Paris, Sizergh Castle, Hatton Garden and Waltham Abbey re-erected in the museum. *Quarto. 6 vols. Each has 24pp of text and 16pp of plates. Original printed boards.* £18

218 **Viollet-le-Duc, (Eugène)** Dictionnaire raisonnée du mobilier Français de l'époque Carlovingienne à la Renaissance *Paris, Morel 1872-5*
Remarkable survey of mediaeval furnishings, household objects, costume and armour, based on Viollet's encyclopedic knowledge and his feeling for the Gothic and perceptive even where mistaken. Volume 1 deals mainly with furniture, volume 2 with utensils, volumes 3 and 4 with dress, jewellery and toiletry, volumes 5 and 6 with armour. Scarcer than Viollet's 'Dictionary of Architecture'. *Octavo. 6 vols. (4) + 437 + (1)pp; (4) + 478 + (2)pp; (4) + 506 + (2)pp; (4) + 498 + (2)pp; (4) + 488 + (2)pp. There are some 2000 text illustrations and 90 plates including several chromolithos. Contemporary quarter morocco, gilt tooled spines.* **Illustration at end of section.** £120

219 **Viollet-le-Duc, (Eugène)** Dictionnaire raisonée du mobilier Français (Volume I) *Paris, Bance 1858*
The original issue in one volume of the first part of the Dictionary. It contains all the material specific to furniture and was issued originally as a separate publication. *Octavo. (4) + 437 + (1)pp with text illustrations and plates. Contemporary quarter morocco.* **Illustration at end of section.** £32

220 **(Waals, Peter) Alexander, Russell** The furniture and joinery of Peter Waals . . . with an introduction by Russell Alexander *Chipping Campden, The Alcuin Press 1930*
A pictorial record of the domestic furniture in the English 'craftsman' tradition which came out of the workshop at Chalford, Gloucestershire, of Peter Waals. Waals, a cabinet maker trained in Holland, had been employed by Barnsley and Gimson and was foreman-manager of the Daneway workshops until Gimson's death in 1919. The illustrations show simple pieces soundly constructed with elegant lines. *Quarto. 8pp and 26 plates with 39 photographic illustrations. Publisher's paper wrappers. Preserved in cloth folder.* £40

221 **Walker, W.** Designs for furniture *London c 1880*
302 designs for hall & library, dining room, drawing room and bedroom furniture, Talbert-ish Jacobean or classical styles; the sectional title pages are signed 'R Davey invt 77' and are in a bolder, Japanese influenced manner. *Folio. 50+(2) litho plates. Original cloth.*
£55

222 **William Wallace & Co Ltd.** Catalogue of a cabinet makers, builders, decorators, upholsterers *London c 1910*
Only a run-of-the-mill firm of furnishers and decorators, but their catalogue begins with a bang with 'Design for a Hall in the Cairene style' (featuring 'Armenian rugs, Persian saddle-bags and Kejim draperies') and is an object lesson in the art of advertising furniture and furnishings. *Oblong folio. 139pp including 4ff of coloured illustrations of linoleum and beds, many other illustrations. Original wrappers.*
£42

223 **Ward-Jackson, Peter** Victoria & Albert Museum. English furniture designs of the eighteenth century *London, HMSO 1958*
A selection, handsomely produced and extensively annotated, from the V & A's superb collection of drawings and pattern books. Introductory chapters set them in the context of English furniture history. *Quarto. (8)+68+(4)pp and 280pp of plates. Original cloth.*
£10

224 **Waring & Gillow Ltd** Some examples of Warings' furniture *London (c 1925)*
Complete catalogue of Waring & Gillow's furniture 'unequalled for artistic effect and durability', showing their commanding position in the trade. *Oblong folio. Approximately 250pp (one leaf defective) with many illustrations of which some are coloured and a further 6 plates. Original printed boards.*
£25

225 **Watson, F. J. B.** Louis XVI furniture *London, Tiranti 1960*
Scholarly, well-illustrated survey by the recent Keeper of the Wallace Collection. *Small quarto. (6)+162pp and 204pp of plates. Original cloth.*
£4

226 **Weaver, Sir Lawrence** High Wycombe furniture *London, Fanfare Press 1929*
High Wycombe has been famous for its chairs since the end of the 18th century and this is an attractive sketch of furniture making and makers in the town down to the 1920s. *Quarto. 84pp including frontispiece and 52 plates. Original decorated cloth.*
£8

227 **Wells, Percy A.** Furniture for small houses. A book of designs for inexpensive furniture with new methods of construction and decoration *London, Batsford 1920*
Octavo. x+35+(1)pp with 57 plates of sketches and photos (1 coloured). Original cloth.
£7

228 **Wells, Percy A.** Design in woodwork *London, Batsford 1934*
Octavo. xii+60pp, frontispiece, and 46 plates. Original cloth.
£4

229 **White, John P.** A complete catalogue of garden furniture and garden ornament *Bedford 1906*
Trade catalogue of a firm specializing in garden decoration. They list seats, chairs, tables, sundials, trellises, statues, vases, pergolas, bridges and gates, and every item is illustrated. Clients of the firm listed at the end include King Edward VII and Count Tolstoy. *Folio. 112pp including many text illustrations, and 2 coloured, 1 photogravure plates. Original decorated cloth.*
£20

230 **White, John P.** Garden furniture and ornament *Bedford (c 1910)*
Greatly enlarged version of the preceding catalogue, showing garden art at its pre-1914 apogee. *Folio. 240pp with many illustrations, and 3 coloured plates. An incomplete copy lacking 4 leaves.*
£20

231 **William Whiteley Ltd** Whiteleys furniture *London (c 1920)*
Furniture catalogue of one of the greatest furnishing businesses of its time. *Oblong quarto. 156pp with many illustrations. Original decorated wrappers.* £18

232 **(Woelfer, Marius)** A collection of plates of garden furniture *Germany (c 1826)*
A set of 35 lithographic plates of early 18th century garden furniture, garden buildings, gates, railings (and gondolas) in a mixture of chinese, gothick and neo-classical styles. These are probably the plates of Marius Woelfer's 'Sammlung von . . . architektonischen Garten-Verzierungen' published in Gotha c1826 (Berlin Cat 3387), but we have not had access to a copy of that work which is very scarce and not in the British Museum. *Octavo. 35 litho plates. Contemporary marbled-paper wrappers, with library label of 'Leopold Billek, Zeichenlaehrer in Teltsch'.* £38

233 **Young, Dennis & Barbara** Furniture in Britain today *London, Tiranti 1964*
Trilingual survey (English, German, French) of recent British furniture. Designers include Robin Day, Roland Gibbard, Robert Heritage, R. D. Russell. *Quarto. (168)pp including 310 illustrations. Original cloth.* £5

234 (Zanuso, Marco) **Dorfles, Gillo** Marco Zanuso designer *Rome, Editalia 1971*
Examples of Zanuso's work illustrated include chairs, television sets, and sewing machines. *Quarto. 150+(4)pp including many illustrations. Original cloth.* £4

235 **Cescinsky, Herbert** English furniture of the eighteenth century *London, Routledge 1911*
Cescinsky's first book on furniture, showing his familiarity with the material and providing a lucid account of 18th century furniture in relation to historical events and the other arts. (See also items 22-25). *Quarto. 3 vols. Each has 383+(1)pp and over 375 illustrations. Contemporary half morocco.* £90

236 **Ecke, Gustav** Chinese domestic furniture *Peking, Henri Vetch 1944.*
Important study based on much material not now accessible, with excellent photo plates and measured drawings. *Folio. (12)+49+(1)pp and 161+(1) plates. Original cloth portfolio. Limited edition of 200 copies.* £75

237 **Ecke, Gustav** Chinese domestic furniture *Rutland, Vermont, Tuttle 1973*
Facsimile reprint. *Folio. (12)+49+(1)pp and 162 plates. Original cloth.* £15

238 **Fra by og kirke** Norsk Folkemuseums samlinger *Kristiania, Norsk Folkemuseum 1912*
Illustrations of Norwegian furniture and ironwork from the 16th century. *Octavo. (8)+84pp with over 100 photo illustrations. Original decorated wrappers (with a pleasant Art Nouveau front cover).* £4

239 **(Gimson, Ernest)** (Catalogue of Gimson exhibition) *Leicester, 1969*
Good representative exhibition of Gimson furniture, metalwork and drawings, and the catalogue has much incidental information on Gimson, the Barnsleys and Peter Waals. *Octavo. 46pp. Original wrappers.* £2

240 **Jewson, Norman** By chance I did rove *Privately published 1973*
Reminiscences of Gimson's last surviving pupil, himself a very able architect and draughtsman in the Gimson – Barnsley vein. *Octavo. x+126pp with 3 text illustrations, litho frontispiece, 8 monochrome and 4 litho plates. Original cloth.* £3

241 **Prignot, Eugène** Le siège moderne *Liège, Claesen 1885*
Chairs and sofas in all styles from Louis XII to Louis XVI, illustrated on tinted litho plates. (See also item 152). *Folio. Litho title and 25 litho plates. Original printed board portfolio, worn.* £18

242 **(Pugin, A. W.)** Furniture in the House of Lords *London, HMSO 1974*
Definitive account of the furniture designed for the Lords by the younger Pugin. *Octavo. 24pp and 12 plates. Original wrappers.* £1

243 **Rudd, J. H.** Practical cabinet making and draughting *London, Benn 1912*
Octavo. (10)+172pp including many illustrations. Original cloth. £4

244 **Strange, Thomas Arthur** English furniture, decoration, woodwork & allied arts during the last half of the seventeenth century, the whole of the eighteenth century, and the earlier part of the nineteenth *London, McCorquodale (c 1900)*
Reproduces a very large number of designs from English furniture pattern books. *Octavo. (4)+368pp including very many illustrations. Original cloth, morocco spine.* £14

245 **Tinti, Mario** Il mobilio fiorentino *Milan & Rome, Bestetti & Tumminelli (c 1925)*
A study of Florentine furniture from the late 14th to the early years of the 16th century including ecclesiastical woodwork and furniture pieces. A pictorial survey with good photographs enlivened by reproductions of early paintings showing appropriate pieces. *Large quarto. 78+(4)pp and 320 full-page photo plates. Publisher's cloth; ex library of Edward Craig.* £45

246 **Wells, Percy A. & John Hooper** Modern cabinet work furniture & fitments. An account of the theory & practice in the production of all kinds of cabinet work . . . third edition revised *London, Library Press 1922*
Octavo. xii+386pp including many text illustrations, and 53 plates. Original cloth. £4

218-9

Interior Design

301 **Diderot, D. & J. L. d'Alembert** (Encyclopédie). Recueil de planches sur les sciences, les arts libéraux, les arts méchaniques, avec leurs explication *Paris, Briasson, David, Le Breton & Durand 1762-72*
Extracts of the sections relating to interior design, and various interior parts and fittings. See item 1701 in the catalogue for full details of the publication. *Each section listed is folio, preserved in paper wallet.*

a **Menuisier en batimens.** (Carpenter & joiner)
A very full coverage of this craft with two vignettes: one of the timber yard with workers cutting planks, the other inside the workshop with joiners shaping and constructing various parts. The remaining illustrations show joints, moulding, architectural woodwork of columns, cornices, niches etc., tools, while a final group of plates is concerned with the technical details of cutting curved timbers for arches, vaults, etc. *38 engraved plates with over 400 illustrations and 16pp text.* £55

b **Miroitier metteur au teint. Miroitier.** (Mirror polisher & tinter)
The making of mirror glass became an expanding trade in 18th century France with the extensive use of mirrors in interior schemes. The two workshop views show slightly different methods of silvering the glass but include rubbing and smoothing the tin, pouring mercury on the tin sheet, amalgamating the mercury with weights and fixing the tin and glass together. The tools and implements shown include details of the special stone table with its raised edges to prevent the mercury from escaping, the draining frames, etc. *Two parts in one. 8 engraved plates numbered I-II, I-VI, with 75 illustrations, and 2pp text.* £68

c **Marbrerie.** (Marbler)
Vignette of the mason's yard showing measuring, cutting and dressing of the marble, and a worker shaping a tomb. For the rest, 6 plates show designs for marble tiles with different arrangements, and inlays for the decoration of chimneys, arches, vaults and floors. 5 plates show the designs of the floors of the great Parisian churches: l'Église des 4 Nations, La Sorbonne, Nôtre Dame, the Val de Grace, and the Dôme des Invalides. The final 3 plates show 51 tools. *11 engraved plates of which 3 double-page, with 88 illustrations, and 2pp text.*
£8

302 **Adam, Robert & James** The works in architecture of the late Robert and James Adam, Esqs. Complete in three volumes. Containing plans, elevations, sections, and detail, of the principal buildings, public and private, erected in Great Britain in the reign of George the Third. With designs of every kind, both for interior and exterior decoration. One hundred and twenty-five plates. Engraved by Bartolozzi, Piranesi, Zucchi, Pastorini, Cunego, &c., &c. *London, the authors 1773 and Priesley & Weale 1822*

The definitive edition of the Adam's monumental publication issued posthumously and concentrating on Robert Adam's major schemes such as Kenwood, Syon, Luton Park, Shelburne House (now Lansdowne House) and Wynne House, as well as work for the royal family.

Robert Adam's fame rests far more on his interior designs than on his exterior facades or his planning arrangements. His belief that the contents of a room should be in perfect harmony with the architectural forms led him to design not only interior decoration but also the furniture, fittings and decorative objects: carpets, curtains, cornices, lamps, wall lights, wine coolers, firegrates, clocks and even small pieces such as inkstands. The ideas he had formed during his travels in Italy and Dalmatia were able to find their greatest scope where he was responsible for the complete expression of an interior. In these projects he revived the light and elegant decoration used in the private apartments of the ancient Romans and produced furniture of harmonizing grandeur and simplicity. The designs which are illustrated are mostly in the rectilinear style of his mature period and show the qualities of 'delicacy, gaiety, grace and beauty' which he admired so much in the ancients. The present publication, (most of which had appeared in parts between 1773 and 1786) is made up of restrikes of the copperplates which had been sold in the sale of the Adam Office in 1821. Priestley and Weale had bought all the coppers and the residue of sheets of the Adams' published and unpublished designs. They planned an extensive programme of republishing but only the 'Works' ever came to any fruition. The original typesheets were used for all of Volume I together with the original impressions of the engravings for Part I. In Volume II the text was reset and the plates restruck. A third volume was added consisting of plates of the coppers which had never previously been issued. This very rare third volume provides more illustrations of schemes which had appeared in the earlier parts as well as some new ones and includes the large double-plate view of the Adelphi; interiors and details of furniture at Syon; details of Shelburne House; the lodges in Green Park; the garden pavilion at Oaks for the Earl of Derby; and ceilings and details for Wynne House; as well as William Adam's designs for Edinburgh University. *Elephant folio. 3 volumes in one. Engraved frontispiece, 2 letterpress titles, and 5 parts: 12 + 10 + 4 + 6 + 6pp (each including part title) and 40 engraved plates (8 numbered plates to each part); letterpress title, (8)pp and 40 engraved plates (in 5 suites each with 8 numbered plates); letterpress title, (2) + 2pp and 25 unnumbered engraved plates. Old marbled-paper boards, quarter calf.*
Illustration opposite. £3250

303 **Adam, Robert & James** The works in architecture *London, the authors 1773-1786*

Separate parts from the original edition of the 'Works': large broadsheet engravings with accompanying text in English and French.

a **Designs of Sion House,** a magnificent seat of His Grace the Duke of Northumberland. Volume I. Number I. London, for the authors and sold by T. Becket, 1773.
The suite includes drawings of the gateway with its architectural details, design and perspective view of the bridge, a general plan, 2 sections of the hall with details, and the designs for various pieces of furniture. Syon was, perhaps, the most neo-classical of Adam's creations even though it was based on a Jacobean interior framework on which he imposed a variety of geometrical shapes and decorations. *Broadsheet. 7 + (1 blank)pp of text including title, and 8 engraved plates of which 1 double-page. Preserved in paper wallet.* £90

b **Designs of Lord Mansfield's Villa at Kenwood,** in the County of Middlesex. Volume I. Number II. London, the author and sold by T. Becket, 1774.
Besides plan, 3 elevations, perspective view and details of the exterior decoration, the suite includes two elevations of what is perhaps Adam's finest room – the library with its fine proportions, effective spatial treatment incorporating screened apse ends, and its tunnel vaulted ceiling. A plate of the decoration of this latter feature is also included as well as mirrors, sideboard with its plate and drinking vessels, cutlery urns and wine cooler designed for the house. *Broadsheet. 10pp of text including title, and 8 engraved plates of which 1 double-page. In paper wrappers.* **Illustration opposite.** £100

302, 303b

c **Designs of Luton House in Bedfordshire,** one of the seats of the Earl of Bute. Volume I. Number III. London, for the author and sold by T. Becket, 1775.
Adam's original plan, the altered plan, 4 elevations, details of architectural decoration, a dressing room, ceilings, curtains, pelmets, candlesticks and a fireplace for the Prime Minister's country house. Adam designs for the main house were never completed as he intended. Two large fires gutted the interiors and subsequent major remodellings considerably altered the exterior form. *Folio. 3+(1)pp and 8 engraved plates. Quarter red morocco.* £40

d **Designs of the House of Sir Watkin Williams Wynn,** Baronet, in St James's Square. Volume II. Number II. London, for the authors and sold by Peter Elmsly, 1786.
Two plans, 2 elevations, a screen wall, architectural details, two ceilings in fine contemporary colouring, and an organ case for the music room of 20 St James's Square. The interiors of this house have been maintained in a fine state of preservation and the illustrated dining room and music room ceilings remain as excellent examples of Adam's elegant linear style of the 1770s. *Folio. 3+(1)pp and 8 engraved plates. Quarter red morocco.*
£40

304 **Adam, Robert & James** The works in architecture *Dourdan, Thézard 1900-1902*

A facsimile edition of all three volumes of the Adams' designs. Generally considered to be the best of the reprints of the works to have been published. *Folio. 3 volumes in two. 30pp and 40 plates; 12pp and 40 plates; 8pp and 25 plates. Quarter morocco.* £110

305 (Adam, Robert) **Damie Stillman** The decorative work of Robert Adam *London, Tiranti 1966*
Excellent study of Adam's interior work, largely based on the Adam drawings in the Soane Museum. *Octavo. viii + 119 + (1)pp and 173 photo illustrations.* £5

306 **Adams, Maurice S. R.** Modern decorative art. A series of two hundred examples of interior decoration, furniture, lighting fittings and other ornamental features *London, Batsford 1930*
Mostly taken from the work of Maurice Adam's own interior decorating business. *Quarto. vi+(2) 240pp including many illustrations, and with 3 folding designs in pockets at end. Original cloth.* £11

307 **Arrowsmith, H. W. & A.** The house decorator and painter's guide; containing a series of designs for decorating apartments, suited to the various styles of architecture *London, Thomas Kelly 1861*
This collection of interior designs (with plates showing mainly wall schemes and applied decoration) is the epitome of the widely eclectic tastes of the 1830s and 40s. Of particular interest are the Elizabethan rooms and furnishings which were brought into fashion at this time. The firm of Arrowsmith, working from New Bond Street, London, were decorators to Queen Victoria. Abbey Life: 3. *Quarto. iv + 120pp and 61 plates (39 aquatint and 22 outline etching) of which 2 printed in sepia, 24 hand-coloured, 2 hand-tinted. Original blind stamped cloth.* £115

308 **Artistic houses** being a series of interior views of a number of the most beautiful and celebrated homes in the United States with a description of the art treasures contained therein *New York, 1883 (Blom reprint 1971)*
Interiors which illustrate the taste of the American millionaire of the 1880s – Pierpont Morgan and W. H. Vanderbilt's houses are included – and also more progressive trends – Louis C. Tiffany's Moorish cum Japanese flat in East Twenty Sixth Street, New York. *Quarto. 2 vols in one. (6)+184pp and 22 plates; (6)+184+(14)pp and 35 plates. Original cloth.* £20

309 **Aviler, C. A. d'** Cours d'architecture, qui comprend les ordres de Vignole, avec des commentaires ... nouvelle édition, enrichié de nouvelles planches, & revue & augmentée de plusieurs desseins conformes a l'usage présent, & d'un grand nombre de remarques, par Pierre-Jean Mariette *Paris, C. A. Jombert 1756*
D'Aviler's 'Cours d'Architecture', first published in 1691, and a work that enjoyed enormous prestige among French architects through its association with the name and doctrines of Vignola, appeared in second and third editions in 1710 and 1720. By the middle of the 18th century there was a demand for an updated edition, and, as Mariette explains in a very informative preface, the sections of it that required the most revision were those that dealt with interior decoration and ornamental features. Thus the descriptions and plates of such things as chimneypieces, windows, doors, mouldings and ironwork are special to this edition and not found in earlier ones; and the examples chosen are drawn, Mariette states, from the best recent French buildings. *Quarto. 1 vol bound as two. 6+(2)+xxxviii+(10)+408+(40)pp and 82 full-p and 1 smaller engraved plates, engraved title, 69 folding engraved leafs (of which 11 carry 2 engravings) together numbered to 81. Contemporary full calf, rebacked.* £125

310 **Bagge (Eric) & (Bernard) Huguet** Gazette du Bon Ton. No 10. Un boudoir et quelques meubles *Paris, Editions Lucien Vogel & Bon Ton (1920)*
Sumptuous boudoir furniture pieces with rather over-blown lines in either red lacquer with gilt-bronze mounts or gilded wood. *Four chromolitho plates numbered XLV-XLVIII. Publisher's printed-paper wrappers.* £8

311 **Bankart, George P.** The art of the plasterer. An account of the decorative development of the craft chiefly in England from the XVIth to

the XVIIIth century *London, Batsford 1908*
The best English account of the subject, with sections on stucco-duro in Italy and in England, sgraffito, wattle and daub, plasterwork generally, pargetting, the eighteenth century 'degeneration', the work of the Adam brothers and more recent trends. *Octavo. viii + (3) + (1) + 350pp including 472 illustrations. Original cloth.* £25

312 **Bankart, George P. & G. Edward** Modern plasterwork construction. Casting and fixing; fibrous, solid, and reinforced *London, Architectural Press (1926)*
Technical guide to the construction and fixing of plaster work. *Folio. 5ff text and 33 plates of working drawings. Original quarter cloth portfolio, repaired.* £15

313 **Barley, M. W.** The house and home. A review of 900 years of house planning and furnishing in Britain *London, Studio Vista 1971*
Relates architecture and furnishing to prevailing social conditions, with special emphasis on the 16th and 17th centuries. *Octavo. 208pp including 239 photo illustrations. Original cloth.* £6

314 **Battersby, Martin** The decorative twenties *London, Studio Vista 1971*
A survey of the interior decoration, fashion, furniture, ceramics, glass, textiles and other decorative arts of the decade in which a new generation of designers began to make their mark by their reaction against the luxury furniture of the early part of the century in favour of more functional forms moving towards either a stark simplicity or a use of ornament strictly applied to the form. *Quarto. 216pp with many monochrome illustrations and 41 colour plates. Original cloth.* £8.50

315 **Battersby, Martin** The decorative thirties *London, Studio Vista 1971*
A follow-up to the previous item recording the diversity of taste and trends in interior design, furnishing and the applied arts during the decade, from the stark simplicity of modernism through the intricacies of bizarre surrealism to the decadent luxury of the immediate pre-war years. *Quarto. 208pp with many monochrome illustrations and 23 colour plates (several full-page). Original cloth.* £8.50

316 **Berain, J(ean)** (Cheminées). Suite H. *(Paris, the author c 1700)*
Ten designs for chimney-pieces with low or tall mirrors, some with pilaster strips between each pair. Similar designs were introduced as part of the new decoration for royal apartments at Versailles at the end of the 17th century. First issue. Berlin Cat 343. Destailleur Notices p 163. *Untitled suite of 5 engraved plates with sizes varying from 248:315 × 278:319mm, with wide margins. In paper wallet.* £38

317 **Berain, J(ean)** (Cheminées) *(Paris, the author c 1700)*
Ten designs for chimney pieces similar to those described above. This suite shows designs with more complex details. Between each pair of chimneys is an arabesque pilaster or wall furniture: candelabra, wall-lights, plaques, console tables, vases, etc. First issue. Berlin Cat 343. Destailleur Notices p 164. *Untitled suite of 5 engraved plates, average size 225 × 328mm, with good margins. In paper wallet.* £45

318 **Berain, J(ean)** Desseins de cheminées dediez à Monsieur Jules Hardouin Mansart. Suite 1 *Paris, the author (c 1700)*
Designs probably intended for the new interiors of the Château de Meudon executed in 1699. One of the arabesque panels shown, and a chimney-piece, are known to have been used in the Cabinet du Dauphin. The chimney-pieces have tall mirrors with arched heads and broken-curved outlines, fireplace openings of diverse forms, and supports of pilasters, herms, or consoles with masks, shells and palmettes. First issue. Berlin Cat 343. Destailleurs Notices p 163. Guilmard p 91. *Title and 4 unnumbered engraved plates with sizes varying from 300 × 270mm to 262 × 383mm; wide margins. In paper wallet.* £50

319 **Berain, J(ean)** (Cheminées), Suite 8 *Paris, Thuret (c 1711)*
More chimney-piece designs, variations of preceding suites. Second issue. Berlin Cat 343. Destailleur Notice p 164. *Untitled suite of 5 unnumbered engraved plates, average size 300 × 325mm, with good margins. In paper wallet.* £32

320 **Beunat, Joseph** Recueil des dessins d'ornements d'architecture de la manufacture de Joseph Beunat, à Sarresbourg, et à Paris *(Sarresbourg & Paris, 1813)*

A trade catalogue illustrating over 700 decorative designs with details from rosettes to candelabra, and including full room designs complete with ground plans. The drawings were provided by some notable designers of the day then beginning their careers. Several plates were drawn by A. P. Giraud with dates varying from May to October 1813, others are signed Normand fils. The drawings are minutely detailed, with measurements, and are in impeccable Empire style. It is not altogether clear for what medium the decorations were intended. It is most likely that they were carried out in 'carton pierre', a substance closely analogous to papier-maché and much favoured in France, or in stone-mastic for which Heiligenthal were later known. Whatever the material the Beunat firm, which was continued by Heiligenthal at Strassbourg, was an important international agent for the distribution of Percier & Fontaine decorations throughout Europe. Berlin Cat 1387. *Small folio. 86 etched plates including title. Contemporary stippled-paper boards, vellum spine.* **Illustration below.** £240

321 **Beunat, Joseph** Recueil des dessins d'ornaments d'architecture de la manufacture de Joseph Beunat à Sarresbourg, et à Paris. – Tarif des ornaments d'architecture de la manufacture de J. Beunat, à Sarresbourg (Meurthe), du 1er octobre 1819, dont le dépôt général est établi Rue Sainte-Avoye, N° 63, hôtel Moutholon *Sarresbourg & Paris, Roussel & Jullet (c 1848) – Paris, l'Imprimerie de Gill, 1819 (but later c 1848)*

Later issue of the catalogue after the take-over by the larger firm. Here 10 more plates have been added of which two bear the imprint 'J. Jos. Heiligenthal Fab.^{c} et Decors a Strasbourg successeur de J. Beunat de Sarrebourg.' The detailed price list has the address of the depot deleted and altered in ink to 'Chez Roussel rue Michel le Comte N°18'. *Quarto. 2 vols in one. 95 plates including title, of which 1 lithographed and the rest etched; 8pp. Nineteenth century paper boards, half calf, rebacked.* **Illustration below.** £180

320-321

322 **Bielefeld, Charles Frederick** On the use of the improved papier-mâché in furniture in the interior decoration of buildings and in works of art *(London, the author c 1842)*

The wide use to which the Victorians put papier-mâché as a medium of decoration was largely due to this improved method patented by Charles Bielefeld about 1830. Subsequently it was used both in public and private interiors and even for exteriors like shop fronts. It was cheaper, safer, and as durable as plaster, could be mass-produced in a large and intricate variety of patterns and did not require specialised skills to fix. Bielefelds were one of the most successful manufacturers with works in the Strand, London and showrooms in Liverpool. The grand scale on which they worked is testified to by the decoration in the temporary House of Lords, the Grocers' Hall, several London clubs and even in the British Museum. This version of their trade catalogue contains over 1000 different items, from simple leaves and rosettes to elaborate capitals, tables and complete organ canopies. All are fully illustrated and examples are shown of panels and ceilings made up from individual items. A postscript leaf quotes press reviews with dates up to April 1842. *Quarto. 11 + (1) + 2pp, frontispiece and (127) etched and lithographed plates; vignette on title-page shows a view of the works in the Strand. Original blind-stamped cloth.* £185

323 **Bielefeld, Charles F.** Tariff of ornaments manufactured in the improved papier mâché *(London, J. B. Nichols & Sons for the manufacturers c 1845)*

Price list for 1100 items ranging from 1½d for 2½ft of mitre leaf to the extraordinary high price (for this catalogue) of £8 for a corinthian capital after the fashion of those at Tivoli. *Octavo. 37 + (3 blank)pp. Publisher's printed wrappers, in folder.* £18

324 **Biet, J.-E.** Souvenirs du Musée des Monumens Français. Collection de 40 dessins perspectifs gravés au trait réprésentant les principaux aspects sous lesquels on a pu considérer tous les monumens reunis dans ce musée. Dessinés par M. J-E. Biet et gravés par MM. Normand père et fils avec un texte explicatif par M. J-P Brès *Paris, the author 1821*

During the revolutionary period the principal monuments from looted cathedrals and churches were concentrated in the church of the Petits-Augustins in Paris, converted for use as a museum under the direction of Alexandre Lenoir (1761-1839). These interior views show the museum just before its suppression, in its finished form with the royal tombs from Saint Denis, and an 'Élysée' (a central garden) with the tomb of Heloise and Abelard. *Folio. (2) + xii + 40pp, with engraved title, (1) + 40 engraved plates and an engraved plan. Original printed boards, morocco spine and corners. Slightly foxed.* £110

325 **Black, Misha** Public interiors. An international survey *London, Batsford 1960*

Octavo. 192pp including 261 illustrations. Original cloth. £15

326 **Blondel, Jacques-François** De la distribution des maisons de plaisance, et de la décoration des édifices en général *Paris, Jombert 1737-8*

Blondel's first published work, and an important source book of rococo designs of the mid century, surveys most aspects of the country house in an effort to point out the rights and wrongs of proportion, composition and interior planning. There are many engraved plates of interiors and furnishings (including such objects as candelabra and vases). A copy of the first edition, second issue. Fowler 49. Berlin Cat 2400.
Quarto. 2 vols. (8) + xvi + 198pp with 10 engraved text figures, and 44 numbered plates; viii + 180pp with 2 engraved text figures, and 111 irregularly numbered plates. Contemporary full calf, rebacked, gilt tooled spines. £240

327 **Blondel, Jacques-François** De la distribution des maisons de plaisance et de la décoration des édifices en général *Paris, 1737-8 (Gregg reprint 1967)*

Quarto. 2 vols. 398pp and 155 plates. Original cloth. £10

328 **Blondel, J. F.** Decorations extérieures & intérieures des XVIIe & XVIIIe siècles. Monuments, décoration des apartements, boiseries & plafonds, mobilier, ferronerie, jardins, etc. *Paris, Ch. Massin (c 1910)*

Reprint of the plates of Blondel's 'Livre Nouveau ou règles des cinq ordres d'architecture', his 'Cours d'architecture' and his 'Maisons de plaisance', rearranged according to subject. A useful collection of material. *Folio. (4) + 19 + (1)pp and 225 plates. Original portfolio.* £35

329 **Borsato, Giuseppe (and Giuseppe Vallardi)** Opera ornamentale di Giuseppe Borsato pubblicata per cura dell' I.R. Accademia di Belle Arti di Venezia . . . con cenni storici dell' ornato decorativo Italiano di Giuseppe Vallardi Milanese *Milan, Vallardi 1831*

Designs for interiors and furniture by Borsato (1771-1849), Professor of Ornament at the Accademia in Venice. They are in the same spirit as those of Percier and Fontaine, and it comes as no surprise that Borsato contributed to the Venetian edition of Percier and Fontaine's 'Recueil' (item 453). *Folio. (8) + 24pp and 60 engraved plates. Quarter straight grain red morocco.* £150

330 **Boucher, (Juste-François)** (Cahiers d'ameublement et décoration interieur) *Paris, Le Pere & Avaulez (c 1775)*

Boucher, the younger, also designed architectural details and interior fitments as well as furniture (see item 14). His designs reflect the simple, formal treatment which became fashionable in interior arrangements in small private houses in France after 1770 and are excellent examples of neo-classical decoration. The following suites are the original issues from his works. Berlin Cat 1267. Guimard p 230.

a **21e Cahier. Cheminées à la moderne.**
Typical chimney-pieces: small, low, rectangular in shape, and surmounted by large mirrors set within rectangular frames decorated with great restraint. *Six plates numbered 121-126. Average size 325 × 200mm. In paper wallet.* £18

b **22e Cahier. Panneaux avec porte.**
Designs for wall panels with matching doors, including examples of door with mirror panels or window openings. *Six plates numbered 127-132. Average size 330 × 200mm. In paper wallet.* £24

c **26e Cahier. Portes à placard.**
Designs for main doors given an architectural treatment. *Six plates numbered 151-156. Average size 330 × 205mm. In paper wallet.* £20

d **27e Cahier. Cheminées à la moderne.**
Details of rectangular chimney openings with simply-decorated shallow mantel, supported by pilasters or consoles. *Six plates numbered 157-162. Average size 200 × 327mm. In paper wallet.* £18

e **44e Cahier. Dessus de porte.**
Eleven designs for overdoors with classical motifs, in painted grisaille or bas relief. In small houses overdoors and panel heads frequently formed the only ornamentation on plain panelled walls. *Six plates numbered 259-264. Average size 325 × 200mm. In paper wallet.* £25

331 **Boucher, Juste-François fils** Receuil de décoration intérieur *Paris, Librarie centrale des Beaux-Arts (c 1890)*

Facsimile reprint of the Chereau edition of 1775 of Boucher's interior designs showing elevations of wall schemes, panelling and alcoves for various types of rooms including libraries and bathrooms, as well as some designs for double-doors, buffets, altars, and some furniture pieces. The designs are reprints of the originals recorded in Guilmard p 231 A-P. *Folio. (8)pp and 60 plates in exact facsimile of the original engravings. Marbled-paper portfolio with ties.* £35

332 **(Breuhaus, Fritz August)** Das Haus in der Landschaft. Ein Landsitz unserer Zeit nach den Entwurfen des Architekten Fritz August Breuhaus *Stuttgart, Hoffmann (1927)*

Breuhaus's Landhaus Andreae, built by him in 1925-26 and completely furnished with the work of contemporary German industrial designers, is here recorded in many pages of illustrations. *Quarto. 16pp including 5 plans, and 60pp of photo plates and 3 coloured plates. Original cloth.* £10

333 **Broadcasting House** *London, BBC 1932*

Description of the building, with many illustrations of interiors and details. The architect was Val Myer and the interiors were chiefly by Raymond McGrath (see items 1232-3), with assistance from Wells Coates, Chermayeff and Maufe. *Quarto. 30pp, with 116 illustrations and accompanying text, and several coloured plans. Original cloth.* £12

334 **Bullet, (Pierre)** Verschyde schoorsteen mantels nieulykx geinventeert door Mr Bullet, etc. *Amsterdam, Reiner & Josua Ottens (c 1700)*

Simple chimney pieces of the type found in modest houses after 1680 and in the less important apartments of larger buildings. The examples are pirated Dutch copies taken not only from the inventions of Bullet but also from Francard, Pierre and Jean le Pautre, and from Vennekool. Berlin Cat 3787. *22 numbered engraved plates, sizes varying from 130:172 × 211:285mm, with good margins. In paper wallet.* £60

335 (Burges, William) **Pullan, R. P.** The House of William Burges *London 1886*

A group of plates which are actual mounted photographs of the contents of Burges' house, showing principally carving and metalwork, and the group includes a general view of Burges' study. *13 folio plates, numbered 1, 4-9, 11, 13, 14, 16, 18, 22. Preserved in cloth folder.* £60

336 **Carrington, Noel** Design and decoration in the home *London, Country Life 1938*

Octavo. 144pp including 281 illustrations. Original cloth. £10

337 **Carrington, Noel** Colour and pattern in the home *London, Batsford 1954*

Octavo. 160pp including many illustrations. £8

338 **Cassell's Household Guide:** being a complete encyclopaedia of domestic and social economy and forming a guide to every department of practical life *London, Cassell (c 1880)*

Deals both with household management and the furniture, decoration and contents of the house. Evidently much used by middle class Victorian housewives, and its canons of taste, however conventional, reflect contemporary fashions. Incorporates useful indices. *Quarto. 4 vols. iv + 394pp; (2) 39 + 8pp; (2) + 381 + (1)pp; (2) + 397 + (1)pp, with many text illustrations. Each vol has additionally a colour frontispiece and 1 colour plate. Original decorated cloth.* £30

339 **Chamblin, Bullet de** Décoration ... de la maison de M. Dodun *(Paris, Jean) Mariette (1727)*

Interior decoration of the salon, anti-room and grand cabinet of the house of M. Dodun, the Comptroller of Finances. The house in rue de Richelieu, Paris, still exists but the fine rococo decoration, recorded only in these plates, was destroyed or removed in the 19th century. A suite from Mariette's 'Architecture françoise'. *Oblong folio. 6 engraved plates, average size 230 × 325mm, with good margins. In paper wallet.* £42

340 **(Chauveau, F.)** (Portes du Palais des Tuileries) *(Paris, c 1670)*

A very fine suite of large engravings of doors in the Louis XIV style, from the Tuileries palace. The designs which were probably made under the direction of Le Brun show two-leafed doors with superimposed rectangular and square panels decorated with trophies, cartouches and the attributes of the royal family. Every detail of the door is shown including the ornamental and highly decorated locks, bolts, and hinges. *Folio. 8 unnumbered engraved plates without title or signature. Average size 380 × 225mm. Good impressions. In paper wallet.* £65

341 **Clément d'Armont, Loïc & Michel Lacroix** Cheminées des pays de la Loire du Moyen Age au XVIIIe siècle. Préface de M. André Chastel *Paris, the authors & Léonce Laget 1973*

Traces the technical and decorative evolution of the fireplace up to the end of the 18th century in 100 examples from modest buildings in the area between Blois and Angers. *Large quarto. xxviii + 404pp including 300 full-page measured drawings and 100 photographic illustrations. Publisher's cloth.* £6.50

342 **Condy, Nicholas** Cothele, on the banks of the Tamar, the ancient seat of the Rt Honble the Earl of Mount Edgcumbe. With a descriptive account... by the Rev. F. V. J. Arundell *London, for the author (c 1840)*

A fine set of interior views straight out of Walter Scott: 'What interest, then, must attach to Cothele, when not only the building remains as it stood in the time of Henry VII, but all the rooms retain their ancient furniture, and the latest is not more modern than the reign of Elizabeth! What an exquisite feast for the antiquary, and not less so to every one possessing the slightest longing for an insight into the ancient mansion of an old English knight!'. The book carries no publication date but is dedicated to an Earl of Mount Edgcumbe who inherited in 1839. Abbey Scenery: 414. *Folio. 35+(1)pp, with dedication leaf, plan and 17 tinted lithographs (including title) by Day & Haghe. Contemporary quarter morocco, gilt decorated cloth boards.* **Illustration above.** £85

343 **Conran, Terence** The House Book *London, Mitchell Beazley Publishers Ltd 1974*

A 'Habitat' view of how to achieve a style in interior design, with sections on each aspect and contributions from a large number of design journalists and specialists in the individual fields. *Oblong quarto. 448pp including several hundred coloured photographic illustrations. Publisher's decorated boards.* £10.95

344 **Conway, Moncure Daniel** Travels in South Kensington with notes on decorative art and architecture in England *London, Trübner 1882*

The best 19th century account of the genesis and collections of the South Kensington Museum, coupled with an admirable essay on contemporary London interiors (Owen Jones's interior for Alfred Morrison's house in Carlton House Terrace; George Aitchison's work for Frederick Lehmann and Lord Leighton; Alma-Tadema's house by Morris & Co). Bedford Park gets a chapter to itself at the end. *Octavo. 234pp with text illustrations. Original cloth.* £15

345 **Crouch, Joseph & Edmund Butler** The apartments of the house their arrangement furnishing and decoration *London, (Unicorn Press) 1900*

Designs for interiors by a Birmingham architectural partnership: they were influenced both by the Arts and Crafts movement and by the prevailing fashion for neo-Elizabethan and neo-Stuart furnishings, and half timber, open beams, etc. are recurring themes. *Octavo. xii+197+(5)pp and 139 illustrations mostly on plates. Original cloth.* £15

346 **Curran, C. P.** Dublin decorative plasterwork of the seventeenth and eighteenth centuries *London, Tiranti 1967*

Octavo. x+124pp and 4 colour plates and 164pp of monotone plates. Original cloth. £5

347 **Daly, César** L'architecture privée au XIXe siècle. Nouvelles maisons de Paris et des environs. Première série (-Deuxième série-Troisième série) *Paris, Librairie Générale de l'architecture 1870, 1872, 1877*

Daly (1809-93), founder and editor of the 'Revue Générale de l'Architecture', was one of the leading architectural theoreticians of the day and better equipped than any one to record the domestic architecture of Paris as it developed under the Second Empire. These three series of volumes provide a splendid record of the new Paris of Baron Haussmann (to whom the work is dedicated) with plans, elevations, details and coloured interior views; the third series, devoted to interior painting, is particularly fine (and scarce). *Folio. 3 series in 8 vols. First series: (Hotels privés) 32pp with 5 illustrations, and 57 engraved plates; (Maisons à loyer) (4)pp and 103 engraved plates; (Villas suburbaines) (4)pp and 81 engraved plates. Second series: (Décorations extérieures et interieures) 6 + 2 + 2pp and 76 engraved plates; (Villas-chalets-jardins) 12pp and 82 plates; (Décorations intérieures) 12pp and 80 plates. Third series: 12 + 4 + 4pp and 55 chromolitho plates; 8 + 4 + 4pp and 55 chromolitho plates. Series 1 and 2 are bound in contemporary quarter red morocco, gilt tooled spines; Series 3 in contemporary quarter brown morocco.* £325

348 **Decker, Paul** Fürstlicher Baumeister, oder: Architectura civilis *Augsburg, Peter Dettleffsen (vol 2: Joh. Jak. Lotter) for Jeremiah Wolff, 1711 (Anhang zum ersten Theil: 1713)-1716*

Paul Decker (1677-1713) one of the most important exponents of German Baroque, went to Berlin to study under Schlüter then returned to his native Nuremberg to become architect of Salzbach in Bavaria and later to the Bayreuth Court where his influence is clear, for instance in Ranz's Hermitage built between 1715 and 1718. He had little opportunity of putting his grandiose fantasy to practical test, but in the pages of his book he designed one of the most complete palace schemes any King of the time could have wished for. These designs, superbly engraved by the best masters of the period, show an extension of the high-point of baroque building, sculpting and quadratura painting, while at the same time spreading the taste for Louis XIV decoration as defined in the work of Berain. Berlin Cat 1990. Cicognara 487. Fowler 97. Guilmard pp 419-420. *Oblong folio. 3 parts in one. (10)pp, engraved frontispiece and 59 engraved plates (some folding); title leaf and 40 engraved plates (some folding) in the Anhang; title leaf and 32 plates (some folding). The two main titles in red and black. Marbled-paper boards, quarter morocco.* **Illustration below.** £950

348-9

349 **Decker, Paul** Fürstlicher Baumeister oder: Architectura civilis. Erster Theil *Augsburg, Peter Detleffsen for Jeremiah Wolff 1711*
The first part only of the previous item. This part is devoted almost exclusively to the interiors of Decker's imaginary palace and shows the plans, wall schemes, ceilings, panel decoration, interior features of all the main rooms. *Folio. (20)pp, engraved frontispiece and 59 engraved plates. Contemporary full calf, gilt.* **Illustration on previous page.** £250

350 **Decoration of the English home** New series. Nos. 1-20 *London, July 1934-December 1936*
A monthly periodical devoted to modern trends in interior decoration, more radical than 'The Studio' and 'Homes and Gardens'. Contributors to these issues include Maurice Adams, Paul Nash, R. D. Russell, John Piper and Edward Carrick. *Quarto. 2 vols. Cloth.*
£40

351 **Delaunay, Sonia** Compositions couleurs idées *Paris, Moreau (c 1930)*
An important collection of abstract designs by this remarkable artist and colourist. See also item 1307. *Folio. (4)pp and 40 coloured plates on card paper. Original cloth folder with printed upper cover. Preserved in cloth box.*
£140

352 **DeVoe, Shirley Spaulding** English papier maché of the Georgian and Victorian periods *London, Barrie & Jenkins 1971*
Octavo. xviii + 193 + (1)pp with 180 text illustrations and frontispiece. Original cloth. £9

353 **Down, H. Ashford** The art of window display. A complete guide to modern methods of shop window publicity, shop lighting, interior display and the work of the display man *London, Pitman 1931*
Octavo. xii + 214pp including 124 text illustrations. Original cloth, ex library. £5

354 **Downing, Alexander Jackson** The architecture of country houses; including designs for cottages, farm-houses, and villas, with remarks on interiors, furniture, and the best modes of warming and ventilating *New York, D. Appleton & Co 1854*
The last and best-known work of Downing (1815-52) the landscape gardener and architect who was the American counterpart of Loudon, and dominated American domestic architecture and decoration in the second quarter of the nineteenth century. The book contains well illustrated and informative chapters on interior decoration and furniture, and promotes the 'bracketed style' which was very influential in America, particularly in the trans-Atlantic interpretation of the Eastlake style. The first edition. *Octavo. x + 484pp including over 250 text illustrations and 37 sepia printed wood engraved plates. Original decorated cloth. Slightly dampstained copy.*
£45

355 **Downing, A. J.** The architecture of country houses ... with a new introduction by J. Stewart Johnson *New York, 1854 (Dover reprint 1969)*
Octavo. xxiv + (2) + 484pp with text illustrations, and 37 full-page plates. Original wrappers.
£2.25

356 **Dupuy Frères** (Catalogue of mouldings for plasterwork) *Paris (c 1900)*
Folio. 44pp of plates (of which 22pp photo plates). Cloth. Ex Waring & Gillow studio copy.
£17

357 **Edwards, Frederick jun.** Our domestic fire-places: a treatise on the economical use of fuel and the prevention of smoke. With observations on the patent laws. Second edition *London, Robert Hardwicke 1865*
Study and discussion of types of grate and of ventilation by a manufacturer of 'smokeless' fire grates. He illustrates designs already patented and his own improvements on them. *Octavo. viii + 110pp, and 16 unnumbered plates with facing text leaves. Original blind stamped cloth.*
£20

358 **Elder-Duncan, J. H.** The house beautiful and useful. Being practical suggestions on furnishing and decoration *London, Cassell 1907*
A practical view of interior decoration from an experienced architectural journalist, capable of dismissing Art Nouveau as 'ephemeral rubbish' but a loyal follower of Morris who features furniture designed by F. L. Griggs, a piano by Lutyens, etc. A useful feature is information on manufacturers' current models and prices. *Quarto. 224pp with many illustrations. Original limp cloth wrappers.* £30

359 **Facey, James William** Practical house decoration. A guide to the art of ornamental painting, the arrangement of colours in apartments and the principles of decorative design. With some remarks upon the nature and properties of pigments *London, Crosby Lockwood 1886*
Short but surprisingly comprehensive handbook to decorative painting (covering colours and colour theory, polychrome work, ornament, symbolism, and all forms of wall covering). *Octavo. xii + 184pp including 55 text illustrations. Original blind stamped cloth.* £11

360 **Ferrari, Giulio** Lo stucco nell' arte Italiana *Milan, Hoepli (c 1905)*
Excellent illustrated survey of Italian plasterwork from Etruscan times, with many examples of the Baroque and Rococo periods. *Quarto. 21 + (3)pp and 205 + (1) photo plates. Original cloth.* £45

361 **Feuchère, Leon** L'art industriel. Recueil de dispositions et de décorations intérieures comprenant des modèles pour toutes les industries d'ameublement et de luxe (etc) *Paris, Goupil (1853)*
Designs for interiors and furnishings for the most palatial mansions of the period. No expense is spared and no style neglected – Louis XV, Byzantine, Gothic, Renaissance, Moorish, Chinese. The resulting ensembles are undeniably luxurious and they foreshadow the bourgeois palaces that were erected in Paris at the height of the Second Empire. *Folio. (4)pp and 72 engraved plates. Cloth, with original printed paper wrappers pasted on front and back covers.* £110

362 **Folnesics, Josef** Alte Innenräume Österreichischer Schlösser Paläste und Wohnhäuser. Zweite Auflage *Vienna, Anton Schroll 1921*
The interiors of some of the most famous 18th century Austrian buildings: palaces in Vienna, the Residenz at Salzburg, and the country seats of Prince Liechtenstein, Count Lamberg and Count Czernin. *Folio. (4)pp and 120 photo plates. Original cloth portfolio.* £28

363 **(Ford, Richard)** Apsley House and Walmer Castle. Illustrated by plates and description *London, John Mitchell and P. & D. Colnaghi 1853*
A sumptuous illustrated record of the Duke of Wellington's London and Kentish residences The chromolitho plates are by Boys, Dibdin, Dillon and Nash and are intended to bring before the eye 'the actual aspect of sites and objects left exactly as when He (the Duke) quitted them for the last time'. The text by Ford, author of a famous guide to Spain and an expert on Velazquez, does an admirable job in relating the plates (mainly interior views) to the Duke's life and personal characteristics and shows how nearly the houses and their contents reflected the Duke's personality. *Folio. Litho title (by Hanhart), (8) + 7 + (1)pp and 10 chromolitho plates. Original cloth portfolio, morocco spine.* £180

364 **Fowler, John & John Cornforth** English decoration in the eighteenth century *London, Barrie & Jenkins 1974*
Full study of all aspects of 18th century decoration in relation to the social history of the period. *Folio. 288pp with 40 colour illustrations and 234 monochrome illustrations. Original cloth.* £10

365 **Fréchet, André – Dufrêne, Maurice** (editors) Intérieurs modernes. Mobilier & décoration. 44 ensembles exécutés et présentés par des artistes décorateurs français modernes. – Ensembles mobiliers. 2me série *Paris, Ch. Moreau (c 1920, 1927)*
Two works from the important series on French contemporary decoration published in the twenties and thirties by Moreau and now invaluable as a record of that period. In a series of

photographic plates Fréchet illustrates the interiors and furniture of the generation of rational and restrained designers who had come to the fore in the second decade of the 20th century: Follot, Rapin, Bouchet, Groult, Jourdain, Bagge and the distinctive and elegant Ruhlmann. Dufrêne shows the later style of these designers together with others such as Sognot, Lalique, Sue et Mare, Poiret, and Levard all practising the style now known as Art Deco. *Folio. 2 works in one. (8)pp and 31 of 32 photolitho plates; (4)pp and 32 photolitho plates. Original portfolio with printer's decorative label.* £65

366 Grandjean de Montigny, (A.) Plan, coupe, élévation et détails de la restauration du palais des états et de sa nouvelle salle à Cassel, en Westphalie *Paris (1810)*

The author, a pupil of Percier and Fontaine, worked at Cassel for King Jerome of Westphalia (Napoleon's younger brother) between 1810 and 1814. Here he records his alteration for the King of the former Musée Frédéric (built for the Landgraf Friedrich II in 1769-79) and his construction of a new neo-classical chamber for the Westphalian parliament. Berlin Cat 2171. *Folio. (6)pp and 10 engraved plates. Contemporary marbled paper boards, with the original printed paper wrappers bound in.* £150

367 Granet, Jean Joseph (Histoire de l'Hôtel royal des Invalides) *(Paris, Desprez 1736)*

The Invalides was built to designs by Libéral Bruant between 1670 and 1677 and its great domed chapel was added by J. H. Mansart during the 1680s. The interior of the chapel, decorated with murals by La Fosse, Jouvenet, Coypel and others, was not completed until after 1708, and Granet's was the first publication on the Invalides to illustrate it. The present item comprises the plates of the book only, but these were its most valuable feature – the text was unsatisfactory and had to be rewritten by Pérau (see item 449) – and the engravings of the chapel by C. N. Cochin are found here in their earliest state. Berlin Cat 2504. *Folio. 104 engraved plates numbered 1-103 and 16*; plates 3-20, 29-32, 37, 63, 75, 88 and 101 are double-page. Contemporary full mottled calf, gilt tooled spine.* £185

368 Greenwood, W. E. The Villa Madama Rome. A reconstruction *London, Tiranti 1928*

A monograph on one of the most important villas of the Italian Renaissance, the Villa Madama, built for Cardinal Giulio de' Medici by Raphael, Peruzzi and Giulio Romano. This was an attempt to reconstruct a classical villa suburbana as near as possible to that described by Pliny. Greenwood concentrates on the internal decoration of the villa carried out by Raphael and his pupils. Next to the Vatican Loggie decorations these designs have been among the most important influences on later generations practising the decorative arts. Greenwood reconstructs the ruins in a blaze of colour which was intended to be a source of inspiration for the mural decorators of the twenties, and also provides a thoroughly documented textual description with historical notes. *Quarto. (2)+viii+76pp 16 monochrome and 18 colour plates containing 44 drawings and photographs. Original decorated cloth. Author's presentation copy with his signature.* £32

369 Guilmard, D. La décoration au XIX siècle. Décor intérieur des habitations. Composé dessiné ou exécuté par les principaux artistes décorateurs de Paris *Paris (c 1870)*

Folio. 40 tinted litho plates of interiors and details by Collette after Prignot, Sauvestre and others. Contemporary quarter morocco, marbled paper boards. £65

370 Halfpenny, William & John Rural architecture in the Chinese taste, being designs entirely new ... with full instructions for workmen ... the whole invented and drawn by Willm & Jno Halfpenny architects ... the 2d edition, 1752 *London, Sayer 1752*

A pattern book intended to cater for the prevailing demand of the period for 'Chinese' designs. Of special interest here are the Halfpennys' plates of Rococo-Chinese furniture, door and window frames, and chimneypieces. The book occupies an important place in the history of Chinese influence on 18th century European architecture (it was well-known in Germany and North America as well as in Britain). *Octavo. Engraved title, 8+8+8+(2)+2pp and 60 engraved plates (11 folding). Contemporary full calf, rebacked.* **Illustration opposite.** £165

370-3

371 **Halfpenny, William & John** Rural architecture in the Chinese taste ... the 3d. edition *London, Sayer 1755*

The third edition contains 4 additional plates. This is the first state of it, with the date 1755 on the title and dates on the part titles. *Octavo. 8 + 8 + 4 + 8 (misnumbered)pp, engraved title and 64 engraved plates (15 folding). Full contemporary tree calf, gilt and blind tooled, gilt coat of arms on covers.* **Illustration above.** £185

372 **Halfpenny, William & John** Rural architecture in the Chinese taste *London, 1755 (Blom reprint 1972)*

Octavo. 64 plates. Original cloth. **Illustration above.** £4

373 **Halfpenny, William & John** Rural architecture in the Chinese taste ... the 3rd edition *London, Sayer, (c 1760)*

Second, undated state of the third edition. *Octavo. 8 + 8 + 4 + 8pp, engraved title and 64 engraved plates (of which 15 folding). Original embossed paper wrappers with contemporary hand colouring. An uncut copy. Preserved in drop-back box.* **Illustration above.** £200

374 **Haweis, Mrs. H. R.** The art of decoration *London, Chatto & Windus 1881*

Octavo. xxiv + 408pp including 74 text figures. Original cloth. £9

375 **Heaton, Aldam** Beauty and art *London, Heinemann 1897*
A collection of essays, covering inter alia interior decoration and furniture, and rather unexpectedly offering one of the liveliest bibliographical surveys of furniture pattern books. *Octavo. xi + (1) + 208 + (2)pp including hand coloured title-page. Original cloth.* £10

376 **John Aldam Heaton & Co.** (Catalogue of chimney pieces, glass, decoration, furniture) *London (1900)*
Trade catalogue illustrated by photo plates by Waterlows, including some coloured reproductions of wall and ceiling paper designs. *Folio. 59ff, mostly of plates. Original decorated gilt stamped cloth.* £25

377 **Aldam Heaton & Co. Ltd.** (Catalogue of wallpaper, stained glass, furniture, etc.) *London (1920)*
Quarto. (6)pp and 45 photo plates. Original cloth. £16

378 **Hessling, Egon** Die schönsten Hausthüren und Thore Berlins und seiner Umgebung ausgefuhrt in holz ... *Berlin, Hessling (c 1895)*
First series. *Folio. Title, (4)pp and 40 photo plates. Original printed portfolio.* £15

379 **Higgins, W. Mullingar** The house painter; or, decorator's companion: being a complete treatise on the origin of colour, the law of harmonious colouring, the manufacture of pigments, oils, and varnishes; and the art of house painting, graining, and marbling *London, Thomas Kelly, 1841*
Higgins, formerly Professor of mechanical and experimental philosophy at Guy's Hospital, designated himself an architect and seems to have designed a shop in Staines as well as the grandstand at Ascot racecourse. He wanted to improve the general standard of house painting and raise the taste of decorating. He believed his work to be the only complete treatise on house-painting and it certainly includes more of the basic philosophy and aesthetics of the subject by discussing the origin, philosophy and harmony of colours and their emotive qualities besides including the practical application of paintwork, and concludes with a brief history of house painting. The illustrations which include 15 examples each of wood graining and marbling are interesting for being executed by hand with a brush and varnish to show exactly what effect could be obtained. *Quarto. iv +(2) + 233 + (1)pp and 30 hand-painted and varnished plates. Publisher's embossed cloth.* £80

380 **Hirth, Georg** Das Deutsche Zimmer der Gothik und Renaissance des Barock-, Rococo- und Zopfstils. Dritte stark vermehrte Auflage *Munich, Hirth 1886*
Comprehensive historical study with a large number of relevant illustrations. *Quarto. xii + 452pp including 370 text figures. Cloth.* £10

381 **Hoffmann, Herbert** (editor) Schöne Raume. Zweite Folge. Eine Sammlung ausgefuhrter Wohn- und Schlafräume, Arbeitszimmer, Buchereien, Speisezimmer, Kuchen und Kinderzimmer *Stuttgart, Hoffmann 1936*
Illustrated survey of contemporary interior design: with extensive coverage of work by Martin Elsaesser, Josef Op Gen Oorth and Walther Sobotka. *Quarto. 104pp with 169 illustrations. Original printed wrappers.* £18

382 **Holme, Charles** (editor) Modern British domestic architecture and decoration *London, The Studio 1901*
Features designs by Frank Brangwyn (stained glass, enamels, carpets, furniture), Crouch & Butler, Ambrose Heal, Selwyn Image, C. R. Mackintosh, Baillie Scott, Voysey and many others. *Large octavo. 212pp (of which pp 33-212 are illustrations). Contemporary quarter cloth.* £20

383 **Holmes, John M.** The art of interior design and decoration *London, Longman 1951*
On the theory of interior design. *Octavo. xii + 196pp with many illustrations. Original cloth.*
£4

384 **Homes and Gardens** (called Our Homes and Gardens until 1923) *London, June 1919-May 1939*
Vols 1-20. Complete run for the interwar period of this periodical devoted to the contemporary English house, its decoration, its furniture and fittings, and its garden. Each monthly number has an article on an interesting new house or conversion, by architects and designers who include Baillie Scott, Clough Williams-Ellis, Oliver Hill, Maurice Adams, Robert Atkinson, C. H. B. Quennell and many others – and articles in the late 1930s feature such emerging stars as Basil Spence, Hugh Casson and Seely & Paget. Houses of well-known personalities are also prominent; those covered in 1938 include Emlyn Williams, Ivor Novello, the Duke of Kent and Adolf Hitler (a very eulogistic article on his Bavarian chalet published in November 1938). Otherwise there is much material on furniture, light fittings and interior decoration; on modern developments in heating and kitchen planning; and on garden planting and layout. *Quarto. 20 vols, each containing 12 monthly issues totalling approximately 450 pages, with very many photo illustrations. Original cloth.* £325

385 **The House Decorator and School of Design** Nos. 1–28. *London, 18 June-24 Dec 1880*
The first 28 issues of a weekly journal devoted to decoration and design. Each issue contains 16 pages, partly filled by articles on carpentry and interior decoration – and partly by trade news. Contributors include J. W. Facey (see item 359). The front page of each issue carries a design for a piece of furniture, ornament or a building. *Folio. 416 + 32pp and 1 litho plate bound in at end. Cloth.* £15

386 **Ionides, Basil** Colour and interior decoration *London, Country Life 1926*
Octavo. xiv + 82pp, and 34pp of monochrome plates, 8 colour plates. Original quarter cloth. £6

387 **Ionides, Basil** Colour in everyday rooms. With remarks on sundry aspects of decoration *London, Country Life 1934*
Octavo. 116pp, colour frontispiece and 40pp of plates. Original cloth. £8

388 **George Jackson & Sons** Part of the collection of releive decorations as executed in papier maché & carton pierre, by George Jackson & Sons, Rathbone Place, London *London, the authors and John Weale 1849*
An early and distinctly impressive trade catalogue, illustrating much of the firm's stock (and work carried out by the firm at Ironmongers' Hall, the Mansion House, St Paul's, Knightsbridge, St Saviour's, Southwark, and in Westminster Abbey for Queen Victoria's Coronation). Like many trade catalogues this is a composite production, the lithographic plates being in part by C. Graf, in part by Day & Haghe, and in part by Day & Son, and although two plates are apparently absent it is likely that their omission from this issue of the catalogue is deliberate (the items illustrated on them no longer being in stock). *Folio. Title, 2pp and 65 litho plates numbered 1-30, 32-50, 52-63 and (2) unnumbered. Cloth.* £150

389 **George Jackson, & Sons Ltd.** (Examples of a few architectural ornaments, etc., manufactured in fibrous plaster, carton pierre, and wood) Volume 1 Ceilings, friezes, cornices *London, 1902*
Quarto. (8)pp text and 105 litho or photo plates. Original boards, morocco spine. A letter from the firm dated June 1914 and loosely inserted regrets that the catalogue is very old 'as with the thousands of models and moulds we have got we find it is impossible to publish another'. £40

390 **Jacobson & Co.** (Plaster and cement stucco mouldings) *New York, 1915*
Trade catalogue. *Quarto. 196pp, mostly of plates. Original cloth.* £18

391 **Jennings, H. J.** Our homes and how to beautify them. Third edition *London, Harrison 1902*
Practical guide to interior decoration, the author relying heavily on Messrs Waring & Gillow for examples of furniture and for illustrations of decorative schemes. *Octavo. 254pp including 98 text illustrations and 46 plates. Original quarter vellum.* £9

392 **Jennings, Arthur Seymour & Guy Cadogan Rothery** The modern painter and decorator. A practical treatise on house, church, theatre and public buildings painting and decorating *London, Caxton Publishing Co (1924)*

Three-volume guide to the painting and decorating business, vol 1 essentially on painting and materials, vol 2 on wallpapering and other sidelines, vol 3 on design, style and the relation of decoration with architecture. *Octavo. 3 vols. x + 196pp and 36 plates; viii + 196pp and 36 plates; viii + 180pp and 36 plates. Original cloth.* £18

393 **Jourdain, Francis** Gazette du Bon Ton, No 6. Un studio, un coin de feu, une chambre à coucher et une chambre d'enfants *Paris, Editions Lucien Vogel & Bon Ton, July 1920*

Four varied interiors illustrating the simplicity of Jourdain's style where everything is reduced to its basic elements and adapted to a precise end. Jourdain was one of the earliest exponents of the new modernism and the founder of the Salon d'Automne. *Four litho plates, partly coloured, numbered XXIX-XXXII. Publisher's printed-paper wrappers.* £10

394 **Jourdain, M.** English decoration and furniture of the early Renaissance (1500-1650). An account of its development and characteristic forms *London, Batsford 1924*

The first half of the book is devoted to decoration (woodwork, carving, inlay, painting, plasterwork, etc.), the second to furniture. Fully illustrated by photographs and measured drawings. *Folio. xviii + 306pp with 427 text illustrations and 10 plates, 8pp subscribers list. Original cloth.* £28

395 **Jourdain, M.** English decorative plasterwork of the Renaissance *London, Batsford (1926)*

Scholarly study of English plasterwork from 1540 to the age of Adam, with an index of recorded plasterers. Her illustrations are largely drawn from G. P. Bankart's private collection of photographs (cf. item 311). *Quarto. xiv + 258pp with 200 illustrations. Original cloth.* £30

396 (Jourdain, Margaret) **Lenygon, Francis** Decoration in England from 1660 to 1770 *London, Batsford 1914*

Margaret Jourdain's first important book, published under the pseudonym Francis Lenygon. The illustrations for it had been collected by Col. H. H. Mulliner, 'who was a gun-mounting fan, a furniture collector and Autolycus purchaser of all kinds of businesses' and had sold Batsfords his blocks and the rights in them for £900 (Bolitho: A Batsford Centenary, p 53); and Mulliner's contribution presumably prevented Jourdain from taking the credit for her accompanying text. *Quarto. x + 296pp with 354 text illustrations, 5 coloured. Original cloth.* £28

397 **Jourdain, M.** English interiors in smaller houses. From the Restoration to the Regency, 1660-1830 *London, Batsford (1923)*

Very handsome pictorial study, illustrating inter alia a number of London interiors now destroyed. *Quarto. (8) + 202pp, frontispiece and 211 illustrations. Original cloth.* £15

398 **Jourdain, M.** English decoration and furniture of the later XVIIIth century (1760-1820). An account of its development and characteristic forms *London, Batsford (1922)*

Quarto. xvi + 269 + (1)pp with 426 illustrations. Original cloth. £35

399 **Jourdain, Margaret** English interior decoration 1500 to 1830. A study in the development of design *London, Batsford 1950*

This brings together the sections on decoration from her earlier books, revised in the light of thirty years research. The material added includes examples of decoration in America in the colonial period. *Quarto. xii + 84pp and 128pp of monochrome plates, 5 colour plates, some text illustrations. Original cloth.* £25

400

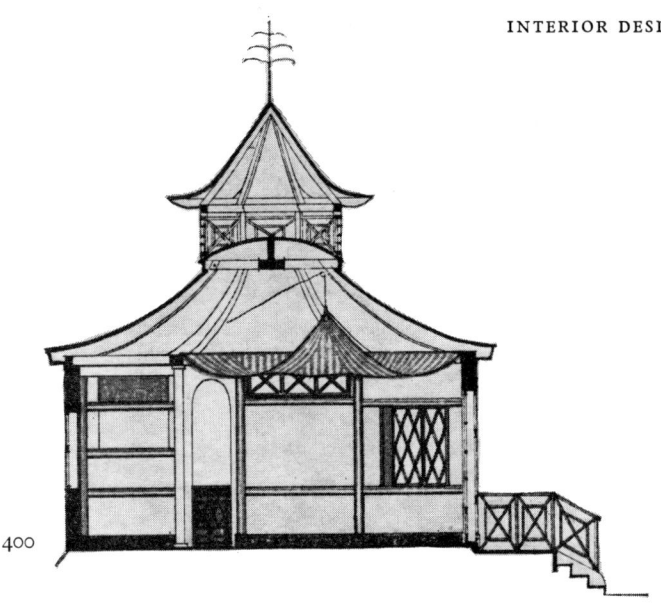

400 **Kampmann, Hack** (editor) Liselund *Copenhagen, 1918*
Essays on the cottage and 'jardin Anglais' erected at Liselund by Andreas Kirkerup for Antoine Bosc de la Calmette in 1792-5. Every detail of the exterior and interior of the main building and the associated garden pavilions is recorded in accompanying plates and the book provides a good idea of the furnishings of a cottage orné of the 1790s. *Folio. 58 + (4)pp, 40 photogravure plates and 58 plates carrying plans and drawings. Limited edition. Quarter morocco, marbled-paper boards, gilt tooled spine, uncut.* **Illustration above.** £48

401 **Kelly, Alison** The book of English fireplaces *London, Country Life 1968*
Brief but well illustrated historical study. *Quarto. 96pp including 111 photo illustrations. Original cloth.* £4

402 **Koch, Alexander** Handbuch neuzeitlicher Wohnungskultur. Band (1). Speisezimmer *Darmstadt, Koch 1913*
Designs for dining rooms and their fittings by over 120 contemporary architects. Those best represented are Bertsch, Breuhaus, Ino Campbell, Josef Hoffmann, Lossow & Kuhne, Niemeyer and Von Seidel. *Octavo. (8)pp, frontispiece and 196pp of plates. Original decorated cloth, rebacked.* £25

403 **Langley, Batty** The city and country builder's and workman's treasury of designs: or the art of drawing and working the ornamental parts of architecture *London, S. Harding 1741*
Designs by Batty and Thomas Langley which include examples of windows, chimney pieces, patterns for floors and cabinet making, altar pieces, pulpits, tombs, clocks, marble tables, sundials, chests of drawers, bookcases and ceilings. Of all Langley's pattern books this – which ran through a number of editions from 1740 onwards – had the widest appeal to craftsmen and their patrons. *Quarto. (2) + 22pp and 186 + (14) engraved plates. Contemporary full calf, rebacked.* £140

403a **Langley, Batty** The city and country builder's and workman's treasury of designs *London, 1750 (Blom reprint 1969)*
Quarto. 240pp with illustrations. Original cloth. £10

404 **Le Nôtre, (A) & (J) le Blond** (Pavillons en treillage) *Paris, J. Mariette (c 1720)*
Lattice-work arcades, arches, pavilions, niches and shelters from Le Nôtre's gardens at the Hôtel de Louvois in Paris, the chateaux of Sceaux and St Cloud, together with some designs by Le Blond. A suite from Mariette's 'Architecture à la Mode'. Guilmard p 130. *Quarto. 6 numbered engraved plates, average size 220 × 305mm. Hinged into marbled-paper boards, half calf.* £48

405 Le Pautre, Jean & Jean Marot (Intérieurs et decorations) *Paris & Antwerp, Le Blond, Pierre Marriette, Moncornet, Pierre Mariette fils (c 1650–1700)*

An interesting collection of engraved and etched plates by the two most important French ornamental engravers of the mid seventeenth century. Jean le Pautre (1618-1682) was one of the most important figures in the creation of the Louis XIV style. His vast body of engraved designs disseminated the style throughout Europe, his inventions were quickly copied in Holland, Germany and England. Fourteen of his suites of designs, mainly early le Blond issues, are incorporated in the collection and show alcoves, panel decoration, vases, salts, ceilings, doorways, friezes, fountains, basins and garden ornament. The two other suites are by the elder Marot (see item 1515) and are particularly good designs for alcoves and ceilings. A detailed description and collation is available on request. *Oblong quarto. 16 suites and 1 odd plates making 121 engraved plates in all. Eighteenth century full red morocco. A collection made at the beginning of the 18th century by Francis Columbine, Colonel of Foot whose book-plate, dated 1708, is on the fly leaf.* **Illustration below.** £345

406 Le Pautre, Jean Lambris à la françoise, nouvellement inventées et gravée *Paris, Pierre Mariette fils (c 1740)*

Interior wall elevations for large apartments in the style created by Lebrun and his team for the royal palaces. The designs here show decorated panels, doors and windows framed by columns or pilasters. These must be late issues of plates made about 1680 but they are only recorded with this imprint. (Oeuvres suite 32). Destailleur Notices p 97. Guilmard p 71. *Six numbered engraved plates, varying in size from 143 × 212 to 153 × 221mm, with good margins. In paper wallet.* £20

407 Le Pautre, Jean Lambris à la romaine *Paris, Pierre Mariette 1661*

Rich baroque interiors using a mixture of architectural features, painting, sculpture and stucco modelling. Later issues give this suite a different title calling it 'Trumeaux et Lambris pour la Decoration des Appartemens.' (Oeuvres suite 31). Destailleur Notices p 84. *Six numbered engraved plates, averages size 250 × 125mm, with good margins. In paper wallet.* £42

408 Le Pautre, J(ean) Les lanbris *(Paris) le Blond (c 1650)*

Overdoors, cartouches, ceiling corners, pendentives and spandrels enriched with figures modelled in the round. (Oeuvres suite 16). *Six numbered engraved plates, average size 222 × 150mm. Fine impressions with good margins. In paper wallet.* £36

409 Le Pautre, J(ean) Alcoves à l'italienne nouvellement inventées et gravées *Paris, Jollain 1665*

Alcoves enclosed by curtains to ward off the draughts were an essential part of bedroom apartments in the 17th century. The openings are decorated with motifs of cupids, masks, and cartouches upholding garlands and swags, and flanked by columns, pilasters, richly decorated panels or carved doors. Berlin Cat 314. Destailleur Notices p 90. *Six unnumbered plates, average size 150 × 215mm, with good margins. In paper wallet.* £42

410 Le Pautre, J(ean) Alcoves à la romaine designez et gravez de nouveau *Paris, P. Mariette (c 1668)*

In the time of Louis XIV alcoves took on the aspect of a stage. Here the seriously conceived decoration is enlivened by their use as a setting for historical scenes. (Oeuvres suite 60). Destailleur Notices p 91. Guilmard p 72. *Six unnumbered plates varying in size from 150 × 216 to 173 × 224mm. Good margins. In paper wallet.* £42

411 Le Pautre, (Jean) (Grand cheminées) *Paris, Jean le Blond, (c 1660)*

Typical chimney-pieces in the early Louis XIV style: large features forming the focal point of a room and setting the treatment of the walls. The overmantels are decorated with reliefs or paintings, the fireplace openings have ornamental firebacks or are closed off by panelled doors. *Six unnumbered engraved plates, average size 292 × 220mm with wide margins. In paper wallet.* £45

412 Le Pautre, J(ean) Grandes cheminées à la romaine *Paris, P. Mariette 1663*

Chimney-pieces 'à la romaine' were set flush to the wall with the shaft embedded in its thickness. These are typical designs of the period – rising the full height of the wall, with a large opening, a painted or sculptured overmantel flanked by elements of the orders or figure sculpture, and surmounted by a cornice holding putti, fames, or eagles. (Oeuvres suite 46). Destailler Notices p 86. Guilmard p 72. *Six numbered engraved plates, average size 325 × 235mm with wide margins. In paper wallet.* £45

413 Le Pautre, (Jean) (Cheminées et lambris) *(Paris), le Blond (c 1660)*

Excellent examples of Louis XIV apartment interiors concentrating on the elevations of the chimney walls but showing typical examples of panelling arrangements, the relation of the architectural members, and the types of door designs. Destailleur Notices p 93. *Six numbered engraved plates, average size 150 × 213mm. Fine impressions. In paper wallet.* £45

414 Le Pautre, Jean Cheminées à la moderne *Paris, Pierre Mariette 1661*

Designs showing the evolution of the chimney-piece where it has diminished in size so that the overmantel ends in a pyramid motif made up either of figures, putti holding frames, or of a large throat decorated in a variety of forms. (Oeuvres suite 48). Guilmard p 72. Destailleur Notices p 84. *Six numbered engraved plates, average size 212 × 150mm with wide margins. In paper wallet.* £35

415 Le Pautre, Jean Architecture van verscheidene nieuwe poorten, kamer-deuren, schoorsteen-mantels, kerken, altaaren, galderyen, cabinetten, alkoves, solder-stukken, enz *Amsterdam, Cornelis Danckerts, (c 1680)*

A wide selection of Le Pautre's designs showing a range in the fields of architectural features, interior designs, ornamental decoration, furniture, vases, church fitments and ironwork. Le Pautre's designs were pirated in the Netherlands almost as soon as they had appeared in France. *Small folio. Letterpress title in Dutch and French and 82 engraved plates made up from ten suites of which 25 doors and windows, 6 iron gates and railings, 6 portes-cocheres, 6 room-doors, 6 church facades and porches, 6 chimney-pieces, 6 interiors, 4 cabinets, 6 vases, 6 alcoves, 5 frames. Eighteenth century marbled-paper boards, vellum spine, repaired.* £150

416 **Le Pautre, P(ierre)** Cheminées et lambris à la mode executez dans les nouueaux bâtiments de Paris *Paris, N. Langlois (c 1690)*
An important suite of designs by Pierre le Pautre showing the chimney forms which developed between 1680 and 1690, in France, as a result of the invention of bent flues which caused the upper cornice to be lowered to eye level. This was then decorated with vases and other ornaments. Two half designs to a plate. *Six unnumbered engraved plates including title. Average size 200 × 135mm, with wide margins. Stitched in marbled-paper wrappers.* £40

417 **(Le Pautre, Pierre)** (Fonds de riches salons) *(Paris), Mariette (c 1720)*
Pierre le Pautre was one of the most able assistants employed by Mansart in the office of the 'Bâtiments du Roi' and one of the leading spirits in the invention of a style of decoration which heralded the rococo. For twelve years his designs provided the main source of ideas for interior decoration. The present suite shows room elevations with arrangements of doors, chimneys and windows in a style introduced at Versailles in 1701 and closely resembling the decoration of the 'Apartement du Roi' at the Trianon. A suite from Mariette's 'Architecture à la mode'. Guilmard p 98. *Oblong folio. 7 engraved plates, average size 190 × 300mm, with large margins. In paper wallet.* £35

418 **(Le Pautre, Pierre)** (Cheminées à la royalle à grand miroir et tablette avec lambris de menuizerie) *Augsburg, Jeremiah Wolff (c 1715)*
Reverse copies of the suite originally issued by Langlois in Paris. The original designs were made by Pierre le Pautre in the 1690s and issued c 1698. They show chimney pieces with small fireplace openings surmounted by tall mirrors and crowned by acanthus scrolls. The designs are similar to those carried out in the Château de la Ménagerie but are rather more advanced showing developments towards the style with which Le Pautre changed the course of French decoration. *Six numbered engraved plates, suite 113 of Wolff's collection. Average size 195 × 135mm, with wide margins. In paper wallet.* £30

419 **Le Pautre, (Pierre)** (Pavillons en treillage) *Paris, J. Mariette (c 1720)*
Lattice-work pavilions, palisades and fountain niches of the early 18th century. Work of this kind was short lived and was one of the first things to disappear when a garden was neglected. A suite from Mariette's 'Architecture à la Mode'. Berlin Cat 3458 & 359(7). Guilmard p 130. *Quarto. 6 unnumbered double-p engraved plates. Average size 280 × 195mm. Hinged into marbled-paper boards, half calf.* £36

420 **Leroux, J(ean) B(aptiste)** Nouveaux lambris de galeries, chambres, et cabinets *Paris, J. Mariette (c 1720)*
Early designs by Leroux showing the style of interior decoration which Pierre le Pautre had developed at the turn of the century: a series of tall slender features – mirrors, windows, doors – alternating with wall panels sparingly decorated. Leroux was one of the most active architects of the first half of the eighteenth century who was employed mainly on finishing and decorating buildings erected by other architects. The suite is from Mariette's 'Architecture à la mode'. Berlin Cat (4032) Guilmard p 249. *Six engraved plates including title; plates numbered 1-5, and final plate unnumbered. Average size 165 × 275mm. Tipped on to grey paper and preserved in paper wallet.* £24

421 **Leroux, (Jean-Baptiste)** Decorations interieurs ... de l'Hôtel de Roquelaure à Paris *Paris, (Jean) Mariette (1727)*
Part of Leroux's decorative work of 1724-6 showing the schemes for the vestibule, two ante-rooms, a bedroom and the small cabinet conceived in an accomplished version of early rococo which was current at the beginning of the decade. Three of the rooms shown still survive in the hôtel which is now the office of the Ministère des Travaux Publiques, but the remaining decorations were altered in the 1730s. The plates appeared in Mariette's 'Architecture françoise'. Berlin Cat 4048. Guilmard p 249. *Oblong folio. 6 engraved plates with 8 elevations. Average size 245 × 375mm. In paper wallet.* £30

422 **Liénard, (Michel)** Spécimens de la décoration et de l'ornementation au XIXe siècle *Liege, Claesen (1872)*
A large collection of designs suitable for the interior decoration of the 19th century house –

whether that house was built in a renaissance or an 18th century manner. The plates are of the high standard associated with the Claesen firm (see also item 152). *Folio. Litho frontispiece, litho title, printed title in red, 4 + 4pp text and 125 litho plates. Contemporary quarter calf.* £45

423 **Loftie, W. J.** A plea for art in the house ... and the importance of taste in education and morals. Second edition *London, Macmillan 1877*
Contains a good chapter on furnishing and furniture. *Octavo. x + (2) + 100pp including text illustrations. Original cloth.* £9

424 **Loukomski, G-K.** Le Kreml (Kremlin) de Moscou. Ses cathedrales ses palais et ses tresors d'art *Paris, Nilsson (c 1925)*
Impressive illustrated record of the Kremlin's architecture, decoration and contents (ironwork, thrones, crosses, robes, chalices, chandeliers, armour, guns), made the more evocative by the light and shadow in the photographic plates. *Quarto. viii + 29 + (5)pp, with 120 plates carrying mounted photographs. Original decorated portfolio.* £45

425 **Loukomski, G-K.** La vie et les moeurs en Russie de Pierre Le Grand a Lénine *Paris, Leroux 1928*
Quarto. viii + 48pp and 107 photographic plates. Original wrappers. £18

426 **Loukomski, G-K.** Mobilier & décoration des anciens palais impériaux Russes (Musées du Peuple) *Paris, Van Oest 1928*
Beautifully produced study of the furniture and decoration of the imperial palace at Tsarskoie Selo, created by Rastrelli for the Empress Elizabeth, refitted by Charles Cameron for Catherine the Great and with 19th century neo-classical additions. *Quarto. 48pp and 215 photo illustrations on 84 plates. Original decorated wrappers, uncut.* £45

427 **Luthmer, Ferdinand** Malerische Innenräume moderner Wohnungen. In Aufnahmen nach der Natur.–Malerische Innenräume aus Gegenwart und Vergangenheit *Frankfurt am Main, Keller 1886–92*
Very handsome photogravure plates of German interiors, with introductory remarks by Luthmer, who was Director of the Kunstgewerbeschule at Frankfurt. *Folio. 4 vols. Title, 20pp and 25 plates; title, (4)pp and 25 plates (23 photogravure, 2 chromolitho); title and 25 plates; title and 25 plates. The last 2 vols are a continuation of the original work under a different title and we are uncertain whether a text should accompany them. 3 vols in original printed paper portfolios, cloth spines, and 1 vol in original printed wrappers.* £50

428 **Magne, H. Marcel** Les chefs-d'oeuvre du style Louis XVI. Première série. Décorations intérieures *Paris, Ducher (c 1910)*
Interiors from Paris, Versailles and Fontainebleau. *Folio. (8)pp and 40 photo plates. Original printed boards.* £12

429 **Marot, D(aniel)** Nouveaux lievre de cheminées à la Hollandoise *(Amsterdam, the author 1712)*
Daniel Marot, the son of Jean Marot and a pupil of Jean le Pautre was a gifted designer and engraver forced to flee France in 1685 because he was a Protestant. He took refuge in Holland and worked for a time in England. This suite from his 'Oeuvres' shows him as the creator of an important provincial variant of the late Louis XIV style with ideas derived from the engraved work of Pierre le Pautre (see items 416-9). His designs had a profound influence on English decoration and were responsible for introducing into this country a type of debased classical Baroque. Berlin Cat 356(12). *Six unnumbered engraved plates, average size 245 × 170mm, with good margins. In paper wallet.* £38

430 **Masson, Andre** Le décor des bibliothèques du moyen âge à la révolution *Geneva, Droz 1972*
A learned and well-written study of library interiors in France, Italy, England, Portugal and Czechoslovakia. *Octavo. (4) + 204 + (2)pp and 60pp of plates. Original cloth.* £10.50

431 **McClelland, Nancy** The practical book of decorative wall-treatments *Philadelphia, Lippincott 1926*
Octavo. 273+(1)pp and 8 colour plates, about 200 monochrome plates. Original decorated cloth. £10

432 **Meissonier, J(uste) A(urèle)** La maison de Sieur Brethous *Paris, Huquier (c 1750)*
One of the three great inventors of French Rococo Meissonier had ambitions also as an architect. These are his only remaining designs for an entire house executed c 1733 and still standing in Bayonne. The most interesting parts of the designs are the two plates which show the interior elevations of the rooms on each floor. The basic treatment is traditionally French but is given uncharacteristic forms in the plastic boldness of the window, door and mirror frames and in the asymmetry of the motifs of the carving. Suite A of the Oeuvres. Berlin Cat 378. *11 engraved plates including title, numbered 1-9, *,**. Suite lettered A. Sizes varying from 140 × 145mm to 156 × 255mm. Tipped on grey hand-made paper, preserved in wrappers.* £90

433 **Meissonier, J(uste) A(urèle)** Sallon de la Princesse Sartorinski en Pologne *(Paris), Huquier (c 1750)*
Fine plates showing excellent examples of Meissonier's fully developed interior style where

433

all is swirling lines, inversed curves, confronting volutes and shell motifs, rising to a ceiling opening on to multiple perspectives. These projected designs were actually carried out in the no longer extant Palace of Pulawy, c 1735. Suite O of the Oeuvres. Berlin Cat 378. Guilmard p 156. *Three engraved plates numbered 84-86, suite lettered O. Two large plates 315 & 250 × 510mm, one plate 243 × 277mm repaired for small tears. Tipped on hand-made grey paper and preserved in matching wrappers.* **Illustration opposite.** £34

434 Meissonier, J(uste) A(urèle) Cabinet de Mr le Comte Bielenski Grand Marechal de la Couronne de Pologne, executé en 1734 *Paris, Huquier (c 1750)*

Large scale details of the interiors which were the master works of the Rococo and fundamental in the diffusion of the style. The plates show a rich combination of architecture, sculpture and painting and multiple perspectives provided by the reverberations of the reflexions in the mirrors. They include a painted ceiling in the tradition of Pietro da Cortona. Suite P of the Oeuvres. Berlin Cat 378. Guilmard p 157. *Four engraved plates numbered 87-90, lettered P. Sizes varying from 360 × 415mm to 545 × 348mm. Tipped on grey hand-made paper and preserved in matching wrappers.* £110

435 Miller, Fred Interior decoration. A practical treatise on surface decoration. With notes on colour, stencilling, and panel painting *London, Wyman (1886)*

With chapters on Japanese decoration and on its influence in England, and illustrations of 'Japanesque' and other designs by the author. *Octavo. ix+(1)+145+(3)pp and 71 illustrations. Original cloth.* £9

436 Modern French decorative art A collection of examples of modern French decoration with an introduction by Léon Deshairs *London, Architectural Press (1926)*

The publication which first introduced 'modernism' and 'art deco' to a wider English public. The book resulted from the great interest shown in the new style by the English visitors to the Paris exhibition of 1925 and from the number of commissions placed with French designers. The plates illustrate a wide range of designs of furniture, furnishings and decorative objects made by the foremost French designers since 1918. The selection was taken from the magazine 'Art & Decoration' and the introduction was provided by its editor who was also curator of the Bibliothéque des arts décoratifs in Paris. *Folio. xi+(1 blank)pp and 188pp of photographic plates with 670 monochrome illustrations, and 14 full-page coloured plates. Publisher's printed cloth boards.* £45

437 Mollet, (Armand-Claude) Décorations de l'Hôtel d'Évreux à Paris *(Paris) Jean Mariette (1727)*

The Hôtel d'Évreux, now the Élysée Palace, is the official residence of the Président de la République de France. The present suite shows the decoration of the ballroom, an ante-room, and the state bedroom, carried out in the conventional style of the second decade of the 18th century according to the designs of Mollet. Successive decorations and alterations have so transformed the interior that nothing substantial remains of these designs. A suite from 'L'Architecture françoise'. Guilmard p 167. *Four unnumbered engraved plates, sizes 230:262 × 320:362mm with wide margins. In paper wallet.* £40

438 Muthesius, Hermann (editor) Die schöne Wohnung. Beispiele neuer Deutscher Innenräume *Munich, Bruckmann 1922*

Muthesius's selection of interior designs emphasizes the work of Bertsch, Haiger, Heidrich, Hoffmann, Paul, Prutscher, Troost and some of his own schemes. *Quarto. xvi+238pp mostly illustrations. Original cloth.* £15

439 Muthesius, Hermann (editor) Die schöne Wohnung . . . zweite stark erneuerte Auflage *Munich, Bruckmann 1926*

Second edition, with a new introduction on the advent of Expressionism and Constructivism and much new illustrative material; designers covered at length now include Fahrenkamp, Merrill and Riemerschmid. *Quarto. xvi+216pp, mostly illustrations. Original cloth.* £20

440

440 (**Nash, John**) Illustrations of Her Majesty's Palace at Brighton; formerly the Pavilion: executed by the command of King George the Fourth, under the superintendence of John Nash, Esq. architect. To which is prefixed, a history of the Palace, by Edward Wedlake Brayley *London, Nichols 1838*

The most sumptuous illustrated record of the Pavilion and its interior, comprising a text by Brayley, 31 plates in outline or monochrome, and the separate suite of 28 'prints in imitation of the original drawings', all hand-coloured and mounted on card paper. The plates had been executed for Nash by the elder Pugin, with various assistants, between 1818 and 1825, and had been purchased on Nash's death by J. B. Nichols, the publisher. Nichols commissioned Brayley to make a careful survey of the Palace and to write a text to accompany the plates, and the present book is the visually very satisfactory result. Abbey Scenery: 62. *Large folio. 2 vols. (8)+17+(1)pp and 31 engraved plates (1 double-page); dedication leaf, printed contents leaf, 28 handcoloured plates mounted on card paper. Quarter straight grain red morocco, gilt spines, marbled paper sides.* **Illustration above.** £1250

441 **Nash, Paul** Room and book *London, Soncino Press 1932*
Nash's very individual view of interior design and book production, appreciative of Robert Adam, Roger Fry's Omega Workshops, and Raymond McGrath, and learned on the use of patterned paper for book wrappers. *Octavo. xix+(1)+98+(4)pp and 19 plates. Original cloth.*
£20

442 **Nolhac, Pierre de** Versailles. Les intérieurs. Première série (–Deuxième série) *Paris, Morance (c 1930)*
Photographic views of the state rooms of Versailles (sculpture, bronzes, mirrors, woodwork,

furniture). *Folio.* 2 vols. *Each with (8)pp text and 60 photo plates. Original portfolios, cloth spines, printed boards.* £45

443 Nouveau livre d'porte d' la chambre *Amsterdam, R. & J. Ottens (c 1700)*
Designs for doors and their surrounds in the typical Louis XIV style as found in the royal apartments. A Dutch copy of French designs. *Six numbered engraved plates, average size 211 × 148mm. Good impressions with wide margins. In paper wallet.* £18

444 Oppenord, G(illes) M(arie) Sixième livre contenant de feux ou grilles d'atres de cheminée *Paris, Huquier (c 1748)*
Twelve designs for andirons or upright bars for fire-grates, mostly conceived in the form of antique urns or vases on pedestals. Suite from the 'Moyen Oppenord'. Guilmard p 142. Berlin Cat 383. *Six numbered engraved plates including title, Suite lettered E. Average size 315 × 225mm. In paper wallet.* £48

445 Pain, W(illiam) The carpenter's and joiner's repository; or, a new system of lines and proportions for doors, windows, chimnies, cornices & mouldings, for the finishing of rooms, &c &c a great variety of staircases, on a plan entirely new, and easy to be understood *London, the author 1778*
First edition of a pattern book of interior features and applied ornament in a debased Adam style whose large drawings would have provided easy models from which builders could work. Pain produced many such pattern books which were widely published in America and although nothing is known of any work he actually executed himself his books must have provided models for the interior details in many 18th and 19th century houses in the New World. *Folio. 2 engraved frontispieces, (14)ff and 67 engraved plates numbered I-XLVIII, L-LXI, ★XXXIX, ★XLVII, A-D, P. Marbled-paper boards, quarter calf.* £75

446 Papers read before the Incorporated Institute of British Decorators Vol. I, London 1900–13 *London (1913)*
Contains three papers by J. D. Crace, the Institute's President (see item 1421), and contributions by Metford Warner, Shuffry and others. *Octavo. Approximately 200pp. Original cloth.* £15

447 Parsons, Frank Alvah Interior decoration its principles and practice *New York, Doubleday 1916*
The principles, history and application of interior design from an American (and rather independent minded) point of view. *Octavo. xiv + 284pp and 67 plates. Original cloth.* £10

447a Patmore, Derek Colour schemes and modern furnishing *London, Studio 1947*
Quarto. 36pp and 72pp of plates. Original cloth. £4

448 (Paul, Bruno) Popp, Joseph Bruno Paul *München, Bruckmann, (c 1916)*
A very extensive early monograph on Paul which already shows his full dimension as one of the most intelligent and personal designers of the twentieth century. Although the book records the work of not more than a single decade it includes four very different major architectural works, several houses and parts of the Berlin museum buildings, and has a large introductory section on exhibition rooms, ships' interiors and furniture, especially the 'Typenmöbel' (the first-ever unit furniture) designed for the Deutsche Werkstätten as early as 1910. Paul had also been the first to make designs for quantity-machined furniture in 1906. As Pevsner ('Pioneers of the modern movement', pp 199–200) sums up: 'we see a personal taste utterly different from the Viennese as well as from Behrens'. Paul and the Deutsche Werkstätten do not mind a touch of the tradition; they dislike principles of inhuman rigidity; comfort, cleanliness and the abolition of tawdry fuss is all they desire. This attitude enabled them to popularise the new style in Germany . . . to effect a change of taste throughout the country, which Gropius, the most uncompromising German innovator, might not have been able to bring about'. *Quarto. (6) + 252 + (2 blank) pp (with 319 illustrations), 7 collotype plates (2 double-page) and 4 colour plates. Original lettered cloth.* £28

449 **Pérau, Gabriel-Louis Calabre** Description historique de l'Hotel royal des Invalides *Paris, Desprez 1756*

Granet's history of the Invalides (see item 367) was not wholly satisfactory and the Abbé Pérau was commissioned to produce this emended version; the sections on the Invalides as an institution had the benefit of the comments of the then officials and the section on its architecture was revised with assistance from the architect François Franque. The plates were largely repeated from Granet but they do not exactly correspond in number and arrangement. *Folio. (4) + xii + 104pp and 108 engraved plates; plates 2, 4-18, 20-5, 34-7, 42, 68, 80, 93, 106 are double-page. Contemporary full mottled calf, gilt tooled spine, panelled sides with gilt fleurs-de-lis at corners.* £210

450 **Percier, C. & P. F. L. Fontaine** Recueil de décorations intérieures, comprenant tout ce qui a rapport a l'ameublement. . . *Paris, the authors and P. Didot 1812*

Percier and Fontaine, two Grand Prix architects whose taste and skill in the handling of classical ornament won them the patronage of Napoleon, were the dominant figures in architecture and the associated arts under the Empire and virtually created the Empire style. Their most important commissions were for the interiors and furnishings of Napoleon's apartments at the Louvre, the Tuileries, Malmaison, Fontainebleau, St Cloud, and Compiègne, and this selection from their interior designs for the Emperor and other clients made their elegant linear style internationally known and imitated; its influence is evident in the furniture designs of Thomas Hope (item 94). *Folio. (4) + 43 + (1)pp and 72 engraved plates. Quarter calf, marbled-paper boards.* £190

451 **Percier, C. & P. F. L. Fontaine** Receuil de décorations intérieures *Paris, the authors and J. Didot 1827*

Second edition. A reissue with a new title page, otherwise identical to the first edition. *Folio. (4) + 43 + (1)pp and 72 engraved plates. Quarter morocco.* £160

452 **Percier, C. & P. F. L. Fontaine** Recueil de décorations intérieures, comprenant tout ce qui a rapport à l'ameublement *Paris, 1812 (Gregg reprint 1971)*

Quarto. 48pp and 72 plates. Original cloth. £9

453 **Percier, C. & P. F. L. Fontaine** Raccolta di decorazioni interne che comprende quanto si riferisce all' addobbamento . . . riveduta la traduzione de Francesco Lazzari . . . con notevoli giunte di Giuseppe Borsato *Venice, Antonelli 1843*

Italian translation with a parallel, French text, of the authors' 'Recueil' (item 450). It incorporates a supplement of 48 plates, accompanied by French and Italian text, illustrating designs by Borsato for interiors in Venice and its environs; they are neo-classical in style and chiefly date from the 1820s and 1830s. *Folio. 177 + (1)pp and 120 plates numbered 1-72 and 1-48. Quarter morocco, marbled-paper boards.* £120

454 **Pfnor, Rodolphe** Architecture décoration et ameublement époque Louis XVI dessinés et gravés d'après des motifs choisis dans les palais imperiaux, le mobilier de la couronne, les monuments publics et les habitations privées *Paris, Morel 1865*

Decorative details taken mainly from the Petit Trianon and the boudoir of Marie Antoinette at Fontainebleau. *Folio. (4) + 44pp and 50 plates. Quarter morocco, marbled paper boards. Gillow & Co copy.* £45

455 **Phillips, R. Randall** The modern English interior *London, Country Life (c 1930)*

Designs for the various rooms of the house selected from the work of leading British architects of the inter-war period. Guy Dawber, P. Morley Horder, Ionides, Lutyens and Clough Williams-Ellis figure prominently. *Octavo. 32pp and 192pp of photo illustrations. Original cloth.* £15

456 **Pierretz, A(ntoine), the elder** Divers desseins de cheminées a la royalle *Paris, la veuve F. l'Anglois dit Chartres (c 1650)*

First issue of a fine set of chimney designs in the style of the mid-seventeenth century. The chimneys are of the pyramidal type where the hood has contracted so much that the mantle ends in a pyramidal motif composed of figures, vases, trophies, putti holding garlands, or with a chimney throat decorated with acanthus leaves. One design bears the cipher of Louis XIIII while another resembles a chimney actually executed c 1645 in the Château de Tanley. Berlin Cat 3778. *13 numbered etched plates including title; plate size 200 × 135mm. Stitched in marbled-paper boards.* £45

457 **Pineau, (Nicholas)** Desseins de buffets et lambris *(Paris), Jean Mariette (1727)*

One of the principal designers responsible for the 'genre pittoresque' style, Pineau fixed the character and detail of the type of decoration which was destined to prevail in France until the last quarter of the 18th century. This suite from Mariette's 'L'Architecture françoise' illustrates the range of his work in wall designs for dining-rooms with buffet tables and water basins, for a bedroom with an alcove, and for reception rooms showing the panel decoration arranged to agree with pier-glasses, casement windows, doors and chimneys. *Six unnumbered engraved plates, average size 300 × 212mm, with wide margins. In paper wallet.* **Illustration below.** £60

458 **Pineau, (Nicholas)** Desseins de cheminées *Paris, (Jean) Mariette (1727)*

Chimney-pieces and wall decoration showing the lightness, delicacy and elegance of Pineau's work as well as the wealth of invention. The designs range from the simple – where the decoration is confined to the mirror-head and the panel above – to the very rich – where natural motifs are mixed with abstract designs and each panel is decorated in a different way. Pineau's asymmetrical forms are only just beginning to creep into his designs at this stage and it is interesting to see their early development. From 'Architecture françoise'. *Folio. 6 numbered engraved plates, average size 300 × 215mm, with good margins. In paper wallet.* £48

457

459 **Piranesi, Gianbattista** Diverse maniere d'adornare i cammini . . . Diverse manners of ornamenting chimneys and all other parts of houses taken from the Egyptian, Tuscan and Grecian architecture with an apologetic essay in defence of Egyptian and Tuscan architecture *Rome, Salomini 1769*

This statement on the decoration of rooms develops the theory Piranesi had first propounded a few years earlier: of a creative eclecticism in which the manipulation of the elements of classical taste in an imaginative way would create a contemporary style of decoration. This view he advocates in the trenchant 'apologetic essay' which prefaces the magnificent plates. Where previously he had upheld one position in the 'Greek versus Roman' controversy emphasising the Etruscan sources as the basis of classical forms he now accepts not only Greek but also Egyptian motifs as the sources of new ideas. His justification for this liberal approach to design was based on the belief that the Romans themselves had taken liberties with the basic forms and so had created works of great richness and diversity. Piranesi selects the chimney-piece as the main subject to illustrate his 'diverse manners' since he regarded it as a completely modern element of interior decoration which had no place in classical design. In this way he demonstrates the application of his theory of creative eclecticism to the needs of his time.
The book was of vital importance to Robert Adam who used Piranesi's theories to justify his own decorative style and to validate the diversity of elements in his own designs. It provided him with a new source of inspiration by suggesting a wide variety of ornament and more diverse sources. Specific influences are apparent in Adam's innovations of the 1770s and '80s, particularly in the form of the group of new chimney-pieces and the Etruscan rooms which were conceived at that period. *Large folio. (4) + 35 + (1 + 2)pp (with decorative etched headpiece and tailpiece), and decorative etched double-page title-dedication, 71 etched plates on 70 ff numbered 1-66, I-II, and 3 unnumbered. The plates usually bound with the 'Apologia' are found at the end of the volume, and the preliminary unnumbered plate has a letterpress 'Avviso al publico' on the verso. Marbled-paper boards, quarter calf, gilt.*
Illustration opposite. £820

460 (Plaisir de France) **Hillerin, Jean de & Alfred Marie** Styles de France. Objets et collections de 1610 à 1920 *Paris, Le Rayonnement Français (c 1925)*

Examples of bronze and metalwork, clocks and lightholders, gold and silverwork, porcelain, glass and mirrors, chronologically arranged to facilitate identification of styles and photographed in settings in order to suggest the placing and disposition of similar objects. *Quarto. 222pp with 365 photographic illustrations of which 50 coloured. Publisher's gilt decorated paper boards; slip case.* £15

461 **Platz, Gustav Adolf** Wohnraüme der Gegenwart *Berlin, Propylaen Verlag 1933*

Very comprehensive collection of designs for interiors and their fittings, drawn from the work of nearly every modern architect of consequence from Norman Shaw to Behrens, Le Corbusier and Poelzig. Probably the best overall view of modern interior design up to the early 1930s. *Octavo. 517 + (3)pp and 15 colour plates, hundreds of illustrations in text. Original cloth.* £40

462 **(Poilly, F.)** Nouvelles cheminées à paneaux de glace executées dans quelques hôtels de Paris *Paris, N. Langlois (c 1690)*

Chimney-piece designs of the type which were prevalent about 1690 and were made popular through the publications of Pierre le Pautre. These designs show mainly the type with low mirrors surmounted by pictures, but two plates illustrate designs where the mirrors occupy the whole of the panel of the chimney-breast. The drawings include large scale details of moulds and cornices. Berlin Cat 3783. Guilmard p 95. *Six unnumbered engraved plates, size 170 × 265mm, trimmed close to plate mark and mounted on old paper. Stitched in marbled-paper boards.* £45

463 **Praz, Mario** An illustrated history of interior decoration from Pompeii to Art Nouveau *London, Thames & Hudson 1964*

The merits of this book are concealed rather than revealed by the title: it is in fact a study of the representations of interiors in paintings of the masters – 'a kind of retrospective exposition of the furnishing of rooms in Europe in the last centuries'. *Folio. 396pp including 400 illustrations (65 coloured). Original cloth.* £15

459

464 Pricke, Robert The architects store-house; being a collection of several designes of frontispieces, doors and window-cases, cieling-pieces, alcoves, chimney-pieces and fountains (etc) *London, Pricke 1674 (Gregg reprint 1967)*

One of the earliest architectural pattern-books put together from the copies of foreign designers which Pricke kept in his shop for sale, and including copies of the engravings of the Le Pautres, Marot, Pierretz, Francini, and other similar French engravers. *Folio. (4)pp and 50 plates. Original cloth.* £6

465 Pricke, Robert The ornaments of architecture. Containing compartments shields, mantlings, foldige, festones, monuments for tombs, alphabets of large letters plain and enrich'd, with the order of making them. With some new designs for carving and painting of eminent coaches *London, Pricke 1674 (Gregg reprint 1967)*

Companion volume to the previous item with the ornament drawn again from foreign engraved works including the designs of Mitelli and Della Bella. *Folio. 50 unnumbered ff. Original cloth.* £6

466 Putnam, J. Pickering The open fireplace in all ages ... new edition, revised and enlarged *Boston, Osgood 1882*

History of fireplace design, with a section at the end devoted to fireplaces built by the author and other American architects of his day. *Quarto. xiv+(2)+204pp with 55 plates. Original decorated cloth.* £18

467 Pyne, W. H. The history of the royal residences of Windsor Castle, St James's Palace, Carlton House, Kensington Palace, Hampton Court, Buckingham House, and Frogmore *London, Harrison for Dry 1819*

Notable for its very fine coloured aquatint plates of interiors. Pyne was associated in its publication with J. B. Papworth, who had experience of furniture and interior design, and this may account for the fact that only 10 of the 100 plates show exteriors and the remainder interiors; the exterior plates, incidentally, have two colours printed, blue for the sky and brown for the buildings, while the interiors have only one colour printed, the remaining colouring being done by hand. The drawings for the plates were done by Wild, Stephanoff, Cattermole and Westall, and the engraving by Sutherland, Bennett, Reeve, Baily and Havell. *Quarto. 3 vols. (6)+ii+188+(2)+21+(1)pp and 31 aquatint plates; (6)+88+(2)+28+(2)+88pp and 37 aquatint plates; (6)+80+(2)+92+16pp and 32 aquatint plates. Contemporary quarter red morocco, gilt tooled spines, gilt edges.* £450

468 **Racinais, Henry** Un Versailles inconnu. Les petits appartements des roys Louis XV et Louis XVI au château de Versailles *Paris, Lefebvre 1950* Limited edition

Quarto. 2 vols. 189 + (7)pp; (7)pp and 157pp of plates. Original cloth, preserved in slipcase.

£30

469 **Die Raumkunst in Dresden** *1906 Berlin, Wasmuth (1906)*

Illustrations of interior designs by Albin Muller, Henry Van de Velde, Bruno Paul, Richard Riemerschmid, Peter Behrens and others, on large photographic plates. *Folio. 5 parts, containing 70 photo plates. Original printed wrappers. Preserved in cloth folder.* £100

470 **Roberts, Henry D.** A history of the Royal Pavilion, Brighton, with an account of its original furniture and decoration *London, Country Life 1939*

A full history, particularly good on the furniture and interior decoration, for which it prints the accounts and identifies designers and craftsmen. *Quarto. xviii + 224pp, 53 photo plates and 20 text illustrations. Original cloth.* £15

471 **Roeper, Adalbert** Sammlung von Öfen in allen Stilarten vom XVI bis Anfang des XIX Jahrhunderts. Zweite Auflage *Leipzig, Schumann (1920)*

An unexpectedly glamorous assemblage of stoves – tiled, glazed and gilded – in styles ranging from late mediaeval to neo-classical, and attractively illustrated. Reissue of a book first published in 1895. *Folio. (8)pp and 60 photo plates. Original cloth portfolio.* £45

472 **Rothery, Guy Cadogan** Chimneypieces and inglenooks. Their design and ornamentation *London, Laurie (1912)*

A historical survey, dealing primarily with British examples; the most recent are the work of such architects as Barry Parker, Baillie Scott and Ashbee. *Octavo. xii + 239 + (1)pp with illustrations. Original cloth.* £8

473 **Rouyer, Eugène** Les appartements privés de S.M. l'Impératrice au palais des Tuileries décorés par M. Lefuel architecte de S.M. l'Empéreur *Paris, Librairie Polytechnique 1867*

The Emperor and Empress concerned are not Napoleon and Josephine but Napoleon III and Eugénie, and Lefuel's interiors are as distinctly Second Empire as Percier and Fontaine's (items 450-3) are Empire. Rouyer's text identifies them as being of 'le style Napoleon III', which he describes as 'un prolongement ... et une adaptation des styles antérieures aux besoins ... de la seconde moitié du dix-neuvième siècle'. *Folio. Title, 10pp and 21 unnumbered engraved plates. Contemporary quarter morocco.* £35

474 **Ruhlmann, (Émile-Jacques)** Gazette du Bon Ton. No 9. Une salle de bains et deux pages de croquis *Paris, Éditions Lucien Vogel & Bon Ton 1920*

These designs for a bathroom in white marble and gold mosaic with dressing table, massage couch and sunken bath, illustrate beautifully the feeling for sumptuous decor and individual luxury of this designer who dominated French decoration in the twenties. *Four litho plates printed in gold, numbered XLI-XLIV. Publisher's printed-paper wrappers.* £6

475 **Rutter, John** Delineations of Fonthill and its abbey *Shaftesbury, for the author 1823*

A history and illustrated guide to William Beckford's fantastic Gothic palace, describing the building in its entirety and taking the visitor through the seventy-six rooms which the public could visit. Furnishings, colour schemes, and notable objets d'art are mentioned. Abbey Scenery: 418. *Quarto. xxiv + 112 + (8)pp and 13 engraved plates (3 aquatint), 1 large folding map. Contemporary quarter morocco. Large paper copy.* £125

476 **Schübler, Johann Jacob** Nouveau livre de chemines, avec outres ornemens et diverses mebles à la moderne *(Augsberg), Joh. Christoph Weigel (c 1715)*

Schübler's versions of the Berain style of chimney-piece (see items 316-9). Like the French suites of the period these plates are divided along the vertical axis so that each plate provides two designs. The decoration of the chimney breast shows an astonishing variety of ideas and an overloading of ornamentation with globes, mirrors, clocks, swags and vases. The plates also include details for all types of fireplace furniture: and irons, screens, firebacks and baskets. Berlin Cat 3803. *Six numbered plates including title, average size 292 × 190mm. Stitched in marbled-paper wrappers.* £35

477 Schübler, Joh. Jacob Neu-inventirte zirliche u: bequeme Stuben-Oefen *Nurenberg, heirs of Joh. Chr. Weigel (1728)*

Twelve stoves, some with ovens and including one with a compartment and accessories for spit-roasting a chicken. The designs are set in elaborately detailed interiors and are followed by sections and hundreds of constructional and decorative details. Even without the text this remains a fascinating suite and forms one of Schübler's more decorative works. Berlin Cat 3836. *Small folio. Decorative engraved title and 24 unnumbered engraved plates, average size 265 × 170mm. Bound in marbled-paper boards, morocco spine.* £45

478 Schübler, Johann Jacob Unterschiedliche Cabinets und Alcoves, mit curieusen Chamin und Ofen ausgeziert *Augsberg, hiers of Jeremiah Wolff (c 1730)*

Part Two of the 'Werck'. Designs for studies and alcoves including a dining alcove with a drinking fountain, and a study with a two-way stove which heats rooms on both sides. Berlin Cat 98. *Letterpress title and 6 numbered engraved plates, average size 305 × 180mm with wide margins. In paper wallet.* £30

479 Schübler, Johann Jacob Neu-erfundene Camine und ausserordentliche Stuben-Ofen *Augsburg, heirs of Jeremiah Wolff (c 1730)*

Part Fourteen of the 'Werck'. Elaborate and ingenious designs for fireplaces and stoves each with its own special practical feature, and all designed to give the maximum of heat with the minimum of fuel. Berlin Cat 98. *Letterpress title and 6 numbered engraved plates, average size 290 × 180mm. Some plates repaired for tears around edges. In paper wallet.* £36

480 Scott-Mitchell, Frederick Practical gilding, bronzing, lacquering, and glass embossing (etc.) *London, Trade Papers Publishing Co. 1914*

Octavo. 175+(11)pp, text illustrations, frontispiece and 2 plates of coloured samples. Original cloth. £15

481 Serres, J. T. Pro bono publico. Splendor with economy combined. A short treatise on the interior decoration of houses, by J. T. Serres, Painter to His Majesty; H.R.H. the Duke of Clarence; and the Right Hon. the Board of Admiralty. A.D. 1813 *London, the author 1813*

John Thomas Serres (1759-1825), a well-known marine painter, made an unfortunate marriage to a Miss Olivia Wilmot and in 1808 was forced to leave London for Edinburgh because of his wife's debts and behaviour; she was later to claim that she was Princess Olive of Cumberland, the legitimate daughter of George III's brother. On his return to London Serres appears to have found employment as an interior decorator and in this pamphlet he advocates the use of painted canvas hangings as a substitute for actual frescoes or wallpaper in the houses of gentlemen who were leaseholders only and not in a position to commission permanent wall decorations. *Octavo. 28pp. Wrappers.* £15

482 Sluyterman, K. Old interiors in Holland *The Hague, Nijhoff 1908*

A standard work on Dutch interiors. *Folio. (4)+22pp and 100 plates. Original cloth portfolio.* £18

483 Smith, H. Clifford Buckingham Palace. Its furniture, decoration & history . . . with introductory chapters on the building and site by Christopher Hussey *London, Country Life (1930)*

A record of the history and contents of Buckingham Palace which combines all the best features of such publications: detailed information on the house and its owners based on original research (Carlton House and the Brighton Pavilion are also discussed); coverage of unexecuted schemes; a full listing of the contents (furniture, paintings, objets d'art, clocks) with names of the craftsmen responsible for them; extensive illustrations; and crisp white paper. *Quarto. xxiii+(1)+299+(1)pp and 351+(6) illustrations on 170 plates (6 in colour). Original cloth.* £20

484 (Spurling, Percival) Legends of the Worshipful Company of Plaisterers *London, 1886*

Ribald ditties on plasterers and their craft. Much the best is one comparing plasterers to beavers, which concludes:

    And Beavers are we still tonight,
    Mated to Beaveresses,
    Who, like their foremothers, delight
    In broad-tailed silken dresses.

Octavo. 42pp. Original decorated cloth. Author's presentation copy. £8

485 Stengel, Walter Alte Wohnkultur in Berlin und in der Mark im Spiegel der Quellen des 16–19 Jahrhunderts *Berlin, Hessling 1958*

Thorough and interesting history of the interior furnishings of Berlin houses based on original documents, with a good bibliography and index. *Octavo. 256pp with 20 text illustrations, colour frontispiece, and 52pp of photo plates. Original cloth.* £5

486 (Stevens, Alfred) The works of Alfred Stevens sculptor painter designer in the Tate Gallery . . . by Kenneth Romney Towndrow *London, Tate Gallery 1950*

Catalogues Stevens' cartoons and drawings for the interior of Dorchester House. *Quarto. xxii+138pp and 27 photo plates. Original cloth.* £4

487 Strange, Thomas Arthur An historical guide to French interior furniture, decoration, woodwork & allied arts during the last half of thes, seventeenth century, the whole of the eighteenth century, and the earlier part of the nineteenth *London, McCorquodale (c 1900)*

The illustrations, mostly drawn from the holdings of the Victoria and Albert Museum and the Wallace Collection, are numerous and are arranged usefully under subject and designer (Le Pautre, Marot, and Meissonier are covered in depth). *Octavo. (4)+400+(2)pp very many illustrations. Original cloth, morocco spine.* £15

488 Stratton, Arthur The English interior. A view of the decoration of English homes from Tudor times to the XIXth century *London, Batsford (1920)*

Weighty, well-illustrated survey of the interiors of larger English houses; it includes measured drawings of panelling, etc. *Quarto. xxviii+86+(2)pp, with xivpp list of subscribers, 82 text illustrations, and 115 plates. Original cloth.* £15

489 Stritt, H. G. Gestaltete Raüme. Eingeführt mit einem Geleitwort von Gert von Klass *Baden-Baden, Wesel (c 1965)*

Designs for interiors by Hans Georg Stritt, an architect working at Freiburg im Breisgau since 1940. *Square quarto. (8)+250pp mostly illustrations. Original cloth.* £10

490 Süe (Eugène) & (André) Mare Gazette du Bon Ton. No 5. Aménagement d'une loge d'actrice. *Paris, Editions Lucien Vogel & Bon Ton June 1920*

Details from one of the earliest schemes carried out by the newly-formed partnership of two of the foremost designers of the twenties: La Companie des Arts Français. Designs are for a mirror, fitted dressing table, a stool and curtain drapes, with a view of a corner into which they fit in the dressing-room of a well-known actress. *Four chromolitho plates numbered XXV–XXVIII. Publisher's printed-paper wrappers.* £10

491 **Tatham, Charles Heathcote** The gallery at Brocklesby, in Lincolnshire; the seat of the Right Honourable Lord Yarborough *London, T. Gardiner 1811*
The picture gallery which Tatham built for Lord Yarborough to house an inherited collection of Old Masters. Tatham's etched plates are detailed enough to identify individual paintings as well as illustrating furniture and decor. *Folio. (6)pp and 6 etched plates numbered I-VI. Blue paper boards.* £80

492 **Tatham, Charles Heathcote** The gallery at Castle Howard, in Yorkshire; the seat of the Earl of Carlisle, K.G. *London, T. Gardiner 1811*
Tatham refitted the west wing of Castle Howard as a sculpture gallery and museum to contain Lord Carlisle's collection of classical antiquities, and this illustrates the completed interiors. *Folio. 6pp and 6 etched plates numbered I-VI. Quarter morocco.* £125

493 **Taut, Bruno** Ein Wohnhaus *Stuttgart, Keller 1927*
Octavo. (6)+118+(2)pp and 1 folding plate of colour samples, many illustrations. Original cloth. £28

494 **Thompson, Francis Benjamin** (editor) The universal decorator *London, George Vickers 1858-1859*
A collection of articles extracted from journals, periodicals and standard works, on all aspects of the applied arts and decoration. Writings by such notables as Eastlake on 'Strengthening oil painting panels', Sydney Smirke on 'Architectural colouring', Westmacott on 'Polychrome in sculpture', and Russell Brandon on 'Ancient timber framing', are interspersed with original contributions by the editor, Edward Shelton, W. H. Hillyard and J. W. Ross on such subjects as golden glass, shell cameos, encaustic tiles, and paper hanging. The illustrations were by William Gibbs. The work first appeared in fortnightly parts of two leaves of text and two plates. *Quarto. 3 vols in one. iv+108+(2)pp and 52 chromolitho plates; (2)+107+(3)pp and 52 chromolitho plates; (2)+87pp and 41 chromolitho plates; many illustrations in text, text pages with decorative margins. Quarter morocco.* **Illustration below.** £85

495 **Thompson, Francis Benjamin** (editor) The universal decorator. A complete guide to ornamental design including designs for cabinet makers, wood carvers, metal workers, Birmingham, Sheffield and the Potteries, scrolls, panels, and general ornament, alphabets, initials and monograms *London, Houlston & Wright (c 1860)*
A later edition of the previous item re-arranged and much expanded, proving the wide appeal to all classes which the publication claimed to have. *Quarto. xi+(1)+512pp with many text illustrations, and 238 litho plates of which 112 in one colour, 11 in two or more colours. Original quarter calf. Subscriber's copy.* **Illustration below.** £110

294-5

496 **Tingry, P. F.** The painter and varnisher's guide; or, a treatise, both in theory and practice, on the art of making and applying varnishes; on the different kinds of painting; and on the method of preparing colours ... second edition, corrected and improved, by a practical chemist *London, Sherwood Neely & Jones 1816*
Widely used collection of recipes for paints, enamel, varnishes and glues, published at Geneva in 1803 (Tingry was Professor of Chemistry there) and first published in England in the following year. *Octavo. xxxii+412+(4)pp, 1 folding table, 2 engraved plates. Original boards, cloth spine, uncut.* £35

497 **Trueb, Aug.** Räume und Menschen *Stuttgart, Hädecke 1923*
Designs for interiors, carpets and wallpaper in the modern idiom – and in lurid colour. *Quarto. 66pp and 25 mounted colour plates. Original quarter cloth.* £8

498 **Turner, Laurence** Decorative plasterwork in Great Britain ... with an introduction by Arthur T. Bolton *London, Country Life 1927*
Historical study of the subject up to the Adam period; Turner's terms of reference include Scotland and the illustrations are particularly good. *Folio. xxxviii+271+(1)pp, including frontispiece and 348 illustrations. Original cloth.* £35

499 **Tynecastle Company** (Catalogue of Tynecastle canvas: vellum: textures: leathers: mosaics: wood mouldings: compo: adaptable & fibrous plaster) *Edinburgh (c 1925)*
Illustrated catalogue of Tynecastle products, principally for the decoration of walls and ceilings; the firm offers to decorate ship saloons and railway cars in Tynecastle canvas and fibrous plaster. *Folio. (8)+344pp with many illustrations. Original cloth.* £15

500 **Vacquier, J.** Le style empire. Décorations extérieures et intérieures, mobilier, bronzes. Troisième édition *Paris, Contet 1920*
First series only – but really good photo plates of Parisian buildings of the Empire period. *Folio. (4)+12pp and 42 photo plates. Original portfolio, marbled-paper boards.* £18

501 **Vanherman, T. H.** Every man his own house-painter and colourman. The whole forming a complete system for the amelioration of the noxious quality of common paint, a number of invaluable inventions, discoveries and improvements *London, I. F. Setchel 1829*
Vanherman, a former house-painter, divulges the secrets of the trade (much against the wishes of his fellow practitioners) by giving simple instructions on the choice of tools and materials, the preparation of paints, oils, varnishes and colours, and their application both internally and externally. The most vital piece of information imparted is the author's own recipe for 'aromatic paint' which produced practically no offensive smell. *Octavo. xxvi+111+(1 blank)pp. Publisher's cloth.* £15

502 **Viollet-le-Duc, Eugène Emmanuel** De la décoration appliquée aux édifices *Paris, Ballue 1880*
A short essay displaying Viollet's combination of scholarship, lucidity, and hostility to the Beaux-Arts brand of architecture. *Quarto. (4)+45+(3)pp with 23 text figures. Cloth.* £30

503 **Ware, I(saac)** Designs of Inigo Jones and others *(London, the author c 1735)*
Palladian interior features showing the executed designs of the architects Inigo Jones, Lord Burlington, William Kent and Colen Campbell. The examples include chimney-pieces, ceilings, staircases, mouldings, alcoves, screens, room schemes and wall elevations from places such as Houghton, Stowe, Somerset House, Chiswick, etc. Berlin Cat 2274. Fowler 437. *Large octavo. Engraved title with engraved tablet on verso, 5 full-page engraved plates of contents on (3)ff and 48 engraved plates (of which 5 double-page given two numbers each to take the numbering to 53). Contemporary full-calf gilt.* **Illustration opposite.** £150

503

504 **Watson, Rosamund Marriott** The art of the house *London, Bell 1897*

Collection of essays reprinted from the Pall Mall Gazette, on how to fill a house and what with. Nothing more recent than about 1815 will do for Miss Watson. *Octavo. xii + 186pp including 32 text illustrations and 8 plates. Original cloth.* £5

505 **Weaver, Sir Lawrence** Exhibitions and the arts of display *London, Country Life 1925*

Weaver was responsible for the display of British exhibits at the Wembley exhibition of 1924 and he bases this book on Wembley, with discussions and excellent illustrations of the layout and grouping of the exhibits. Comparisons are made between Wembley and the exhibitions at Munich and Gothenburg in 1922 and 1923. *Quarto. xx + 106pp, colour frontispiece, 366 illustrations (partly on 22 colour plates and 80pp of monotone plates). Original cloth.* £16

506 **Weaver, Sir Lawrence** Tradition & modernity in plasterwork *London, G. Jackson & Sons 1928*

Effectively a history of and advertisement for the Jackson firm of plasterers (for whose catalogue see item 389). Weaver mentions their links with Robert Adam and Owen Jones, and illustrates much of the firm's recent work for architects such as Lutyens, Reilly, Herbert Baker and Richardson & Gill. *Quarto. Frontispiece and 64pp including 46pp of plates. Original quarter vellum.* £15

507 **Wegert, Friederich** Die Farbe als Stimmungselement. Flächen- und Raumlösen in Malerei und Spritztechnik *Munich, Verlag G. D. W. Callway (1929)*

Sixty-five pleasing illustrations show examples of wall schemes, single motifs and repeat patterns for interior decoration. Muted colours and sprinkled-paint technique are used to create a mood, cause a disintegration of plane and surface, or, expand the space. The designs have a very strong period flavour. *Folio. (6)pp and 24 numbered chromolithograph plates. Publisher's printed portfolio.* £36

508 **Wharton, Edith & Ogden Codman** The decoration of houses *New York, Scribners 1919*
Favours Louis XV and Louis XVI decorative precedents. *Octavo. xxii+204pp and 56 photo plates. Original cloth.* £4

509 **Whiteman, G. W.** Some famous English country homes from the time of Henry VIII to the Regency *London, Antique Collector 1951*
Includes illustrations of the interiors of some of the best known English country houses. *Quarto. viii+172pp including 155 illustration. Original cloth.* £5

510 **Whittock, Nathaniel** The decorative painters' and glaziers' guide; containing the most approved methods of imitating oak, mahogany, maple, rose, cedar, coral, and every other kind of fancy wood ... designs for decorating apartments ... the art of staining and painting on glass ... – Supplement to the decorative painters' guide *London, Isaac Taylor Hinton 1827, Sherwood, Gilbert & Piper 1832*

The author proudly points out in his preface that his work needs no apology. Indeed, there is no precursor in English which treated the same subjects in such depth or covered such a wide rang within this particular field. Whittock, who was painting and drawing master at the Univeersity of Oxford was a prolific illustrator and author and was one of the first to produce works with lithograph illustrations systematically coloured by hand. The present work was quickly acknowledged as a valuable addition to works on decoration and new issues and additions soon followed.

In 1832 a Supplement appeared with illustrations of sixteen specimens of marbles from the Radcliffe Library which had only just been made available to public inspection, and resulted in some very fine plates. The original part of the work was reissued with a new title page to form a third edition, but the Supplement was also available separately to purchasers of the former issues, to be added to them as has been done here. *Octavo. 364+(4)+ivpp and 85+17 lithographed plates of which 46 hand coloured or tinted and several finished with gum arabic. Original marbled-paper boards, rebacked.* **Illustration below.** £165

511 **Whittock, Nathaniel** The decorative painters' and glaziers' guide ... *London, Isaac Taylor Hinton 1828*
Second issue before the addition of the Supplement. *Quarto. 332+(4)pp and 86 lithographed*

plates (numbered 1-74, with one plate bearing two numbers and 13 bis plates) of which 31 are hand coloured or tinted several finished with gum arabic. Original marbled-paper boards, quarter calf, rebacked using original spine. Waterstaining on a few plates. **Illustration opposite.** £115

512 **Whittock, Nathaniel** The decorative painters' and glaziers' guide... *London, Sherwood, Gilbert & Piper 1841*
Fourth issue with the Supplement an integral part of the work. *Quarto. iv+364+(4)pp and 84 lithographed plates of which 32+16 hand coloured or tinted and several finished with gum arabic. Publisher's embossed cloth.* **Illustration opposite.** £140

513 **Wilde, Oscar** Art and decoration. Being extracts from reviews and miscellanies *London, Methuen 1920*
Octavo. (8)+205+(1)pp. Original cloth. £9

514 **Willett, Ralph** A description of the library at Merly in the county of Dorset *London, John Nichols for the author 1785*
A lavish folio volume with parallel French and English texts describing the library built by Ralph Willett (1719-95) to house his collection of early typography, travel, Americana, etc. Its chief internal feature was the plasterwork of the ceiling, a series of allegorical designs on the theme of the origin and progress of civilization which Willett planned and a Mr Collins executed. These are fully represented in the plates of this book; the smaller ceiling panels portray persons as various as Zoroaster, Alfred and Manco Capac and the large oval centre panel shows George III being introduced by Britannia to Drake, Burghley, Newton, Bacon, Locke, Inigo Jones and Wren, while Collins is glimpsed 'leaning on the balustrade... peeping into the temple'. The book, Willett and his library are the subject of an article by Alan Thomas in 'The Book Collector', Winter 1963. *Folio. (4)+14pp, including title with engraved vignette, and 25 engraved plates on 24ff (2 folding). Contemporary full calf, neatly rebacked.* £280

515 **Wilson, Jose & Arthur Leaman** Colour in decoration *London, Studio (1972)*
Recent interior design work in colour. *Quarto. 160pp with many colour illustrations. Original cloth.* £8

516 **Wohnraüme und Dielen aus Alt-Schleswig-Holstein und Lübeck** Mit einer einleitung über Nord-Elbische Wohnungskunst von Professor Dr G. Brandt *Berlin, Verlag für Kunstwissenschaft (1918)*
Provides good illustrative coverage of North German interiors from the 16th century to the Biedermeier period. Lübeck as a member city of the Hanseatic League provides some of the handsomest houses. *Folio. (8)pp and 40 photo plates. Original cloth portfolio.* £30

517 **Wohnungskunst das bürgerliche Heim** Illustrierte Halbmonatshefte für Wohnungskunst Innenarchitektur und Kunstgewerbe *Darmstadt, Oct-Dec 1909, 1910, 1911*
54 numbers of this periodical launched in April 1909 (and united since July 1909 with the Munich fortnightly 'Die Raumkunst'). They constitute the issues for the last three months of 1909 and for the years 1910 and 1911 in their entirety. They cover the work of German architects and interior designers based in the Rhineland and Bavaria, with special reports on outside events, e.g. the second general meeting of the Deutsche Werkbund. *Quarto. 54 issues with many illustrations. Original decorated wrappers.* £35

518 **Wollin, Nils G.** Modern Swedish decorative art *London, Architectural Press 1931*
Quarto. xxxpp and 208pp of photo plates. Original cloth. £14

519 **Wright, Lawrence** Home fires burning. The history of domestic heating and cooking *London, Routledge 1968*
Octavo. ix+(1)+219+(1)pp with text illustrations. Original cloth. £3.75

520 **Yerbury, F. R.** (editor) Modern homes illustrated *London, Odhams (1947)*
Domestic architecture and design in the post-war world. *Octavo. 320pp many illustrations and plans and lxxii pp adverts). Original cloth.* £4

521 **Baillie Scott, M. H.** Haüser und Gärten ... ins Deutsche übersetzt von Wilhelm Schölermann *Berlin, Wasmuth 1912*
German translation of Baillie Scott's 'Houses and Gardens', published in 1906 and highly recommended by Muthesius and others. The illustrations of interiors, furniture, etc are reproduced from the English edition. This translation seems not to be known by Kornwolf (item 716). *Folio. xii+132pp, with 14 coloured plates and other photo illustrations. Original cloth.* £35

522 **Campen, Jacob van – Quellinius, Hubertus** Afbeeldin van't stadt huys van Amsterdam. – Prima (... Secunda) pars praecipuarum effigierum ac ornamentorum amplissimae Curiae Amstelrodamensis, maiori ex parte, in candido marmore effectorum *Amsterdam, Frederck de Witt (1665)-1668*
Second edition of Vennekol's plates illustrating the architecture and interiors of van Campen's Amsterdam town hall (1648-1655) one of the largest buildings in Holland, and the grandest of all European town halls, now the Royal Palace. Jacob van Campen was the most influential Dutch architect of the 17th century and the originator of what Summerson has called 'that Anglo-Netherlandish manner which had been the national (English) idiom since the time of Charles I'. This very complete coverage of the architecture of the exterior and interior and the illustrations of much of the decoration is together with the two magnificent volumes on the sculptural decoration which was the work of Aert Quellijn (1609-1668) of Antwerp. His brother Huybrecht drew and etched the plates and had published a small collection (48 plates) while work was still in progress. When he returned to Antwerp in 1665 he sold his entire stock of prints and maps to the publisher Frederick de Witt who also bought the rights to the architectural plates which had originally been issued by Danckerts in 1661. De Witt then issued the present three volumes as a complete pictorial record of Holland's most ambitious building project. *Elephant folio. 3 vols in one. Engraved title, engraved portrait of van Campen, and 29 engraved plates; engraved title, portrait of Aert Quellijn, engraved index and 48 plates; engraved title, engraved index and 55 engraved plates. A special set of plates mounted on sheets of laid paper and preserved between contemporary boards made into a drop-back box.* **Illustration opposite.** £460

523 **Marshall, H. G. Hayes** Interior decoration to-day *Leigh on Sea, F. Lewis 1938*
Many illustrations of interiors, furniture and fabrics of the 1930s (from London, Paris and New York). *Quarto. 288pp, mostly illustrations. Original cloth.* £8

524 **Mulliner, H. H.** The decorative arts in England during the late XVIIth and XVIIIth centuries *London, Batsford 1923*
Mulliner collaborated with Margaret Jourdain under the pseudonym 'Francis Lenygon' (see item 396). This publication under his own name has good illustrations of furniture, upholstery, bookbindings, etc. *Folio. (340)pp, with 256 photo illustrations. Original cloth.* £14

525 **Nouveaux intérieurs français** 4e série *Paris, Charles Moreau (c 1935)*
Another of the records in the Moreau series of interior design and furniture of the inter-war years. Here the modernist movement is shown in full spate represented by the rational approach, smooth lines, and formal simplicity of designers and decorators such as Roux-Spitz, Sognot, Adnet, Drouet, Dupré-Lafon, Djo-Bourgeois, Bacharach, Kahn, Chareau, and Barret. *Small folio. (8)pp and 45 (of 48) heliotype photoplates. Publisher's printed portfolio with ties.* £40

526 **Patmore, Derek** Decoration for the small home *London, Putnam 1938*
Quarto. xiv+(2)+208+(16)pp, including 65 photo plates. Original cloth. £4

522

527 **French interior design and furniture** from 1650 to 1930 in contemporary prints. An exhibition

A collection specially assembled, of contemporary prints of French interior schemes, furniture and decoration from the style of Louis XIV to the twenties and Art Deco. The French Court Style is represented by, among others, the works of the Le Pautres, Jean Marot, Berain and Mansart, the Regency style with Lassurance, Leroux, and Vassé, and the extravagances of the Rococo with Mollet, Pineau, and Meissonier. Blondel, Boucher, Lalonde and DelaFosse illustrate the transitional period and early Neo-Classicism while the styles of the Directoire, the Consulate and the First Empire are typified in the works of Percier and Fontaine, Beauvallet and Normand. Coloured illustrations from the magazine 'Collection de Meubles et Objets de Gôut' cover the period from the Revolution to the Second Empire. Mid nineteenth century eclecticism is typified by César Daly from his famous series of 'Décoration intérieur peinte' with representations of the designs of artists and painter-decorators such as Ouri, Denuell, Charton and Guillaume. The influence of industrial growth on furniture design is reflected in prints from the late nineteenth century semi-pattern books of furniture designers and makers, and these merge into examples of the 'Style Moderne'. The twenties and Art Deco is shown in a group of lithoprint photographs by exhibitors at the Salon d'Automne: Dufrène, Jallot, Leleu, Süe et Mare, etc.

The collection consists of examples of the work of more than 40 designers and includes not only illustrations of furniture pieces and wall schemes from the various periods and styles but particular features such as doors, windows, ceilings, chimney pieces, overdoors, and examples of the different types of decoration which emphasise the changes in detail that constitute the content of a style. Particular schemes are included, from the royal buildings, from Parisian hôtels, provincial châteaux and from private houses, some still extant, others which disappeared long ago and for which these illustrations represent the principal source for the study of their original schemes.

The prints are fully catalogued and an accompanying booklet provides notes on each designer or artist, and supplies a short historical and descriptive text to accompany each plate. In this way the illustrations are suitable and ready for immediate display or exhibition. A detailed list is available on request. *100 plates including copperplate line engravings, hand-coloured engravings, litho, tinted litho, chromolitho, and photolitho. In portfolio.*
Illustration below. £400

528 English interiors, decorative details, and furniture, from the seventeenth to the twentieth century, in contemporary or early prints. An exhibition

A specially assembled collection of contemporary prints showing the transformation of taste in English decoration and furniture up to the beginning of the present century.
The prints start with the introduction of italianate classicism by Inigo Jones and John Webb, seen mainly through the eyes of the English Palladians: Kent, Flitcroft and Vardy, who are also represented by their own designs, together with those of Lord Burlington, Colen Campbell and others. Their designs show the planning and arrangements of interiors as well as details of interior features. Further examples come from the 18th century pattern books both of the major architects such as Gibbs and Chambers and of the minor builders as Swan and Batty Langley. Ornamental details and furniture include the japanning patterns of Stalker and Palmer, and the exuberant designs of Thomas Chippendale. The great age of neo-classicism is shown in the works of Adam and Thomas Hope while the grace and elegance of Georgian furniture is illustrated by the designs of Hepplewhite and Sheraton. The nineteenth century opens with illustrations which appeared in Ackermann's 'Repository' including the early gothick of Pugin. The prints continue with such notables as George Smith and the Nicholsons and show the effects industrialisation and new production techniques with the furniture of the mid century and the Great Exhibition pieces, and in designers such as Thomson and Braud, while the continuing influence of exhibitions is shown in the works of Talbert. Examples of commercial 'art furniture' of the end of the century appears in illustrations from 'The Furniture Gazette'.
The foregoing are only a sample of the names which appear on the designs illustrating every aspect of interiors and furniture through two and a half centuries.
The prints are fully catalogued and accompanied by a booklet of notes on the designers and craftsmen with a short descriptive text to accompany each plate showing the place of the design within its historical setting. A catalogued list is available on request. *100 plates including copperplate line engravings, hand-coloured engravings, uncoloured and hand-coloured aquatints, litho, chromolitho, photolitho and collotype. In portfolio.* **Illustration above.** £400

529 **European decoration,** furniture and interiors from 1650 to 1930 in contemporary prints. An exhibition

In this particular collection all the principal designers in the two previous collections are represented by their most typical designs to provide a balance between interiors, decorative features, ornamental decoration, and furniture forms. To these is added a substantial German section with representative prints of a wide range of craftsmen from the early forms of Guckeisen and Ebelmann and the mannerist extravagances of Dietterlin through the lavish baroque inventions of Schübler and Decker, the traditional furniture pieces of Rump, the rich rococo of Hoppenhaupt and Hertel, and the selections of ornament from decorators such as Feichtmayer, Bichel, Nilson and Habermann to the Biedermeier style and nineteenth century designs. A passing look is given to work in the Netherlands in the prints of Vredeman de Vries and Crispin de Passe. Italy is represented with the decorative work of the Caracci, the ornamental designs of de Santi, Giardini's silverwork, and the furniture of Albertoli. Other prints include designs of Swedish furniture.

The collection provides a visual display which helps us to understand the furniture pieces we see and admire within the context of their period, within their original settings, and their relation to the interior features and other ornamental decoration to which they were married.

The individual prints are fully catalogued, short notes are provided on each artist and designer, and a descriptive text is given for each plate. A catalogued list is available on request. *100 plates including copperplate line engravings, aquatints (some hand-coloured), litho, chromolitho, photolitho and collotype. In portfolio.* £400

Murals, Mosaics and Ceilings

601a Until recent times the great decorative murals on buildings were known only through the interpretations of the engraver. Unlike easel paintings murals could not travel and their influence was consequently limited.
The engraved suites which figure in this section of our catalogue are therefore of great interest and significance for it was through them only that the work of many artists was widely disseminated. Even those who were fortunate enough to have seen the originals would use the prints to restore their fading memories, and what they saw would be the interpretations of draughtsmen and engravers influenced by the particular mannerisms of their period.
More than this, the suites of engravings are sometimes the only surviving records of schemes which have long since disappeared. Others are the only contemporary documentation of the work before subsequent alterations and restorations blurred the artist's original intention. Happily, a great number can hold their own and stand as work of engraving in their own right.

601 **Diderot, D. & J. L. d'Alembert** (Encyclopédie). Recueil de planches sur les sciences, les arts libéraux, et les arts méchaniques, avec leurs explication *Paris, Briasson, David, Le Breton & Durand 1762-72; Livorno 1772-9*
See item 1701 in the catalogue for details of this publication. *The section listed is folio, the plates sizes average 360 × 225mm, and the suite is preserved in a paper wallet.*
a **Mosaïque** (The mosaic worker)
Vignette of the mosaic workshop showing sorting and polishing of the stones, and assembling and finishing framed mosaic pictures and portraits. The remaining illustrations include 1 plate of tools and utensils, and several designs copied from ancient Roman examples including a large illustration of a mosaic at Palestrina: a montage of Egyptian views. *5 plates of which 1 double-page, with 9 illustrations and (1 + 1 blank) pp.*
Illustration on previous page. £15

602 **Ber(r)ettoni, Niccolo** In Templi S. Marie Montis Sancti Sacello D. Anna dicato depictas effigies *Rome, Gio. Girolamo Frezza 1727*
Frescoes from the Capella de Sant'Anna in the church of Sta Maria in Monte Santo, one of the twin churches of the Piazza del Popolo, Rome. Berrettoni's frescoes were painted c 1680, after the church, begun by Bernini in 1664, had been completed by Rainaldi in 1675. The illustrations, drawn by Stefano Pozzi and engraved by Frezza, show the fresco of the dome: God in Majesty upheld by clouds and angels; the putti of the pendentives; and the beatification of St Ann from the lunette. *Seven engraved plates varying in size from 217 × 202mm to 252 × 258mm. Untrimmed. In paper folder.* £42

603 **Blackburne, E. L.** Sketches, graphic and descriptive, for a history of the decorative painting applied to English architecture during the Middle Ages *London, John Williams 1847*
A very handsome book describing a selection of surviving examples of mediaeval decorative painting and illustrating them with chromolitho plates by Day & Son. The text supplies some learned ecclesiological lore on the portrayal of saints and the use of ornament. Abbey: Life 6; Mclean: Victorian Book Design, p 120. *Quarto. Chromolitho title, iv + 88 + (2)pp and 23 chromolitho plates. Contemporary quarter green morocco.* £55

604 **Cortona, Pietro Berrettini da** Galeria dipinta nel Palazzo del Prencipe Panfilio da Pietro Berrettini da Cortona. G. Audran sculps *Paris, N. Poilly (c 1680)*
The decoration of the Palazzo Pamphili with its impressive combination of friezes and ceilings was one of the three great decorative enterprises of the mid 17th century in Rome. The gallery of the palace was built by Borromini in 1646 for Innocent X, and the fresco work was painted by Pietro da Cortona between 1651 and 1654 as a rich monochrome system of undulating framework to support the main scenes which were devoted to the life and apotheosis of Aeneas. Cortona was one of the Italian baroque painters whose work was most influential on the French decorators. His effect was most pronounced on Charles Lebrun and he provided immediate models for such artists as Anguier. The plates, by Audran, are reverse copies of the suite by Carlo Cesio with the same title, published in Rome c1670. *Decorative engraved title, decorative engraved dedication and 14 engraved plates, of which 10 in sizes varying from 278:374 × 483:590mm, 2 of average size 275 × 220mm, and 2 size 278 × 710mm. Used plates, fingermarked in the very wide margins and with inkstain on margin of title but not affecting engraved parts. Preserved in cloth portfolio.* £55

605 **Carracci, Annibale** Galeriae Farnesianae icones Romae in aedibus Sereniss. Ducis Parmensis ab Annibale Carracio ad veterum aemulationẽ posterorumq. admiratioñe cum ipsarum monocromatibus et ornamentis a Petro Aquila delineatae incisae *Rome, Gio. Giacomo de Rossi (1674)*
The ceiling of the Gallery of the Palazzo Farnese, Rome, executed by Annibale Caracci and his assistants between 1597 and 1604, is the first of the great Italian Baroque ceiling frescoes and a milestone, in the development of this particular type of monumental art. Its arrangement pointed forward to the ideas of space and illusion

MURALS, MOSAICS AND CEILINGS

which were to become the characteristic features of the ceilings of the High Baroque and its execution made it one of the most influential works of all time affecting the technique of seventeenth century painting by returning to the classical ideal of balance and logic, of self-contained units carefully arranged to form a coherent and unified whole.

The Farnese ceiling is structurally a coved vault above projecting cornices. The commission was for a cycle of love scenes from Ovid's Metamorphoses, illustrating the Power of Love. Annibale felt that mythological paintings should be seen objectively in isolated frames yet he was unwilling here to apply friezes which he felt were suitable only for rooms with flat ceilings. His compromise solution was to incorporate 'quadri riportati' for the mythological scenes in a 'quadratura' framework, achieving an illusion of ceiling pictures hanging parallel to, or out from the walls. Looking somewhat backwards to the tradition of Mannerist conceits it conveyed the idea of an open-air picture booth between the hanging paintings of which the sky could be glimpsed. Pietro Aquila's engravings catch exactly the spirit of Carracci's work managing to convey something of the spatial complexity which makes the ceiling such an interesting work, while the importance of the scheme is emphasised by the fine portrait of Annibale after Carlo Maratti, an allegorical frontispiece with a full length portrait and a splendid decorative dedication plate. Berlin Cat 4088. *Engraved title, portrait, engraved frontispiece, decorative dedication and 21 numbered engraved plates varying in size from 280:650 × 285: 710mm. Clear impressions with good margins. Preserved in drop-back box.* **Illustration below.** £325

606 **Carracci, Annibale** Aedium Farnesiarum Tabulae ab Annibale Caraccio depictae a Carlo Caesio aeri insculptae atque a Lucio Philarchaeo explicationibus illustratae *Rome, Venanzio Monaldini 1753*
A handsomely produced work with an erudite description of the programme and the iconography of the Farnese Gallery and a full explanation of each mythological scene verified by numerous references to authors both ancient and modern. The Gallery is illustrated in the engravings of Carlo Cesio and the work is enriched by a series of large etched initials on landscape backgrounds, by a group of extra decorative plates including a set of grotesque panels, and a suite of playing putti by Giacinto Gimignani who, like Cesio, was also a pupil of Pietro da Cortona. The publication is completed by a fine roundel tailpiece taking up three-quarters of the final page and depicting the Abduction of Persephone. Cicognara 3376. *Folio. Title (printed in red and black with large etched vignette), (VI) + LXXIV ff and 35 engraved plates (of which 1 portrait, 10 double-p folding, 1 three-p folding, 6 on 3ff). Includes 3 engraved head pieces, 24 engraved tailpieces and 34 etched initials. Nineteenth century marbled-paper boards, half calf, gilt.* £225

607 **Carracci, Annibale** Galeria nel Palazzo Farnese in Roma del Sereniss. Duca di Parma etc. Dipinta da Annibale Caracci intagliata da Carlo Cesio *Rome, Venanzio Monaldini (c 1753)*
Separate issue by Monaldini of the plates of the previous item. Cesio's engravings first appeared in the mid seventeenth century and were later reissued by Arnold van Westerhout (whose imprint they still bear) about 1715. The engravings reproduce, in a large format, all the mythological scenes, show the medallions with their surrounding 'ignudi' groups, include the bronze captives, the putti of the pendentives, and the Virtues, as well as several other details, and show them all in normal perspective. Berlin Cat 4087. *Engraved title and 41 plates on 23 double leaves. Plates numbered 1-30 with nos 22, 23, 26, 27 each having two plates taking the same number, and nos 24 & 25 having four plates each with the one number. Plate sizes vary from 98 × 153 to 375 × 745mm, with wide margins. Untrimmed copy with good impressions. Preserved in drop-back box.* £150

608 **Carracci, Annibale** Gallerie que l'eccelent Annibal Carrache a peinte a Rome dans le Palais de Farnese *Paris, le Blond (c 1660)*
Reverse copies of Cesio's engravings made by Le Febure and Louis de Chastillon soon after the originals had appeared in Rome. The suite is dedicated to Lebrun as Chancellor of the French Academy whose directors had approved the masterpiece as one which should be studied by students in order that they might extract the principles of drawing. The paintings of the Gallery were particularly admired by Lebrun and passages derived from the ceiling can be singled out in several of his monumental works. *Title and 32 unnumbered engraved plates on 22 leaves. Sizes vary from 105 × 160mm to 370 × 722mm, with wide margins. Preserved in drop-back box.* £135

609 **Carracci, Annibale** Imagines Farnesiani cubiculi cum ipsarum monocromatibus et ornamentis Romae in aedibus Sereniss. Ducis Parmensis ab Annibale Carraccio aeternitati pictae. A Petro Aquila delineatae incisae *Rome, Gio. Giacomo de Rossi (c 1675)*
Depictions of frescoes of the Camerino of the Palazzo Farnese, Rome. This cycle was the first monument of Annibale Carracci's grand Roman manner and the indispensable prelude to the decoration of the Galleria Farnese (see item 605). The ceiling was designed to honour the young Cardinal Farnese, whose personal device forms an integral part of the decorative scheme. The programme was probably furnished by Fulvio Orsini for the theme of Virtue. On the vaults and in the lunettes it is developed in mythological and allegorical scenes from the stories of Hercules and Ulysses illustrating the victory of Virtue and Effort over Danger and Temptation. The decorative framework for the paintings was based on north Italian models such as the monochrome decorations in the nave of Parma Cathedral. Berlin Cat 4086. *Thirteen numbered engraved plates, including decorative title; sizes vary from 265:433 × 301:544mm. Fine impressions with wide margins, centre fold visible on some plates; untrimmed. Preserved in drop-back box.* £120

610 **Carracci, Ludovico** Il claustro di S. Michele in Bosco di Bologna dipinto dal famosa Lodovico Carracci e da altri eccellenti maestri usciti dall sua scola; descrito dal Sig. Co: Carlo Cesare Malavasia

e ravvivato all originale con l'esatto disegno, ed intaglio del Signor Giacopo Giovannini pitto bolognesse *Venice, Domenico Lovisa 1715*
The only record of the now lost frescoes of the elder Carracci and his followers in the cloisters of San Michele in Bosco, Bologna. The frescoes, executed in 1604-5 by Ludovico himself, and his pupils Guido Reni, Cavedoni, Garbieri, Brizio, Spada and Massari, depict scenes from the lives of Saints Bernard and Cecilia, as well as some fine telamones figures. During the 17th century the cycle was considered to be Ludovico's masterwork but even at that time the frescoes were suffering from the use of oil on fresco combined with poor ingredients in the plaster. Even more premature decay of the paintings is instanced by the restorative work carried out in 1632 by Guido Reni. This second issue of a work published in 1694 is without the accompanying text by Malvasia which is still noted in the unaltered title. Some of the plates appear to be worn in parts but this is actually an attempt to reproduce the ghostlike effect which the decaying frescoes were in part displaying when these interpretations were made. However, one of the earlier telamones coppers appears to have been lost, since a new plate has been cut with the drawing in a more mannered style which produces a certain individual and dramatic effect. *Folio. Letterpress title and 20 engraved plates (numbered 1-18, 2 unnumbered) of which 4 folding. Lightly stitched in original wrappers, untrimmed. Preserved in folder.* £240

611 Carracci, Ludovico & Guido Reni (Telamones figures from the cloisters of San Michele in Bosco) *(Bologna, heirs of Antonio Pisarri 1694)*
Giovannini's engravings of the fine male figures and figure groups depicted as providing column supports in the frescoes of San Michele in Bosco. These plates are from the first issue of the preceding item. Berlin Cat 4084. *Folio. 4 engraved plates, average size 375 × 230mm. Tipped on handmade paper. Preserved in paper wallet.* £45

612 Croft-Murray, Edward Decorative painting in England 1537-1837. Volume two. The eighteenth and early nineteenth centuries *London, Country Life 1970*
The second part of Mr Croft-Murray's study of painting as employed in the decoration of ceilings, walls and woodwork in English buildings. It begins with the work of G. A. Pellegrini and M. Ricci, Venetian painters who came to England in 1708, and covers all important work in the field down to B. R. Haydon's plans for the decoration of the new Houses of Parliament. *Folio. 382pp including 156 illustrations. Original cloth.* £18

613 Gélis-Didot, P. La peinture décorative en France du XVIe au XVIIIe siècle *Paris, Librairie General de l'Architecture (1885)*
Examples of decorative painting from the Louvre, Versailles, Fontainebleau, Chantilly and many provincial public buildings. A companion volume to that by Gélis-Didot and Laffillée (item 614). *Folio. (8) +8+(240)pp with text illustrations and 60 chromolitho plates. Cloth portfolio.* £85

614 Gélis-Didot & P. & H. Laffillée La peinture décorative en France du XIe au XVIe siècle *Paris, Librairies-Imprimeries Réunis (c 1885)*
Over 600 examples of early painting and decoration in French ecclesiastical buildings extending from the paintings in the baptisteries and crypts of romanesque churches to the walls of the great cathedrals and the chapel shrines. *Folio. 6 parts in 1. (vi) +xiv+ (192)pp with many text illustrations, and 60 unnumbered chromolitho plates. Publisher's cloth with original printed-paper part wrappers preserved.* £90

615 Giulio Romano (Frescoes and ceilings from the Palazzo del Té, Mantua) *(Rome c 1640)*
Illustrations of Giulio's powerful frescoes from the Duke of Mantua's pleasure palace showing details of the vault paintings representing the Temple of Heaven and scenes from the Fall of the Giants. An unsigned and unrecorded work. *Six etchings; sizes vary from 188 × 216mm to 213 × 287mm. In paper wallet.* £65

616 Giulio Romano (L'entrée de l'Empereur Sigismond à Mantoue) *Paris, Claudia B. Stella 1675*
Representations of the triumphal entry into Mantua of the Holy Roman Emperor

Sigismund, King of Hungary and Bohemia (1368-1437) after a painted and stucco frieze in one of the rooms of the Palazzo del Té, at Mantua which had been carried out by Primatticio and Mantovano under the direction of, and from designs by, Giulio Romano. This is the first impression of the plates engraved by Antoinette Bouzonnet Stella which are usually known only from the 18th century restrikes by Chereau and Jombert (see Berlin Cat 1074). This later issue has the dedication to Colbert on the first plate burnished out and replaced by a title. *Twenty-five numbered engraved plates with an average height of 165mm and widths varying from 323mm to 415mm. Good margins. In folding cloth case.* £75

617 Goldicutt, John Specimens of ancient decorations from Pompeii *London, Rodwell & Martin 1825*
A small but very elegant collection of mural and mosaic designs from Pompeii, illustrated by handcoloured engraved plates. *Quarto. (2)pp and 20 coloured engraved plates (including title). Cloth, original printed label on upper cover.* £50

618 Gruner, Lewis Fresco decorations and stuccoes of churches & palaces, in Italy, during the fifteenth & sixteenth centuries with descriptions by Lewis Gruner, and, A comparison between the ancient arabesques & those of the sixteenth century by Mr A. Hittorff *London, John Murray, P. D. Colnagi (etc) & the authors 1844*
A fine coverage, by the artistic mentor to Prince Albert, of Italian Renaissance interior decorative work principally by Raphael and his studio, his pupils Giovanni da Udine and Giulio Romano, with some examples by Corregio, Pensile, Peruzzi, Pinturicchio and Luini. The illustrations show the Vatican Logge, the Villa Madama, the Farnesina, the Villa Lante, the Palazzo del Té and the Ducal Palace at Mantua, and the Camere di S. Paolo in Parma, ending with a group of ecclesiastical buildings principally showing the Certosa at Pavia. The plates were adaptations of those published by Thürnmer and Gutensohn in 1834. Special hand coloured copies of this work were produced but the ordinary run of the work was intended to be coloured by the client and an interesting final plate furnishes an aid to colouring the rest with a key of 56 coloured symbols linked by numbers and letters to more than 150 small details. *Folio atlas and quarto text volumes. (6)pp and 46 numbered engraved plates; xvi+72pp and 4 numbered litho plates with 43 illustrations. Atlas in 19th century marbled-paper boards, red morocco spine, gilt. Text in original printed wrappers.* **Illustration below.** £260

618

619 Gruner, L. The decorations of the garden-pavilion in the grounds of Buckingham Palace. Engraved under the superintendence of L. Gruner ... with an introduction by Mrs Jameson *London, John Murray 1846*
The decoration of the garden pavilion was carried out at the wish of Queen Victoria and Prince Albert to encourage wider use of fresco painting in Britain. A large octagon room was painted with frescoes on subjects from Milton's Comus, by artists who included Maclise, Dyce, Landseer and Eastlake; and two smaller rooms in Pompeian and 'Romantic' styles, the latter with frescoes from designs by Gruner derived from the novels of Sir Walter Scott. A thoroughly Victorian miscellany. *Folio. 11+(1)pp, with a large wood engraving on half title, and 15 plates (of which 6 chromolitho, the others engraved). Original gilt stamped red cloth, rebacked. With presentation inscription from Gruner.* £110

620 **Hutton, Edward** The Cosmati: the Roman marble workers of the XIIth and XIIIth centuries *London, Routledge 1950*
Quarto. xii+62+(2)pp and 64pp of plates, coloured frontispiece. Original cloth. £9

621 (Lebrun, Charles) **Massé, Jean-Baptiste** La Grande Galerie de Versailles, et les deux salons qui l'accompagnent *Paris, l'Imprimerie Royal 1752*
The Grande Galerie, or, the Galerie des Glaces, and the two rooms which lead to it: the Salon de Guerre and the Salon de la Paix, were the creation of Mansart and Lebrun. Their decorative and architectural ensemble forms a complete summary of the Louis XIV decorative style. The engravings presented here concentrate on Lebrun's ceiling paintings which depict the life of Louis XIV from 1661 to 1678. Louis' achievements are represented in allegorical form with the King as a Roman Emperor surrounded by the gods and goddesses of antiquity and symbolic figures representing the King's friends and enemies. This programme was portrayed in 9 large paintings, 12 small canvasses and 6 grisailles.
The drawings for the volume were carried out by Massé (1687-1767) who spent twenty-five years on the task. The effort exhausted his financial resources, caused bad feeling with the engravers he employed (including notables such as Aubert, Audran, Cochin, Duflos, Laurent Simoneau, Surugue and the Tardieux) and in the end the work was coolly received by the public. However, Louis XV was well pleased with Massé's efforts and to show his gratitude rewarded the artist by appointing him Keeper of the Royal Paintings, and recompensed him by purchasing the original drawings (now in the Louvre). Berlin Cat 4026. *Large folio. (4)+18pp and 55 engraved plates of which 23 double-p, 26 single-p, and 6 two page (numbered 1-52, 12**, 13**, 14**). Contemporary green morocco, gilt tooling on boards and spine.* £360

622 (Lebrun, Charles) **Surugue, Louis** Grand Escalier du Château de Versailles dit Escalier des Ambassadeurs ordonné et peint par Charles le Brun ecuyer Premier Peintre du Roy *Paris, Louis Surugue (c 1725)*
The only complete record of the Great Staircase at Versailles, the first room to be illuminated by a glass skylight, which was built between 1671 and 1679 and destroyed in the mid 18th century in order to make more apartments. The staircase was one of the most spectacular of the schemes at Versailles in the third quarter of the 17th century and the final and finest example of the co-operation between LeVau who supplied the plan and Lebrun who provided the decorative designs. The engravings show the novelty of the plan which had to be fitted into a wide but shallow room, and the splendour of the decorations. These latter are shown both in their total effect and with details of the painted Ionic columns, the imitation tapestries which filled the gaps between, the open loggia with the symbols of the four continents combined with allegories praising the virtue and achievements of Louis XIV. This copy contains 8 additional plates which are not part of the main work but show paintings from the Grande Galerie of the Palais Royal. Berlin Cat 4025. *Large folio. Engraved title, 9 plates of engraved text on 5ff with large decorative engraved headpiece, engraved initial, engraved tailpiece and 24 numbered engraved plates of which 5 double-p; 8 engraved plates, not part of the main work. Half red morocco.* £360

623 **Le Pautre, Jean** Plafons à la romaine nouvellement inventez et gravez *Paris, Jollain 1665*
Twelve ceiling designs with a central geometrical space painted to represent a heavenly scene, and surrounded by a heavily decorated frame intended to be executed in paint and stucco. *Six unnumbered engraved plates each with two designs. Average size 145 × 212mm, with good margins. In paper wallet.* £45

624 **Le Pautre, J(ean)** Quart de plafons nouvellement inventés et gravés *Paris, P. Mariette (c 1670)*
Similar designs to the previous suite conceived in a richer manner with more complex decoration. (Oeuvres suite 41). Destailleur Notices p 101. Guilmard p 71. *Six numbered engraved plates, average size 150 × 220mm, with good margins. In paper wallet.* £42

625 **Le Pautre, (Jean)** (Desseins de plafonds) *(Paris), Moncornet (c 1670)*
Complete ceiling designs of which three have a central painted panel and three are

composed of bands and panels of stucco with figure decoration. (Oeuvres suite 35). Guilmard p 71. *Six unnumbered engraved plates, average size 138 × 192mm. In paper wallet.* £36

626 Le Pautre, J(ean) Nouveau dessins de plafons *Paris, J. Marriette (c 1720)*

More complex ceiling designs with covings decorated in painting and sculpture and quadratura designs using architectural perspectives for 'trompe l'oeil' effects. (Oeuvres 34). Destailleur Notices p 101. Guilmard p 71. *Six unnumbered plates, average size 156 × 215mm, with wide margins. In paper wallet.* £30

627 L'Orange, H. P. & P. J. Nordhagen Mosaics. Translated by Ann E. Keep *London, Methuen 1966*

Mosaic work of the Roman and early Byzantine period. *Quarto. x + 92pp and 110pp of photo plates, 4 additional colour plates. Original cloth.* £6

628 Lysons, Samuel Figures of mosaic pavements discovered at Horkstow in Lincolnshire *London 1801*

The first part of Lyson's work on the Roman antiquities discovered in Britain, which had appeared under the title of 'Reliquae Britannico-Romanae'. This part illustrates the mosaics which had been discovered accidentally in the gardens of Horkstow Hall in 1796. The hand-coloured illustrations include a map of the area showing the position of the find in its relationship to other Roman remains in the area, a landscape view of the estate showing the position of the pavement, and details of the various remains of the mosaic compartments together with a conjectual restoration of the whole floor design by the elder Robert Smirke. *Broadsheet. Hand coloured aquatint title, (4) + 4pp and 7 coloured aquatint plates of which 4 double-page folio. A special copy produced in a limited number, contemporary hand-coloured to resemble drawings. Quarter morocco modern binding with original publisher's label on front cover.* £75

629 (Manni, Domenico Maria) Azione gloriose degli uomini illustri fiorentini, espresse co'loro ritratti, nelle volte della Reale Galleria di Toscana *(Florence, Ignazio Orsini c 1750)*

A rare work which illustrates the magnificent decorations of the Uffizi Gallery, most of which are still extant. The volume arose out of the desire of the Grand Duke of Tuscany, Francis of Lorraine (who had succeeded the Medici in 1737) to have made pen drawings of decorations of the Gallery. This inspired Ignazio Orsini to commission Guiseppe Menabuoni to draw the ceilings of the south and west corridors for publication, and to employ the antiquarian and historian, Domenico Maria Manni, to write the accompanying explanatory text. The decorations of these corridors had been planned by Leopold Medici in consultation with his librarian Ferdinand de Maestro, Canon Lorenzo Pantiatichi, and Alessandro Segni. The paintings which were begun in 1658 depicted, on the west corridor, the various branches of learning, and portraits of celebrated Florentines were intermingled with grotesques and scenes representing the exploits of the cities of the state of Tuscany, and the deeds of their inhabitants. The south corridor was devoted to the virtues of the Grand Dukes, the Council of Florence, the Florentine saints and the founding of various Orders. The decoration was carried out by the foremost painters of the period: Cosimo Ulivelli, Jacopo Chiavistelli, Angiolo Gori, and their pupils and followers. The work provided a fortunate record of the complete scheme, for a fire in 1762 seriously damaged the end of the west corridor, destroying 12 sections of the ceiling and nine portraits. Berlin Cat 4103. *Oblong folio. Engraved title, engraved portrait, (4)pp and (52)ff text, 52 engraved plates. Eighteenth century marbled-paper boards, calf spine. A very fine copy.* **Illustration opposite.** £750

630 Morgan, Thomas Romano-British mosaic pavements: a history of their discovery and a record and interpretation of their designs *London, Whiting 1886*

Excellent survey of Roman mosaic pavements discovered in Britain up to the 1880s, with accurate colour illustrations. *Octavo. xxxiv + 323 + (1)pp, frontispiece and 34 plates (some coloured and folding). Original decorated cloth.* £22

631 **Murbach, Ernst** The painted Romanesque ceiling of St Martin in Zillis *London, Lund Humphries 1967*
Quarto. (6) + 48pp and 88pp of photo illustrations (mostly colour). Original cloth. £5

632 **Pinturicchio (Bernardino di Betto di Biago)** (Vita del Papa Pio II nel Bibliotheca Piccolomini del Duomo de Siena) del et sculp da Raim(ondo) Faucci *(Siena), Franc. Xav. Rossi (1771)*
Pinturicchio's decorative perspective paintings in the cathedral library at Siena, built c1494 for Cardinal Francesco Piccolomini to receive the valuable books which Pope Pius II had left to the town of Siena. Pinturicchio's programme carried out 1503-7 depicts scenes from the life of Aeneas Silvio Piccolomini, afterwards Pope Pius II. The cycle, with its arabesque decorated pilasters and fine colour harmonies is judged to be Pinturicchio's finest work and Faucci provides the standard 18th century interpretation of the work. *Broadsheet. 10 engraved plates of average size 555 × 330mm. Stitched in nineteenth century, marble-paper wrappers.* £30

633 **Polidoro (Caldara) da Caravaggio** (The story of Niobe) *Rome, Arnold van Westerhout (c 1710)*
Scenes etched by Giovanni Battista Galestruzzi, from the Story of Niobe on the façade of the Palazzo Cesi, Rome, which had been painted in grisaille by Polidoro about 1527. Polidoro da Caravaggio (c1500-1543) was one of the more inventive artists of the circle of Raphael, and achieved a particular fame by painting vast panoramic friezes of monochrome scenes from the history of ancient Rome, and from the mythologies, across the façades of many Roman palaces. (see also item 1626). Second issue Berlin Cat 4171:4. Bartsch III nos 18-22. *Five numbered etched plates with imprint and signature on plate 3, lettered at the corners to show matching sections. The plates have an average height of 115mm and vary in width from 125 to 344mm. With wide margins. In paper wallet.* £30

634 **Polidoro (Caldara) da Caravaggio** Polydori Caravagensis insignia monocromata ... *Rome, Gio. Giacomo de Rossi (c 1670)*
Illustrations of the frieze decorations from the façade of the Palazzo Gaddi in Via della Maschera d'Oro, Rome, painted in monochrome by Polidoro and Maturino c1527 but which no longer survives. The illustrations show the embarkation of troops from Africa, the loading of boats, and end with a naval battle at Ostia. The work was drawn and engraved by Pietro Santo Bartoli. *Eight numbered engraved plates, sizes 160 × 445mm. With centre fold marks visible, two plates repaired for small centre tears: three plates cut to plate mark along bottom edges, otherwise good margins. In cloth portfolio.* £80

635 **Polidoro (Caldara) da Caravaggio** (Scenes from the façade of the Palazzo Milesi, Rome) *Rome (c 1675)*
Various scenes from history and from the mythologies etched by Galestruzzi from the decoration of the Palazzo Milesi, in Via della Maschera d'Oro. The scenes include a Rape of the Sabines, and, Saturn castrating Uranus (see plate 194 no 223 in Italian Drawings in the British Museum: Raphael his Circle). *Six numbered etched plates. Sizes vary from 110:118 × 124:171mm. Good impressions with wide margins. In paper wallet.* £40

636 **Polidoro (Caldara da Caravaggio)** (The story of Hannibal) *(Rome c 1675)*
Scenes which appear to be part of the life of Hannibal, drawn by Galestruzzi and etched by Giovanni Francesco Venturini. It is not certain on which palace façade these scenes appeared. Berlin Cat 4181:3 suggests one in the Via della Maschera d'Oro. They could be more scenes from the Palazzo Milesi. *Five numbered etched plates with an average height of 153mm and widths varying from 85mm to 152mm. Good impressions with wide margins. In paper wallet.* £45

637 **Polidoro (Caldara) da Caravaggio** Sabinarum raptum a Polydoro Caravagien celeberr pictore delineatum *(Rome c 1710)*
A little known engraving of Polidoro's monochrome frieze showing the Rape of the Sabines from the space between the first and second floors of the Palazzo Ricci near Corte Savella, Rome, painted c1524. The frieze still exists but has been much restored and is not easy to see. Drawings of parts reproduced on two of the plates are in the British Museum (see Italian Drawings in the British Museum: Raphael & his Circle, no 221, plate 193). A second issue of earlier engravings now deleting imprint and signatures. *Three numbered engraved plates with an average height of 175mm and widths varying from 450 to 492mm; joined to make one long frieze. Good margins. In paper wallet.* £35

638 **Ponce (Nicolas)** Arabesque antiques des Bains de Livie, et de la Ville Adrienne, avec les plafonds de la Ville-Madame, peints d'après les dessins de Raphael *Paris, the author 1789*
Grotesque ceiling decorations showing the ancient Roman originals from the 'grottoes' of the palaces and villas of the Roman Emperors and their Renaissance counterparts as executed by the studio of Raphael. Renewed interest in this type of decoration had been manifest after the excavations of Professor Felice had uncovered sixteen rooms of the Golden House of Nero in 1774-5. Berlin Cat 3953. *Folio. (4)pp and 15 engraved plates. Original green-paper boards. Untrimmed.* £58

639 **Raphael Sanzio da Urbino** Psyches et Amoris nuptiae ac fabula a Raphaele Sanctio Urbanate Romae in Farnesianis hortis transtyberim ... Expressa a Nicolao Dorigny ad similitudinem delineata et incisa *Rome, Domenico de Rossi, 15 August 1693*
Engravings by Dorigny after the frescoes in the loggia on the ground floor of Agostino Chigi's Villa Farnesina on the Tiber carried out 1517-1518. The theme is the fable of Psyche taken from The Golden Ass by Apuleius. The framework of the ten spandrels and eight lunettes is shown in nine plates. Beginning with the wall communicating with the Chamber of Galatea the plates work clockwise round the room showing the story of Cupid's love for Psyche and the jealousy of Venus. They conclude with a large plate each for the two great frescoes on the ceiling, conceived as tapestry hangings pinned over a frame of garlands, leaves and fruit: The Council of the Gods, and, The Wedding Banquet. The frescoes, based on preparatory drawings by Raphael, were executed by his assistants Gaudenzio Ferrari, Raffaelline del Colle and Giulio Romano. Giovanni da Udine painted the beautiful arbour framework which continues the greenery of the garden outside. The engravings were carried out in such a form that they were probably intended to be hand coloured.
This suite contains the extra plate showing the Triumph of Galatea from a neighbouring room, which in some copies is replaced by figures of Prudence, Force and Moderation. Berlin Cat 4066. *Large folio. 12 numbered engraved plates including title. Sizes average 380 × 660mm and 390 × 700mm with the final plate 525 × 365mm. Fine impressions with good margins, untrimmed. Original blue-paper wrappers, preserved in cloth portfolio.* £90

640 Raphael Sanzio da Urbino Picturae Raphaelis Sanctij Urbinatis ex aula et conclavibus Palatij Vaticani ad publicum terrarum orbis ornamenturis in aereas tabulas nunc primum omnes deductae explicationibus illustratae *Rome, Domenico de Rossi 1722*

Engravings by Francesco Aquila after Raphael's Vatican frescoes whose balanced and classically poised compositions are some of the finest examples of the High Renaissance style at its apogee. The plates show the principal scenes of the decorations of the four inter-communicating rooms in the north wing of the Palace, known collectively as the Stanze, and executed for the Popes Julius II and Leo X, between 1509 and 1524. The rooms are illustrated in the reverse order of the usual approach by visitors, beginning with the Sala di Constantino whose frescoes, simulating tapestries hanging from the wall and illustrating The End of Paganism and the Establishment of the Church of Rome, are shown in seven plates. Five plates show the Stanza dell'Eliodoro with its theme of Divine Intervention on Behalf of the Church, and include a fine example of the ceiling decoration which is now in very poor condition. The Stanza della Segnatura, intended as the library of Julius II, containing Raphael's masterpieces 'The School of Athens' and 'The Disputa', is shown in five plates, while the final four plates illustrate the Stanza dell'Incendio whose frescoes celebrate the Glorification of the Power of the Pope.

The work contains three extra plates by Bartoli which do not form part of the series, and which join together to make a large scene of the Adoration of the Magi. Berlin Cat 4064. *Large folio. 22 engraved plates including title, numbered 1-19 (with no 3 consisting of four coppers); 3 unnumbered plates. Average size 480 × 680mm. A completely untrimmed copy. Original blue paper wrappers, preserved in cloth portfolio.* £185

641 Raphael Sanzio da Urbino Paulus Athenis per Epicuraeo . . . (The School of Athens) *Rome, Gio. Giacomo de Rossi 1648*

The engraving by Philippe Thomassin of Raphael's famous masterpiece in the Vatican Stanza della Segnatura. Thomassin, a French engraver who settled in Rome in 1585, originally published his work in 1617 and dedicated it to the Professor of Medicine, Giovanni Battista Figoni. This is the second issue. *One illustration on 2 coppers, 397 & 407 × 490mm. A fine impression with good margins.* £45

642 Raphael Sanzio da Urbino Loggie di Rafaele nel Vaticano (. . . che contiene volte ed i loro respettivi quadri . . . il compimento degli ornati, e de' bassirilievi antichi) *Rome, (Marc Pagliarini c 1769-1777)*

Raphael's Loggie decorations are among the most influential decorative schemes of all times and the present suite of engravings, which were the first comprehensive survey of the work, still forms the most important record of the frescoes. They were made while the decorations still retained their freshness and clarity, before subsequent restoration was carried out on the frescoes and before preservation treatment had been given to the stucco work. The three parts include a view looking down the gallery, a large scale plan of the Loggie with an overall view of the wall elevations, while the doors, pilasters, paintings of the vaults, the decoration of the embrasures of the windows and the spandrels of the vaults are shown in large scale detail. The work was engraved by Giovanni Volpato and Giovanni Ottaviani after the drawings of Pietro Camporesi and Ludovico Tesco, under the general editorship of Gaetano Savorelli who also provided some of the drawings. The engravings were intended to be hand coloured after the original works. Berlin Cat 4068. See also the following item. *Three parts. Engraved title with view and portrait, 4 engraved plates of doors of which 2 lettered A and 2 lettered B, 14 engraved plates of wall decorations numbered I-XIV, and 3 engraved plates joined to make one large elevation with plan; 13 engraved plates of lunettes and vault frescoes numbered I-XIII; 12 engraved plates of pilaster decorations numbered 1-12 each made from two coppers, and 1 etched plate of the Vatican Museum with plan, section and view, by Gau & Liman, Rome, 1817. Preserved in two quarter morocco drop-back boxes with morocco labels.* **Illustration on next page.** £560

643 Raphael Sanzio da Urbino Loggie di Rafaele nel Vaticano . . . Seconda parte che contiene . . . volte ed i loro respettivi quadri *Rome, Marc Pagliari c 1776*

Splendid individual coloured illustrations of the lunettes over the windows and the matching section of vault above, from Raphael's Vatican Loggie. Each of the thirteen **vaults** contain four frescoes united by illusionistic designs **of** perspective architectural decoration and grotesques of coloured and gilded stucco. The scenes are devoted to stories from the Bible.

The engravings which are from a copy to the previous item have been excellently hand coloured in gouache to imitate the original fresco colouring, and the gilded stucco of the original has here been picked out in gold paint. Each example makes a fine decorative work and provides an excellent idea of the beauty and richness of the originals in their early state. Giovanni da Udine's fruit garlands in the lunettes stand out from a deep blue ground, delicate grotesques and arabesques ornament the soffits and spandrels of the arch, and perspective trompe l'oeil decoration forms a background to each historiated scene. *Each item is made from two engravings joined together to give an average size of 605 × 555mm, coloured in gouache and gold paint by a contemporary hand; backed on stiff paper, in card mount.*

a **God appears to Isaac.** From the fifth vault. £45

b **Joseph interprets the dreams of his brothers.** From the seventh vault. £55

c **Moses receiving the tablets of the law.** From the ninth vault. £50

d **The triumph of David.** From the eleventh vault. £50

e **The judgement of Solomon.** From the twelfth vault. **Illustration below.** £55

642/643e

644 **Raphael Sanzio da Urbino** Architettura ed ornati della Loggia del Vaticano opera de celebre Raffaele Sanzio da Urbino *Venice, Santini 1783*

Excellent Venetian copies of the previous item 642. The scale and format of both these works makes them particularly suitable for display or exhibition. *Folio. 3 parts in 2. Decorative engraved title, and 28 engraved plates numbered I-XIV, I-XIV; engraved title with view and portrait, 4 engraved plates of doors of which 2 numbered A and 2 numbered B, 3 engraved plates of plan and wall elevation, 13 etched and aquatinted plates of lunettes and spandrels numbered I-XIII; 13 etched and aquatinted plates of vault frescoes numbered I-XIII. Fine impressions with wide margins. Contemporary stippled-paper boards, quarter calf, rebacked. Ex library.* £280

645 **Raphael Sanzio da Urbino** Logge del Vaticano *Rome, Niccola de Antoni (1802)*
The pilaster decorations of the Loggie engraved by Carlo Lasinio, Professor of etching at the Academia of Florence and later Keeper of the Camposanto Museum at Pisa. Lasinio was one of the foremost practitioners of outline engraving and an experimenter in the colour process. However, this suite, carried out under the direction of Francesco Rainaldi, was executed in the conventional manner. Berlin Cat 4070. *Large folio. Decorative engraved title and 13 engraved plates numbered I-VIII, II-VI. Nineteenth century marbled-paper boards, morocco label, half calf, rebacked.* £35

646 **Raphael Sanzio da Urbino** Imagines Veteris ac Novi Testamenti a Raphaele Sanctio Urbinate in Vaticani Palatii Xystis mira picturae elegantia expressae *Rome, Gio. Giacomo de Rossi 1675*
The historiated scenes from the vaults of the second floor of the Vatican Loggie, forming the cycle which is popularly known as 'The Bible of Raphael'. The fifty-two frescoes are devoted principally to stories from the Old Testament with the final vault treating of scenes from the Life of Christ. The engravings, by Pietro Aquila and Caesar Fantetti are dedicated to Queen Christiana of Sweden and include her portrait. Berlin Cat 4062. *Oblong folio. Engraved title with dedication and portrait, engraved frontispiece and 52 numbered engraved plates. Large paper copy with fine impressions; frontispiece repaired and stain in the wide margin, otherwise a good clean copy, uncut. Contemporary paper boards, quarter calf, rebacked.* £70

647 **Raphael Sanzio da Urbino** Eminentissimo ... Camillo Maximo ... Parerga, atque ornamenta, ex Raphaelis Sanctij prototypis ... in Vatican Palatij Xystis.-Imagines Veteris ac Novi Testamenti a Raphaele Sanctio Urbinate in Vaticani Palatii Xystis mira picturae elegantia expressae *Rome, Gio. Giacomo de Rossi (c 1675)*
Two suites of engravings of part of the Vatican Loggie decorations including the Bible scenes of the previous item. The other suite, engraved by Bartoli, shows classical motifs and groups of painted stucco decorations by Giovanni da Udine from the soffits and spandrels of the Loggie vaults. Giovanni reinvented a technique which had been lost since antiquity to provide the stucco medium, and he drew the inspiration for his motifs from the chambers of the buried ruins of the Golden House of Nero which had been excavated not many years before. The first and final plate are interesting for showing the Studio at work on the Loggie and for illustrating Giovanni experimenting to discover the correct mixture for his material and making notes on his findings. Berlin Cat 4063 (records an incomplete copy). *Oblong folio. 2 works in one. 43 numbered engraved plates on 22ff including title; engraved title with dedication and portrait, engraved portrait, engraved frontispiece, and 52 numbered engraved plates. Contemporary green vellum, rebacked.* £85

648 **Raphael Sanzio da Urbino** D. Nicolao Simonellio ... Raphaelis Urbinatis monumenta.-Serenniss.mo Principi Leopoldo Medices ... Imagines, ab Hetruriae legatione ad Pontificatum ... in aulaeis Vaticanis, textili monocromate elaboratas.-Eminentissimo ... Camillo Maximo ... Parerga, atque ornamenta *Rome, Gio. Giacomo de Rossi (c 1675)*
A series of three suites of engravings of the works of Raphael by Pietro Santi Bartoli, a pupil of Poussin, and one of the leading exponents of the classical revival in the second half of the seventeenth century. The series includes the Medici tapestries showing the achievements of Giovanni de'Medici and his rise to the Papal throne. See also the previous item for the third suite. Cicognara 3600. Berlin Cat 1668 & 4063 (records incomplete copy). *Oblong folio. 3 works in 1. 15 unnumbered engraved plates including decorative title; decorative engraved title and 14 numbered engraved plates; 43 numbered engraved plates including title. Foxed. Contemporary marbled-paper boards, calf spine.* £65

649 (Raphael Sanzio da Urbino) **Engelmann, G.** The lodges of Raphael; from the celebrated frescoes in the Vatican, representing some of the principal historical subjects of the old and new testament. Drawn by M. M. Weber, Aubry-le-Comte, Chrétien, d'Hardivillier,

Zuiger and other eminent artists in Paris *London & Paris, John Hearne (c 1820)*
A standard subject for illustration since the 17th century here brought up-to-date with the use of the new medium; crayon lithography. This must have been one of the earliest books of its type and one of the first to cover the work of Raphael in that medium while at the same time it provided the standard 19th century interpretation of the paintings. Up-and-coming lithographic draughtsmen were employed and the finest continental commercial lithographer transferred the work to stone. *Large folio. Letterpress title and 52 numbered litho plates. Publisher's cloth. Ex library.* £40

650 (Raphael Sanzio da Urbino) **Bellori, Gio. Pietro** Descrizione delle mimagini dipinte da Raffaelle d'Urbino nel Palazzo Vaticano, e nella Farnesina alla Lungara, con alucini ragionamenti in onore dell sue opere, e della pittura, e scultura di. Gio. Pietro Bellori. In questa nuova edizione accrescinta anche della vita del medisimo Raffaelle descritta da Giorgio Vasari *Rome, hiers of Gio. Lorenzo Barbiellini 1751*
Small pocket edition of a work first published at the end of the seventeenth century (see below) and here prefaced by Vasari's 'Life of Raphael.' *Duodecimo. Engraved portrait frontispiece, viii + lxiiii + 268pp including engraved coat-of-arms on verso of title-page and 2 woodblock diagrams in text. Contemporary full vellum.* £40

650a (Raphael Sanzio da Urbino). **Bellori, Gio. Pietro** Descrizzione delle imagini dipinte da Rafaelle d'Urbino nelle camere del Palazzo Apostolico Vaticano *Rome, G. K. Boëme 1695 (Gregg reprint 1968)*
An important work for understanding the resurgence of interest in the works of Raphael in the second half of the 17th century. The greatest art historian of the period describes the Camere frescoes of the Vatican and the Cupid and Psyche series in the Villa Farnesina, with an explanation of their iconography and themes. His commentary on the restorations of Raphael's work in the Farnesina loggia and the Carracci paintings in the Galleria Farnese (see items 605–8) provides a detailed defence of the work carried out by his friend Maratta. *Quarto. Portrait frontispiece and (8) + 112pp. Publisher's cloth.* £8

651 **Richardson, George** A book of ceilings, composed in the style of the antique grotesque: designed and etched by George Richardson, architect *London, for the author 1776*
Richardson states in a preface dated 22 March 1774 that he had been employed under 'these eminent masters Messrs Adam of the Adelphi . . . in drawing and designing upwards of eighteen years', and his ceiling designs are in the Adam manner; one, indeed, is for Lord Scarsdale's house at Kedleston for which the Adam brothers were largely responsible. *Folio. Title, engraved frontispiece, ii + (4) + ii + 11 + (1)pp and 48 engraved plates (1 double-p). Quarter calf.* **Illustration below.** £150

652 **Richardson, George** A book of ceilings *London, 1776 (Gregg reprint 1968)*
Folio. 20pp and 29 plates. Original cloth. **Illustration below.** £10

651-2

653 **Richardson, George** A collection of ceilings decorated in the style of the antique grotesque; containing designs fit for adorning halls, parlours, antichambers, libraries, dining rooms, drawing rooms and other principal apartments . . . the second edition *London, for the author 1793*

The text gives additional details of Richardson's work at Kedleston (see preceding item) but omits some information, on other projects, that is found in the first edition. *Folio. 12pp, engraved dedication leaf and 48 engraved plates (1 double-p). Quarter calf.* £120

654 **Rubens, (Peter Paul)** La gallerie du palais du Luxembourg peinte par Rubens, dessinée par les S.s Nattier, et gravée par les plus illustres graveurs du temps *Paris, Duchange 1710*

Probably the most important single cycle of Rubens entire 'oeuvre' the Marie de Medici paintings illustrate better than anything else the artist's abundant energy and tireless invention. The series, which commemorates and glorifies the various stages of the stormy career of the Queen-Mother of France, was commissioned by her for the great gallery of her Luxembourg Palace which was completed in 1620. It was perhaps the exigencies of the commission with its twenty-one paintings, and the demands of the French court, which necessitated the master painting over a groundwork provided by his studio, that led to the development of the freedom and fluency which marks Rubens' style after 1625, the year in which the commission was completed.

The present collection of engravings, several years in the making, was based on drawings made by J. M. Nattier and used specialist engravers for the plates: Bercy for the lettering, Edelinck for the portraits, Audran for about half the plates and the portrait of Rubens after Van Dyck, Alex Loir on three further plates, and a number of others including Picart. Berlin Cat 4319. *Large folio. Title, portrait of Rubens, text leaf, dedication (with portrait of Marie de Medici), two portraits plates (Francesco de Medici and Joanna of Austria: the Queen's parents), and 21 plates of which 3 double-leaf; engraved throughout. Average plate size 505 × 350mm. Eighteenth century marbled-paper boards, half oasis, rebacked.* £65

655 **Saward, B.C.** Decorative painting: a practical handbook on painting and etching upon various objects and materials for the decoration of our home *London, Upcott Gill (c 1900)*

Octavo. xx + 216pp with text illustrations; 16pp adverts. Publisher's decorated cloth. £8

656 **Skinner, John** Mosaic pavement discovered at Wellow *1823*

Four coloured plates, on a scale of one inch to a foot, of the mosaic pavement of the Roman villa at Wellow in Somerset, unearthed in 1737 and again uncovered in 1807. The drawings for the plates were made by the antiquarian John Skinner (1772-1839). *Oblong broadsheet. 4 coloured plates (1-3 mounted on 1 linen backed sheet) measuring 280 × 685mm, 235 × 685mm, 235mm; 650 × 450mm. Lacks the accompanying plan. Preserved in brown cloth folder.* £25

657 **Smith, Henry Ecroyd** (Remains of Roman mosaic pavements in Britain) *York, the artist 1849-50*

Four large chromolitho plates of mosaics at Aldborough, Yorks (the Roman town of Isurium) and Leicester. *Broadsheet. 4 chromolitho plates average size 730 × 525mm. Preserved in brown cloth folder.* £20

658 **Society of Antiquaries** The Painted Chamber. Vetusta Monumenta. Volume VI. Plates XXVI-XXXIX *London, Society of Antiquaries 1842*

The only published record of the wall paintings of the Painted Chamber in the Palace of Westminster which were destroyed in the fire of 1834. This series of paintings once formed a fine example of the work of Master William of Westminster, Master Walter of Durham and his son Master Thomas, the three creators of the Court Schools of Henry III and Edward I, which marked the zenith of English medieval art. The paintings, showing stories from the histories of the Old Testament and the events from the Book of the Maccabees in a contemporary fashion, were neglected over the years and covered by whitewash and blue paper. Their remains reappeared in 1819 during the course of alterations to the Chamber but were obliterated soon

afterwards. The present plates were made from the drawings of Charles Stothard who was commissioned to record the works at their appearance in 1819, and are preceded by a historical account of the Chamber and a description of its paintings, by John Gage Rokewode, the director of the Society.
The first two plates show, in addition, architectural details of the building and views of the interior of the Chamber made by William Capon in the 1790s. *Large folio. 37+(1)pp and 51 illustrations on 14 engraved plates numbered XXVI-XXXIX of which 10 hand coloured. Buckram binding with original title from printed wrapper preserved and mounted on the first leaf.* £55

659 (Viollet-le-Duc, Eugène) **Ouradou, Maurice** Peintures murales des chapelles de Nôtre-Dame de Paris éxécutées sur les cartons de E. Viollet-le-Duc *Paris, A. Morel 1870*
Full details of the decorative schemes of each of the twenty-nine chapels of the great cathedral which had been designed by Viollet-le-Duc as part of his great restoration programme of the 1850s under the influence of the renewed interest in polychromatic decoration. The painting was actually executed by Courtin and particular care was taken in the application of the colours and in the mixing of their tones allowing for the disposition and the quality of the light on the different sides of the building, the distance of the viewer, the reflective quality of the surfaces and the effect of the stained glass reflections. The drawings and supervision of the work was by the Inspector of the Works. *Folio. (4)+26pp and 62 chromolitho plates numbered A, B, 1-60. Preserved in portfolio, with published printed-paper front wrapper.* £80

660 **Wagner, Ludwig** Moderne Decorations-Malereien in farbiger Ausführung *Düsseldorf, Wolfrum (c 1901)*
Mural paintings executed for clients in Essen, Düsseldorf and Duisburg. *Folio. Title and 32 chromolitho plates. Original portfolio.* £32

661 **Zanotti, Giampietro** Le pitture di Pellegrino Tibaldi e di Niccolo Abbati esistenti nell'instituto di Bologna *Venice 1756*
Zanotti (1674-1765), a painter, engraver and art historian, was Secretary of the Accademia Clementina at Bologna and author of a history of the Accademia and the school of artists associated with it. In the present book he describes and illustrates the decorations of the two most famous rooms of the Palazzo Poggi, home of the Accademia and the Institute of Arts and Sciences of Bologna. They contained frescoes by Tibaldi (1527-1596) and by Abbati (1512-1571), which had been greatly admired by Annibale and Agostino Caracci. The plates for the book were engraved by Bartolommeo Crivellari (1725-1777) and in two cases by Crivellari's master Joseph Wagner. Berlin Cat 4080. *Folio. Engraved frontispiece, (6)+45+(1)pp, including title vignette, 8 engraved initials, 6 engraved headpieces and 6 engraved tailpieces, 2 engraved portraits and 41 engraved plates. Contemporary calf, gilt and blind tooled.* £125

662 **Fowler, William** (Mosaic pavements, stained glass, tiles, etc) *1796-1809*
These extremely handsome hand-coloured engravings were issued separately by Fowler (1761-1832), an architect and builder at Winterton, Lincolnshire, from about 1796 onwards. They fall into two series. The first, issued in collected form in October 1804, are predominantly engravings of mosaic pavements from Roman villas in the East Midlands and Yorkshire, with a few plates of mediaeval encaustic tiles and stained glass. The second series, commenced in March 1805 and completed in 1809, are mostly of stained glass (they include a fine series of windows from Aston Hall, Birmingham) but include one plate of a font and one of the chapter house at Southwell. Their value lies in their strict fidelity to the originals from which they are taken: Sir Joseph Banks's view, expressed at the time of their publication, was that 'Others have shown us what they thought these remains ought to have been, but Fowler has shown us what they are, and that is what we want'.
Owing to the circumstances of the plates' issue, complete sets of them are seldom found and Lowndes states that not more than 30 or 40 copies were completed of the two series (a third series, issued in 1824, is even rarer). This copy contains 55 plates, but that total includes a duplicate dedication leaf, and 54 plates is the number called for by Lowndes. No text accompanies them.

662

Hardie (English Coloured Books, pp 13-14) describes Fowler's work as one of the last examples of the hand colouring of line engravings before the introduction of colour printing. *Folio. 55 engraved hand-coloured plates with black hand-coloured edges, mounted on contemporary white card paper as issued. The total is made up by 3 dedication leaves (one a duplicate), 18 plates of mosaics (one of a Cosmati pavement in Canterbury Cathedral), 5 plates of tiles, 26 plates of stained glass, and 3 miscellaneous plates. Contemporary full straight grain red morocco extra, with extensive gilt and blind tooled panelled decoration on covers, gilt tooled spines and inner dentelles. Gilt armorial device of Duke of Buccleuch in centre of covers, with badge of Order of Thistle suspended (which indicates that the binding dates between May 1812, when the 4th Duke received the Thistle, and his death in April 1819). Some wear at edges and other slight damage to covers (carefully repaired), but still a very fine binding.* £900

663 Lasinio, Carlo Pitture a fresco del Campo Santo di Pisa intagliate da Carlo Lasinio *Florence, Molini, Landi & Co 1812*

Large outline illustrations of one of the most important mural cycles of northern Italy, the Campo Santo frescoes at Pisa. These were executed on the walls of the cloistered quadrangle of the city burial ground which provided a very suitable extensive and unbroken area for a large historiated cycle. Painting extended for over two centuries before the whole programme was complete. Among the artists working on the schemes were Francesco da Volterra, Andrea da Firenza, Antonio Veneziano, Spinello Aretino, Piero di Puccio, possibly Taddeo Gaddi, and Benozzi Gozzoli who painted the extensive final sequence. Some of the most interesting and earliest of the frescoes, (which give the clue to the meaning of the entire programme) the Triumph of Death, the Last Judgment, the Inferno, and, the Anchorites of the Thebaid, are now believed to be by Francesco Traini and not by Andrea Orvagna as Vasari stated. The scenes uphold the eremitical idea and the contemplative life as a solution to moral and economic problems.

Many of the frescoes were damaged or destroyed by a wartime fire in 1944 and a large part of the remaining cycle was removed from the walls to prevent complete deterioration as the roof of the cloisters had been destroyed. This tragedy did have a happy solution as it revealed one of the most extensive and important groups of sinopie drawings so far discovered in Italy. The present engravings were made by Lasinio when he was Keeper of the Campo Santo Museum and were probably intended for hand colouring. The majority of the engravings first appeared in 1810 accompanied by a quarto text by Professor Giovanni Rosini, who tried to take all the credit for the work, with the result that this second issue appeared soon after with a text abstracted from Rosini's notes and those of Professor Sebastiano Ciampi. *Large folio. Double-page title with engraved vignette, 11 + (1 blank)pp and 40 double-page engraved plates. Contemporary marble-paper boards, quarter calf, rebacked.* £165

664 **Price, John Edward** A description of the Roman tessellated pavement found in Bucklersbury; with observations on analogous discoveries *Westminster, Nichols 1870*
Contains much useful information on the history and construction of mosaic floors, and on the topography of Roman London. *Quarto. (2) + 78pp, chromolitho frontispiece, 1 chromolitho and 3 litho plates. Disbound. Large paper copy, uncut and unopened.* £15

665 **Rice, David Talbot** The church of Haghia Sophia at Trebizond *Edinburgh, University Press 1968*
The most remarkable feature of this monastery church is a series of mid 13th century wall paintings by Byzantine artists, and their iconography, style, dating and technique is discussed in detail by Professor Talbot Rice. They are well illustrated on colour and monochrome plates. The book also gives a complete description of the architecture, sculpture and interior of the building. *Folio. xxii + 275 + (1)pp, with colour frontispiece and 12 colour and 80 monochrome plates. Publisher's cloth.*
We have purchased the last remaining copies of this handsome book and are selling them at £10

666 **Rothery, Guy Cadogan** Ceilings and their decoration. Art and archaeology *London, Laurie, (c 1912)*
Octavo. xiv + 282pp with 28 photo plates. Original decorated cloth. £5

667 **Sherrill, Charles H.** Mosaics in Italy, Palestine, Syria, Turkey and Greece *London, Bodley Head 1933*
Octavo. xiii + (3) + 304pp, frontispiece and 16 photo plates. Original cloth. £5

668 **Society of Antiquaries** (Roman mosaic pavements at Wellow, Somerset; Stunsfield, Oxfordshire; Cotterstock, Northants) *(London), Society of Antiquaries 1737, 1738*
Plates produced in the second half of the 1730s for private distribution to the Members illustrate the chief interests of the Society at that period when it was dominated by the search for the remains of classical antiquity. Three engravings from drawings by James West reproduce the fine tesselated pavements at Wellow, discovered in 1737; the large floor at Stunsfield discovered as early as 1712 and which disappeared long ago is after drawings of Thomas Hearne, engraved by George Vertue; while the more formally designed floor at Cotterstock discovered at the full height of the interest, was drawn by George Lynn and engraved by William Bogdani. *Five large engravings measuring approximately 205 × 145mm with attractive contemporary hand-colouring in three or more colours.* £45

Design and Exhibitions

785

701 **Arbeiten der Österreichischen Kunst-Industrie aus den Jahren 1868-1893** *Vienna (1893)*
Illustrations of objects of metalwork, glass, etc produced in Austria in the period. Parts 3-5 only. *Folio. 3 vols. Each containing 10 plates (numbered xxi-xxx, xxxi-xl, xli-l). Original gilt decorated cloth portfolios.* £30

702 **The Art Journal** *London, 1847-1902*
A very long run in excellent condition of this primary source for Victorian taste in the fine and applied arts. Published monthly with extensive coverage of international and local exhibitions, annual reviews of art sales with prices, and staunch support for the Royal Academy, it represents the High Victorian euphoria induced by the Great Exhibition and its successors, and it covers all the major developments in art and art theory during the Victorian period. Contributors include Christopher Dresser, Norman Shaw, Sir Rutherford Alcock, Basil Champneys, Lewis Day, E. W. Godwin, Lethaby, G. B. Shaw, Gosse, McColl on his bindings and Ashbee on jewelry and in 1891 on his own electric light fittings. *Quarto. 55 vols forming a complete run for the years 1847 to 1902; the volumes are numbered 9-16, New Series 1-19, and from 1881 onwards they carry the year date only. The 1847 and 1848 volumes appeared under the title 'The Art Union'. The set is uniformly bound in contemporary quarter red morocco, gilt tooled spines and gilt edges.* £825
a *Some single volumes in various bindings available for the same period.* each £15

703 **Art Journal** The Art Journal illustrated catalogue. The industry of all nations, 1851 *London, George Virtue for the Art Journal 1851*
An illustrated catalogue of the decorative and ornamental exhibits at the Great Exhibition of 1851. Over 1500 objects are figured and 526 exhibitors – of whom 135 are continental, and 20 American – are mentioned in the text. A preliminary essay gives a history of the Great Exhibition project and there are five other essays on aspects of the exhibition; R. N.

Wornum's essay on 'The exhibition as a lesson in taste' is informative. This catalogue was one of the most influential of those produced for the Great Exhibition. *Quarto. xxvi + xvi + viii + viii + viii + xxii + 328pp, including over 1500 woodcut illustrations. Original gilt and blind stamped blue cloth, gilt edges. Presentation copy to Lord Northwick, with his bookplate. (This copy has an engraved plate showing 'Cupid Captive' bound as frontispiece; other copies recorded by us have plates of 'Sabrina' and 'St. George' in this position, while some do not have a frontispiece; it does not seem that a frontispiece was integral to the book as issued).* £30

704 **Art Journal** The Art Journal illustrated catalogue 1851 *London, Virtue 1851*
Another copy. *Original gilt and blind stamped cloth (not a presentation copy).* £12

705 **Art Journal** The Art Journal illustrated catalogue, 1851 *London, 1851 (David & Charles reprint 1970)*
Original cloth. £6

706 **Art Journal** The Art Journal illustrated catalogue – Catalogue of the Exhibition of Art-Industry in Dublin, 1853 *London, Virtue 1851 (1853)*
Quarto. xxvi + xvi + viii + viii + viii + xxii + 328pp; viii + 64pp with nearly 400 woodcut illustrations. Contemporary quarter green morocco, gilt tooled spine. £24

707 **Art Journal** Illustrated catalogue of the International Exhibition 1862 *London, Virtue 1862*
Art objects of every description (metalwork, jewelry, ceramics, furniture). Designers include Alfred Stevens, Burges, Norman Shaw and J. P. Seddon. *Folio. xii + 324pp including many illustrations. Contemporary full green morocco, rubbed at hinges.* £30

708 **Art Journal** Illustrated catalogue of the International Exhibition 1862 *London, 1862 (EP reprint 1973)*
Folio. xii + 324pp. Original cloth. £6

709 **Arts & Crafts** Arts and Crafts essays. By members of the Arts and Crafts Exhibition Society *London, Rivington 1893*
First edition. Essays expounding the principles of the Arts and Crafts movement, with a preface by William Morris himself. Contributors include Walter Crane, Somers Clarke, Emery Walker, Cobden-Sanderson, Lethaby, Reginald Blomfield and Sedding. *Octavo. xviii + 420pp including 6 text figures. Original cloth, uncut.* £17

710 **Arts & Crafts** Arts and Crafts essays *London, Longman 1899*
Second edition. A reprint of the preceding item. *Octavo. xviii + 420pp including 6 text figures. Original boards, cloth spine.* £10

711 **Arts & Crafts** Handicrafts and reconstructions. Notes by members of the Arts & Crafts Exhibition Society *London, Hogg 1919*
Twelve postwar essays carrying on the ideals of the Arts & Crafts movement in a changed social framework. Lethaby contributes an introduction and an essay on 'Education and Industry', and May Morris writes on weaving. *Octavo. (6) + 139 + (1)pp. Original printed wrappers.* £10

712 **Arts décoratifs de Grande-Bretagne et d'Irlande** Exposition organisée par le gouvernement Britannique. Palais du Louvre, Pavillon de Marsan, Avril-Octobre MCMXIV *London (HMSO) 1914*
Exhibition primarily devoted to the Arts and Crafts movement, with a special section on William Morris. Introductory essays accompanying the catalogue are by Walter Crane, Emery Walker, Sydney & Douglas Cockerell, May Morris and others. There are illustrations of over 200 of the exhibits and there is an excellent index. *Quarto. cxc + 168pp and 127 plates. Contemporary full green morocco, gilt panelled sides, gilt edges.* £32

713 **Art Treasures Examiner** The Art-Treasures Examiner: a pictorial, critical, and historical record of the Art-Treasures exhibition, at Manchester, in 1857. Illustrated by upwards of 150 engravings on wood (etc) *Manchester, Ireland (1857)*

Notes on the 1857 Manchester exhibition and the works of art shown there; the main emphasis is on the paintings but furniture and objets d'art are also covered. Coloured views of the exterior and interior of the Exhibition building are included. *Folio. (8)+vii+(1)+ 300pp including many wood-engraved illustrations and 2 colour plates. Contemporary quarter calf, gilt tooled spine.* £15

714 **Ashbee, C. R.** Craftsmanship in competitive industry. Being a record of the workshops of the Guild of Handicraft, and some deductions from their twenty-one years' experience *Chipping Campden, Essex House Press (1909)*

Ashbee founded the Guild of Handicraft in London in 1888 under the influence of Ruskin and Morris, and it produced work in the Morris tradition until dissolved in 1907. Here Ashbee argues the case for Guild organizations and discusses their economic viability. (See also items 903-4). *Octavo. (4)+258+(2)pp including frontispiece and several illustrations. Original quarter cloth.* £25

715 **(Ashbee, C. R.)** Arts and crafts at Campden *Campden (c 1905)*

Trade catalogue of the Guild of Handicraft Ltd, with exterior and interior views of their workshops, and photo illustrations of 40 objects from their range of silver, copper and brass work, jewelry, furniture and carving. (See also item 903). *Oblong octavo. 16pp. Original printed wrappers. In paper folder.* £30

716 **(Baillie Scott) Kornwolf, James D.** M. H. Baillie Scott and the Arts and Crafts movement. Pioneers of modern design *Baltimore, Johns Hopkins 1972*

The first biography of Baillie Scott, with full references, list of works, bibliography, etc. *Quarto. xxx+(2)+588+(4)pp including 268 text illustrations. Original cloth.* £13

717 **Berlage, H. P.** Inleiding tot de kennis van de ontwikkeling der toegepaste kunst *Rotterdam, Brusse 1923*

Five lectures by Berlage on the development of applied art, delivered to students of the Dutch School of Commerce at Rotterdam, illustrated by examples of the work of contemporary Dutch designers. *Octavo. 77+(3)pp and 64pp of plates. Original printed paper wrappers.* £35

718 **Blount, Godfrey** Arbor vitae. A book on the nature & development of imaginative design for the use of teachers handicraftsmen & others *London, Dent 1899*

A manual of design written at the height of Arts and Crafts fervour; 'it is because the movement has instinctively preferred to carve wooden bowls, beat brazen plates, and weave honest cloth and linen, instead of setting them to paint pictures, that we are justified in believing that a real renaissance is possible'. *Quarto. viii+240pp including many illustrations. Original cloth, uncut.* £15

719 **Crane, Walter** The bases of design *London, Bell 1898*

Octavo. xx+366pp including many illustrations. Original decorated cloth. £10

720 **Crane, Walter** Line and form *London, Bell 1904*

Intended by Crane as a companion volume to 'Bases of Design'. Published in 1900 and reprinted in 1901 and 1904. *Octavo. xvi+288pp including many illustrations. Original decorated cloth.* £9

721 **Crane, Walter** Ideals in art. Papers theoretical practical critical *London, Bell 1905*

Collection of essays and addresses on all aspects of design. *Octavo. xiv+288pp including many illustrations. Original decorated cloth.* £15

722 (Crane, Walter) **Konody, P. G.** The art of Walter Crane *London, Bell 1902*

Crane supplied illustrations and designed the cover for this study of his work. *Folio. xiv+148pp, frontispiece and many illustrations. Original decorated cloth.* £70

723 **Davis, Owen W.** Art and work. As shown in the several artistic industries employed in the use of marble, stone, and terra-cotta; metal, wood, and textile fabrics; as well as in the various details associated with decorative art *London, Batsford 1885*

Davis was an architect and industrial designer working in the spirit of Matthew Digby Wyatt (see item 797), and the book is chiefly devoted to his own designs, which include work for Gillows, Copelands and Schoolbred & Co., and to designs by Wyatt. *Quarto. 36pp and 85 litho plates. Original cloth.* £30

724 **Davison, T. Raffles** (editor) The arts connected with building. Lectures on craftsmanship and design delivered at Carpenters Hall *London, Batsford 1909*

Thirteen lectures by nine contributors; the most important are two by Voysey on 'Ideas and Things' and Baillie Scott's lecture on 'Ideals in building, false and true'. *Octavo. xiv+224pp including many illustrations. Original decorated cloth.* £15

725 **Dekorative Kunst** Illustrierte Zeitschrift für angewandte Kunst. (Vol 1-10) *Munich, 1898-1902*

The first ten volumes of this influential periodical launched at the high point of the Art Nouveau movement to propagate Art Nouveau ideals. Fittingly, the opening volume begins with a contribution by S. Bing (see item 743) and features Van de Velde, Lichtwark, Schumacher, Voysey and Cobden-Sanderson. Subsequent volumes deal at length with work by Ashbee, Behrens, Berlage, Baillie Scott, Bruno Paul, Otto Wagner and Louis Comfort Tiffany and many others. Of particular interest is the series of articles on progressive trends in the applied arts in Britain by Muthesius; they date from the period when he was cultural attaché to the German embassy in London and his appreciation of the Glasgow school (discussed in vol 3 and again, with particular reference to C. R. Mackintosh, in vol 8) reflects its immense contemporary impact. *Quarto. 10 vols. Each volume with many illustrations of Art Nouveau architecture, furniture, interior fittings, metalwork, glass, etc. Original decorated cloth.* **Illustration below and at end of section.** £650

725

726 **De La Motte, Philip** Choice examples of art workmanship selected from the exhibition of ancient and mediaeval art at the Society of Arts. Drawn and engraved under the superintendence of Philip De La Motte *London, Cundall & Addey 1851*
Examples of mediaeval and renaissance metalwork, enamelling, maiolica and glass. *Large octavo. (6) + 14pp and 60 litho plates. Original decorated paper boards printed in four colours and black, gilt studs at corners. (See McClean: Victorian Book Design, p142). Bookplate of Lord Northwick.* £22

727 **Derrington & Sons** Illustrated catalogue of bricks, tiles, drain pipes, sanitary ware, chimney pots, grates, ranges, etc. *Birmingham (c 1900)*
The firm describe themselves as 'brick manufacturers and builders' merchants'. A feature of the catalogue are the partly coloured illustrations and a section of full colour plates of plain and encaustic tiles. *Quarto. (2) + 65ff including many illustrations. Original printed wrappers.* £16

728 **Design and Industries Association** Design and industry. A proposal for the foundation of a Design and Industries Association *(London, 1915)*
Pamphlet issued under the names of C. C. Brewer, Ambrose Heal, F. E. Jackson, J. H. Mason, H. H. Peach, H. T. Smith and H. Stabler (the acting Committee) setting out the ideas behind the foundation of the Association and calling for support. The Association was modelled on the Deutscher Werkbund and this pamphlet is the first issued by an organized body of British opinion to make the German equation between sound design and efficiency in use. *Octavo. 18 + (2)pp, enclosing printed circular. Original wrappers. In cloth folder.* £20

729 **(Deutscher Werkbund)** Deutsche Form im Kriegsjahr. Die Ausstellung Köln 1914. (Jahrbuch des Deutschen Werkbundes 1915) *Munich, Bruckmann 1915*
The Deutscher Werkbund, founded by Muthesius, had as its object the bringing of design into a closer relationship with industrial requirements – reacting against the amateurish element in the Arts and Crafts movement. This exhibition included designs by Muthesius, Behrens, Bruno Paul, and (the one Arts and Crafts survivor) Henry Van de Velde. *Octavo. (4) + 44pp and (4) + 168pp of plates. Original boards.* £25

730 **Die Form ohne Ornament** Werkbundausstellung 1924 (Bücher der Form . . . erster Band) *Stuttgart, Deutsche Verlags-Anstalt 1925*
Designs for furniture, metalwork and pottery by German designers of the time. *Octavo. 22 + (2)pp and 90pp of plates. Original cloth.* £15

731 **Dowling, Henry G.** A survey of British industrial arts *Benfleet, Lewis 1935*
Ironwork, glass, textiles, pottery, furniture, etc. A preface summarizes design trends of the 1930s. *Quarto. 57 + (7)pp and 100 plates. Original cloth.* £17

732 **Dresser, Christopher** The rudiments of botany, structural and physiological: being an introduction to the study of the vegetable kingdom, and comprising the advantages of a full glossary of technical terms. *London, Virtue 1860*
This sets out the essentials of Dresser's attitude to botany – 'the idea has been kept strongly in sight, that a plant in its most elementary form is extremely simple; and that all plants, however far extened, are nothing more than repetitions or aggregations of this simple unit' – and Dresser intended that the book should also assist the art student. *Octavo. xxii (misnumbered) + 434pp including 560 text illustrations. Contemporary cloth.* £40

733 **(Dresser, Christopher)** Christopher Dresser 1834-1904. Pottery, glass, metalwork. An exhibition arranged by Richard Dennis, John Jesse. 3 October to 27 October 1972 *London, Fine Art Society 1972*
Important catalogue which gives overdue recognition to the work of one of the foremost

Victorian industrial designers – for the Linthorpe and Ault potteries, for Clutha glass, for Elkington silverware. *Small folio. 36pp including many illustrations. Original wrappers.* £4

734 Eisler, Max Österreichische Werkkultur *Vienna, Schroll 1916*

Recent work by members of the Austrian Werkbund (Josef Hoffman et al). Interiors, furniture, pottery, glass, and sculpture are illustrated. *Octavo. 262pp including many illustrations (and a list of members of the Werkbund). Original boards.* £22

735 (Engelhardt, Knud von) Frederiksen, Erik Ellegaard Knud v. Engelhardt arkitekt & bogtrykker 1882-1931 *Copenhagen, 1965*

Engelhardt was both architect and a designer of metalwork, lettering and silverware. *Octavo. 127+(3)pp with many illustrations. Original wrappers.* £6

736 Farleigh, John The creative craftsman *London, Bell 1950*

A study of the artist craftsman, including interviews with Bernard Leach, Leslie Durbin, Sydney Cockerell etc. *Octavo. xii+268pp and 24pp of plates. Original cloth.* £5

737 Farleigh, John Design for applied decoration in the crafts *London, Bell 1959*

Octavo. 128pp including 41 text figures and 16pp of plates. Original cloth. £4

738 Farleigh, John (editor) Fifteen craftsmen on their crafts *London, Sylvan Press 1945*

Octavo. viii+132pp including 12pp of illustrations. Original cloth. £4

739 Farr, Michael Design in British industry. A mid-century survey *Cambridge, University Press 1955*

Contains a foreword and postscript by Pevsner explaining the relationship between this and his own earlier study (item 771), and contrasting the two. *Octavo. xxxviii+332+(2)pp and 88pp of plates. Original cloth.* £15

740 (Festival of Britain) Design in the festival. Illustrating a selection of well-designed British goods in production in the Festival year 1951, with an introduction by Gordon Russell (etc.) *London, HMSO for Council of Industrial Design 1951*

Octavo. 132pp including many illustrations. Original wrappers. £4

741 Fisher, John An illustrated record of the retrospective exhibition held at South Kensington, 1896 *London, Chapman & Hall 1897*

An exhibition of 256 designs from schools of art (all illustrated). *Folio. xiipp and 156 plates. Preserved in original cloth folder.* £17

742 Geddes, Norman Bel Horizons *Boston, Little Brown 1932*

This sets out Bel Geddes's design philosophy and records his ideas – revolutionary in their day – for the design of cars, liners, trains, airports, theatres, restaurants, gas stoves and window displays. An important statement of the views of an advanced American designer of the 1930s. *Quarto. xx+294pp with 222 illustrations. Original cloth.* £25

743 **Geffroy, Gustave** Les industries artistiques Françaises et étrangères à l'exposition universelle de 1900 *Paris, Librairie Centrale des Beaux-Arts (1900)*

A special feature of the exhibition was the 'Art Nouveau Bing' house, designed with its contents by De Feure, Colonna and Gaillard under the supervision of the Art Nouveau propagandist Samuel Bing (see also item 725). Geffroy's catalogue does justice to it and a wide range of other exhibits (Daum glass, Lalique and Tiffany jewelry, etc.). Britain's contribution – despite the 'tres joli pavillon de M. Lutens' (sic) – was limited to Heal and Waring and Gillow furniture. *Folio. (4)+62+(2)pp including 33 text illustrations and 99 (of 100) photogravure plates (4 coloured). Lacks plate 51. Quarter red morocco.* £65

744 **Gloag, John** Industrial art explained *London, Allen & Unwin 1934*
Octavo. 192pp and 16pp of plates. Original cloth. £4

745 **Gloag, John** (editor) Design in modern life *London, Allen & Unwin 1934*
Essays on aspects of design by Maxwell Fry, Gordon Russell, and others. *Octavo. 138pp and 40pp of plates, 1 large folding table. Original cloth.* £9

746 **Gloag, John & Grace Lovat Fraser** Plastics and industrial design ... with a section on the different types of plastics ... *London, Allen & Unwin 1945*
Octavo. 166+(2)pp and 48pp of plates. Original cloth. £5

747 **(Goldscheider)** L'Évolution artistique. Revue destinée à la diffusion des idees d'art moderne dans l'industrie et contenant des reproductions d'oeuvres d'artistes des groupes 'La Stèle' et 'Evolution'. Fascicules de Janvier à Juin (de Juillet à Décembre) 1926. Textes par Yvanhoé Rambosson *Paris, Goldscheider 1926*

The Goldscheider firm had its own pavilion at the 1925 exhibition; this review publicizes bronzes, ceramics, lamps executed for it by Art Deco designers and is a striking reflection of post-1925 enthusiasm for Art Deco work. Note that, despite the title, the text is in English and therefore intended for the Anglo-American market. *Quarto. 2 vols. Each volume with title leaf, (24)pp and 48 plates, many coloured. Names of designers and measurements of objects illustrated are given on tissues facing each plate. Original quarter calf, gilt decorated boards.*
Illustration below. £150

747

748 (Great Exhibition 1851) **Royal Commission for the Great Exhibition of the Works of Industry of all Nations, 1851** Official descriptive and illustrated catalogue. In three volumes. – First (Second) report of the Commissioners for the Exhibition of 1851, to the Right Hon Spencer Horatio Walpole, etc. – Official descriptive and illustrated catalogue supplement. Three volumes. – Reports of the juries on the subjects in the thirty classes into which the exhibition is divided. In four volumes. – Supplement to the first report of the Commissioners, containing engravings of the medals and certificates prepared too late for insertion in their proper places. – Cases containing medals distributed to those who had organised the exhibition *London, W. Clowes & Sons for the Royal Commission (1851) 1852, (1853) 1852, 1853*

A special Commissioner's copy of the catalogue which provides a complete record of the exhibits, exhibitors, and prize winners in the largest and most lavish exhibition ever assembled. The exhibition was divided into four main sections: Raw Materials, Machinery and Mechanical Inventions, Manufactures, and Sculpture and the Plastic Arts, and, in itemizing and describing the various objects and processes shown, the catalogue provides a mine of information on the state of industry and the industrial arts in the mid 19th century. The 'Reports of the Juries', of which only 130 presentation copies were prepared, are important for being the only publications, which were **illustrated with Talbot's calotype photographs,** that have been preserved in good condition. Gernsheim, in his 'History of Photography' (1969, p 174) states that 'the negatives of these Crystal Palace photographs had been taken by C. M. Ferrier of Paris on albumenized glass plates, and Hugh Owen of Bristol by a calotype process. Henneman's positives were printed on Talbot's silver chloride paper, also called "plain salted paper" . . . One hundred and fifteen magnificently bound sets of the "Reports of the Juries", each four-volume set containing 155 photographs size 8½in × 6½in, were presented to the Queen, Prince Albert, Cabinet Ministers, foreign governments, the Colonies, the Exhibition Commissioners, the British Museum and a few other institutions'. The remaining fifteen sets were given to Talbot in payment for his work. (Gernsheim is, in fact, in error over the number of photographs, there are 154 photographs and 1 lithograph). The majority of sets of this work, consisting of not only the 'Report of the Juries' with their 154 calotypes, but the special Commissioner's copy of the catalogue, were presented to the heads of royal households and libraries so are rarely found for sale, and are scarcely ever sold, as here, with the accompanying medals. *Folio. 11 volumes in 9, and case of medals. Official Catalogue, 3 vols: Lithographic title, (4) + cxcii + (508)pp (with misnumbering) and 40 lithographic plates (some misnumbered), 1 large folding coloured map, 2 unnumbered double-p lithographic plates (of which 1 coloured) and many text illustrations, some full-page; (6) + 524 (numbered 479-1002)pp and 184 lithographic plates (numbered 41-224), with many text illustrations, some full-page; (4) + 468 (numbered 1003-1470) + (2)pp and 170 lithograph plates (numbered 225-394) with many text illustrations, some full-page. Reports of Juries: ccv + (1) + 358pp with photo frontispiece and 4 photographic plates; (2) + iv + 512 (numbered 359-870)pp with photo frontispiece and 44 photographic plates; iv + 461 (numbered 871-1332) with photo frontispiece and 43 (of 44) photographic plates (missing plate bound in vol 4); (2) + iv + 496 (numbered 1333-1828), photo frontispiece and 59 photographic plates, 3 coloured litho plates. Reports of Commissioners, bound with Supplement to Official Catalogue: (2) + liv + 211 + (3)pp; 76pp; (4) + 62 (numbered 1471-1532)pp. Supplement to Report of Commissioners: (6)pp with 7 steel engraved plates. Medals: 5 bronze medals; Council 89mm; Exhibitors 44mm; Jurors 64mm; Service 47mm; Prize 76mm, diameters. Full red morocco, gilt stamped device with royal cipher in centre of boards and a small device with cipher on spine; gilt key pattern tooled revers; blue silk end papers and flyleaf backing, with gilt royal coat-of-arms and ciphers on inside front cover. Binding by Riviere. The copy is that presented by the Commissioners to Lieutenant George Montague Stopford, RE, Adjutant to the detachment of Royal Sappers and Miners which, according to the Official Catalogue 'was permitted by the Master General of the Ordnance to bring their military discipline and business knowledge to aid in the arrangements of the Exhibition'. Stopford rose to rank of Major and died in 1860.* **Illustration opposite.**

£5500

749 (Great Exhibition 1851) **Royal Commission for the Great Exhibition of the Works of Industry of all Nations, 1851** Official descriptive and illustrated catalogue. In three volumes *London, W. Clowes & Sons for the Royal Commission 1851*

Standard copy of the catalogue (see above). The first volume deals with the sections on Raw Materials and Machinery and contains nearly 100 page list of articles displayed and 75 pages of names of exhibitors and such. The second volume catalogues the Manufactures

748   and Fine Arts sections and records the exhibits from the Colonies; while the final volume deals with foreign exhibits and representatives. *Folio. 3 vols. Lithograph title, (4)+cxcii+ 508pp numbered 1-478 (but with numeration 193-208, and 465-478 repeated) and 40 lithograph plates, 1 large folding coloured map, 2 double-p litho plates (1 coloured) and many text illustrations, some full-page, (and 72pp adverts); (6)+524 (numbered 479-1002)pp and 182 lithograph plates with many text illustrations some full-p; (4)+468 (numbered 1003-1470)+(2)pp and 170 lithograph plates with many text illustrations, some full-p. Original embossed and gilt-decorated cloth.*   £120

750 (Great Exhibition 1851) **Commission for the Great Exhibition of the Works of Industry of all Nations, 1851** Official and descriptive catalogue. Supplementary volume. . . . First and Second Reports of the Royal Commissioners *London, W. Clowes & Sons for the Royal Commission (1853)*

The desire to issue the Official Catalogue before the Exhibition closed led to the omission of many illustrations and descriptions to many important items whose manufacturers had been slow in commissioning illustrations or had not realised the importance of the catalogue as a form of advertisement. It was therefore decided to publish this further volume to rectify the omissions, correct mistakes in the earlier works and further give full appreciation to the contribution of India in the Exhibition. The publication was issued together with the summing-up reports of the organisers. As this was a later issue it is found far less frequently than the other volumes. *Folio. xxvi+(2)+62 (numbered 1471-1532)pp and 126 litho plates of which 5 double-p; liv+211+(1)pp and 1 double-p coloured litho plates, 2 large folding plans; (2)+76pp. Nineteenth century marbled-paper boards, quarter calf.*   £85

751 (Great Exhibition 1851) **Royal Commission for the Exhibition of the Works of Industry of all Nations, 1851** Reports by the Juries on the subjects in the thirty classes into which the Exhibition was divided. Presentation copy *London, William Clowes & Sons for the Royal Commission 1852*

The standard copy of the 'Reports' for the Exhibitors and issued in one volume without the calotypes of the special four volume sets. Over £20,000 was put aside for prize awards and these were given in the form of two medals: a larger Council Medal awarded for 'important novelty of invention or application, either in material, or processes of manufacture or originality combined with great beauty of design'; and a smaller Prize Medal for 'excellence in production or workmanship... utility, beauty, cheapness, adaptation to particular markets... being taken into consideration'. 30 classes of items were judged and the judges, usually eight to a panel, included Michael Faraday for Mining & Metallurgy, Joseph Hooker for Foods, George Rennie for Machinery & Tools, Sir John Herschel for Scientific Instruments, Samuel Courtauld for Silk and Velvet, Thomas de la Rue & A. Firmin Didot for Printing & Bookbinding, E. E. Chevreul for Printing and Dyeing Fabrics, Henry Hope (of Hope Diamond fame) and Lewis Grüner (see items 618-9) for Precious Metals and Jewelry, E. Ebelman for Ceramics, J. C. Crace for Decorative Furniture & Furnishings, Antonio Panizzi, C. R. Cockerell, John Gibson and A. W. Pugin for Sculpture and Plastic Arts, and Hector Berlioz for Musical Instruments. *Folio. (6)+cxx+867+(1)pp with some text illustrations; 16pp adverts for the Official Catalogue. Original blind stamped and gilt decorated cloth.* £40

753

752 (The Great Exhibition 1851) **Nash, J. N., (L.) Haghe and (J.) Roberts** Dickinson's comprehensive picture of the Great Exhibition of 1851. From originals painted for H.R.H. Prince Albert by Messrs. Nash, Haghe and Roberts, R.A. *London, Dickinson Bros & Her Majesty's Publishers 1854*

The most complete pictorial record of the Great Exhibition beginning first with the areas devoted to particular nations in the order of Europe, the Near East, China, America, the Far East and the colonies with particular emphasis on France (4 views), Tunis (3 views) and India (7 views). The work then moves on to the areas devoted to special subjects including stained glass, furniture, fabrics, and machinery, and ending with a view of the exterior of the building, a general view of the British Section, and finally the Closing Ceremony. Ten of the plates bear Nash's signature with a date usually of 1852, while the remainder are unsigned. The work was published under the 'Express sanction of H.R.H. Prince Albert' to whom it was dedicated, and who had commissioned the original paintings. Abbey: Scenery of Great Britain 251. *Broadsheet. 2 parts. (27)ff of text with blank versos including title in black and red; (27)ff of text with blank versoes including title in black and red; 55 loose chromolitho plates with hand-coloured finish; each 370 × 485mm on 423 × 582mm. One part in publisher's original printed wrappers. Preserved in drop-back box.* £780

753 **(The Great Exhibition 1851)** Recollections of the Great Exhibition of 1851 *London, Lloyd Brothers & Co and Simpkin Marshall & Co 1st September 1851*

A very fine series of selected views of the interior of the Exhibition, much more specific in their viewpoint than the previous item. The areas devoted to five countries are shown: China, Russia, Turkey, India (with 2 views) and France (with 3 views). A selection of the Fine Arts section is shown and three views of the Sculpture Gallery with each view concentrating on a particular statue. Of special interest to the subjects in this catalogue are the illustrations of the furniture sections, the Queen's Retiring Room, the textiles of the Bradford Court, the metalwork of the Birmingham Court and the Sèvres porcelain in the French Court. The artists responsible for the illustrations include Jno Absolom (9), H. C. Pigeon (5), W. Goodall (5) and C. T. Dolby (4) and the plates were lithographed by Day & Sons. Abbey: Scenery of Great Britain 246. *Twenty-five tinted litho plates with much hand-colouring (and including decorative title) averaging in size 275 × 375mm mounted on card 425 × 585mm, and 1 leaf of text listing plates and artists. Preserved in drop-back box.* **Illustration opposite.** £875

754 **Holme, Charles** (editor) The art-revival in Austria. (Special summer number for 1906) *London, The Studio 1906*

Articles by Ludwig Hevesi, Hugo Haberfeld and A. S. Levetus on Austrian painting, architecture and decorative art. Hoffman, Moser and the Wiener Werkstätte figure prominently. *Octavo. (4) + viii + xvi + viii + viii + xiipp, with many illustrations. Original printed wrappers.* £16

755 **Holme, Charles** (editor) Arts and crafts. A review of the work executed by students in the leading art schools of Great Britain and Ireland. Special autumn number of 'The Studio' *London, The Studio 1916*

Small folio. iv + 204pp including many illustrations, some coloured. Original cloth. £10

756 **Holme, Geoffrey** Industrial design and the future *London, The Studio 1934*

A crusading study, sub-titled 'A challenge to the producer' and dedicated to 'the man who dared to try – Franklin Roosevelt' with replies by Frank Lloyd Wright, Chermayeff, Howard Robertson, etc to a questionnaire on design. *Octavo. 160pp including 80pp of illustrations. Original cloth.* £18

757 **Illustrations of Art Manufactures** ancient & modern; drawn from examples in various museums, private collections, and the best British & foreign productions of the present time. Vol 1 *London, Newbery & Co. (mid 19th century)*

Illustrations of furniture, metalwork, glass, and similar items. Probably all published. *Quarto. Title,(4) + 24pp and 36 numbered litho plates. Quarter blue morocco.* £40

758 **Industrial Art** a monthly review of technical and scientific education at home and abroad. Edited by J. H. Lamprey. Vol 1. July to December, 1877 *London, Hardwicke & Bogue 1877*

Octavo. vi +(2) + 184pp with 157 woodcut illustrations. Original cloth. £14

759 **(International Exhibition 1925)** Reports on the present position and tendencies of the industrial arts as indicated at the International Exhibition of Modern Decorative and Industrial Arts, Paris, 1925 *London, Department of Overseas Trade (1927)*

Reports by British critics on all sections of the exhibition, which form the most complete record in any language of the exhibition which gave Art Deco its identity. *Quarto. 208pp and 152pp of monochrome plates, 10 colour plates. Original cloth.* £30

760 **Knight, Charles** (editor) The arts and industries of all nations; or pictorial gallery of arts: illustrating the progress of painting ... manufactures, trades, etc, etc, from the earliest period to the present time ... illustrated with steel engravings, executed in the first style of art, and

nearly four thousand engravings on wood London, J. G. Button (1857)
Extensively illustrated part-published book, aimed at the public who had visited the Great Exhibition and its successors of the 1850s. The first volume concentrates on the applied arts, with illustrations of such objects as a Jacquart loom, sideboards, bookcases, etc, and also has an historical introduction on the exhibition movement, while the second volume is devoted to architecture, sculpture, and painting. *Folio. 2vols. (8) + xl + 388pp with coloured frontispiece, engraved vignette on title and 23 steel engraved plates; (8) + 404pp with coloured frontispiece, engraved vignette and 23 steel engraved plates. Original quarter morocco, gilt tooled spines, gilt edges.* £75

761 Kunst und Kunsthandwerk am Bau 250 Arbeiten in Stein, Eisen, Holz und anderen Werkstoffen. Zweite Auflage Stuttgart, Hoffmann 1938
Octavo. 206pp, mostly of illustrations. Original cloth. £9

762 Lethaby, W. R. Art and labour. A reprint of two articles London, Design & Industries Association (c 1922)
Octavo. 15 + (5)pp. Original wrappers. £4

763 (Moore, Albert) **Baldry, Alfred Lys** Albert Moore his life and works London, Bell 1894
Moore (1841-93), best known as a painter, also did decorative work – murals for Coombe Abbey and St Alban's, Rochdale, and designs for mosaics and tiles – and was an early friend of the architect W. E. Nesfield. *Folio. xii + (2) + 109 + (3)pp with many illustrations and photogravure plates. One of 60 copies printed on large paper, with a set of proof plates inserted. Original decorated linen covered boards with brass corner studs, gilt edged.* £100

764 (Moore, Albert) **Baldry, Alfred Lys** Albert Moore his life and works London, Bell 1894
Another copy of the ordinary edition. *Folio. xii + (2) + 109 + (3)pp with illustrations and photogravure plates. Original cloth.* £25

765 (Morris, William) A brief sketch of the Morris movement and of the firm founded by William Morris to carry out his designs and the industries revived or started by him London, Morris & Co. 1911 (Privately printed by the Chiswick Press)
Square octavo. 63 + (1)pp, frontispiece and 8 plates. Original wrappers. Barry Parker's copy.
£25

766 William Morris & Co (Ruskin House) (Trade catalogue of metal casements, stained glass, decorative ironwork) London (c 1910)
Large, well illustrated catalogue of the firm's products which shows an appreciation of advertizing and display techniques and is produced in a manner not far removed from the Morris/Burne Jones tradition. But this was not *the* William Morris firm, or for that matter a firm belonging to the empire of W. R. Morris (Lord Nuffield), but a firm directed by a quite different William Morris who was in active control of it when this catalogue was issued. It lists an impressive selection of its clients and one cannot help thinking that some of them had intended to patronize the real Morris firm. The catalogue also serves the purpose of showing the provenance of much weak early 20th century glass signed 'Morris'. *Folio. 200pp illustrated throughout. Original printed and decorated canvas.* £50

767 Naylor, Gillian The Arts and Crafts movement. A study of its sources, ideals and influence on design theory London, Studio Vista 1971
Octavo. 208pp with many illustrations. Original cloth. £4.80

768 Papini, Roberto Le arti d'oggi. Architettura e arti decorative in Europa Milan, Bestetti & Tumminelli 1930
Dedicated to 'Benito Mussolini cittadino onorario di universa' but provides, for all that, a comprehensive view of recent architectural and decorative work in Europe; its Italian authorship means that Milanese and Venetian designers and architects are featured, and so are several in Austria, Hungary and Czechoslovakia. *Folio. 22 + (2) + (8)pp and 434pp of plates. Original cloth.* £20

769 **(Paris Exhibition 1844)** Exposition des produits de l'industrie Française en 1844. Rapport du Jury Central *Paris, Fain & Thunot 1844*
The Paris exhibition of 1844, and its successor of 1849, were the direct inspiration for the Great Exhibition of 1851 and set the precedent for much of its organization and procedure. These are the reports of the Jury on the exhibits of 1844, with separate sections for textiles, metalwork, machinery, precision tools, chemical products, the beaux arts, pottery and the arts not covered elsewhere. As a whole they give a complete view of French art and industry at that date. *Octavo. 3 vols. lxxii+880pp; (4)+ 978pp; (4)+842pp. Contemporary full panelled red morocco, gilt tooled spines, gilt edges. A very fine set bound by Lebrun for King Louis Philippe.* £120

770 **(Paris Exhibition 1878)** The Society of Arts Artisan reports on the Paris Universal Exhibition of 1878. *London, Sampson Low 1879*
Parties of skilled workmen from Britain were sent to Paris for the Exhibition of 1878 under the auspices of the Society of Arts, in order to view the exhibits and report on them. The reports published in this volume are a selection from the 168 submitted. They are all based on the writers' trade and technical experience and in addition to information on aspects of manufacture and design they give details of comparative trade conditions, hours of work, etc in the pottery, glass and furniture trades in England and France. (Many other trades are treated similarly). *Octavo. ix+(1)+664pp; 6pp of advertisements. Original cloth.* £35

771 **Pevsner, Nikolaus** An enquiry into industrial art in England *Cambridge, University Press 1937*
Based on research by Pevsner in 1934-5 when newly arrived in Britain and working at Birmingham University. A pioneer survey in which the subject matter was as fresh to the investigator as his questions were novel to those investigated; and still stimulating reading. *Octavo. xiv+234+(2)pp including 22pp of illustrations. Original cloth.* £18

772 **Pevsner, Nikolaus** Pioneers of modern design from William Morris to Walter Gropius *New York, Museum of Modern Art (1957)*
Octavo. 152pp with 137 illustrations. Original cloth. £4

773 **Pye, David** The nature of design *London, Studio Vista 1972*
Excellent study of the basic theory of design by the Professor of Furniture Design at the Royal College of Art. *Octavo. 96pp with text illustrations. Original wrappers.* £1.50

774 **Read, Herbert** Art and industry. The principles of industrial design *London, Faber 1934*
First edition. An influential book on the theory of industrial design and strikingly illustrated. *Octavo. 144pp with many illustrations. Original cloth.* £10

775 **Read, Herbert** Art and industry. The principles of industrial design *London, Faber 1944*
Second edition. *Octavo. 188pp with many illustrations. Original cloth.* £5

776 **Read, Herbert** (editor) The practice of design *London, Lund Humphries 1946*
Essays on aspects of design by Milner Gray, Frederick Gibberd, Misha Black and others. *Octavo. 228pp with illustrations. Original cloth.* £8

777 **Richards, Charles R.** Art in industry. Being the report of an industrial art survey conducted under the auspices of the National Society for Vocational Education and the Department of Education of the State of New York *New York, 1922*
Reports on the costume, textile, jewelry, silverware, furniture, lighting, wallpaper, ceramics and printing trades; and, at some length, on art education in the U.S.A. and in Europe. *Octavo. (6)+499+(1)pp. Original boards, cloth spine.* £18

778 **Sala, George Augustus** Notes and sketches of the Paris Exhibition *London, Tinsley Brothers 1868*
A reproduction of articles which had first appeared in the 'Daily Telegraph' and are here augmented by further considerations, conclusions and revised attitudes. The author, a much travelled journalist and prolific writer, believed it to have been 'very hard work to get through the Exhibitions of '51, of '55 and of '62; but '67 made sight-seeing easy, and opened a Royal road of instruction in technics and the applied sciences'. *Octavo. 396pp. Original cloth.*   £14

779 **Scheidig, Walther** Crafts of the Weimar Bauhaus 1919-1924. An early experiment in industrial design *London, Studio Vista 1967*
Quarto. 150pp including 96pp of illustrations (44 coloured). Original cloth.   £8

780 **Society of Industrial Artists** Designers in Britain 1851-1951 *London, Wingate 1951*
A survey of industrial design in the year of the Festival of Britain. Includes coverage of current work and historical essays by Milner Gray and Pevsner. *Small folio. 306pp including many illustrations. Original cloth.*   £9

781 **The South Kensington Museum** Examples of the works of art in the museum and of the decorations of the building with brief descriptions *London, Sampson Low 1881*
Etchings of objects in the South Kensington collections by students of the Art Schools. *Folio. 2 vols. (8)pp and 96 plates with accompanying text leaves; 80 plates with accompanying text leaves. Original cloth (not uniform).*   £15

782 (Stevens, Alfred), **Armstrong, Walter** Alfred Stevens. A biographical study by Walter Armstrong *Paris, Librairie de l'Art 1881*
Much of Stevens' work was in the field of applied arts and this biography gives a full account of it, singling out for special praise his doors for the School of Mines in Jermyn Street; his stoves for Hooles (see item 873) and his porcelain for Mintons; his interior for Dorchester House in Park Lane; and his design work for a commercial firm of interior decorators. *Folio. Engraved frontispiece, title in red and black, 47+(1)pp and 1 plate. Original decorated cloth, covers badly faded but internally in good condition. Edmund Gosse's copy, with presentation inscription from the critic J. W. Comyns Carr.*   £30

783 **The Studio** An illustrated magazine of fine & applied art *London, 1893-1912*
The first of the modern art periodicals of the nineties, featuring Beardsley, Brangwyn and Voysey in its initial volume, and remaining well abreast of contemporary trends. It was very influential abroad and its coverage of British decorative design and domestic architecture (Voysey and Baillie Scott are recurring contributors) is particularly good. Other valuable features are its coverage of foreign art exhibitions and articles on modern art by D. S. MacColl and the best British critics of the day. *Quarto. Vols 1-56 (lacking 53).* *Vols 1-39, 43-44 in publisher's cloth, vols 40, 42 and 45 in quarter morocco, remainder in cloth or original printed wrappers. Chamberlain 2347.* **Illustration below and opposite.**   £385

Some single volumes between 8 and 70, various bindings.   each £8

783

784 **The Studio Yearbook of Decorative Art** *London, 1906*
A comprehensive guide year by year to the most advanced British and European design from the Edwardian period to the age of the boutique. Extensive American coverage from 1922 onwards. Fully illustrated, partly in colour. *Quarto. Vols 1-61. Publisher's cloth or wrappers as issued.* £700
a *Most volumes available separately.* each £12

785 **Tallis, John** Tallis's history and description of the Crystal Palace, and the exhibition of the world's industry in 1851; illustrated by beautiful steel engravings, from original drawings and daguerreotypes, by Beard, Mayall, etc, etc. *London, Tallis (1851)*
History of the Great Exhibition and description of the exhibits, with many illustrations of fans, furniture and fountains (and many other objects), all in excellent mid-Victorian taste. *Quarto. 3 vols bound in 6. 268pp; 262pp and 110pp, with 145 steel engraved plates. The title pages to vols 2 and 3 and the contents lists for each volume are bound at the end of the sixth part. Original gilt decorated blue cloth.* **Illustration at head of section.** £110

786 **The Technical Educator** an encyclopaedia of technical education *London, Cassell (1870-3)*
Information on all aspects of technical education, including articles on building, mechanics, drawing, colour and colour theory (an important series of articles by A. H. Church), and museums. But its real significance is that it contains the run of 31 essays on 'Principles of Design' by Christopher Dresser, later to be printed in book form under the same title. These discuss every aspect of design – ornament, furniture, carpets, textiles, pottery, glass, metalwork, silverware – and make plain Dresser's importance as a designer and teacher. A number of Dresser's own designs are illustrated and these include some of the greatest originality: a tea pot that could pass as the work of an advanced designer of the 1920s or 1930s and a sketch of an ornamental design 'exemplifying power', remarkable for its symbolic evocation of growth in the manner of the Art Nouveau. *Quarto. 4 vols in 2. iv+412pp; iv+412pp; iv+412pp; iv+428pp. Each vol has a chromolitho frontispiece and many text illustrations. Contemporary quarter morocco.* £45

787 **Transactions** of the National Association for the Advancement of Art and its application to industry, Liverpool meeting, 1888 *London, 1888*
Speakers at this inaugural meeting of the Association included Lord Leighton, Alma-Tadema, Holman Hunt, Alfred Gilbert, Crace, T. G. Jackson, Walter Crane, William Morris, Cobden Sanderson, Patrick Geddes and J. D. Sedding, and their speeches are printed in full in this volume. *Octavo. xxii+408pp. Original cloth.* £35

787a **Transactions** of the National Association for the advancement of Art and its application to industry, Edinburgh meeting MDCCCLXXXIX *London, 1890*
A feature of this second meeting was a course of 'Free evening lectures and meetings for working folk' delivered by Morris, Crane, Emery Walker and Cobden-Sanderson. Speakers at the main meeting included G. F. Watts and Ashbee as well as many of those who had participated in 1888. *Octavo. xv+(3)+485+(1)pp. Original cloth. M. H. Spielmann's copy with pencilled notes on his own address to the meeting (printed in full pp 272-81).* £40

788 **Triggs, Oscar Lovell** Chapters in the history of the Arts and Crafts movement *1902 (Blom reprint 1972)*
Octavo. 198pp. Original cloth. £4

789 **(Van de Velde, Henry)** Henry Van de Velde zum 100 Geburtstag. *Stuttgart, Wurttembergischer Kunstverein 1963*
Catalogue of the centenary exhibition, with an assessment of Van de Velde by Robert Delevoy, descriptions of the exhibits (paintings, designs, furniture, pottery, silverware) and a bibliography. *Octavo. 52pp and 36pp of photo plates. Original wrappers.* £3

790 **Victoria & Albert Museum** Exhibition of Victorian and Edwardian decorative arts. Catalogue *London, HMSO 1952*
Extremely useful catalogue of the exhibition held in 1952 to mark the centenary of the Museum of Ornamental Art (the V & A's precursor). Exhibits numbered 960 and the catalogue, arranged by the late Peter Flood, is a mine of information on their designers and manufacturers. *Octavo. 150pp. Original wrappers.* £1

791 **Waring, J. B.** Masterpieces of industrial art & sculpture at the International Exhibition, 1862 *London, Day & Son 1863*
Magnificently produced chromolitho record of the 1862 Exhibition, in which Waring took a prominent part as organizer of the architectural, glass, earthenware, furniture, jewelry and goldsmith's work exhibits. Waring himself wrote the English text: a French translation accompanies it; and the chromolithography was supervised by W. R. Tymms and executed by Tymms, Albert Warren and G. MacCulloch. *Folio. 3 vols. 11 + 100ff and 100 chromolitho plates; 2 + 100ff and 100 chromolitho plates; 2 + 101ff and 101 chromolitho plates. Each volume has additionally a chromolitho title. Publisher's full red morocco, decorated in blind to an entrelac pattern and fully gilt-tooled with floral ornaments and panels for main title and shields of Europe, Asia, Africa and America; gilt edges.* £150

792 **Welch, Robert** Design in a Cotswold workshop *London, Lund Humphries 1973*
The work of a silversmith and stainless steel designer operating from Campden seventy years after Ashbee. *Oblong quarto. 64pp including many illustrations. Original cloth.* £2.95

793 **Wettergren, Erik** L'art décoratif moderne en Suède … traduit du Suédois par Virgile Pinot *Malmo, Musée de Malmo (1925)*
This is a record of recent Swedish work in the applied arts written for the 1925 Paris Exhibition. It gives prominence to Gate and Hald's Orrefors glass. *Quarto. (6) + 185 + (1)pp including many illustrations. Original wrappers.* £10

794 **Wettergren, Erik** The modern decorative arts of Sweden *London, Country Life (1927)*
English translation of the preceding item. *Quarto. (8) + 204 + (4)pp including many illustrations. Original quarter cloth.* £12

795 **White, Gleeson** (editor) Practical designing. A handbook on the preparations of working drawings *London, Bell 1893*
Guide to the mechanics of design by a number of experts. Different writers deal with the design of carpets, textiles generally, pottery, tiles, metalwork, stained glass, bookbindings, wallpaper. The first edition of a widely used handbook. *Octavo. viii + 327 + (1)pp including many text figures. Original decorated cloth.* £6

796 **Wingler, Hans M.** The Bauhaus, Weimar, Dessau, Berlin, Chicago *Cambridge, Mass., MIT Press 1969*
History of the Bauhaus, by the director of the Bauhaus Archiv, fully documented, extensively illustrated, and containing biographical notes on its staff and students, as well as information on the work of its various craft workshops (pottery, metalwork, textiles, cabinet making, etc.) and on its general philosophy of design and building. *Folio. xviii + 653 + (1)pp, many photo illustrations and 24pp of colour illustrations. Original cloth in slipcase.* **Illustration opposite.** £37.50

796

797 **Wyatt, M. Digby** The industrial arts of the nineteenth century. A series of illustrations of the choicest specimens produced by every nation at the Great Exhibition of Works of Industry, 1851. Dedicated, by permission, to His Royal Highness the Prince Albert *London, Day & Son 1851-3*

The most sumptuous of the publications connected with the 1851 exhibition. It was published in forty parts, each containing four chromolithograph plates, between October 1851 and March 1853 in an edition of 1300 copies. The publishers' main aim, Wyatt writes in a postscript, was 'to demonstrate, upon a great scale, the capabilities of colour-printing as an auxiliary to industrial education' and the plates are truly a credit to Day & Son and the lithographer Francis Bedford. Just as valuable today is the text that accompanies them, mainly by Wyatt himself but including contributions by T. Everall Jones, C. Fowler and Burges (the last writing on furniture and stained glass). It gives much information on the objects illustrated, their manufacturers and designers, and Wyatt throughout relates the exhibits to contemporary trends in design and ornament. *Folio. 2 vols. They contain in all xii+(8)pp, 2 chromolitho titles and 158 chromolitho plates each with an accompanying leaf of text. Original quarter morocco, cloth boards with gilt stamped decoration, gilt edges.*   £400

798 **Yapp, G. W.** Art industry. Furniture, upholstery, and house-decoration. Illustrative of the arts of the carpenter, joiner, cabinet-maker, painter, decorator, and upholsterer *London, Virtue (c 1880)*

Yapp compiled the catalogue of the 1851 exhibition and was associated with several similar ventures, and this is a selection from the finest art industry exhibits at international exhibitions from 1851 onwards. The text mentions manufacturers and designers, describes technical features of interest and makes judgments that reflect approved mid-Victorian taste. *Folio. vi+76pp and 151+84+47+33+5 plates. Original decorated cloth.*   £75

799 **Design Magazine** *London, The Design Council 1949-1974. Numbers 1-312 (lacking 12 issues)*

Folio. 18 vols bound, the remainder in original wrappers as issued.   £280

725

Metalwork

801 **Diderot, D. & J. L. d'Alembert** (Encyclopédie). Recueil de planches sur les sciences, les arts libéraux, les arts méchaniques, avec leurs explication *Paris, Briasson, David, Le Breton & Durand 1762-72; Livorno 1772-79*

Extracts of the sections dealing with base metals: iron, pewter, lead, tin, etc. and their related crafts. A detailed description of the main work can be found in item 1701 in the catalogue. *Each section is folio, the plates sizes average 360 × 225mm, and is preserved in a paper wallet.*

a **Forges ou art du fer** (Forging)
A complete work giving full details with 20 large views of all the processes involved in the production of iron. It is divided into 5 sections:
I: The exploitation of the ore and its preparation which includes its extraction and oxidation, early types of smelting furnaces, removing from the matrix, and details of early types of crushing mills.
II: The furnaces and the casting of pig iron. Plates show plans and elevations of furnaces, types of blast pumps, details of bellows and battons, the processes of charging the furnaces, making the pig moulds, pouring the molten iron and examining and weighing the pig iron.
III: The processes of making commercial iron. Plans, sections and details of the furnaces, making the moulds in earth and sand, casting from ladles and the necessary conduit pipes.
IV: The forge where the pig iron is converted into bars. Includes details of particular examples of two types of fired forges, the processes of crushing and reforging the puddle iron, forging, stretching and trimming the bars.
V: Various types of casting. This section includes large scale plans of the foundry, views of the foundry shed with the processes of making and tying iron rods, details of the rolling mills for shaping and moulding iron, trimmers and cutters. The final plates show plans and sections of large double-geared foundries and large washing and crushing machines.
A complete visual survey of the iron industry. *52 plates (of which 13 double-page) with 288 illustrations, and numbered I-X, I-X, I-XII, I-VII, I-XI, I-II and 45+(1 blank)pp text.* £150

b **Serrurier** (Art-metalworker & locksmith)
A complete book on hardware with a wide variety of plates both informative and decorative. The vignettes show the blacksmith's shop and the iron yard where the wares are made from the iron rods of the previous suite. Illustrations include plates of building and boat irons, examples of balconies, balustrades, grills and railings. Two double-plates with designs for gates include the gates at the Château de Maison. Other plates of decorative ironwork lead to keys, locks with their mechanisms, and show different types for doors, drawers and coffers. Further plates show padlocks, hinges, window hasps, window frames and panels, mouldings, shutters, carriage-work and carriage springs. Finally the suite is complete with the forging tools, bench tools and 2 large plates showing a detailed design of a tilt-hammer. *57 engraved plates of which 2 double-page, and 12pp text.* £120

c **Plombier** (Plumber)
The technique of working lead in sheets or pipes. The first part shows the methods of a small workshop with three views of the smelting furnace, cooling the lead into sheets, on tables and in tubes, working the lead to make pipes, and weighing the pipes. Detailed drawing of pipe moulds, tools and other necessary equipment are included. The second suite shows similar processes as carried out in a large foundry and concentrates on plans, elevations, and sections of the foundry, with drawings of the cutting and rolling machine and its water-powered wheel, and in addition a large view of the rolling shop with the machinery in action. *7 engraved plates with 64 illustrations, and 2pp text; 12 engraved plates of which 6 single-page, 3 double-page, 3 three-page folding, and 6pp of text.* £35

d **Potier d'étain. Potier d'étain bimbelotier** (Pewterer and his wares)
Of these two suites concerned with pewterware, one concentrates on the workshop techniques with details of the different moulds and their parts, the machinery and the tools which are used, while the second suite illustrates the various finished products showing designs for plates, trays, vases, ewers, candlesticks, incense boats, chalices, altar-crosses, crosiers and lamp covers, with one plate of the special moulds for making several vases of the same shape at one time. *2 parts in one. 9 engraved plates with 315 illustrations, and 3+(1 blank)pp text.* £35

e **Ferblantier** (Tinsmith)
A simple suite with 62 illustrations of tools and a vivid workshop scene showing the tinsmiths making coffee pots on an anvil, soldering a pot, filing down the metal work, and fitting a lid, etc. *2 engraved plates and (1+1 blank)pp text.* £9

f **Coutelier** (Cutler)
A craft with which Diderot was well familiar (his father was a master cutler) and this is apparent in the superb workshop view where the furnace tucked away in one corner and the ornate serving counter and show cases form the backcloth to a splendid picture of a worker inclined on the board of the grindstone which is turned by a huge hand wheel. The rest of the plates illustrate the tools of the trade and a detailed view of the grindstone and its parts. *2 engraved plates with 53 illustrations, and 1+(1 blank)pp of text.* **Illustration at head of section.** £9

g **Chaudronnier** (Coppersmith)
The suite deals with the three types of coppersmith and shows a workshop view of each one followed by the tools of the trade and the finished pieces. The first part deals with the making of cooking pots and pans, the second part with the making of copper plate, and the third with the making of musical instruments and shows processes in the formation of trumpets, hunting horns, kettle drums, loud-speakers, and ear trumpets. *4 engraved plates with 85 illustrations, and 2pp text.* £17

h **Ciseleur et damasquineur** (Chaser and inlayer)
The workshop vignette shows workers cutting a sword blade, chasing the hilt, firing, burnishing and polishing pieces and applying gold thread to a work. The remaining illustrations are tools of the profession. *2 engraved plates with 91 illustrations and 1+(1 blank)pp.* £9

i **Armurier** (Armourer)
Medieval knights in chainmail and plate armour together with individual illustrations of various types of swords, daggers, lances, shields and helmets of former times. *2 engraved plates with 32 illustrations and 1+(1 blank)pp text.* £5

802 Ayrton, Maxwell & Arnold Silcock Wrought iron and its decorative use *London, Country Life 1929*

On the use of wrought iron in architecture in England to the middle of the eighteenth century; fully illustrated and with sections on Tijou, and on smiths in Wales, the West of England, and the Midlands. Quarto. Frontispiece, (8)+196pp and 239 photo illustrations. Original cloth. £20

803 **Barbezat & Cie** Ornements en fonte de fer *Paris (c 1859)*
The very extensive trade catalogue of one of the best known French ironwork manufacturers. Items illustrated include balconies and balustrades and all kinds of ornament for gates and railings; pumps, fountains, grates, umbrella stands; tables, vases, light fittings; church furnishings; statues (human and animal); and drainpipes. The catalogue was evidently adapted to changes in the firm's stock and the numbering of its pages shows considerable additions and deletions to have been made in the printing process, 27 of the pages being left blank and 15 being given 'bis' numbers. *Folio. Title, (4) + 200pp (numbered 1-177, A-C, with 15 bis numbers and 10 blank unnumbered pp; of the numbered pages 18 are represented also by blanks, the rest are litho plates with several illustrations to a page) 1 extra folding litho plate. Original blind stamped cloth.* £165

804 **Barnard Bishop & Barnards** Fire grates, mantels, & accessories *(Norwich c 1910)*
Trade catalogue, with a large number of designs for fireplaces and their fittings showing Aesthetic Movement and Art Nouveau influence. Who on earth was the firm's principal designer? (One design is stated to be by L. F. Day – see items 1212, 1344 – but the inference from that is the remainder were not). *Quarto. 116pp with many photo illustrations. Original decorated paper boards.* £25

805 **Barnard, Bishop & Barnards** Stove designs *(Norwich c 1910)*
Clearly influenced by Art Nouveau with recurring sunflower motifs in the decoration. *Eight photographic plates.* £12

806 **Berain, (Jean)** (Pièces de serrureries) *Paris, the author (c 1695)*
Thirty-nine designs for ironwork railings and balustrades for the royal buildings several of which include the cipher of Louis XIV. Berain adapts his usual combination of strapwork and arabesque ornament with a fine feeling for the inherent properties of the material. First issue. Berlin Cat 343. Destailleur Notices p 164. *Untitled suite of 5 engraved plates in sizes varying from 303:345 × 270:292mm, with wide margins. In paper wallet.* £55

807 **(Birmingham brass fittings)** Catalogue of the metal fittings for curtains, beds, commodes, doors, bells, etc. *Birmingham (c 1823)*
An early trade catalogue of a firm manufacturing the above articles. The catalogue is not dated but is printed on paper carrying the watermark dates 1820 and 1821 and has the owners name and the date 1823 in ink. Bound at the end are three plates of brass cornice rods on paper watermarked 1823, together with a price list for cornice rods carrying the name of Messrs Yates and Hamper, of Birmingham and London.
The catalogue illustrates over 400 different items, presumably all executed in brass, which appear to be intended as accessories to furniture and interior woodwork. The stock numbers that appear by the illustrations go up to numbers over 11000 and the inference is that this is the catalogue of a firm that played a major part in the furniture accessories business and had done so for a long period. The objects illustrated are indeed designed in an Adamesque, late 18th century manner and it would be interesting to correlate them to the brass fittings found on Hepplewhite and Sheraton furniture. Trade catalogues of the 1820s are uncommon, especially so in this field, and this is a particularly interesting one with good engraved plates. *Oblong quarto. 1 leaf with mounted printed index, and 68 engraved plates (of which 12 are folding). There are 3 further engraved plates and 1 leaf price list as described above. Original marbled paper boards, morocco spine.* **Illustration below.** £385

808 **Bordeaux, Raymond** Serrurerie du moyen-age. Les ferrures de portes . . . avec dessins par Henri Gerente et G. Bouet *Oxford, Parker 1858*
Mediaeval ironwork as used in the decoration of doors and for bolts, locks and keys, illustrated by 40 litho plates by Bouet and many text figures. Despite the title, this was a publishing enterprise of J. H. Parker of Oxford (as the imprint shows) and the book owes as much to drawings supplied by J. C. and C. A. Buckler as it does to drawings by Gerente and Bouet. *Octavo. vi + 127 + (1)pp with 40 litho plates and numerous text illustrations. Original gilt-stamped red cloth.* £90

809 **Burlington Fine Arts Club** Exhibition of chased and embossed steel and iron work of European origin *London 1900*
Good representative collection of armour, door furniture, etc., catalogued by J. Starkie Gardner and G. F. Laking. *Large quarto. xxi + (1) + 82pp, with 70 plates. Original cloth, spine repaired.* £42

810 **Bury, (J. B. M.)** Modèles de serrurerie accompagnés des détails qui doivent en faciliter l'exécution et d'examples géométraux gravés par Normand, Hibon, Thierry, Olivier, etc. *Paris, Librairie Centrale d'Architecture (c 1855)*
Engravings of decorative ironwork in Paris, ranging from late 17th century examples in the Marais district to work by Percier and Fontaine and the author. Features illustrated include gates, balconies, railings, window and door frames and shop fronts. There is a useful explanatory text. *Folio. 15 + (1)pp and 56 engraved plates. Original printed paper boards, cloth spine.* **Illustration below.** £110

811 **Caillouet** Cahiers de serrureries *Paris, Basset, J. Chereau; & Augsburg, J. M. Will c 1770 & 1788*
Collection of plates from both the French and German suites of Caillouet's ironwork designs showing balconies, railings, garden gates, staircases, balustrades, altar rails with grilles, and lampholders. Nothing appears to be known about the designer except from these few engraved designs. It is interesting to see that the German suites are not copies of the French publications but are quite different designs. *Folio. 39 engraved plates in all. There are 22 from the French suites: Cahiers II, III, IV & the unrecorded 2, 5, & 8, of which Cahier III is complete in 6 plates. 17 plates are from the German suites: Theils 74-78, & 80 of which Theils 75, 76 & 77 are complete with 4 plates each. Early 19th century marbled-paper boards, quarter calf, gilt decorative spine. Ex library of the decorators V. & R. Baguès with their bookplate on the inside front cover.* £235

812 **Carron Company** Select designs in fire-grates etc. Longden pattern *London (c 1920)*
'Many of the firegrates illustrated in this catalogue... have been specially designed for Royal Palaces, as well as some of the finest and most palatial Mansions throughout the Kingdom'. Catalogue issued to mark opening of new showrooms following acquisition by Carron of Longden & Co. *Octavo 180pp with many illustrations. Original cloth.* £15

813 **(Child & Child)** A description of the pastoral staff given to the diocese of Albany, New York, anno MDCCCXCVII: with representations of the chief parts of the staff *Boston, Merrymount Press 1900.*
The staff was designed by Messrs Child & Child of London. The book was printed by D. B. Updike at the Merrymount Press and designed by Bertram G. Goodhue. *Folio. 9ff and 6 photo plates. Publishers' quarter calf. A copy produced for the printers and not included in the limited edition of 150 copies.* £45

814 **Clarkson, Douglas A.** Ancient iron work from the 13th century *London, Atchley (1860)*
Clarkson was a devout follower of Ruskin and his drawings of ironwork (which include drawings of gates at Frankfurt and Konstanz) are intended to show the superiority of mediaeval craftsmanship and design. He follows Ruskin in denouncing 'the bald and repulsive monotony of the streets of London' and suggests that a reversion to purer and freer forms of iron ornament would be beneficial: why, he asks, should the British Museum, devoted to the peaceful pursuits of literature and science, 'be fenced in and defended by a menacing range of warlike spears' (the railings which still surround it). *Small folio. Litho title, 4pp text and 48 litho plates by Vincent Brooks after drawings by the author. Original cloth.* £40

815 **Clouzot, Henri** La ferronerie moderne. 4eme serie *Paris, Moreau (c 1930)*
Contemporary ironwork by Raymond Subes, Desvallières, Schenck et fils, Poillerat, NICS Frères, Piguet, Brandt. (See also item 864). *Folio. (4)pp and 32 litho photo plates. Original printed paper boards (portfolio).* £45

816 **Comyn, Ching & Co Ltd** Catalogue of metal fitments.– Ventilator catalogue *London 1910, 1909*
Illustrated catalogue of a firm of 'builders, cabinet & upholsterers' ironmongers, workers in brass, iron, bronze, etc. Brass founders'. Much of their work is for domestic use – stair rods, picture hooks, hinges, castors – but they also offer 'highly finished door furniture' and 'antique ironwork' for the quality market, while their ventilators are strictly commercial pieces. *Quarto. (24)+424pp with many illustrations; 44pp with many illustrations. Original cloth.* £16

817 **Contet, F.** Documents de ferronerie ancienne époques Louis XV et Louis XVI *Paris, the author 1911*
Three series of plates illustrating about 400 examples of 18th century ironwork, mainly taken from private mansions but including work in some cathedrals, e.g. Amiens, and for some official buildings. *Folio. 3 vols in 1. 2ff and 40 photo plates in each part. Original half morocco.* £35

818 **Corbin, P. & F.** Illustrated and descriptive catalogue and price list of hardware *Hartford, Connecticut, Case Lockwood & Brainard 1885*
P. and F. Corbin specialized in the manufacture of mortice locks, door knobs and plates and door furniture generally. The frontispiece to the catalogue illustrates their works at New Britain, Connecticut. Bound at the end are supplements numbered three and four, issued respectively in 1890 and (1892). *Quarto. Frontispiece xvi (with addendum leaf numbered xvii)+631+(1)pp, with illustrations throughout; frontispiece 97+(1)pp, with illustrations; 49+(1)pp with illustrations. Original decorated cloth, spine repaired.* £45

819 **Cottingham, Lewis Nockalls** The smith and founder's director containing a series of designs and patterns for ornamental iron and brass work. 1824 *(London, the author 1824)*
Second, enlarged, edition of this influential pattern book for a growing industry. First published in October 1823 as the 'Ornamental metal worker's director', the book contains illustrations of the most recent work done in London in 1822-3 (Cumberland Gates in Hyde Park, gates to Fife House, Vintners Hall, and John Nash's house in Waterloo Palace), a fine series of gas lights and hundreds of examples of rosettes and small Roman and Gothic ornaments 'from drawings & casts in the author's possession'. Cottingham (1787-1847) had a house and private museum in Waterloo Bridge to contain his collection of casts, carvings and ornament and this was later to become the nucleus of the Royal Architectural Museum (the predecessor of the Victoria and Albert Museum). A prospectus bound with this copy shows that plates AI to AV illustrate French ironwork of the Napoleonic period and reveals one of the ways by which British taste was quietly altered by Continental example. *Quarto. Lithotitle and 83 lithoplates numbered 1-58, 60-71, AI-AV, 77-84, all by Hullmandel. Plate 59 was never issued. 2pp prospectus bound in. Quarter morocco, marbled paper sides.* **Illustration above.**
£175

820 **Davis Limited** Illustrated catalogue of general brassfoundry for use of builders, cabinet makers, shop fitters, and ship builders *Birmingham 1910*
Trade catalogue. The firm's products, all illustrated, range from brass knockers to wrought iron coal tongs, via beer taps, coffin screws and bedstead balls. The mind boggles! *Octavo. (2) + xviii + 488pp. Original cloth.*
£18

821 **Demont** Nouveau traité de serrurerie ou Vignole à l'usage des ouvriers serruriers et de tous les constructeurs, avec le système complete de la pose des sonnettes *Paris, P. Marie & A. Bernard (c 1840)*
One of a series of manuals treating of special constructional crafts with techniques and details based on a simple explanatory system which the author chooses to link with Vignola, presumably for its clarity and ease of understanding. The plates, by Marlier, illustrate tools, building irons, and hardware articles, range through patterns for balconies, railings, shutters, doors, furniture mounts, balustrades, locks and their pieces, and finally extended to complete iron constructions with roofs, greenhouses, granaries and bridges. The author shows a special interest in doorbells and the mechanics of their workings. *Quarto. (4) + 20pp and 40 numbered steel engraved plates. Original printed-paper wrappers, preserved in cloth portfolio.*
£130

822 **Designs of ornamental gates, lodges, palisading, and iron work of the Royal Parks . . .** principally taken from the executed works of Decimus Burton, John Nash, Sydney Smirke, Sir John Soane, Robert Stevenson, Sir John Vanbrugh, Christopher Wren *London, John Weale 1841*
Illustrations of the lodges and railings of the London parks and of notable examples of decorative ironworks at the Royal Hospital, Chelsea, Greenwich, Hampton Court, Buckingham House and the Sultan's Palace at Constantinople. The text gives details of improvements carried out in the Royal Parks between 1826 and 1840 and states their cost per annum and per item; there are also plans of the parks. The ironwork at Constantinople, illustrated in the last two plates of the work, had been recently executed for the Sultan by Mr William Dean, of the Phoenix Foundry, Little Bolton. *Folio. 20pp including 2 woodcuts, and 50 full-page engraved plates (plates 9 and 35 misnumbered). Original cloth, morocco spine.*
£90

823 **Eck, Charles Louis Gustave** Traité de construction en poteries et fer, a l'usage des bâtimens civils, industriels et militaires. Suivi d'un recueil des machines appropriées à l'art de bâtir. Traité de l'application du fer, de la fonte et de la tole dans toutes les constructions. Suivi d'un aperçu sur l'art d'ériger les tuyaux de cheminées en briques d'après le nouveau système *Paris, Blosse 1836; Carilian-Goeury & Dalmont 1841*

Two complementary volumes on the use of earthenware, iron and steel in construction. The first is a valuable study of the use of earthenware in the construction of vaults and domes, and of the use of tie-rods in supporting it; the second, primarily concerned with the constructional uses of metalwork, also deals with decorative fountains, lamp standards, etc. *Folio. 2 vols. (6) +72+21+(1)pp and 51+15 engraved plates; (8)+115 +(1)+8+32pp and 63+4+13 engraved plates. Vol I contemporary quarter morocco, gilt tooled spine; vol 2 marbled paper boards, cloth spine.* £220

824 **Ferrari, Giulio** Il ferro nell'arte Italiana . . . terza edizione aumentata *Milan, Hoepli c 1910*

Photographic illustrations of ironwork of Italian buildings from the Middle Ages to the early 19th century. *Small folio. 197+(1)pp including 160pp of illustrations. Original cloth.* £16

825 **Ffoulkes, Charles** Decorative ironwork from the XIth to the XVIIIth century *London, Methuen 1913*

Hinges, grills, locks, door handles, chests, clocks and other items. Ffoulkes' examples are taken from all over Europe. *Quarto. xxxvi+148pp with 80 text figures and 31 photo plates. Original cloth, uncut.* £45

826 **Fordrin, Louis** Nouveau livre de serrurerie *Paris, the author 1723 (facsimile reprint Paris, Calavas c 1900)*

Collection of designs by Louis Fordrin, a member of a well-known family of smiths who did much work for Louis XIV at Versailles. He was largely responsible for the internal ironwork of Nôtre Dame, Paris, which was removed at the Revolution and of which these plates are today the best evocation. *Large folio. 5ff text and 30 plates including title and dedication leaves of original work. Quarter cloth portfolio.* £25

827 **Fournier Frères** Album de serrurerie de luxe. Principaux modèles créés depuis 1864 *Paris (c 1865)*

Trade catalogue. Much elaborate door furniture and some rather splendid casement bolts. *Oblong folio. Litho title leaf and 39 litho plates (8 double-p). Original cloth.* £65

828 **Gardner, J. Starkie** English ironwork of the XVIIth & XVIIIth centuries. An historical & analytical account of the development of exterior smithcraft *London, Batsford 1911*

Starkie Gardner, who had a wide practical experience as a designer of ironwork and headed his own metalwork firm (see item 830), was also deeply involved in the history of the subject and largely responsible for the development of the Victoria and Albert Museum's metalwork collection. This is a work of primary importance for 17th and 18th century ironwork, well illustrated with photos by Horace Dan. *Large octavo. xxxvi+336pp including 163 text illustrations and 88 plates. Original cloth.* £18

829 **Gardner, J. Starkie** English ironwork of the XVIIth & XVIIIth centuries *London 1911 (Blom reprint 1970)*

Octavo. 374pp including 163 text illustrations, and 88 plates. Original cloth. £10

830 **J. Starkie Gardner Ltd** Decorative metalwork. Traditional and modern. Volume I *London, Architectural Advertising Ltd 1936*

The firm founded by J. Starkie Gardner (see item 828) was responsible for the decorative metalwork in the RIBA Buildings, the Cumberland and Dorchester Hotels, South Africa House, and many other important buildings of the interwar period, and this is an illustrated record of its products. *Small folio. Title leaf, contents leaf, (150)pp of photo plates, and (20) leaves marking starts of separate sections. Original cloth.* £24

831 **Gautier, Pierre** Divers ouvrages de balustrades cloisons paneaux et autres ornemens pour les serruriers. Faits et inventez par Pierre Gautier maistre serrurier du Roi dans son arsenal de galères à Marseille *(Marseilles) the author 1685*

A series of plates illustrating the ironwork designed by Gautier and his family for Louis XIV's Arsenal des Galères at Marseilles, built for the king by Pierre Puguet (cousin of the more famous architect and sculptor of that name) in 1678. Examples of the Gautiers' ironwork illustrated include panels, gates, banisters, lamp brackets, balustrades, screens, fire-dogs, and fan lights. Crown and fleur-de-lis motifs are incorporated in their pleasant floreated designs.
Thirteen of the plates have the initials of Pierre Gautier and six have the initials J.G., apparently those of Pierre Gautier's son Jean. No other engravings of their work are known. Berlin Cat 1346. *Small folio. Engraved title leaf and 20 engraved plates. Laid on to old paper. Quarter morocco, marbled paper boards.* **Illustration above.** £375

832 **Geerlings, Gerald K.** Wrought iron in architecture *New York 1929 (Bonanza reprint 1957)*
Quarto. v+(1)+202pp with 324 illustrations. Original cloth. £7

833 **Geerlings, Gerald K.** Metal crafts in architecture. Bronze, brass, cast iron, copper, lead, lighting fixtures, tin, specifications *New York, Bonanza (1957)*
Octavo. vi+202pp with 277 figures. Original cloth. £3

834 **Gloag, John & Derek Bridgwater** A history of cast iron in architecture *London, Allen & Unwin 1948*
The only book in English that deals both with the constructional and decorational uses of cast iron, and well illustrated. *Quarto. xx+395+(1)pp and 507 photo illustrations, 6 colour plates. Original cloth.* £25

835 **Griggs, W.** Iron work. 53 plates, from objects and drawings in the South Kensington Museum *London, Griggs 1898*
Principally gates, doors, knockers and other door furniture. *Small folio. (4)pp and 53 plates (3 double-p). Original cloth. Ex library.* £12

836 **Harris, John** English decorative ironwork from contemporary source books 1610-1836 *London, Tiranti 1960*
Examples of ironwork from pattern books and drawings, with an historical introduction and notes. Designers range from Inigo Jones to Henry Shaw. *Quarto. vi+18pp with (154)pp of plates. Original cloth.* £5

837 **Harris & Sheldon Ltd** Architectural metalwork: bronze: shopfronts, grilles, gates, show-cases: staircases *Birmingham (1927)*
Trade catalogue of the firm which had executed commissions for Austin Reed's

Regent Street premises; the Bon Marché, Liverpool; and the J. R. Wadia Trust, Bombay (all illustrated here). *Quarto. Colour frontispiece, 28pp with many illustrations. Original printed wrappers.* £8

838 **(Héré de Corny, Emmanuel)** Recueil des fondations et établissemens faits par le roi de Pologne . . . qui comprend la construction d'une nouvelle place . . . & les bâtimens que Sa Majesté Polonoise a fait élever dans le ville de Nancy pour son embelissement. Nouvelle édition augmentée & corrigée.-Compte général de la dépense des édifices et batimens que le roi de Pologne . . . a fait construire (etc) *Luneville, Claude-Francois Messuy 1762, 1761*
Complete description of the building operations, their cost, regulations, acts and founding charters, and of the workmen and artisans employed. Covers both the actual buildings and their very important ironwork (see also items 841, 842). Attractively produced with engravings of the buildings in the text. The operations at Nancy followed the settlement at neighbouring Luneville of King Stanislas of Poland, father-in-law of Louis XV of France, on his expulsion from his own kingdom; Héré de Corny was his chief architect. *Folio. 2 vols in 1. (8) + xii + 202 (numbered to 201 with an unnumbered page between 187 and 188)pp, with engraved title vignette, 1 engraved headpiece and 1 engraved tailpiece, and 3 large folding engraved plates of ironwork; (2) + 136 (numbered to 135 with unnumbered page after 13)pp, printed mostly in script type, with engraved title vignette, 2 engraved head and 2 engraved tailpieces, and 11 engraved vignettes of buildings. Folding plan of city of Nancy lacking. Contemporary full calf, spine repaired.* £150

839 **Hoever, Otto** (editor) An encyclopaedia of ironwork. Examples of hand wrought ironwork from the middle ages to the end of the 18th century. With an historical introduction by Otto Hoever *London, Benn 1927*
Good pictorial survey of European ironwork, with a short history of wrought iron manufacture. *Folio. 32pp text and 320pp plates. Original cloth.* £35

840 **Jousse, Mathurin** La fidelle ouverture de l'art de serrurier *La Flèche, Griveau 1627 (reprint by W. Griggs for Department of Science and Art 1889)*
Designs for keys and door furniture, published when Jousse was twenty; he later became well known as an architect and draughtsman. *Quarto. (4)pp, title and 26 photolitho plates. Original cloth.* £17

841 **Lamour, Jean** Recueil des ouvrages en serrurerie, que Stanislaus le Bien-Faisant, Roy de Pologne . . . a fait poser sur la place Royale de Nancy . . . avec un discours sur l'art de serrurerie *Nancy, the author (1768)*
A sumptuous publication worthy of its royal inspiration and of its designer, and probably the finest collection of wrought-iron designs to have been published. A vast folding plate of the great gate to the Place Stanislas is accompanied by full-page engravings of virtually all Lamour's Nancy ironwork, and when these are considered alongside the account books (see item 838) this must be one of the best recorded ironwork work commissions ever. Most of the work was executed around 1757 and the engravings of it are by the local artists Nicole père and fils and Collin (some are dated 1759 and 1760). Berlin Cat 1365; Destailleur no 479. *Large folio. Engraved ornamental title, engraved dedication, (10)pp in script type, 20 engraved plates of which 2 are double-page, 1 has a double-width flap attached, and 1 other consists of 4 double-page plates attached three in a row plus one on top. Original marbled paper boards, rebacked.*
Illustration at end of section. £875

842 **Lamour, Jean** Recueil des ouvrages en serrurerie *Nancy 1768 (Nicolas-Digout reprint, Nancy c 1860)*
Lithographic facsimile. *Folio. Ornamental title, ornamental dedication, (6)pp text (with 1 headpiece), 24 litho plates (numbered to 28 to include a 5 sheet folding plate taking 5 numbers). Sheets in quarter cloth portfolio, morocco label on cover.* £40

843 **Le Pautre, (Jean)** (Serrurerie) *(Amsterdam) R. & J. Ottens (c 1700)*
Eleven designs for ironwork gates, a staircase balustrade and a circular window grille. The gate designs range from straightforward models with very simple decoration to more complex designs richly ornamented. Dutch reverse copies. *Six unnumbered engraved plates, average size 220 × 145mm, with wide margins. In paper wallet.* £40

844 **Lethaby, W. R.** Leadwork old and ornamental and for the most part English *London, Macmillan 1893*
Octavo. viii + 148pp with 76 figurative illustrations. Original cloth. £9

845 **Lindsay, J. Seymour** Iron and brass implements of the English house. With an introduction by Ralph Edwards. (Revised edition) *London, Tiranti 1970*
In six sections dealing respectively with the hearth, the kitchen, lighting, smoking, miscellaneous metal items and items used in America in the Colonial period. First published in 1927 and a pioneer study of English domestic metalwork. *Octavo. viii + 88pp and 152pp of plates with 480 drawings of metal items. Original cloth.* £5

846 **Lister, Raymond** Decorative wrought ironwork in Great Britain *London, Bell 1957*
Technical and historical sketch, with a useful bibliography. *Octavo. xii + 266pp with 59 text figures, and 28pp of plates. Original cloth.* £8

847 **Lister, Raymond** Decorative cast ironwork in Great Britain *London, Bell 1960*
History of the use of cast iron and casting techniques. *Octavo. xii + 258pp with 83 text figures, and 8 plates. Original cloth.* £8

848 **Walter Macfarlane & Co.** Illustrated catalogues of Macfarlane's castings. Sixth edition *Glasgow (c 1905)*
The octavo version of the Macfarlane catalogue, photographically reproduced from the quarto edition. *Octavo. Approximately 400pp of illustrations. Original cloth.* £22

849 **Walter Macfarlane & Co.** Illustrated catalogue of Macfarlane's Castings. Seventh edition *Glasgow (c 1909)*
A catalogue of Macfarlane's range of pipes, drains, gutters, ridging and sanitary fittings; their baths are particularly fine and there are colour illustrations of ten of them. At the end there are selections of items from other Macfarlane catalogues (fountains, stable fittings, lamp standards, bandstands, conservatories). *Folio. 400pp with thousands of illustrations, and 5pp of colour plates. Original cloth.* £45

850 **Walter Macfarlane & Co.** Illustrated catalogue of Macfarlane's Castings. Eighth edition *Glasgow (c 1912)*
By this edition Macfarlane's were describing the catalogue as 'the Standard Reference on the subject of Cast Iron Water, Soil and Drain Goods and Gutters' and the sections on ridging and sanitary goods are held over to a later volume. *Folio. 274pp, illustrated throughout. Original cloth.* £35

851 **Marot, Pierre** La place royale de Nancy. Image de la réunion de la Lorraine à la France. Du monument du bien-aimé à la statue du bien-faisant *Nancy, Berger-Levrault 1966*
A sumptuous production marking the acquisition by the Musée Historique Lorrain of a copy of the long-destroyed statue of Louis XV that was the centrepiece of the Place Royale at Nancy (see also items 838, 841-2). Includes the results of the most recent French research on the artists and architects employed on it. Limited to 1000 copies. *Folio. 160pp and 30 coloured plates. Original portfolio containing sheets in original folders.* £45

852 **Metman, Louis & H. Le Secq des Tournelles** Le musée des arts decoratifs. Palais du Louvre, Pavillon de Marsan. Le métal ... première partie. Le fer *Paris, Longuet (c 1905)*
Illustrated record of the museum's holdings of decorative iron objects; with particularly good coverage of locks, keys, cutlery, scissors and other smaller items. *Small folio. Title leaf, 44pp and 130 photo plates illustrating 1485 objects. Quarter cloth portfolio.* £40

853 **Meyer, Franz Sales** A handbook of art smithing for the use of practical smiths, designers of ironwork, technical and art schools, architects, etc. Translated from the second and enlarged German edition. With an introduction to the English edition by J. Starkie Gardner *London, Batsford 1896*
Meyer was Professor in the School of Applied Art at Karlsruhe and his book is based on German traditions and techniques. *Octavo. viii+207+(1)pp with 214 text illustrations. Original cloth.* £15

854

854 **Meyrick, Samuel Rush** A critical inquiry into antient armour as it existed in Europe, but particularly in England, from the Norman conquest to the reign of King Charles II. Illustrated with a series of richly coloured engravings. With a glossary of military terms of the middle ages *London, Bohn 1824*
Practically the first study of English armour as a whole and also, and perhaps more important, a ready source of information and ideas on mediaeval chivalry in all its aspects; it was a favourite book of Sir Walter Scott. The plates were engraved by R. Bridgens after drawings by Meyrick. First edition. *Large quarto. 3 vols. 20+(2)+ lxxvii +(1)+206pp and 30 plates (numbered 1-30 of which 8-25, 27-30 handcoloured); (6)+297+(1)pp and 36 plates (numbered 31-66, all handcoloured except 44); (6)+147+ (135)pp and 14 plates (numbered 67-80 all handcoloured except 80); with a handcoloured initial beginning each chapter. Quarter calf.* **Illustration above.** £325

855 **Moorey, P. R. S.** Ancient Persian bronzes in the Adam collection *London, Faber 1974*
Octavo. 208pp with 188 illustrations and 4 colour plates. Original cloth. £9

856 **Morris Singer Company** (Architectural metalwork) *London (c 1934)*
Trade catalogue of the firm which describes itself as a 'Branch of William Morris & Co (Westminster) Ltd. and incorporating the architectural metal department of "Singers of Frome"'. The firm was responsible for metalwork at the Bank of England, the Daily Telegraph and the RIBA building. *Folio. 52pp with many illustrations. Original cloth.* £7

857 **Murphy, Bailey Scott** English and Scottish wrought ironwork. A series of examples of English ironwork of the best periods, together with most of the examples now existing in Scotland with descriptive text *Edinburgh, Waterston 1904*
Illustrates virtually all the wrought-iron work of any consequence in Scotland, as well as Talman's ironwork at Drayton House, Northamptonshire, William Stanton's work at Belton House, Lincolnshire, the ironwork of various Oxford and Cambridge colleges, and other English specimens. Has detailed measured drawings and collotype photo plates. *Large folio. (14)+14pp and 80 plates. Original gilt stamped cloth.* £40

858 **Thomas O'Brien & Co.** Catalogue no.34 *London, 1896-7*
Catalogue of stoves, chimney pieces, kitchen ranges and general ironwork. *Octavo. xxxii+1104pp with over 1000 text illustrations. Original quarter calf.* £28

859 **T. W. Palmer & Co.** General price list of railings, gates, hurdles, treeguards, ornamental ironwork, wire, cattle & tennis court fences, etc. *London (1933)*
Proprietors of the Merton Abbey Ironworks. The plates illustrate work at Welwyn, Elstree, Mortlake, and elsewhere. *4to. (92)pp, including text figures and illustrations. Original printed wrappers.* £4

860 **Patents for Inventions** Abridgments of Specifications. Class 30, Cutlery. 1897-1900, 1901-4, 1905-8, 1909-15, 1916-20, 1921-5, 1926-30 *London, HMSO 1902-32*
Run for 1897-1930 of specifications for cutlery. Patentees include Elkingtons and Mappin and Webb and all the major manufacturers of razors. *Octavo. 7 vols bound in 2. Contemporary quarter morocco.* £70

861 **Patents for Inventions** Abridgements of specifications 340,001-720,000. Group XIV. Cutlery, furniture, table and toilet articles *London, HMSO 1932-57*
Specifications for the period 1929-52; differently grouped to the earlier series but following on from it. *Octavo. 19 parts of which 4 are bound in 1 vol quarter morocco and 15 are in original wrappers.* £20

862 **Patents for Inventions** Abridgments of Specifications. Class 128. Table articles and appliances. 1897-1900, 1901-4, 1905-8, 1909-15, 1916-20, 1921-5, 1926-30 *London, HMSO 1903-34*
Complete run for 1897-1930 of specifications for such objects as cruets, flower holders, jugs, moustache guards, nutcrackers, plates, napkin rings and trays. Note the Marquis of Graham's gimbal for supporting glasses on his yacht (1898: 11189) and the Baroness von der Osten's special fork for breaking and extracting the flesh of crabs (1903: 25506). *Octavo. 7 vols bound in 2. Contemporary quarter morocco.* £70

863 **Pitt-Rivers, H. A. L. F.** On the development and distribution of primitive locks and keys *London, Chatto & Windus 1883*
Comparative study of locks and keys from as far afield as Weymouth and Yarkand. *Quarto. 31+(1)pp and 10 litho plates each with text leaf of description. Quarter morocco, cloth sides. Author's presentation copy.* £35

METALWORK 141

864 **Poillerat, Gilbert** Ferronerie d'aujourd'hui. Première série *Paris, Moreau (c 1950)*
Features contemporary metalwork by Raymond Subes, by Poillerat himself, and others. A sequel to the series 'La ferronerie moderne' (see item 815). *Small folio. (8)pp and 42 photo plates. Original cloth portfolio.* £22

865 **Pugin, A. Welby** Designs for iron & brass work in the style of the xv and xvi centuries *London, Ackerman 1836*
The first issue of the work with the etched plates printed in two colours. *Quarto. 27 numbered etched plates, all with legend and signature printed in red. Plate 1 repaired for marginal tears. Original cloth, neatly rebacked, with original front printed label in two colours.* £45

866 **Robertson, E. Graeme** Sydney lace. Ornamental cast iron in architecture in Sydney *Melbourne, Georgian House 1962*
Quarto. xvi+198pp with 225 illustrations. Original cloth. £15

867 **Robertson, E. Graeme** Ornamental cast iron in Melbourne *Melbourne, Georgian House 1967*
Full account of the use of cast iron in Victorian Melbourne, with many photographs of the city's surviving 19th century buildings. *Quarto. x+229+(1)pp with many illustrations. Original cloth.* £12

868 **Roeper, Adalbert** Geschmiedete Gitter des XVI-XVIII Jahrhunderts aus Süddeutschland *Munich, Jos. Albert (c 1920)*
Illustrations of 16th century-18th century ornamental gates and railings, from such places as Nuremberg, Regensburg and Augsburg. *Folio. (6)pp and 50 photo plates with 111 illustrations. Original cloth portfolio.* £25

869 **Roeper, Adalbert** Deutsche Schmiedearbeiten aus fünf Jahrhunderten *Munich, Jos. Albert (c 1920)*
Examples of German keys, locks and door furniture ranging from the 14th to the 18th centuries. The plates are very good and not all the pieces are anonymous; there is a magnificent door-knocker by J. Ch. Böckel, the court locksmith at Cassel. *Folio. (6)pp and 50 photo plates with 175 illustrations. Original cloth portfolio.* £30

870 **Rowe Bros & Co** Catalogue of sheet lead, lead pipe, lead soil and ventilating pipe, compo pipe, lead wire, lead tape, window lead, plumbers' and tinmen's solder *Exeter (1930)*
Very sanitary, but their embossed plates and leaded lights are respectable and their extracting roof ventilators veritably mediaeval. *Quarto. xxiv+776pp with over 1000 illustrations, some coloured. Original cloth.* £20

871 **Small, Tunstall & Christopher Woodbridge** English wrought ironwork mediaeval & early renaissance. A portfolio of full size details *London, Architectural Press (c 1920)*
This and the next item provide very detailed drawings of wrought iron features which the authors thought could usefully be copied in contemporary buildings; they are in fact pattern books on the old 18th- and early 19th-century lines. *Quarto. ivpp and 20 plates. Preserved in original cloth portfolio.* £10

872 **Small, Tunstall & Christopher Woodbridge** English wrought ironwork of the late 17th and early 18th centuries. A portfolio of full-size details *London, Architectural Press (c 1920)*
Quarto. iv pp and 20 plates. Preserved in original cloth portfolio. £10

873 **(Stevens, Alfred)** Notes on some works by Alfred Stevens from 1850 to 1857. As shown by the original drawings and models in the possession of Messrs Henry E. Hoole & Co Ltd of Green Lane Works, Sheffield. Selected and arranged by Henry Ingle Potter *Sheffield, Hoole (c 1912)*

Stevens spent the years 1850-7 as resident designer with the Sheffield firm of Hoole Co, manufacturers of metal grates and fenders, and this very interesting pamphlet records his drawings and models preserved by the firm, as well as designs which were in fact executed. *Quarto. 28pp and 56 photo illustrations. Original printed wrappers.* £32

874 **Tavenor-Perry, J.** Dinanderie. A history and description of mediaeval art work in copper, brass and bronze *London, George Allen 1910*

Quarto. xii + 238pp with 71 text illustrations, and 48 plates. Original cloth. £15

875 **Teale Fire-place Company** Designs of fire-places *Leeds, July 1893*

Trade catalogue, incorporating two articles on fireplaces by T. Pridgin Teale, F.R.S.; photographic illustrations of the firm's products; and two very long and impressive lists of those who had purchased them, beginning with 'Her Majesty the Queen, Windsor Castle' and finishing up with the Royal Station Hotel, York. *Quarto. Title, 48pp and 36 plates. Original decorative printed boards.* £28

876 **Thiollet (François)** Serrurerie et font de fer récemment executées. Application aux planchers et combles, aux ponts, escaliers et machines diverses, &. Ornemens en fonte ajustes aux portes, devantures de boutique, grilles, rampes d'escalier, candélabres, cheminées, poêles, & *Paris, Bance Ainé 1832*

Specimens of contemporary ironworks, principally taken from buildings in Paris. Extensive coverage of gates, railings, and balconies and – more unexpectedly – the use of decorative ironwork in shopfronts. *Folio. Engraved frontispiece, (4) + 32pp and 72 engraved plates. Half red morocco, marbled paper sides, gilt tooled spine. Bookplate of Gladys de Grey (Marchioness of Ripon).* £210

877 **Tijou, Jean** A new booke of drawings . . . containing severall sortes of iron worke *London, the author 1693*

The most important English book on ironwork and the rarest (Wing lists two copies only). These designs by Tijou for gates, balconies, staircases and panels were intended for Hampton Court and most were executed, though in a less decisively rococo manner. *Oblong folio. 20 numbered engraved plates, each approximately 260 × 350mm. Cloth folder in slip-case.* **Illustration opposite.** £800

878 **Tijou, Jean** A new booke of drawings . . . reproduced with the addition of a brief account of the author and his works, and descriptions of the plates, by J. Starkie Gardner *London, Batsford 1896*

Facsimile reprint with an introduction by Starkie Gardner discussing Tijou's work at Hampton Court and explaining some of the complications over its attribution to him. *Folio. Decorative title leaf, 8pp and 20 plates. Original printed paper boards, cloth spine.* **Illustration opposite.** £25

879 **Wainwright & Waring Ltd** Catalogue of steel, bronze & aluminium windows, architectural metalwork in wrought iron, bronze & lead, stained & leaded glass *London (c 1935)*

Illustrates work done for Lutyens, Guildford Cathedral, Liberty's, Youngers (brewers) and others. *Folio. 92pp with many illustrations. Original cloth, vellum spine.* £12

880 **Weaver, Lawrence** English leadwork its art & history *London, Batsford 1909*

A very thorough study, never superseded, with sections on fonts, pipes, cisterns, spires, domes, statues, vases, tombs, and smaller lead objects, and extensively illustrated. *Quarto. xv + (1) + 268pp, including frontispiece and 441 illustrations. Original cloth.* £25

METALWORK 143

877-8

881 Weaver, Lawrence English leadwork its art & history *London, 1909 (Blom reprint 1970)*
Quarto. 284pp with 441 illustrations. Original cloth. £10

882 G. Wright & Co Catalogue of grates *Sheffield, Lockwood & Bridges (c 1860)*
Trade catalogue of patent bivalve firegrates, illustrated by handsome litho plates. Oblong folio. 24 litho plates and price lists. Original cloth. £60

883 **Young & Marten** Complete catalogue of requisites for building construction *London (c 1897)*
Young & Marten were a firm of builders and ironmongers based at Stratford, East London, with a substantial clientèle and vague artistic aspirations – they designed their own cut glass and stained glass – and this fine trade catalogue with chromolitho title page and coloured illustrations gives a good picture of the stock of a firm of this kind in the 1890s. *Quarto. 2 vols. Over 840pp in all, illustrated throughout. Original cloth, covers slightly stained, but contents sound.* £70

884 **Young & Marten** (Catalogue of requisites for building construction) *London 1894*
Earlier Young & Marten catalogue featuring a representative selection from the firm's stock. *Quarto. (160)pp and 5 chromolitho plates, many text illustrations. Original printed wrappers.* £20

885 **Preece, John** Gates of Veneto *London, Baker 1968*
Photographs of 17th-18th century ironwork in Padua, Verona, Vicenza and the Veneto. *Small folio. 90pp including frontispiece, and 60 photo plates. Original cloth.* £3

Gold, Silver and Jewelry

901c

901 Diderot, D. & J. L. d'Alembert (Encyclopédie). Recueil de planches sur les sciences, les arts libéraux, et les arts méchaniques, avec leurs explication *Paris, Briasson, David, Le Breton & Durand, 1762-72; Livorno, 1772-79*

Extracts of the sections concerning precious metals, jewelry and related occupations. See item 1701 in the catalogue for full details of the publication. *Each section listed is folio, the plate sizes average 360 × 225mm, and the suite is preserved in a paper wallet.*

a **Fonte de l'or, de l'argent et du cuivre** (Precious metal foundry)
Smelting and casting gold, silver and copper in sand moulds, with a vignette of the smelting shop, details of the furnace and illustrations of the progressive operations of casting in parts. *Six engraved plates with 64 illustrations, and (1 + 1 blank)pp text* £15

b **Argenteur** (Silversmith)
A fine vignette showing workers cutting, chasing, applying silver leaf, and polishing pieces, together with illustrations of the various utensils. *Two engraved plates with 30 illustrations, and (1 + 1 blank)pp text.* £10

c **Batteur d'or** (Gold beater)
Tools, machinery, and a workshop vignette showing melting the gold, beating it, separating the gold leaf and rolling it into thin strips. Details of the rolling machine are included. *Two engraved plates with 22 illustrations, and 1 + (1 blank)pp text.* **Illustration above.** £9

d **Doreur** (Gilder)
An excellent suite showing three types of workshop: a metal gilder's with 75 illustrations of tools and a view of the process of melting down the gold, laying it on the metal, putting on the colour, burnishing, discolouring, and touching up the finished piece; a copper-plate gilder's shop with 22 illustrations of tools and views of the processes of applying gold to the copper sheets; and finally a wood gilder's workshop with 20 illustrations of tools and a view concerned primarily with the gilding of mirror and picture frames. *Four engraved plates and 2pp text.* £17

e **Tireur et fileur d'or** (Drawer of gold thread)
A suite which shows clearly Diderot's fascination with complicated pieces of machinery. The two vignettes illustrate the processes of making the gold wire including the operation of the drawing-frame and the mill for pulling the thread, while the rest of the plates include detailed drawings of the drawing-frame and its parts, the draw-plate with the successively smaller holes which extend the thread and force it to conform to the diameter, the plaiting machine and large scale drawings of a spinning machine which takes 13 bobbins and has all the parts described. *12 engraved plates with 240 illustrations, and 3 + 1 blank pp of text.* £20

f **Orfèvre grossier** (Goldsmith)
Vignette of the goldsmith's workshop, 12 plates of tools, utensils and machines including detailed drawings of the furnaces, the turning lathe and machinery for making the gold filings and pounding the cinders for smelting and burnishing. Seven plates of designs of ewers, vases, altar crosses, candlesticks, tureens, teapots, and various types of table plate and dishes. *19 engraved plates with 345 illustrations, and 4pp of text.* £35

g **Orfèvre-bijoutier** (Goldsmith-jeweller)
The making of small gold and jewelry articles with designs for clasps, rings, bracelets, scissors, watchcases, sword handles and hilts, cane-heads and small boxes. Four plates of tools and utensils and a workshop vignette showing jewel mounting, metal forging, soldering etc, while the master weighs and sells the merchandise. A mixed suite of decorative designs and practical information. *Seven engraved plates with 160 illustrations and 2pp text.* £20

h **Orfèvre-jouaillier, metteur en oeuvre** (Stone-setter)
A jeweller's workshop showing the processes of mounting and setting precious stones. A suite which includes both decorative plates of designs for rings, brooches, earrings, clips, buckles, bracelets, necklaces and pendants, and practical informative illustrations of different cuts of diamonds with drawings of some of the largest and most famous stones of the time, and 4 plates of tools with a half plate illustration of the special work-bench of the stone-setter with all its fittings. *11 engraved plates with 212 illustrations, and 3 + (1 blank)pp text.* £30

i **Diamantaire** (Diamond cutter)
The processes of cutting diamonds, with two vignettes showing the cutting and grinding machine where a worker sprinkles the plate with diamond powder soaked in oil, while another supplies the turning power, and a third grinds two diamonds against each other. *Three engraved plates with 22 illustrations, and 1 + (1 blank)pp text.* £12

k **Gravure en pierre fines** (Gemstone engraver)
A vignette of the engraver working with the treadle-driven engraving lathe, and two plates of tools with detailed drawings of the lathe. *Three engraved plates with 32 illustrations and (1 + 1 blank)pp text.* £9

l **Gravure en medailles et en cachets** (Maker of seals)
The engraving and modelling of medals and seals with two workshop views and two series of tools and instruments for carrying out the operations. *Five engraved plates numbered I-III, I-II, with 74 illustrations and 1 + (1 blank)pp text.* £15

m **Emailleur à la lampe, et peinture en emaile** (Enameller)
An interesting suite of plates which includes 4 fascinating vignettes of workrooms. One shows the enameller at home working in a darkened room with a blow lamp to melt the enamel. The second shows the workroom with the processes of making glass thread and false pearls; the third shows the beads being coloured by the introduction of a drop of liquid in which fish scales have been dissolved, and threading the beads; while a final plate shows the processes of painting and enamelling metal and its final burnishing process. Each view is accompanied by illustrations of the related tools. *Four engraved plates with 50 illustrations and 1 + (1 blank)pp text.* £16

n **Piqueur de tabatières, incrusteur et brodeur** (Snuff-box decorator)
Decorating small boxes and similar articles by inlaying, encrusting, and pricking in gold and silver, often on a shell base. *Two engraved plates with 40 illustrations and (1 + 1 blank)pp text.* £7

GOLD, SILVER AND JEWELRY 147

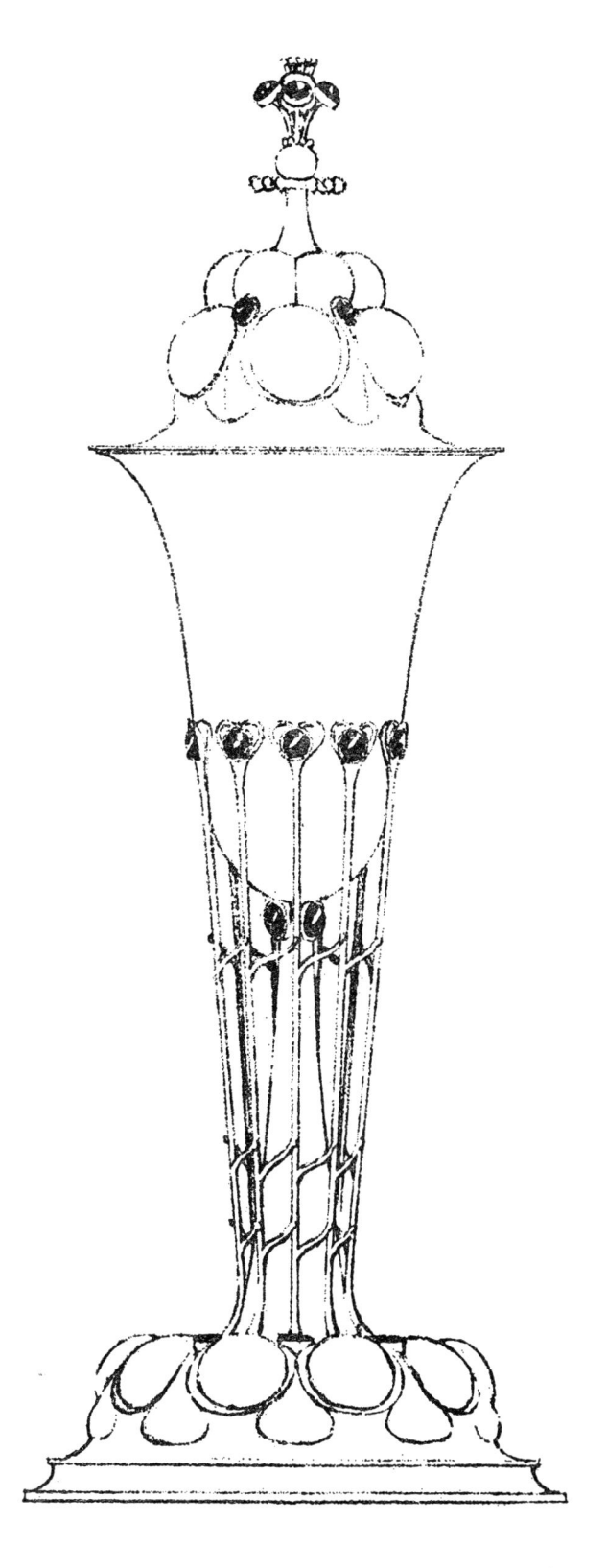

902-3

902 **Ashbee, C. R.** Modern English Silverwork.... A new edition with introductory essays by Alan Crawford & Shirley Bury *London, B. Weinreb 1974*

Ashbee (1863-1942) one of the finest designers of silver and a pioneer of modern design, was the founder of the Guild of Handicraft. This was the most impressive of the ventures of the Arts and Crafts movement and was set up as an organisation to aid craftsmen to withstand the competition imposed by machinery. The Guild exhibited widely in Vienna, Munich, Dusseldorf and Paris, and its work, particularly in silver, exercised strong influences on designers and manufacturers in England, Europe and America. Unfortunately the Guild, which as a group had moved to Chipping Campden in the Cotswolds in 1902, was a commercial failure and was forced into voluntary liquidations in 1908. This volume of designs, showing the silverwork produced by co-operative design in the Guild, was issued soon after the organisation had disbanded. Ashbee's aim was partly to help students to realize that design could be approached on a co-operative and socialist basis and mainly to show the public the originals of the designs that were being plagiarised by commercial firms whose factory imitations had been principally responsible for the financial ruin of the Guild.

This new edition has the same one hundred lithograph plates as the original and thirty-five of these have been coloured by hand in the manner of the earlier edition. Ashbee's text has been retained and prefaced by two introductory essays: 'Charles Robert Ashbee, his life and work' by Alan Crawford, and a critical assessment of the book and of the silverwork of Ashbee and the Guild by Shirley Bury of the Department of Metalwork at the Victoria and Albert Museum. There is, in addition, a bibliographical note on the printed sources.

This new edition, is published in a limited edition of one thousand numbered copies for sale, and twenty-five copies for presentation. *Quarto. xxiv+(2)+34+(2)pp and 100 litho plates of which 35 hand coloured. Publisher's cloth.* **Illustration on previous page and below.** £40

903 **Ashbee, C. R.** Modern English silverwork: an essay by C. R. Ashbee, together with a series of designs by the author drawn upon a hundred separate lithograph plates and coloured by hand, with a descriptive index *London, Essex House Press, 1909*

One of the few surviving copies of the original edition. The book was printed by Ashbee's own Essex House Press at the Norman Chapel, Broad Campden in the Cotswolds in an edition of 200 copies. Many of the plates were delicately coloured by the hands of Ashbee, his friends and members of the Guild. *Quarto. 34+(2)pp and 100 lithograph plates some of which are handcoloured. No 73 of 200 copies. Original cloth, spine repaired, with new label.* **Illustration on previous page and below.** £360

902-3

904 **Anderson, Lawrence Leslie** The art of the silversmith in Mexico 1519-1936 *New York, Hacker 1975*
Reissue of Anderson's major study of the Mexican silver industry (mining, smelting, legislation, craftsmen, hallmarks, artistic trends, the decorative objects produced), which was first published in 1941. *Quarto. 2 vols. 460pp and 183 plates. Original cloth.* £30

905 **(Assay Offices)** Parliamentary Report. Report from the committee appointed to enquire into the manner of conducting the several assay offices in London, York, Exeter, Bristol, Chester, Norwich, and Newcastle upon Tyne *(London) 1773*
An enquiry into the conduct of London and provincial assay offices by a committee of the House of Commons. Their report prints the evidence of witnesses who appeared before them and complete lists of the goldsmiths and silversmiths who at that time had their marks registered at the assay offices. It was the committee's recommendation that 'some further checks and regulations are necessary to be made ... besides those provided by the laws now in being' that brought about the establishment of additional assay offices at Birmingham and Sheffield. *Folio. 88pp. Sheets, uncut, stitched and preserved in cloth box.*
£40

906 **Berain, C(laude)** (Chiffres enlacés contenus dans des cartouches *Paris c 1690*)
Claude Berain was the less-known brother of Jean and a specialist engraver of plate, watch cases, book-plates, silver and gold pieces, as well as an ornamental engraver. Ciphers using the initials of the owner were by far the most common type of decoration for personal articles of gold and silver. They were frequently found on watches, boxes, mirrors, salvers, and plate, and vied in popularity only with heraldic devices but had a much wider use. The plates here show three large designs, headed by a royal cipher, and 12 small designs in groups of four. All the plates are signed by Berain. Berlin Cat 848. Destailleur Notices p 168. Guilmard p 92. *Six engraved plates with 15 designs. Average size 88 × 102mm. Tipped on grey paper and preserved in paper wallet.* £42

907 **Berain, C(laude)** (Dessus de boites *Paris c 1690*)
Designs for rectangular box tops with strapwork and moresque chased ornament surrounding central vignettes with abstract motifs, creatures, a landscape, a putto and a Venus and Cupid scene. The designs would have been copied on tobacco, snuff, or toilet boxes. Destailleur Notices p 168. Guilmard p 92. *12 unnumbered engraved plates, average size 73 × 95mm. Tipped on to grey paper and preserved in a paper wallet.* £60

908 **(Boulenger)** Couverts & petite orfévrerie argent. Coutellerie ebène, ivoire, nacre *(c 1900)*
Trade catalogue of cutlery manufacturers Boulenger, with photo illustrations of their complete range of stock: about six-hundred pieces. *Folio. Title leaf,(1) + 36 (numbered 1-35 and 13 bis) plates. Original cloth.* £42

909 **Brawn, Thomas** Catalogue of ecclesiastical and domestic mediaeval metal work, in gold, silver, brass, and iron; sacred vessels, memorial brasses, metal screens ... spire and gable crosses, and all kinds of architectural metal work *Birmingham (c 1860)*
Brawn's stock in trade shows the influence of the Ecclesiologists and the vigorous litho plates illustrate his wares from chalices to herses, incense boats and ceremonial trowels. One plate is signed 'Geo Tho Robinson archt del des et lith.' *Octavo. 15 + (1)pp and 39 litho plates. Title and plate B1 neatly repaired at margins. Cloth.* £30

910 **P. Bruckmann & Co.** Neue Formen silberner Gefässe *Heilbronn am Neckar, P. Bruckmann & Co. (c 1850-61)*
Trade catalogue of high-class German silverware by a firm with an international clientele who showed their goods at the 1851 Exhibition. The designs, illustrated in full or half size drawings, show all manner of tableware from candlesticks, bells, tongs and napkin rings to the usual eating utensils and table services, all in a rather solid, traditional German style. Loose sheets give price lists in French and German as well as the approximate weight of each piece. The catalogues appear to have been those belonging to the Brussels

representative of the firm. *Folio. 4 parts. 6 + 6 single-page litho plates, 5 + 4 double-page litho plates and 1 single-page loose litho plates and 3 letterpress sheets. Original blue paper wrappers with printed labels. Preserved in cloth. Portfolio.* £285

911 Brunner, Herbert Old table silver. A handbook for collectors and amateurs. Translated by Janet Seligman *London, Faber 1967*
Guide to European table silver, with lists of workshops, facsimiles of marks, names and dates of makers and descriptions of the types of silver utensil found. *Octavo. 224pp including 261 photo illustrations. Original cloth.* £8

912 Bry, J(ohan) Th(eodor) & T(heodor) de (Designs for knife and daggar handles) *Frankfurt, the authors c 1595*
Decorative designs for knife handles by two of the finest Netherlandish-German goldsmiths and ornamental engravers of the late Renaissance. The designs are all similar in style and show grotesque decoration on a black ground as a setting for medallions containing scenes from the Old and New Testaments, allegorical figures, or emblems.

a **Four designs inscribe 'Aer', 'Ignis', 'Terra', 'Aqua'**
Each with a large and small medallion. The designs are cut into the plate-mark following the contours of the design. 'Aer' and 'Ignis' have male figures, emblematic clasped hands and matching grotesque decoration and formed a pair on one plate. 'Terra' and 'Aqua' have female figures, pelican emblems, and matching grotesque decoration, and formed another pair 'en suite'. From 'Mansches de Coutiaus'. Berlin Cat 631:1. Nagler Monographisches III: 678. *Four plates cut into marks, average size 92 × 25mm, mounted on old paper and tipped on hand-made paper. In paper wallet.* £35

b **Four designs originally forming two pairs. Inscribed 'Manus manum lavat Ephes V', 'Fui non sum es non eris Psalm CIII', 'Sine Cerere et Baccho friget Venus', 'Per peccatum mors Genes III'**
Each design has three medallions: a small roundel with an emblem, an arcuated shape with a scene illustrating the saying, and an allegorical female figure in an oval. The outlines of the designs match. Possibly also from 'Mansches de Coutiaus'. *Four plates cut to separate designs, average size 30 × 96mm; mounted on old paper and tipped on hand-made paper. In paper wallet.* £35

c **Four designs; one pair inscribed 'Fides' & 'Justitia' and 'Prudentia' & 'Fortitudo'**
With two female allegorical figures each as well as emblem; the second pair with inscription and with one allegorical figure, but signed T.B. between the designs. *Four designs on 2 plates; sizes 98 × 72mm and 95 × 62mm. Tipped on hand-made paper. In paper wallet.* £60

d **Two designs forming a pair**
Each with alternative arcuated and oval inlay design to one side. Both plates show scenes from the Story of Tobias and an allegorical female figure in an oval set below. The alternative designs also show scenes from the same story and a female allegorical figure. Each handle has a nymph of the 'Fontainebleu' type set in the pommard. *Six illustrations on 2 plates; average size 104 × 42mm. Tipped on hand-made paper. In paper wallet.* £35

e **Four designs**
One plate with three designs, a central full design with a betrothal scene inscribed below 'S Math Chap 19' is flanked by 2 half designs with long inscriptions in French. Signed 'Io Theodori de Bry fe et excud'. The last design is cut to follow the contours, is inscribed in reverse 'II Reg XIII' and shows an inlay scene with a murder at a banquet. *Four designs on 2 plates; sizes 107 × 81mm and 93 × 22mm. Tipped on hand-made paper. In paper wallet.* £55

f **Three designs cut to follow contours. Two form a pair and are inscribed 'Te gunse gayne leven' and 'Van groot tot groten'**
Each with emblem, scene and mythological figure. The third design is similar and is inscribed 'Sine cap fedes' in reverse'. *Three plates, average size 75 × 18mm; mounted on old paper and tipped on hand-made paper. In paper wallet.* £25

913 Bry, Theo & Joa. de (Decoration for sword and daggar scabbards *Frankfurt c 1595*)
Tops and chapes of scabbards with grotesque decoration on black ground inset with medallions. The central decorations include winged putto or lion masks and female allegorical figures of which one is a Minerva, another Lucrezia. The plates are variously signed 'T·B·', 'Theo de Brij fe et excu' and 'I.D. de Brij fac'. *Six engraved designs on 3 plates; one previously cut through centre (separating the two designs) has been rejoined. Sizes vary from 71 × 62mm to 107 × 83mm. Tipped on hand-made paper and preserved in paper wallet.* £75

914 **Bry, Io Theo de & Theo de** (Jewelry and other ornaments *Frankfurt, the authors c 1590*)
Vigorous and attractive designs for belts, buckles, pins, rings and pendants with grotesque decoration on a black ground. Some beautifully imaginative forms intermingle flowers, birds, bees, butterflies and snails, masks, putti and small animals. One design for a pendant with a central oval medallion of Judith and Holofernes is signed 'Io. Theo de Bry', another armband design also has a central oval with Judith holding the head of Holofernes (Berlin Cat 631: 1, 4). Three further plates from Berlin Cat 630:3, Nagler Mon III 1618:15.
20 engraved designs on 6 plates; sizes vary from 17 × 77mm to 86 × 118mm (3 plates of approximately this latter size). Tipped on hand-made paper, preserved in paper wallet. £85

915 **Caglieri, Liborio** Compendio delle vite de santi orefici ed argentieri raccolto de diversi autori *Rome, Bernabo 1727*
Lives of St Eloi and other metalworking saints. Some of them are illustrated at work. *Quarto. (8) + 102 + (6)pp, engraved frontispiece, engraved title vignette and 14 engraved plates by Carlo Gregori. Contemporary vellum. Contents slightly browned.* £28

916 **Cellini, Benvenuto** The treatises of Benvenuto Cellini on goldsmithing and sculpture (made into English from the Italian of the Marcian Codex by C. R. Ashbee) *London, Essex House Press for Edward Arnold, April-October 1898*
The first book to issue from the Essex House Press was also another first – the first English translation of the two treatises on the methods and practice of the sculptor and goldsmith in the Renaissance as set down by that great cinquecento self publicist, Benvenuto Cellini. The publication was specifically intended as a workshop book for the pupils and craftsmen of the Guild of Handicrafts, (to whom it is dedicated) and was meant as a companion volume to J. A. Symonds translation of the 'Autobiography'. Although a practical work full of technical descriptions it is larded with amusing anecdotes and vivid pictures of a Renaissance workshop, and Ashbee has attempted to retain Cellini's graphic touch and narrative brilliance. The illustrations are reproductions of those used in the Plon monograph on Cellini (published in Paris in 1883). The work ends with a glossary of Italian technical terms. *Quarto. xiv + (2) + 164 + (4)pp with 4 woodcut diagrams in text and 11 photogravure full-p plates. Publisher's cloth. From a limited edition of 600 numbered copies.* £68

917 **Cellini, Benvenuto** The life of Benvenuto Cellini, translated from the Italian by John Addington Symonds *London, The Ballantyne Press, 1900*
Second edition of this particular translation, originally published in 1888. The work was decorated and the printing supervised by C. S. Ricketts, and it was seen through the press by C. J. Holmes, future editor of the Burlington Magazine and later director of the National Gallery. *Small folio. 2 vols clxxxci + (1)pp; clxxxciii + (2)pp. Publisher's paper boards, cloth spine, printed label.* £45

918 **Clifford, Anne** Cut-steel and Berlin iron jewellery *Bath, Adams & Dart 1971*
Brief but well-illustrated study of a type of jewelry of which there is otherwise no account in English – and hardly anything in any other language. *Octavo. 96pp, including 57 illustrations, with 4 colour plates. Original cloth.* £3

919 **Cotterell, Howard Herschel** Old pewter its makers and marks in England, Scotland and Ireland. An account of the old pewterer & his craft ... illustrating all known marks and all secondary marks *Rutland, Vermont, Tuttle 1963*
A reprint of English edition, 1929, the work is essential to the study of the subject and incorporates a list of no fewer than 5374 English pewterers. *Quarto. xxii + 432pp, with many text illustrations, and 76 plates. Original cloth.* £20

920 **(Courtauld)** Some silver wrought by the Courtauld family of London goldsmiths in the eighteenth century *Oxford, Shakespeare Head Press 1940*
One of a limited edition of 100 copies printed in red and black on hand-made paper. This

most handsome book describes the silver made by Augustine Courtauld (1686-1751), and by his son, daughter-in-law and grandson down to the 1770s. All the plate described and illustrated derives from the collections of members of the Courtauld family, for whom the volume was published. The historical introduction and technical descriptions are supplied by E. Alfred Jones (see item 940). *Folio. xii + 129 + (1)pp, with 64 plates (of which 4 are photogravure). Title is partly handcoloured. Original patterned boards, cloth spine. Uncut.* £225

921 **Curle, Alexander O.** The treasure of Traprain. A Scottish hoard of Roman silver plate *Glasgow, Maclehose Jackson 1923*

Handsome publication of a hoard of Roman silver bowls, vases and flagons discovered in 1919 on Traprain Law. *Quarto. xvi + 132pp, with 41 plates (some photogravure) and 70 text figs. Original cloth.* £35

922 **Darcel, Alfred** Trésor de l'église de Conques *Paris, Didron 1861*

Description of the superb collection of Carolingian and early mediaeval reliquaries and jewelry preserved at Conques. *Quarto. xii + 76 + (4)pp and 15 engraved plates. Original printed wrappers, repaired. Slightly dampstained.* £25

923 **Delieb, Eric** The Great Silver Manufactory. Matthew Boulton and the Birmingham silversmiths 1760-1790 *London, Studio Vista 1971*

Both the first full-length study of the silver manufacturing side of Boulton's Soho works, and an important contribution to Boulton's biography, tracing connections between Boulton and such people as Robert Adam and James and Samuel Wyatt. *Quarto. 144pp with many illustrations. Original cloth.* £8

924 **Evans, Joan** A history of jewellery 1100-1870. Second edition *London, Faber 1970*

Quarto. 224pp with 34 text figs, and 192pp of plates. Original cloth. £10

925 **(Fabergé, Carl)** A loan exhibition of the works of Carl Fabergé jeweller and goldsmith to the Imperial Court of Russia 1846-1920 *London, Wartski 1949*

Catalogue of the first post-revolution Fabergé exhibition, running to 383 items. Sacheverell Sitwell contributes a foreword. *Octavo. (4) + 28 + (4)pp including 2 coloured illustrations. Original wrappers.* £5

926 (Fabergé, Peter Carl) **Bainbridge, Henry Charles.** Peter Carl Fabergé goldsmith and jeweller to the Russian Imperial court and the principal crowned heads of Europe. An illustrated record and review of his life and work, A.D. 1846-1920 *London, Batsford 1949*

Biographical study, idiosyncratic and often irritating, but partly based on personal knowledge and informative throughout. The illustrations are very good. *Quarto. xxiv + 170pp and 126 plates (some coloured). Original cloth.* £30

927 **(Fizaine)** Catalogue of silverware *Paris (c 1880)*

Trade catalogue of a range of silver table ware, strong in salt cellars, cruets, sauce boats and tea pots, illustrated both by litho plates and actual photographs. The litho plates carry the address 'Paris, Fizaine, rue Notre-Dame-de-Nazareth, 45' at the bottom left corner and we assume that to be the firm of manufacturers involved. *Folio. 24 folio sheets measuring 600 × 450mm containing 118 objects numbered 1 to 118 reproduced in litho; sheets 1-8 are lithographed by Jannin, 9-11 carry no imprint and 12-24 are by Becquet Frères. There are also 8 mounted photographs. Preserved in cloth folder.* £95

928 **Giardini, Giovanni** Promptuarium artis argentariae ex quo, centum ... tabulis propositis, ... educi possunt novissimae ideae ad cujuscumque generis vasa argentea, ac aurea invenienda ac conficienda *Rome, Fausto Amideo 1750*

A collection of designs for gold and silverwork, in two books; the first part devoted to ecclesiastical instruments (chalices, reliquaries, monstrances, candelabra, incense burners), the second to secular pieces (lamps, candelabra, clocks, coffee pots with cups, table centres, stirrups and buckles).

Giardini (1646-1722), one of the most important silversmiths of his day in Italy, was born in Forli but worked in Rome from 1673 when he became a master silversmith. By 1677 he was successful enough to be employing four assistants and in 1699 was in charge of the Papal Foundry. Among his noted pieces in precious metals are a reliquary at Giubbio, a sword presented by the Pope to Prince Eugène of Savoy, two candlesticks for Cardinal Francesco Barbarini's private chapel, and a mace (now in the V & A Museum). Giardini also worked in other metals, casting artillary for the Castel Sant'Angelo, the Monte Cavallo clock bell, bronze decorations for Fontana's tomb of Queen Christina, and the lid of the font in St Peter's.

The designs show Giardini's varied, lively and vigorous style which is in the mainstream of Roman baroque with overtones of mannerism and just a hint of rococo forms. Although the artist was not an innovator and his designs had no perceptible influence outside Italy where fashions were changing, his forms were clearly the patterns adopted by the Italian silversmiths who, resisting the changing fashion, remained faithful to the baroque tradition. This is illustrated by the necessity for this posthumous reissue of the plates which had originally been published in 1714 under the title 'Disegni diversi'. The first book was then dedicated to Giardini's patron Pope Clement XI whose coat-of-arms appears on 17 plates; the second part was dedicated to the Roman Academy of Design. Giardini's drawings were formerly in the Berlin Kupferstischerkabinett and were engraved by Maximilian Joseph Limpach of Prague who worked with his brother in the Vatican printing works. Berlin Cat 1142. Our copy is an early issue of this second edition which strangely still retains the two dedication leaves of the first, and a plate dedicated to Clement XI. (We are indebted to Mr John Bury for the information in this description).

Folio. 2 letterpress titles each with engraved vignette, 2 engraved dedication leaves, and 100 engraved plates. Quarter calf, contemporary marbled-paper boards. **Illustration below.**

£225

928-9

929 **Giardini, Giovanni** Promptuarium artis argentariae *Rome, Fausto Amideo, 1750*

Standard issue of the previous item which omits the dedication leaves and has the inscription to Pope Clement XI (who had died in 1721) burnished out. *Folio. 2 letterpress titles with engraved vignettes, and 100 engraved plates. Quarter calf.* **Illustration on previous page.** £180

930 **Grande argenterie** *Schaffhausen & Neuchâtel (c 1900)*

Trade catalogue of silver plate manufacturers, not named but presumably Swiss as text and plates were printed respectively in Schaffhausen and Neuchatel. They produced napkin rings, tumblers, tea sets, sauce boats, etc. *Oblong quarto. Contents leaf and 50 photo plates. Original quarter morocco.* £36

931 **Grimwade, Arthur** Rococo silver 1727-1765 *London, Faber 1974*

Octavo. xxi+(1)+74pp and 96pp of plates, colour frontispiece. Original cloth. £8.50

932 **Hayward, J. F.** Huguenot silver in England 1688-1727 *London, Faber 1959*

Octavo. 89+(3)pp and 96pp of plates. Original cloth. £5

933 **Heal, Sir Ambrose** The London goldsmiths 1200-1800. A record of the names and addresses of the craftsmen their shop-signs and trade-cards *Cambridge University Press 1935 (David & Charles reprint 1972)*

Lists nearly 7000 goldsmiths, 1500 of their shop-signs and 350 trade-cards. *Octavo. xii+280pp text and 80pp of plates. Original cloth.* £6

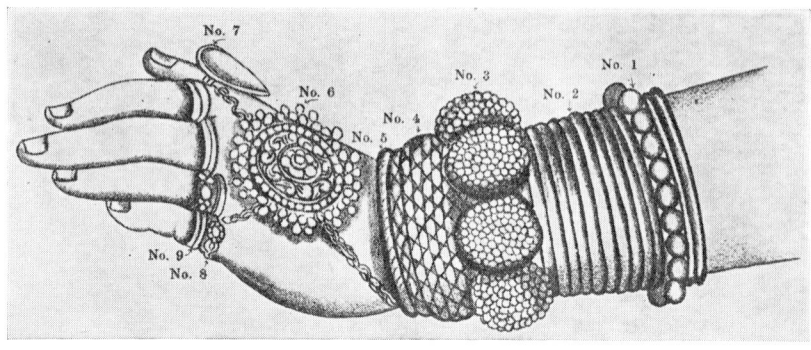

934

934 **(Hendley, T. H.)** The Journal of Indian Art and Industry, volume XII, nos. 95-107 *London, W. Griggs 1906-9*

These numbers of the Journal are entirely devoted to the publication in parts of Colonel Thomas Holbein Hendley's extensive study of Indian jewellery. Hendley (1847-1917) served for 27 years in Jaipur and Rajputana with the Indian Medical Service, and subsequently as Inspector General of Civil Hospitals, Bengal, and had opportunities for studying the jewelry both of major Muslim and Hindu rulers and of ordinary Indian citizens. He takes the jewelry of each part of India in turn, beginning with Delhi and then covering Rajputana and Malwa, the Punjab, the Bombay Presidency (including Aden), the Central Provinces, Madras, Bengal, Tibet, Nepal and Burma. Each of the thirteen parts includes twelve or more plates, of which two are usually coloured, and the whole work contains 189 pages of text and 167 plates, describing and illustrating 1,138 objects. *Folio. 13 parts in original printed paper wrappers. Mint condition.* **Illustration above.** £40

935 **Holland, Margaret** Old country silver. An account of English provincial silver, with sections on Ireland, Scotland and Wales *Newton Abbot, David & Charles 1971*
Octavo. 240pp, colour frontispiece and 16pp of plates. Original cloth. £3.50

936 **Holme, Charles** (editor) Modern design in jewellery and fans *London, The Studio 1902 (Special winter number for 1901-2)*
Essays on French, British, Austrian, German, Belgian and Danish jewelry etc. An important record of Art Nouveau taste. Aymer Vallance's contribution on British design recognizes the pre-eminence of Ashbee. *Octavo.(8)+6+8+10+8+4+4+4+(8)pp, 35+52+8+8+8+8 plates, 1 printed silk specimen. Cloth, original printed wrappers laid down on front and back covers.* £30

937 **Hughes, G. Bernard** Antique Sheffield plate *London, Batsford 1970*
Sheffield plate was first manufactured in the 1740s by Thomas Bolsover, and this is a history of the industry and of its products between then and the middle of the 19th century, with information on makers, marks and techniques. *Octavo. 304pp and 269 illustrations on plates. Original cloth.* £6

938 **Hughes, George Ravensworth** The Worshipful Company of Goldsmiths as patrons of their craft 1919-53 *London, Company of Goldsmiths 1965*
Quarto. (6)+62+(76)pp and many photo illustrations. Original wrappers. £2

939 **Jackson, Charles** An illustrated history of English plate ecclesiastical and secular, in which the development of form and decoration in the silver and gold work of the British Isles . . . is delineated and described *London, Holland Press 1967*
First published in 1911 but still the only complete study of the subject down to the end of the Georgian period. Over 1500 illustrations show everything from mustard pots to maces. *Quarto. 2 vols. xxxviii+(2)+466pp;(4)+(620)pp, with frontispiece, 76 plates and 1,506 text figures. Original cloth.* £30

940 **Jones, E. Alfred** The old royal plate in the Tower of London including the old silver communion vessels of the chapel of St Peter ad Vincula within the Tower *Oxford, Fox Jones 1908*
Scholarly, well-illustrated description of the royal plate – as distinct from the regalia – which includes standing salts, tankards, maces and trumpets. *Quarto. xxxiv+(2)+78+(2)pp with 6 text illustrations and 22 photogravure plates. Original cloth.* £28

941 **Julienne, (E) & E. Goesin** Journal du bijoutier *Paris (c 1865)*
Set of twenty litho plates of jewelry designs by Eugène Julienne from the 'Journal du Bijoutier', together with six plates of jewelry and ornament by Goesin. *Small folio. 26 litho plates. Quarter cloth.* £16

942 **King, Thomas, H.** Orféverie et ouvrages en métal du moyen-âge mésurés et dessinés d'après les anciens modèles *Bruges, 1852*
Measured drawings of mediaeval chalices, censers, lamps, ciboriums and other types of religious vessel. King intended them as working drawings from which craftsmen could copy. *Folio. 2 vols. Title leaf, 4+(2)pp and 100 plates (7 double-p); title leaf, 3+(1)pp and 100 plates (16 double-p). Contemporary quarter calf, neatly rebacked.* £120

943 (Lamerie, Paul de) **Phillips, Philip A. S.** Paul de Lamerie citizen and goldsmith of London, a study of his life and work A.D. 1688-1751 *London, Holland Press 1968*
Reprint of Phillips's biography, first published in 1935. Phillips discovered much new information on De Lamerie's family and career and established his connection with William Hogarth (who started in life as apprentice to a silver engraver). There are illustrations of a wide range of De Lamerie silver with accompanying descriptions. *Folio. xvi+116pp and 82pp of plates. Original cloth. Limited edition of 500 copies.* £18

944 **Le Pautre, Jean** (Vases ou burettes) *Paris, le Blond (c 1645)*
Early issue of these most interesting wine jugs, altar cruets, and oil pitchers, in the antique style as seen through Le Pautre's highly fertile imagination. The designs owe much to those of Polidoro (see item 1624) and are set (two to a plate) on long tables, against landscape or tapestry backgrounds, or within interiors with figures, and bordered with richly decorative frames. *Six numbered engraved plates, average size 155 × 220mm. Good margins. In paper wallet.* £45

945 **Le Pautre, Jean** Vases ou burettes à la romaine *Paris, Nicolas Langlois, 1661*
A similar suite to the previous item with the designs of the vases occupying more of the plate area, their handles more delicate and slender, and their settings those of ancient Rome similar to the manner depicted by Poussin. An early issue. (Oeuvres 99). Destailleurs Notices p 85. Guilmard p 75. *Six unnumbered engraved plates, average size 150 × 215mm. In paper wallet.* £45

946 **Le Pautre, (Jean)** (Salière et cartouches) *Paris, le Blond (c 1650)*
Untitled suite showing salt cellars within heavily decorated frames. One of the few suites of designs to give some idea of the form these pieces took in the early Louis XIV period. An early issue. (Oeuvre suite 105). Destailleur Notices p 103 (later issue). Guilmard p 74. *Six unnumbered plates, average size 147 × 216mm. Good margins. In paper wallet.* £60

947 **Le Pautre, (Jean)** (Torchère avec riches encadrements) *Paris, le Blond (c 1660)*
The only recorded issue of this suite of large candelabra with figures resting on intricate bases ornamented with leaf and animal motifs, the whole supporting a dish-like tray. The designs are set against landscape backgrounds and are contained within rich plastic frames. All such pieces at Versailles were executed in precious metals but the majority were melted down during the economic stringencies towards the end of the reign of Louis XIV. Destailleur Notices p 104. *Six unnumbered engraved plates, average size 300 × 220mm, with wide margins. In paper wallet.* £72

948 **Lewis, M. D. S.** Antique paste jewellery *London, Faber 1970*
A careful historical and technical account of a neglected and complex subject. *Octavo. 80pp with 18 text figures and 48pp of plates. Original cloth.* £5

949 **Massé, H. J. L. J.** The pewter collector. A guide to British pewter, with some reference to foreign work ... revised, with additions, by Ronald F. Michaelis *London, Barrie & Jenkins 1971*
Octavo. xiv + 280pp and 16pp of plates. Original cloth. £8

950 **Meissonier, J(uste Aurèle)** Chandelière de sculpture en argent *Paris, Huquier (c 1750)*
Meissonier, the designer who had the greatest single influence on the development of the rococo style, was first heard of as a designer of gold and silver, receiving his 'mastership' in 1724. This suite which shows the full flowering of his style is, in fact, three views of a candlestick with a spiralling form and putti, shown from different angles which give a totally different impression. It is an important suite, often lacking in otherwise complete copies of the 'Oeuvres'. According to Fiske Kimbal it is crucial in the origin of the 'genre pittoresque' showing it 'fully formed in the hands of Meissonier'. The piece was designed in 1728. Suite B from the 'Oeuvres'. Berlin Cat 378. *Three engraved plates including title, numbered 10-12 and lettered B. Average size 266 × 213mm, cut close to plate marks at top and bottom. Tipped on hand-made paper and preserved in matching wrappers.* £50

951 **Meissonier, (Juste Aurèle)** Huitième livre *Paris, Huquier (c 1750)*
Really beautiful designs which make excellent decorative plates. The suite, made up of thirty-five gold and silver designs includes the earliest works for the crown: sword-guards for the king's marriage regalia of 1725. The remaining designs consist of 12 most imaginative snuff-box designs based on variations of the shell palmette, tobacco-box lids with chased pictorial designs, a walking-stick head, and watch-backs using the 'morceau de

fantaisie' forms (see item 1503b). Suite H of the 'Oeuvres'. Berlin Cat 378. Destailleur Notices p 228. Guilmard p 155. *Six engraved plates numbered 49-54, lettered H. Sizes varying from 167 × 157mm to 303 × 222mm. Tipped on hand-made blue paper and preserved in matching wrappers.* £150

952 Meissonier, J(uste) A(urèle) Neuvième livre *Paris, Huquier (c 1750)*
Meissonier's flowing line and intricacy of form make these designs for table-silver quite breathtaking illustrations. They include designs for salt cellars, beautifully imaginative oil bottles, superb tureens and Meissonier's earliest known design: a finger-bowl for the Duc de Bourbon, made in 1723. These designs were very influential on porcelain makers in Saxony and England. Suite I of the 'Oeuvres'. Berlin Cat 378. Destailleurs Notices pp 228-9. Guilmard p 156. *Six engraved plates numbered 55-60, lettered I. Sizes varying from 180:250 × 237:321mm; one plate cut to plate mark on one side, otherwise good margins. Tipped on hand-made blue paper, in matching paper wallet.* **Illustration below.** £110

952

953 Meissonier, J(uste) A(urèle) Dixième livre *Paris, Huquier (c 1750)*
More stunning designs for table plate including bon-bon dishes, candelabra and candle snuffers, and a series of salt cellars whose shell forms provided the inspiration for several porcelain factories in the second half of the 18th century, among them those of Chelsea and Bow. Suite K of the 'Oeuvres'. Berlin Cat 378. Destailleur Notices p 229. Guilmard p 156. *Six engraved plates numbered 61-66. Sizes varying from 178:255 × 250:237mm. Three plates cut to plate mark on one side, otherwise good margins. Tipped on blue hand-made paper, in matching folder.* £110

954 Meissonier, J(uste) A(urèle) Livre d'orfèverie d'église. Troisième livre *Paris, Huquier (c 1750)*
More conventional than most of Meissonier's designs yet still rich in scrollwork and shell-like forms and with asymmetrical tendencies this suite includes designs for altar crosses, a chalice, a candlestick, a hanging lamp and an incense burner, and shows Meissonier's contribution to ecclesiastical silverwork. Suite N of the 'Oeuvres'. Berlin Cat 378. Destailleur Notices p 230. Guilmard p 156. *Six engraved plates numbered 78-83, lettered N. Two plates 480 × 220mm, the rest average 390 × 198mm, and are cut to plate mark at top and bottom. Tipped on blue hand-made paper; in matching wrappers.* £65

955 **Navarro, Antonio de** Causeries on English pewter *London, Country Life (c 1906)*
Octavo. xvii + (1) + 176pp including 72 plates. Original cloth. £10

956 **Oman, Charles** Caroline silver 1625-1688 *London, Faber 1970*
Octavo. 73 + (3)pp and 96pp of plates. Original cloth. £6

957 **(Parisien goldsmiths)** Les grands orfèvres de Louis XIII à Charles X *Paris, Hachette 1965*
A detailed account of Parisian goldsmiths and their products in the 17th-19th centuries, useful for its illustrations and a table of makers' marks as well as for its text. *Quarto. 336pp with many illustrations. Original cloth.* £15

958 **Pasini, Antonio** Il tesoro di San Marco in Venezia *Venice, Ongania 1886*
A description of the objects preserved in the treasury of the basilica (altar plate, reliquaries, vestments), with fine chromolithograph plates. The oldest pieces date from the Byzantine period and the quality of the early mediaeval goldsmiths' work – including the famous Pala d'Oro in the basilica proper – is most impressive. *Folio. Chromolitho frontispiece, xx + (2) + 153 + (21)pp and 100 chromolitho plates. Contemporary quarter morocco, ex library copy.* £30

959 **Patents for inventions** Abridgments of the specifications relating to watches, clocks, and other timekeepers. Abridgements . . . Part II A.D. 1857-1866. Abridgements . . . Part II A.D. 1867-1876 *London, Eyre & Spottiswoode 1858; 1871; 1883*
Octavo. 3 vols. viii + 130 + 10pp; xii + 176 + (4) + 15 + (1)pp; viii + 94 + (34)pp. Original printed paper wrappers. £18

960 **Pugin, A. Welby** Modèles d'orfèvrerie, argenterie, etc.-Modèles de ferronerie, serrurerie et bronzerie. Style des 15e et 16e siécles *Paris, Noblet et Baudry (c 1850)*
Mid 19th century undated French editions of Pugin's 'Designs for gold and silversmiths' and 'Designs for iron and brass work', showing his influence on contemporary French taste. *Quarto. 2 works in 1. Engraved title and 27 litho plates; engraved title and 26 litho plates. Contemporary quarter calf, marbled paper sides.* £18

961 **Report on Clock and Watch Makers Petitions** *London 1798*
Evidence submitted to a Committee of the House of Commons on the adverse effects for the clock trade of a recently imposed duty on clocks and watches. Manufacturers in Clerkenwell (the London centre of the industry) and Birmingham give details of its effect. *Quarto. 27 + (1)pp. Sheets, sewn as issued.* £15

962 **Rossi, Filippo** Chefs d'oeuvre de l'orfèvrerie *(Paris) Arts et métiers graphiques (1956)*
An illustrated record of Italian goldsmiths' work from the 13th century to the 18th century. *Quarto. 239 + (3)pp with text illustrations, coloured frontispiece and 83 coloured plates. Original cloth.* £15

963 **Rowe, Robert** Adam silver 1765-1795 *London, Faber 1965*
Silver of the age of Robert Adam – some of it designed by him – studied in the context of the establishment of the Birmingham and Sheffield Assay offices, with unpublished material from the papers of Matthew Boulton. *Octavo. 96pp text and 96pp of plates. Original cloth.* £6

964 (Sabattini, Lino) **Ponti, G. & B. Munari** Lino Sabattini *Milan, Bestetti 1972*
The work of a leading modern Italian silversmith. *Octavo. (74)pp of mainly photo illustrations. Original cloth.* £3

965 **Shaftoe, W(illia)m** (Representation of an antique silver plate decorated with bas reliefs) *London, the artist, 31st May 1736*
An exact, full size, representation of a silver salver weighing 148 ounces, found in the

sands of the river Tyne at Corbridge, Northumberland (the Roman garrison of Corstopitum on Hadrian's Wall) in 1735. The fine relief sculpture, the iconography of which is not clear, shows the deities Diana, Minerva, Ceres, Vesta and Apollo, together with various animals. The piece, which has a beautifully designed border of vine-leaves, fruit, and tendrils, is probably a ceremonial plate and is believed to date from the late fourth century A.D. The engraving, dedicated to the Duke of Somerset, on whose land the piece was found, was executed by Gerrard van der Gucht after Shaftoe's drawing. *Line engraving 465 × 522mm (18¼ × 20½ins). In paper wallet.* £30

966 Smith, H. Clifford Jewellery *London, Methuen 1908 (EP reprint, 1973)*
History of jewelry from Egyptian times, fullest on the 16th and 17th centuries. *Octavo. xlvii+(1)+410pp and 54 plates. Original cloth.* £6.75

967 Statz, Vincenz Gothische Einzelheiten. 6te partie. Gold, Silber, und Kupferarbeiten *Liège, Ch. Claesen 1867*
Part 6 of a series of drawings of Gothic details; this is the part that deals with metalwork. *Small folio. (2)pp and 38 litho plates (12 folding and 2 coloured). Contained in cloth folder preserving original printed paper front cover.* £18

968 Streeter & Co. Catalogue of gems *London, c 1895*
Trade catalogue with illustrations of the firm's jewelry, and a handbook to the various kinds of precious stones. *Octavo. 61+(3)pp including 28pp of colour-tinted illustrations of jewelry (330 items illustrated in all). Original cloth.* £10

969 (Tassie, James & William) Gray, John M. James and William Tassie. A biographical and critical sketch with a catalogue of their portrait medallions of modern personages. *Edinburgh, Patterson 1894*
James Tassie (1735-1799) developed a process for the reproduction in enamel paste of classical cameos and intaglios which made him an international reputation. He also modelled in wax, and cast in enamel, portrait medallions of many of his contemporaries – Gray catalogues 493 such medallions – which he exhibited at the Society of British Artists and the Royal Academy. Gray's book remains the only critical study of Tassie and of his nephew and successor, and his catalogue of the medallions – with notes on dimensions and signatures and the identity of the sitters – has not been superseded. *Octavo. xii+174pp and 18 plates. Original cloth, uncut.* £100

970 (Tassie, James & William) Gray, John M. James and William Tassie. A biographical and critical sketch *Edinburgh, 1894 (Holland Press reprint 1975)*
Octavo. 186pp and 18 plates. Original cloth. £10

971 Tatham, Charles Heathcote Designs for ornamental plate, many of which have been executed in silver, from original drawings *London, T. Gardiner 1806*
Most of these designs for plate are for candlesticks, candelabra and table ornaments. Tatham's patrons for whom these were executed included Lords Camden, Carlisle, Spencer and Yarborough and Sir Watkin Williams-Wynn. *Folio. (4)+3+(1)pp and 41 etched plates. Quarter calf, marbled paper boards.* £150

972 Ticher, Kurt Irish silver in the rococo period *Shannon, Irish University Press 1972*
Octavo. (8)+28+(2)pp and 112pp of photo plates. Original cloth. £5

973 J. J. Wainwright & Co. Price list of jewellery and all the latest novelties *Birmingham, 1882*
Catalogue of a firm of Birmingham jewellers, full of the trinkets and small heavily decorated items of jewelry for which Birmingham was famous, and not free from whimsy; their latest novelty was 'Ye Spider and Ye Flie' jewelry. *Octavo. 40pp, many illustrations. Original wrappers.* £10

974 **Wardle, Patricia** Victorian silver and silver-plate *London, Barrie & Jenkins 1970*
Coverage of silversmiths (Armstead, Morel Ladeuil, Dresser), plate manufacturers (Elkingtons of Birmingham) and external patronage and influences. *Octavo. 238pp with 22 text figures, and 48pp of photo plates. Original cloth.* £2.50

975 **Waring, J. B.** (editor) Examples of metal-work & jewellery, selected from the Royal and other collections. Edited by J. B. Waring. Chromo-lithographed by F. Bedford. Drawings on wood by R. C. Dudley. With an essay by M. Digby Wyatt, architect *London, Day & Son 1857*
Waring and Matthew Digby Wyatt collaborated in a number of publications which gave expression to the taste and mid-Victorian artistic ideals which Owen Jones and others had formulated and which flourished in the years following the Great Exhibition. Here Wyatt describes and sumptuous chromo-litho plates illustrate a range of jewellery, plate and armour. *Folio. (38)pp, chromolitho title and 17 chromolitho plates. Original gilt decorated cloth.* £85

976 **Wilkinson, Wynyard R. T.** Indian colonial silver. European silversmiths in India (1790-1860) and their marks *London, Argent Press 1973*
Surprisingly enough, the first book published on this subject. Excellent photographic illustrations of marks. Limited edition. *Quarto. viii + 172pp with over 200 illustrations. Original cloth.* £12

977 **(Will, Jean Martin)** Des encensoirs à la mode antique *Augsburg, Jean Martin Will (c 1785)*
A suite of incense burners, one of a series of plates published by Will which showed the new neo-classical style applied to the design of small pieces. Most were derived from French examples or were direct copies of the current Parisien designers. Berlin Cat 188. Guilmard p 460. *Four etched plates, numbered suite 99:1-4. In paper wallet.* £25

978 **Wilson, H.** Silverwork and jewellery. A text-book for students and workers in metal. *London, John Hogg 1903*
A volume in the series of 'Handbooks on the Artistic Crafts' edited by Lethaby (see item 101). *Octavo. 356 + (2)pp including 16 plates and 169 text figures. Original boards, cloth spine.* £8

979 **Wyatt, M. Digby** Metal-work and its artistic design *London, Day & Son 1852*
A substantial contribution to the literature of metalwork, with lengthy essays on the theory of metal design, on metalworking techniques and on the history of the subject. It also has Day & Son's usual splendid plates, chromolithographed by Bedford from drawings of Renaissance and mediaeval metalwork; the drawings are by Wyatt, Burges, F. C. Penrose, Charles Barry junior and others. *Folio. (iv) + lii pp and 50 chromolitho plates (including title). Original gilt stamped cloth, rebacked.* £160

980 **Wyatt, M. Digby** Specimens of ornamental art workmanship in gold, silver, iron, brass, and bronze, from the twelfth to the nineteenth centuries. Fifty large plates in gold and colours, of the choicest examples, with a history of the art in Italy, England, France, Germany, and Spain; together with its theory and practice *London, Day & Son 1852*
Wyatt's considered views on decorative metalwork, handsomely illustrated by chromolitho plates by Bedford. Wyatt (1820-1877) was exceptional among architects of his age and standing for his knowledge of the fine arts and his European horizons and in 1851 had been made Secretary to the executive committee of the Great Exhibition. Burges was his pupil and he pays generous tribute to Burges's 'deep study of the mediaeval arts' in his preface. *Large folio. Chromolitho title, letterpress title in red and blue, lii + (2) + 81 + (1)pp and 49 chromolitho plates (numbered to 50 to include title). Original gilt and blind stamped cloth.* £165

GOLD, SILVER AND JEWELRY 161

981 **Yapp, G. W.** Metal-work. Illustrating the chief processes of art-work applied by the goldsmith, silversmith, jeweller, brass, copper, iron and steel worker, bronzist, etc. etc. *London, Virtue (c 1880)*
Companion volume to Yapp's Art Industry (item 798). *Folio. vi + 76pp and 104 + 61 + 58 + 41 + 28 + 25 + 3 chromolitho plates. Cloth.* £75

982 **Younghusband, Sir George & Cyril Davenport** The crown jewels of England *London, Cassell 1919*
Illustrated description of the regalia by the Keeper of the Jewel House in the Tower of London and a colleague. *Small folio. viii + (4) + 84pp, coloured frontispiece and 18 coloured plates. Original cloth. Ex library.* £10

983

983 **Aveline, P(ierre)** Livre de têtes antiques gravées d'après les pierres et cornalines du Cabinet du Roy *Paris, Francois Chereau 1754*
Portraits taken from the most famous of the French collections of gems show 5 heads of women, 7 famous Roman men, 6 mythological figures and the rest anonymous. Guilmard p 173 declares that this suite of engravings is recorded but that he himself had never seen it. *Engraved decorative title and 20 numbered engraved plates, average size 145 × 103mm. Laid on old blue paper, preserved in paper wallet.* **Illustration above.** £65

984 **Braun, Edmund Wilh.** Die Silberkammer eines Reichsfursten (das Lobkowitz'sche Inventar). Werke Deutscher Goldschmiedekunst der Spatgotik und Renaissance *Leipzig, Klinkhardt & Biermann 1923*
A 17th century inventory, illustrated by contemporary drawings (reproduced in facsimile), of the Lobkowicz family's gold and silver plate. *Octavo. 32pp, with 36 photo plates. Original boards.* £15

985 **Caldicott, J. W.** The values of old English silver and Sheffield plate, from the XVth to the XIXth centuries *London, Bemrose 1906*
A guide to silver prices for collectors, not of much use in that direction today but still interesting for its illustrations of silver objects and details of their dimensions and weights. *Large quarto. (10) + 293 + (5)pp, with 87 plates. Original cloth.* £12

986 **Markham, Christopher A.** Pewter marks and old pewter ware domestic and ecclesiastical *London, Reeves & Turner 1909*
Octavo. xvi + 316pp with 102 text illustrations and 2 plates. Original gilt decorated cloth. £8

987 **(Recueil de pierres gravées antiques)** (*Paris, c 1780*)
A collection of fine quality French engravings of cameos, without a title-page and the plates giving a caption and indication of the type of stone but no signature of the engraver. The majority of the gems are heads, principally of famous Romans, while others are of animals and mythological figures, and a few show inscriptions. A final group of plates illustrate engraved stones of a later date with busts of kings, emperors and popes, from Frederick Barbarossa to Pope Julius II, and including Elizabeth of England. *Quarto. 76 engraved plates numbered 1-25, 27-76, 2*. Cloth boards, morocco spine gilt.* £45

988 **Spilsbury, John** A collection of fifty prints from antique gems, in the collections of The Right Honourable Earl Percy, The Honourable C. F. Greville, and T. M. Slade, Esquire *London, John Boydell 1st January 1785*
The only known publication of John Spilsbury who kept a print shop in Covent Garden and sold the works of his better known brother, Jonathan. The standard of engraving is about what one would expect but many of the gems are interesting. Charles Greville, who owned over half of the originals, was the nephew of Sir William Hamilton. Perhaps his greatest claim to fame was a 'discreet arrangement' with his uncle, after which Greville's mistress left London for Naples and independent fame as Lady Hamilton, but the two men also swapped other gems, some of which are recorded here. *Quarto. (4)pp and 50 numbered engraved plates (of which 7 laid in). Contemporary marbled-paper boards, quarter calf.* £60

989 **Vico, Aeneas** Ex gemmes et cameis antiquorum aliquot monumenta ab Aenea Vico Parmen incis per illustri et excellent. mo D.o D Dominico Panarolo Rom.o in patrio Lyceo medicine professori *Rome, Gio. Giacomo de Rossi (c 1660)*
A little known and generally uncatalogued suite of engravings by Aeneas Vico which concentrates on reproducing mythological scenes and standard figure groups which formed part of the iconography of classical Roman art and provided much source material for Renaissance and later artists. Several of the illustrations show Bacchanalian revelries, sacrificial rituals, the heroes of mythology and classical groups and events such as the Birth of Venus, a triton and nereid, Bellerophon and Pegasus, Apollo and Daphne, etc. *34 engraved plates including decorative engraved title; size varying from 85 × 72mm to 95 × 145mm. Laid on old blue paper, preserved in paper wallet.* £125

990 **Cassini, Giovanni Maria** Novus thesaurus gemmarum veterum ex insignioribus dactyliothecis selectarum cum explicationibus *Rome, the author 1797*
A very handsome set of this collection of 400 engraved plates of gems and ornament, issued in four separate volumes in 1780, 1782, 1786 and 1797 and exceedingly scarce in this collected form. The publication is based on material collected by Antonio Francesco Gori (1691-1757) for a new edition of his 'Thesaurus Gemmarum Antiquarum' of 1750, and the gems are engraved against ornamental backgrounds based on motifs from Raphael's Vatican Loggie and from the frescoes of the Baths of Titus. The drawings for the plates were done by Vincenzo Brenna (1745-1820), architect and painter who later worked in Poland and Russia, designing the Imperial Library at St. Petersburg. The engraver, Giovanni Maria Cassini, a pupil of Piranesi who specialized in architectural and perspective views of Rome, seems at first to have taken a subordinate part in the publication – the preface to the first volume suggests that the original impetus to it was given by Venanzio Monaldini – but later took on the entire responsibility for it.
The engravings are arranged in suites of ten. Within each suite the ornamental backgrounds are repeated for each plate and only the gem representation in the centre changes. The style of the plates is classical, with arabesque patterns and grotesques, gryphons, etc.
Works of reference commonly list this book as by Giovanni Battista Passeri (1694-1780), whose classification of gems under 24 headings is printed in volume 1 (pp 1-12), but Passeri died before the publication of the first volume and had no connection with the later ones. Guilmard p 337 (vols 1 & 2 only). Cicognara 2960. Brunet IV p 420. Not in Berlin Cat. or Avery. *Folio. 4 vols. Engraved title, iv + 28 + (2)pp, 100 engraved plates; engraved title, xxiv + 24pp, with (1) + 100 engraved plates; engraved title, xv + (1) + 19 + (1)pp, with (1) + 100 engraved plates; engraved title, engraved dedication leaf, (4) + 16pp, with 100 engraved plates. Contemporary quarter mottled calf, gilt tooled spines, patterned paper boards. From the library of John, Duke of Bedford, with his bookplate.* £1250

Ceramics

1001 b

1001 **Diderot, D. & J. L. d'Alembert** (Encyclopédie). Recueil de planches sur les sciences, les arts libéraux, les arts méchaniques, avec leurs explication *Paris, Briasson, David, Le Breton & Durand 1762-72, Livorno 1772-79*

Extracts of the sections relating to ceramics. See item 1701 in the catalogue for a detailed description of the background to the plates. *Each section listed is folio and preserved in a paper wallet.*

a **Potier de terre** (Earthenware potter)
View of a small pottery shop where earthenware stoves, pipes, ovens, and containers for chemicals are made. Three plates show the various types of vessels and objects, 4 plates details of a simple wheel, 4 plates of a compound wheel, and 4 plates of a special potters wheel. *18 engraved plates of which 1 double-page with over 200 illustrations, and 3 + (1 blank)pp.* £30

b **Fayancerie** (China potter)
Two vignettes show a pottery yard with the pits for storing and preparing the clay, and the interior of a finishing shed with racks of pots drying out. The other illustrations include plates of finished articles (78 illustrations), tools and utensils including various types of wheels, molds, and saggers, plans, elevation, and a sectional view of an up-draught kiln, and a plate of clay mills including a view of a horse-turned wheel. The explanation to the plates is preceded by short notes on the history of ceramics in France, types of clay, processes before firing, ways of placing the pots in the kiln, and details of various types of pottery.
12 engraved plates with 187 illustrations, and 5 + (1 blank) pp. **Illustration above.** £38

1002 (Allen, Herbert). **Rackham, Bernard** Victoria and Albert Museum. Department of Ceramics. Catalogue of the Herbert Allen collection of English porcelain *London, HMSO 1923*
Rackham's notes on the history of individual factories and his descriptions of the pieces (indicating artists and provenances) make this more than just a catalogue. *Octavo. Frontispiece, xvi + 172pp and 100pp of plates. Original cloth.* £16

1003 **Andrae, Walter** Coloured ceramics from Ashur and earlier ancient Assyrian wall-paintings *London, Kegan Paul 1925*
Sumptuous publication of ceramic objects and glazed wall paintings discovered in the Deutsche Orient-Gesellschaft's excavations in and around the Assyrian city of Ashur. *Large folio. xii + 78pp and 36 coloured plates, 48 text illustrations. Original cloth.* £65

1004 **Barnard, Julian** Victorian ceramic tiles *London, Studio Vista 1972*
Basically a study of the ceramic tile industry in Britain between 1830 and 1900, with much information on manufacturers, styles and designers. It also includes a section on American art-tile companies. *Quarto. 184pp with 115 illustrations on 72pp of plates. Original cloth.*
£4.80

1005 **Barrett, Franklin A.** Worcester porcelain and Lund's Bristol. Second edition *London, Faber 1966*
This is an entirely rewritten version of the 1953 first edition, which it replaces. *Octavo. 92 + (2)pp and 96pp of plates, 8 colour plates. Original cloth.* £6

1006 **Barrett, Franklin A. & Arthur L. Thorpe** Derby porcelain 1750-1848 *London, Faber 1971*
Octavo. 206 + (2)pp and 96pp of plates, 8 colour plates. Original cloth. £10

1007 **Bell, R. C.** Tyneside pottery *London, Studio Vista 1971*
Pottery produced in and around Newcastle from 1740 to modern times. *Quarto. 152pp with many illustrations. Original cloth.* £5

1008 **(Bennett, Richard)** Catalogue of the collection of old Chinese porcelains formed by Richard Bennett, Esq. Thornby Hall, Nottingham *London, Gorer (1911)*
Quarto. 80pp and 58 coloured plates. Original cloth. £18

1009 **Berendsen, Anne (and others)** Tiles. A general history *London, Faber 1967*
The only comprehensive book on the subject in English, and contains an extensive and well-illustrated section on Delft tiles. *Small folio. 286pp with many illustrations, some coloured. Original cloth.* £10

1010 **Berling, Karl** Das Meissner Porzellan und seine Geschichte *Leipzig, Brockhaus 1900*
History of Meissen porcelain which is both scholarly and well illustrated – and very handsomely produced. The author was Director of the Kunstgewerbe Museum at Dresden and had access to much archive material as well as to specimens of all periods of Meissen. *Folio. xvii + (1) + 211 + (1)pp with 219 text illustrations and, 30 plates (of which 15 are chromolitho and the remainder photogravure) and a double-page table of marks. Original decorated cloth, gilt edges.* £185

1011 **Blacker, J. F.** The ABC of collecting old continental pottery *London, Stanley Paul 1913*
A more scholarly work than the title might suggest, and covering Hispano-Moresque and Persian pottery as well as European. *Octavo. 316pp and 48 plates. Original cloth, partly uncut.* £9

1012 **Blunt, Reginald** The Cheyne Book of Chelsea china and pottery *London, 1924 (EP reprint, 1973)*
This reprint has a very informative introduction by J. V. G. Mallet and a bibliography. *Octavo. xxxviii + 132pp and 56 plates.* £3.50

1013 **Brears, Peter C. D.** The English country pottery. Its history and techniques *Newton Abbot, David & Charles 1971*
A thorough study of local English earthenware incorporating much original research. All in all one of the best books on the history, techniques and materials of the English potter. *Octavo. 266pp, colour frontispiece, 8pp of plates and 31 text illustrations.* £3.75

1014 **Brongniart, Alex** Traité des arts céramiques ou des poteries considérées dans leur histoire, leur pratique et leur théorie ... deuxième édition, revue, corrigée et augmentée de notes et d'additions, par Alphonse Salvetat *Paris, Béchet jeune 1854*
Second, revised edition of Brongniart's treatise on pottery and porcelain manufacture and manufacturers. As director of the Sèvres factory he had a wide acquaintance with potters in other countries; he was also interested in archaeology and his book is both a historical account of the subject from pre-Roman times and a very full guide to the pottery industry of his own time. The plates illustrate technical processes from a wide variety of countries and periods. *Octavo. 3 vols (1 oblong). xxxi + (1) + 694 + (2)pp and litho map, text figures; iv + 762pp with text figs; (4) + 80pp and 60 litho plates, 3 folding tables. Contemporary quarter morocco, marbled paper boards, with gilt device of Duc de Mouchy on spine and his armorial bookplates.* **Illustration below.** £95

1014

1015 **Brown, William Norman** The art of enamelling on metal *London, Scott Greenwood 1900*
Octavo. 60pp with 28 text figures. Original cloth. £4

1016 **Burlington Fine Arts Club** Catalogue of a collection of European enamels from the earliest date to the end of the XVII century *London, 1897*
Quarto. xxxii + 82pp and 72 photo plates (some coloured). Original cloth. £20

1017 **Burlington Fine Arts Club** Exhibition of early Chinese pottery and porcelain *London, 1911*
Good exhibition largely based on the Eumorfopoulos collection and organized by R. L. Hobson who contributes a scholarly introduction. *Folio. xli + (3) + 97 + (1)pp and 58 plates (chromolitho and collotype). Original cloth.* £48

1018 **Burlington Fine Arts Club** Exhibition of early English earthenware *London, 1914*
A comprehensive exhibition of English pottery to the mid 18th century. There is a preface by J. W. L. Glaisher. *Quarto. xlvi+(2)+150+(2)pp, frontispiece and 50 photo plates. Original cloth.* £42

1019 **Burton, William** A history and description of English porcelain *London, 1902 (EP reprint 1972)*
Octavo. vi+xii+196pp, with 35 plates and 90 other illustrations. Original cloth. £3.50

1020 **Burton, William** A general history of porcelain *London, Cassell 1921*
Comprehensive treatment of the whole field (Chinese, European, English). *Octavo. 2 vols xviii+204pp, colour frontispiece and 65 plates (21 colour); ix+(1)+228pp, colour frontispiece and 45 plates (9 colour). Original cloth, uncut.* £24

1021 **Bushnell, G. H. S. & Adrian Digby** Ancient American pottery *London, Faber 1955*
The pottery of Peru, Mexico and other pre-European civilizations in America. *Octavo. xii+52pp and 80pp of plates, 4 colour plates. Original cloth.* £3

1022 **Butler, A. J.** Islamic pottery. A study mainly historical *London, Benn 1926*
History of Islamic pottery up to the 16th century, at its fullest when dealing with Egyptian lustre ware but also covering the pottery of Spain, North Africa, Persia and Turkey and still an authoritative work of reference. The illustrations are very effective. *Large folio. xxv+(1)+179+(1)pp and 92 plates (some coloured). Original cloth.* £80

1023 **Cahiers de la céramique et des arts du feu** Revue trimestrielle *Sèvres, Société des amis du Musée National de Ceramique 1955-7. Nos. 1-6*
Quarto. Original wrappers, preserved in publishers' dropback box. £18

1024 **(Castleford Pottery)** The Castleford Pottery pattern book 1796 with a preface by Peter Walton, an historical note by Heather Lawrence and a comparison with the pattern book of the Leeds Pottery *Wakefield, EP 1973*
Reprint of a pattern book published by Messrs. Dunderdale of Castleford in 1796; the 1796 title is printed in French and Spanish which shows Dunderdales' reliance on the export trade. *Quarto. xviii+(8)pp and 57 plates. Original cloth.* £2.50

1025 **Chamot, M.** English mediaeval enamels *London, Benn 1930*
A catalogue of the thirty-six surviving examples of English enamel work of the Middle Ages, with a historical commentary. *Quarto. xii+49+(3)pp and 20pp of plates. Original cloth.* £17

1026 **(Chinese & Japanese porcelain)** Versteigerung von Ostasiatischer Keramik von der Han-Periode bis zum 19 Jahrhundert sowie von Gegenständen des Ostasiatischen Kunstgewerbes aus Privatbesitz *Vienna, Glückselig & Wärndorfer 1923*
Sale catalogue of 176 pieces of Chinese and Japanese porcelain from two important private collections. *Folio. 20pp and 14 mounted photographs. Original wrappers.* £9

1027 **Church, W. A.** Patterns of inlaid tiles, from churches in the diocese of Oxford, drawn and engraved by W. A. Church *Wallingford, J. G. Payne 1845*
Small quarto. 3ff and 24 two-tone litho plates. Original wrappers, repaired. £15

1028 **Cooper, Ronald G.** English slipware dishes 1650-1850 *London, Tiranti 1968*
A general history of English slipware, which lists the surviving work of such potters as Thomas and Ralph Toft, Talor, Simpson and Samuel Malkin. *Octavo. vi + 144pp with 84 text illustrations and 160pp of plates carrying illustrations numbered 85-333. Original cloth.* £5

1029 **Coysh, A. W.** Blue and white transfer ware 1780-1840 *Newton Abbot, David & Charles 1974*
Second edition, revised. Includes details of many lesser known firms who specialized in blue-and-white and willow pattern wares. *Quarto. 112pp and 171 photo illustrations. Original cloth.* £3.75

1030 **Coysh, A. W.** Blue-printed earthenware 1800-1850 *Newton Abbot, David & Charles 1972*
Octavo. 112pp and 155 photo illustrations. Original cloth. £3.25

1031 **Cushion, J. P. & W. B. Honey** Handbook of pottery and porcelain marks. Third edition *London, Faber 1965*
Octavo. 478pp with illustrations of marks throughout. Original cloth. £5.50

1032 **Dennis, Richard** Catalogue of an exhibition of Doulton stoneware and terracotta 1870-1925. *London, the author 1971*
A very fully illustrated catalogue of Dennis's large collection as exhibited in London in 1971. *Quarto. (266)pp with over 600 illustrations. Original wrappers.* £5

1033 **Dennis, Richard** Catalogue of an exhibition of pottery at the Fine Art Society. William Moorcroft and Walter Moorcroft 1897-1973. December 1973 *London, Dennis 1973*
An extensive range of Moorcroft pottery, with illustrations of all 494 items. *Small folio. 128pp with illustrations. Original wrappers.* £5

1034 **Donnelly, P. J.** Blanc de Chine. The porcelain of Tehua in Fukien *London, Faber 1969*
Octavo. xiv + 407 + (3)pp and 160pp of plates, 6 colour plates. Original cloth. £15

1035 **Duhamel du Monceau, (Henri Louis)** (Description des arts et des métiers). L'art du potier de terre *Paris, 1773*
Duhamel was the main force behind the Académie Royale de Sciences' publications. This section describes the processes involved in pottery, with special reference to earthenware and to tiles (well illustrated); and has a chapter of 'Observations sur les fabriques de poteries d'Angleterre année 1765', which unexpectedly has more to say on potteries round Newcastle-upon-Tyne than on Staffordshire. *Folio. Title, 84pp and 17 engraved plates (plate 17 repaired for corner tear). Quarter calf.* £90

1036 **Du Sartel, O.** La porcelaine de Chine. Origines; fabrication, décors et marques; la porcelaine de Chine en Europe; classement chronologique; imitations, contrefaçons *Paris, Morel 1881*
A scholarly study. Only 110 copies appear to have been printed. *Folio. (4) + iii + (1) + 230 + (2)pp with 120 text figures and 32 plates (of which 18 chromolitho). Original cloth portfolio, repaired.* £85

1037 **Eaglestone, Arthur A. & T. A. Lockett** The Rockingham pottery... new revised edition *Newton Abbot, David & Charles 1973*
New edition which incorporates the results of the latest research. *Octavo. 160pp. Original cloth.* £3.25

1038 **English Ceramic Circle** The English Ceramic Circle 1927-1948. English pottery and porcelain. Commemorative catalogue of an exhibition held at the Victoria and Albert Museum *London, Routledge 1949*

The exhibits, representing all aspects of 17th and 18th century English ceramics, were contributed by such eminent collectors as Lord Fisher, Dyson Perrins and F. Severne Mackenna. *Folio. xvi + 96pp and 120pp of plates. Limited edition. Original cloth.* £38

1039 **Falkner, Frank** The Wood family of Burslem. With a note on the author by Michael Robert Parkinson *Wakefield, 1972*

Reprint of Falkner's book on the Wood family of potters, first published in 191 2 *Quarto. 118pp and 56 plates, folding table. Original cloth.* £4

1040 **Fisher, Alexander** The art of enamelling upon metal. With a short appendix concerning miniature painting on enamel *London, The Studio 1906*

The illustrations include examples of the author's own enamel painting in a Burne-Jones derived manner. *Quarto. (8) + 38 + (2)pp and 24pp of monochrome plates, 2 colour plates. Original quarter cloth.* £15

1041 **(Franks, Augustus)** Bethnal Green Museum. Catalogue of a collection of oriental porcelain and pottery, lent for exhibition, and described by Augustus W. Franks. Second edition, revised *London, Eyre and Spottiswoode 1879*

Franks (1826-97), on the staff of the British Museum 1851-96, was one of the earliest British collectors of oriental ceramics in a systematic way and the collection catalogued here – with full descriptions, notes and measurements – was presented by him to the British Museum in 1884. *Octavo. xviii + 246pp and 25 plates numbered I-XVIII and A-G Original cloth. This copy has two letters from Franks dated 3 July and 24 August 1880 loosely inserted.* £35

1042 **Furnival, William James** Leadless decorative tiles, faience, and mosaic comprising notes and excerpts on the history, materials, manufacture & use of ornamental flooring tiles, ceramic mosaic, and decorative tiles and faience. With complete series of recipes for tile-bodies, and for leadless glazes and art-tile enamels *Stone, the author 1904*

An admirable history of the tile industry in Europe, Asia and America, and of the tile-making process. Coverage of all the major manufacturers and interesting historical notes on Persian, Indian and Chinese use of decorative tilework. *Octavo. xxii + (2) + 852pp, with 37 plates and 340 illustrations. Original cloth, covers slightly stained but otherwise sound.* £45

1043 **Garner, Harry** Oriental blue and white. Third edition *London, Faber 1973*

Octavo. xxx + 86pp and 100pp of plates, 10 colour plates. Original cloth. £6.75

1044 **Garner, F. H. & Michael Archer** English Delftware. Second, enlarged and revised edition *London, Faber 1972*

Octavo. xxi + (1) + 103 + (1)pp and 136pp of plates, 8 other coloured plates. Original cloth. £7.50

1045 **Giacomotti, Jeanne** French faience *New York, Universe 1963*

A full account of 17th and 18th century faience, covering every region of France and extensively illustrated. *Quarto. (2) + 266 + (4)pp with 52 colour plates and 133 photo illustrations in text. Original cloth.* £9

1046 **Godden, Geoffrey A.** Minton pottery & porcelain of the first period 1793-1850 *London, Herbert Jenkins 1968*

Quarto. xvi + 168pp and 82pp of plates, 12 colour plates. Original cloth. £10

1047 **Godden, Geoffrey A.** Caughley and Worcester porcelains 1775-1800 *London, Herbert Jenkins 1969*
Quarto. xxii + 166pp and 160pp of plates, 10 other colour plates. Original cloth.   £10

1048 **Godden, Geoffrey A.** The illustrated guide to Lowestoft porcelain *London, Herbert Jenkins 1969*
Octavo. xix + (1) + 164pp and 112pp of plates, 8 colour plates. Original cloth.   £5.50

1049 **Godden, Geoffrey A.** Coalport and Coalbrookdale porcelains *London, Herbert Jenkins 1970*
Quarto. xiv + (2) + 156pp and 144pp of plates, 10 coloured plates. Original cloth.   £10

1050 **Godden, Geoffrey A.** Victorian porcelain *London, Barrie & Jenkins 1970*
A general history, with chapters on the principal manufacturers (Coalport, Copeland, Derby, Minton, Worcester) and on the main developments in design. Octavo. 222pp including 102 illustrations. Original cloth.   £3.50

1051 **Godden, Geoffrey A.** Encyclopaedia of British pottery and porcelain marks *London, Barrie & Jenkins 1970*
The only comprehensive encyclopaedia of British marks, illustrating over 4000 of them. Octavo. 766pp and 8pp of plates. Original cloth.   £20

1052 **Godden, Geoffrey A.** The illustrated guide to Mason's Patent Ironstone china *London, Barrie & Jenkins 1971*
Octavo. xiv + 175 + (1)pp and 80pp of plates, 8 colour plates. Original cloth.   £6

1053 **Godden, Geoffrey A.** The illustrated guide to Ridgway porcelains *London, Barrie & Jenkins 1972*
Octavo. xviii + 93 + (1)pp and 80pp of plates, 8 colour plates. Original cloth.   £6

1054 **Godden, Geoffrey A.** British porcelain. An illustrated guide *London, Barrie & Jenkins 1974*
Alphabetically arranged guide to the products of forty major factories, useful for those not recently studied separately. Octavo. 451 + (1)pp including 567 illustrations. Original cloth.   £20

1055 **Gompertz, G. St.G. M.** Korean celadon and other wares of the Koryo period *London, Faber 1963*
Octavo. xviii + 102pp and 96pp of plates, 6 colour plates. Original cloth.   £6

1056 **Gompertz, G. St.G. M.** Korean pottery and porcelain of the Yi period *London, Faber 1968*
Octavo. xx + 106 + (2)pp and 120pp of plates, 8 colour plates. Original cloth.   £6.50

1057 **Gompertz, G. St.G. M.** Celadon wares *London, Faber 1968*
Octavo. 104pp and 36pp of plates, 4 colour plates. Original cloth.   £5

1058 **Green, David** Pottery, Materials and techniques *London, Faber 1972*
Guide to basic techniques for the student. Quarto. 148pp with text illustrations. Original cloth.   £3.50

1059 **Hall, H. Byng** The bric-a-brac hunter; or, chapters on chinamania *London, Chatto & Windus 1875*
Octavo. ix + (3) + 290pp, with an actual photograph of Major Byng Hall captioned 'The bric-a-brac hunter at home'. Original decorated cloth.   £10

1060 (Hancock, Robert) **Ballantyne, A. Randal** Robert Hancock and his works *London, Chiswick Press, 1885*
Describes his varied artistic activities, and includes a catalogue of known works. A well-known portraitist and engraver, Hancock's most famous work was transfer-printing his designs on to china for the Worcester Porcelain Co. *Small quarto. viii + (2) + 51 + (1 blank) + 8pp and 12 plates. Publisher's boards, author's complimentary copy, uncut.* £65

1061 **Haslem, John** The old Derby china factory: the workmen and their productions *London, Bell 1876 (EP reprint, 1973)*
Octavo. xvi + xvi + 256pp and 11 plates. Original cloth. £3.50

1062 **Hayden, Arthur** Spode and his successors. A history of the pottery Stoke-on-Trent, from 1765-1865 *London, Cassell 1925*
As a history of the Spode firm now superseded by item 1187, but this is still interesting on technique and on the history of the pottery industry in general. The illustrations are good. *Octavo. xxiii + (1) + 204pp and 82 plates (24 colour). Limited edition. Original cloth.* £18

1063 **Higgins, R. A.** Greek terracottas *London, Methuen 1967*
Terracotta figures of the classical period. *Quarto. liv + 170pp and 64pp of plates, 4 colour plates. Original cloth.* £7

1064 **Hillier, Bevis** Master potters of the Industrial Revolution. The Turners of Lane End *London, Cory Adams & Mackay 1965*
A family of Staffordshire potters whose fortunes were made by the Industrial Revolution and ruined by the French Revolution. *Quarto. viii + 96pp and 40pp of plates, 4 colour plates. Original cloth.* £9

1065 **Hillier, Bevis** Pottery and porcelain 1700-1914 *London, Weidenfeld & Nicolson 1968*
A study of pottery and porcelain in England, Europe and North America which breaks new ground in relating the articles made to the artistic and, more particularly, the social climate of the time. There are also chapters on marketing, folk pottery, artist potters, collectors and forgers. *Quarto. 386pp including 217 illustrations. Original cloth.* £10

1066 **Hobson, R. L.** Worcester porcelain. A description of the ware from the Wall period to the present day *London, Quaritch 1910*
Handsomely produced and very well illustrated history of the Worcester factory and its products. *Folio. xi + (1) + 208pp, frontispiece and 108 plates (of which 17 chromolitho, the remainder collotype). Original decorated cloth, uncut.* **Illustration below.** £90

1067 **Hobson, R. L.** Catalogue of the Frank Lloyd collection of Worcester porcelain of the Wall period presented by Mr and Mrs Frank Lloyd to the Department of Ceramics and Ethnography in the British Museum *London, British Museum 1923*
391 items are catalogued and all the best are illustrated. *Octavo. xix + (1) + 96pp with 84 photo plates. Quarter cloth, printed board sides.* £22

1068 **Hodgkin, John Eliot & Edith** Examples of early English pottery named, dated and inscribed *1891 (EP reprint, 1973)*
Octavo. xx + 188pp with many illustrations in blue and sepia. Original cloth. £5

1069 **Holgate, David** New Hall and its imitators *London, Faber 1971*
The porcelain produced by the New Hall China Manufactory of Hanley, Staffordshire, 1781-1835. *Octavo. 112pp and 96pp of plates, 8 colour plates. Original cloth.* £7

1070 **Honey, W. B.** Dresden china. An introduction to the study of Meissen porcelain *London, Black 1934*
A lucid guide to Meissen porcelain, concentrating on 18th century material. *Octavo. xvi + 224pp, frontispiece and 60pp of plates. Original cloth. Author's presentation copy to Bernard Rackham.* £20

1071 **Honey, W. B.** German porcelain *London, Faber 1947*
Octavo. xvi + 56pp and 96pp of plates. Original cloth. £8

1072 **Honey, W. B.** Old English porcelain. A handbook for collectors *London, Faber 1948*
Octavo. 292pp and 112pp of plates. Original cloth. £8

1073 **Honey, W. B.** Many occasions. Essays towards the appreciation of several arts *London, Faber 1949*
Octavo. 158pp with plates. Original cloth. £8

1074 **Honey, W. B.** French porcelain of the 18th century. Second edition *London, Faber 1972*
Primarily a study of the soft paste porcelain of Saint-Cloud, Chantilly, Mennecy, Vincennes and Sèvres. *Octavo. xv + (1) + 78 + (2)pp and 96pp of plates, 8 colour plates. Original cloth.*
£8

1075 **Howard, David Sanctuary** Chinese armorial porcelain *London, Faber 1974*
A massive contribution to the history of Chinese export porcelain, listing examples of some 2900 dinner services painted with the arms of British families between 1695 and 1820, and illustrating nearly 2000 of them. The porcelain is classified and dated and there are notes on the families whose arms appear on it, giving details of their connection with China, their social position and family relationships indicated by the heraldry; in fact, this is almost as essential for the student of 18th century English history and society as for the collector of porcelain. Appendices list directors of the East India Company, captains and owners of East Indiamen sailing to Canton, Britons connected with Canton in the 18th century, and others who held positions that brought them into touch with the export porcelain trade. *Quarto. xiv + 1034pp, with 25 colour plates, and nearly 2000 monochrome illustrations in text. Original cloth.* £60

1076 **Hughes, G. Bernard** English and Scottish earthenware 1660-1860 *London, Abbey Fine Arts (1960)*
Octavo. 238 + (2)pp, text illustrations, frontispiece and 46pp of plates, 4 colour plates. Original cloth. £4

1077 **Hughes, Therle & Bernard** English painted enamels *London, Spring Books 1967*
Quarto. 156pp including 83 photo illustrations, and 4 colour plates. Original cloth. £4

1078 **Hurlbutt, Frank** Bow porcelain *London, Bell 1926*
A scholarly study, printing much documentary material (including details of excavations on the Bow factory site), and extensively illustrated. Octavo. xviii + 165 + (1)pp and 56 half-tone, 8 colour plates. Original cloth. £47

1079 **Hurlbutt, Frank** Bristol porcelain *London, Medici 1928*
Important study, with information on history and technique and with extensive documentation. Octavo. xx + 164 + (2)pp and 8 tipped in colour plates, 56 monochrome plates. Original cloth. £60

1080 **Hyde, J. A. Lloyd** Oriental Lowestoft. Chinese export porcelain. Porcelaine de la Cie des Indes. With special reference to the trade with China and the porcelain decorated for the American market *Newport, Ceramic Book Co 1964*
Quarto. (8) + 168pp including 33 plates, and 4 other colour plates. Original cloth. £8.50

1081 **(Importation of earthenware)** An act to permit the importation of painted earthenware, except galley tiles, the manufacture of Europe, to be sold in Great Britain, and for charging the same with a duty ad valorem *London, 1775 (15 Geo. III XXXVII)*
This act repeals an act of 1464 prohibiting the import of painted earthenware and long in abeyance, and imposes a duty on such imports; porcelain, covered by different legislation, is excluded. Folio. (4)pp. £12

1082 **Jacquemart, Albert** History of the ceramic art. A descriptive and philosophical study of the pottery of all ages and all nations. Translated by Mrs Bury Palliser. Second edition *New York, Scribner 1877*
Jacquemart's is the classic 19th century history of ceramics, first published in French, and as a work of reference most authoritative on French potteries. Octavo. (10) + 628pp with 200 text illustrations, and 12 etched plates. Original decorated cloth, gilt edges. £15

1083 **Jenyns, Soame** Japanese pottery *London, Faber 1971*
The first authoritative study in English. Octavo. xiv + 320pp and 120pp of plates, 4 colour plates. Original cloth. £15

1084 **Jenyns, Soame** Later Chinese porcelain. The Ch'ing dynasty (1644-1912). Fourth edition *London, Faber 1971*
Octavo. xvi + 111 + (1)pp and 120pp of plates, 8 colour plates. Original cloth. £5.50

1085 **Jewitt, Llewellynn** The ceramic art of Great Britain from pre-historic times down to the present day. Being a history of the ancient and modern pottery and porcelain works of the kingdom and of their productions of every class *London, Virtue 1878*
First edition of this fullest 19th century history of British pottery, porcelain and tiles. Jewitt's emphasis on research – 'hard literary digging to get at facts and to verify dates, that is not understood, and would scarce be believed in, by the reader who turns to my pages' – marks this out from other publications of the period and makes it a reference work of lasting importance. The reprint by Godden (below) prints the sections on 19th century potters and potteries only, and though of value because Godden corrects factual errors and brings the history of the potteries down to 1900 it loses in his revision and in the omission of less essential information much of the character of the original. Octavo. 2 vols. xiii + (1) + 531 + (1)pp and 4 plates (including frontispiece); viii + 569 + (3)pp and 3 chromolitho plates. The first vol has 888 text figures and the second 786 figures. Original decorated cloth. **Illustration opposite.** £35

1085-7

1086 **Jewitt, Llewellynn** The ceramic art of Great Britain ... new edition, revised *London, Virtue (1883)*

Second edition, 'slightly abridged, printed in smaller type, and compressed into one goodly volume' (to quote the author) but also incorporating new facts not found in the first edition. *Octavo. xii + 642pp with 1816 text illustrations. Original cloth.* £25

1087 (Jewitt, Llewellyn) **Godden, Geoffrey A.** Jewitt's Ceramic art of Great Britain 1800-1900. Being a revised and expanded edition of those parts of The ceramic art of Great Britain by Llewellyn Jewitt, F.S.A., dealing with the nineteenth century *London, Barrie & Jenkins 1972*

Quarto. xxviii + (2) + 282pp, frontispiece and 116 photo illustrations. Original cloth. £8

1088 **John, W. D.** Nantgarw porcelain *Newport, Johns 1948 (with supplements 1956 and 1969)*

Handsome monograph which deals exhaustively with the pottery made at Nantgarw, near Cardiff, in the years 1813-22. *Quarto. xvi + 176pp, colour frontispiece and 63 plates (13 coloured); (12)pp and 8pp of illustrations. Original cloth, with the two supplements in rear pocket. Uncut.* £53

1089 **John, W. D.** Swansea porcelain *Newport, Ceramic Book Co 1958*

Quarto. xxii + (2) + 118 + (2)pp and 20 colour plates, 78pp of monochrome illustrations. Original cloth. £18

1090 **John, W. D.** William Billingsley (1758-1828). His outstanding achievements as an artist and porcelain maker *Newport, Ceramic Book Co 1968*

Billingsley worked successively at the Derby, Pinxton, Torksey, Worcester, Nantgarw, Swansea and Coalport potteries, and this biographical study adds to knowledge of each of the factories. *Quarto. xvi + 97 + (1)pp and 22 colour plates, 50pp of monochrome illustrations. Original cloth.* £15

1091 **John, W. D. & Warren Baker** Old English lustre pottery *Newport, Ceramic Book Co 1962*

Quarto. xx + 132pp, colour frontispiece and 95 plates (13 colour). Original cloth. £15

1092 **John, W. D. & Anne Simcox** Pontypool and Usk japanned wares with the early history of the iron and tinplate industries at Pontypool *Newport, Ceramic Book Co 1966*
Quarto. xi+(1)+88pp, colour frontispiece and 27 illustrations. Original cloth. £8

1093 **Jonge, C. H. de** Dutch tiles. Translated by P. S. Falla *London, Pall Mall 1971*
Octavo. viii+337+(1)pp and 158pp of photo illustrations, 6 colour plates. Original cloth. £10

1094 **King, William** English porcelain figures of the eighteenth century *London, Medici 1925*
A cross-section of portrait figures chosen to illustrate the range produced in England during the eighteenth century; the examples figured are principally taken from private collections. Octavo. xii+16pp, colour frontispiece, 7 colour and 72 monochrome plates. Original cloth. £22

1095 **Koyama, Fujio** Ceramiche orientali *Milan, Silvana 1959*
Chinese and Japanese pottery and porcelain. Folio. 403+(3)pp including many illustrations some coloured. Original cloth. £18

1096 **Lancaster, H. Boswell** Liverpool and her potters *Liverpool, Jones 1936*
Octavo. 96+ivpp, frontispiece and 24pp of plates. Original wrappers. £4

1097 **Lane, Arthur** Italian porcelain. With a note on Buen Retiro *London, Faber 1954*
Octavo. xvi+80pp and 96pp of plates, 4 colour plates. Original cloth. £3

1098 **Lane, Arthur** English porcelain figures of the eighteenth century *London, Faber 1961*
Octavo. xii+148pp and 96pp of plates, 4 colour plates. Original cloth. £4

1099 **Lane, Arthur** French faience. Second edition *London, Faber 1970*
Octavo. xi+(1)+49+(3)pp and 96pp of plates, 8 colour plates. Original cloth. £4.50

1100 **Lane, Arthur** Greek pottery. Third edition *London, Faber 1971*
Octavo. 64pp and 96pp of plates, 8 colour plates. Original cloth. £6

1101 **Lane, Arthur** Later Islamic pottery. Persia, Syria, Egypt, Turkey. Second edition *London, Faber 1971*
Octavo. xvi+134pp and 100pp of plates, 8 colour plates. Original cloth. £7.50

1102 **Latham, Bryan** Victorian Staffordshire portrait figures for the small collector *London, Tiranti 1953*
Octavo. (2)+41+(1)pp and 56pp of plates. Original wrappers. £1.25

1103 **Leach, Bernard** A potter's book. Second edition. (14th impression) *London, Faber 1973*
A guide to design and technique by the most distinguished of British potters, making use of his familiarity with Japanese and Korean working practice. Original cloth. £3.50

1104 (Leeds Pottery) **Hartley, Greens and Co.** Designs of sundry articles of Queen's or Cream-colour'd Earthen-ware, manufactured by Hartley, Greens, and Co. at Leeds Pottery: with a great variety of other articles. The same enamel'd, printed or ornamented with gold to any pattern; also with coats of arms, cyphers, landscapes, &c, &c *Leeds (1814)*

1104-6

The last and fullest edition of the Leeds pottery pattern book. From 1775, when William Hartley joined the Green family in the management of the pottery, to 1820, when the business got into financial difficulties, the Leeds pottery was one of the best-known in Britain and its cream coloured ware was a serious competitor to Josiah Wedgwood's own 'Queen's Ware'. Wedgwood had published a catalogue of his ware in 1774 as a guide for pottery salesmen and customers, and the Leeds pottery replied in 1783 with a much larger catalogue of their ware, illustrating 184 designs on 45 plates. This was reissued in 1785 and 1786, and appeared in a new edition in 1794 and 1814, containing in its final form 221 designs for the ware generally and 48 for items for the tea service.

Printed pattern books of this date and character are rare. Those that exist are particularly useful in identifying manufacturers' products and in understanding their methods of business and sale. This copy of the Leeds pattern book has its title page supplied by a modern type facsimile carrying the date 1783, but it can be shown by the number of plates and by watermarks to be a copy of the fuller 1814 edition. Plates 1-38 and 61-67 are repeated from the 1783 edition (the latter group renumbered) and the remaining plates are later additions. This copy contains two plates numbered 52 carrying quite different designs. *Small folio. Title in type facsimile, 72 engraved plates (numbered 1-71 with 52 repeated), of which 2 folding. Quarter morocco, marbled paper boards.* **Illustration above.** £725

1105 (Leeds Pottery) **Kidson, Joseph R. & Frank** Historical notices of the Leeds Old Pottery . . . with a new introduction by Peter Walton *Wakefield, SR 1970*

Reissue of the Kidsons' history of the Leeds pottery first published in 1892, which complements the Leeds Pattern Book (item 1104) and the recent study by Towner (item 1106). *Octavo. (8) + 162pp and 21 plates. Original cloth.* £2.10

1106 (Leeds Pottery) **Towner, Donald** The Leeds pottery *London, Cory Adams & Mackay 1963*

Includes a photo reproduction of the firm's printed pattern book in the 1814 edition (see item 1104), without really doing justice to the original; but a valuable background study of the pottery. *Octavo. x + 180pp, including photo facsimile of pattern book, and 48pp of plates. Original cloth.* **Illustration above.** £10

1107 **Lehmann, Henri** Pre-Columbian ceramics ... translated by Galway Kinnell *London, Elek 1962*
Octavo. 128pp and 32pp of plates. Original cloth.
£5

1108 **Litchfield, Frederick** Pottery and porcelain. A guide to collectors. New edition, revised and enlarged *London, Truslove 1905*
Based on secondary sources but a fairly extensive handbook. Octavo. xviii + 400pp with many plates and text illustrations. Original cloth.
£8

1109 **Little, W. L.** Staffordshire blue. Underglaze blue transfer-printed earthenware *London, Batsford 1969*
Octavo. 160pp including 108 illustrations of marks, and 64pp of plates. Original cloth.
£6

1110 **Liverani, Giuseppe** La maiolica Italiana sino alla comparsa della porcellana Europea *Milan, Electra 1958*
Quarto. 264 + (4)pp including 83 colour illustrations and other black and white illustrations. Original cloth.
£18

1111 **Loar, Peggy A.** Indiana stoneware *Indianapolis, 1974*
Catalogue of an exhibition of stoneware, mostly 19th century, but with some very recent work, held at Indianapolis Museum of Art April-May 1974. Quarto. 48pp with 94 illustrations. Original wrappers. **Illustration below.**
£4

1112 **Lockett, T. A.** Davenport pottery and porcelain 1794-1887 *Newton Abbot, David & Charles 1972*
Quarto. 112pp with 103 illustrations. Original cloth.
£3.75

1111

1113 **Luxmoore, Chas. F. C.** 'Saltglaze' with the notes of a collector *London, Holland Press (1969)*
A good reprint of one of the best illustrated studies of salt-glazed ware, first published in 1924. *Folio. (2) + 66pp, colour frontispiece and 89 plates each with facing text leaf. Original cloth.* £12.50

1114 **Macht, Carol** Classical Wedgwood designs. The sources and their use and the relationship of Wedgwood jasper ware to the classical revival of the eighteenth century *New York, Gramercy 1957*
Octavo. xvi + 144pp including 64 illustrations. Original cloth. £8

1115 **Mackenna, F. Severne** Cookworthy's Plymouth and Bristol porcelain *Leigh on Sea, Lewis 1946*
First study of Cookworthy (1705-80), the first British manufacturer of true porcelain, and of his potteries at Plymouth and Bristol. *Octavo. 110pp and 58pp of plates. Original cloth. Limited edition of 500 copies. Signed by author.* £30

1116 **Mackenna, F. Severne** Chelsea porcelain. The triangle and raised anchor wares *Leigh on Sea, Lewis 1948*
Excellent monograph on Chelsea porcelain of the 1740s and 1750s, with discussion of the problems and a bibliography. *Octavo. xvi + 90pp and 56pp of plates. Original cloth. Limited edition of 500 copies. Signed by author.* £30

1117 **Mackenna, F. Severne** Chelsea porcelain. The red anchor wares *Leigh on Sea, Lewis 1951*
Chelsea porcelain of the period 1753-58. *Octavo. xvi + 106pp and 78pp of plates. Original cloth. Limited edition of 500 copies.* £24

1118 **(Manning, Anne)** The provocations of Madame Palissy, by the author of 'Mary Powell' *London, Hall Virtue & Co (1853)*
First edition. A romantic novel about the domestic tribulations of Bernard Palissy, the greatest of French potters. *Octavo. (2) + 241 + (1)pp with chromolitho frontispiece. Original blind-stamped cloth. Loose in covers but clean internally.* £9

1119 **(Marks, Murray) Williamson, G. C.** Murray Marks and his friends. A tribute of regard by Dr G. C. Williamson *London, John Lane 1919*
Murray Marks was the first London dealer to specialize in the sale of Chinese blue and white porcelain, and this biographical study is informative on his business and his connections with the artists of the day (Rossetti, Burne-Jones, Whistler). *Octavo. xvi + (2) + 207 + (1)pp, frontispiece and 21 photo plates. Original cloth.* £12

1120 **Marshall, H. Rissik** Coloured Worcester porcelain of the first period (1751-1783) *Newport, Ceramic Book Co 1954*
Quarto. (12) + 305 + (1)pp, with 31 colour plates and 14 + 55 monochrome plates illustrating over 1100 objects. Original cloth. £40

1121 **Medley, Margaret** Yuan porcelain and stoneware *London, Faber 1974*
Octavo. xii + 139 + (1)pp, and 8 colour plates, 124pp of monochrome plates. Original cloth. £15

1122 **Mew, Egan** Old Bow china *London, Jack (c 1910)*
Octavo. 112pp and 16 plates. Original cloth. £4

1123 **Mew, Egan** Royal Sèvres china *London, T. C. Jack (1925)*
Octavo. 90pp and 16 plates (8 coloured). Original cloth. Author's presentation copy. £4

1124 **Mew, Egan** Battersea enamels *London, Medici Society (1926)*
The Battersea enamel factory, active 1750-56, specialized in the reproduction by a transfer process of engraved designs on an enamel surface. *Octavo. ix+(3)+27+(1)pp and 6 colour, 72 monochrome plates. Original cloth.*
£28

1125 (Morgan, William de) **Gaunt, William & M. D. E. Clayton-Stamm** William de Morgan *London, Studio Vista 1971*
Biography, concentrating on De Morgan's contributions to ceramic design and illustrating a range of De Morgan pottery and tiles. *Quarto. 176pp including 144 illustrations (24 coloured). Original cloth.*
£6.40

1126 (Morgan, William de) **Stirling, A. M. W.** William de Morgan and his wife *London, Thornton Butterworth 1922*
Biographical study of the De Morgans, based on personal knowledge and their surviving correspondence and covering De Morgan's role in 'recreating in ceramic work ... the colour of the Persian & the lustre of the great Umbrian craftsmen'. *Octavo. 404pp with text illustrations, frontispiece and 32 photo plates. Original cloth.*
£20

1127 **Morley-Fletcher, Hugo** Meissen *London, Barrie & Jenkins 1971*
Small folio. 120pp with many colour illustrations. Original cloth.
£8

1128 **Mountford, Arnold R.** The illustrated guide to Staffordshire salt-glazed stoneware *London, Barrie & Jenkins 1971*
Based on the evidence of recent excavations as well as on stylistic and documentary considerations. *Octavo. xxi+(1)+88pp and 128pp of plates, 8 colour plates. Original cloth.*
£6

1129 **Neurdenburg, Elisabeth** Old Dutch pottery and tiles ... with annotations by Bernard Rackham *London, Benn 1923*
No. 10 of a limited edition of 100 copies signed by the author and by Rackham. A scholarly treatise and a fine piece of book production. *Quarto. xv+(1)+155+(1)pp and 69 plates carrying 103 coloured and 9 monochrome illustrations. Full contemporary morocco, top edge gilt, uncut and largely unopened.*
£70

1130 **Nicholls, Robert** Ten generations of a potting family. Founded upon 'William Adams, an Old English Potter' by William Turner, F.S.S. and other works on the Adams family *Stoke-on-Trent, Wood Mitchell 1949*
Octavo. xxv+(3)+135+(1)pp with text illustrations, frontispiece and 55 plates. Original cloth.
£10

1131 **Orange, James** Bizen-ware with a catalogue of the Chater collection *Yokohama, Kelley & Walsh 1916*
History, details of technical processes, information on potters, catalogue of Bizen ware collection formed in Yokohama and acquired by Chater. *Octavo. 68pp text and 46 plates numbered 69-115. Original cloth.*
£40

1132 **Pabst, Arthur** Kunstvolle Thongefässe aus dem 16 bis 18 Jahrhundert. Die keramische Sammlung des Freiherrn Albert von Oppenheim in Köln *Berlin, Hessling & Spielmeyer (c 1890)*
Folio. Title leaf, 8pp and 52 photo plates. Cloth portfolio.
£40

1133 **Pauls-Eisenbeiss, Erika** German porcelain of the 18th century *London, Barrie & Jenkins 1972*
A catalogue, fully annotated and illustrated, of the Pauls-Eisenbeiss collection. Volume I is devoted to Meissen porcelain from the beginning to 1760, and Volume II to the porcelain of Höchst, Frankenthal and Ludwigsburg. The detailed treatment and the wide range of material and illustrations make this a work of reference for the subject as a whole. *Folio. 2 vols. 570+(2)pp with illustrations, many coloured; 328+(2)pp with illustrations, many coloured. Original cloth.*
£19

1134 **Plinval de Guillebon** Régine de Paris porcelain 1770-1850. Translated by Robin R. Charleston *London, Barrie & Jenkins 1972*
The first study of the porcelain produced by manufacturers in Paris proper (Dagoty, Darte, Dihl and the workshops of the Comte d'Artois and the Comte de Provence are among those discussed). *Quarto. 362pp with 243 illustrations, many coloured, and 227 reproductions of marks. Original cloth.* £19

1135 **Popelin, Claudius** L'email des peintres *Paris, Levy 1866*
On the artistic use of enamel, with particular reference to the methods of producing the various colours required by artists; and a section at the end wholly devoted to calligraphy. *Octavo. (8) + 208pp with text illustrations and decorated initial letters. Original printed boards. Armorial bookplate.* £30

1136 **Pountney, W. J.** Old Bristol potteries. Being an account of the old potters and potteries of Bristol and Brislington, between 1650 and 1850, with some pages on the old Chapel of St Anne, Brislington *Bristol, Arrowsmith 1920*
History of the Bristol potteries based on local records and excavations. *Octavo. xxxiv + 370pp, coloured frontispiece and 54 plates. Original cloth.* £28

1137 **Pountney, W. J.** Old Bristol potteries *Bristol, Arrowsmith, 1920 (EP reprint 1972)*
An adequate reproduction. *Octavo. xxxiv + 370pp, frontispiece and plates. Original cloth.* £4

1138 **Price, E. Stanley** John Sadler a Liverpool pottery printer *West Kirby, for the author 1948*
Octavo. 103 + (1)pp and 19 plates. Original wrappers. £6

1139 **Prodan, Mario** La poterie T'ang *Paris, Arts et Metiers Graphiques 1960*
Quarto. 186pp with 120 illustrations (34 coloured). Original cloth. £12

1140 **Pugh, P. D. Gordon** Staffordshire portrait figures and allied subjects of the Victorian era *London, Barrie & Jenkins 1970*
Quarto. xi + (1) + 657 + (3)pp including many illustrations. Original cloth. £16

1141 **Pugh, P. D. Gordon** Naval ceramics *Newport, Ceramic Book Co 1971*
Covers both commemorative figures of naval heroes and the china and crockery used in naval messes and hospitals. *Quarto. xxvi + 113 + (1)pp, colour frontispiece and 12 colour plates, 118pp of monochrome illustrations. Original cloth.* £12.60

1142 **Pugh, P. D. Gordon** Heraldic China mementoes of the First World War *Newport, Ceramic Book Co 1972*
China guns, ships, aeroplanes with heraldic emblems – mostly Goss. *Folio. xii + 50pp and 24 plates. Original cloth.* £4

1143 **Rackham, Bernard** Early Netherlands maiolica. With special reference to the tiles at the Vyne in Hampshire *London, Bles 1926*
Scholarly and handsomely produced study of 16th century Netherlands pottery and tiles. *Quarto. xiv + 136pp, frontispiece and 55 plates (11 coloured). Original cloth, uncut.* £42

1144 **Rackham, Bernard** Italian maiolica. Second edition *London, Faber 1963*
Octavo. xvi + 35 + (1)pp and 96pp of plates, 4 colour plates. Original cloth. £3

1145 **Rackham, Bernard** Medieval English pottery. Second edition, revised *London, Faber 1972*
Octavo. xvi + 40pp and 96pp of plates, 8 colour plates. Original cloth. £6.50

1146 **Rackham, Bernard & Herbert Read** English pottery ... with an appendix on the Wrotham potters by Dr J. W. L. Glaisher *London, 1924 (EP reprint, 1972)*
Quarto. xii + 24 + 144pp and 115 plates. Original cloth. £10

1147 **Randau, Paul** Enamels and enamelling. An introduction to the preparation and application of all kinds of enamels for technical and artistic purposes ... translated from the German by Charles Salter *London, Scott Greenwood, 1900*
A comprehensive guide to enamelling processes. Octavo. viii + 188pp with 16 text figures. Original cloth. £9

1148 **Ray, Anthony** English Delftware pottery in the Robert Hall Warren collection, Ashmolean Museum, Oxford *London, Faber 1968*
A scholarly catalogue of an important Delftware collection. Octavo. 248pp and 96pp of plates, 8 colour plates. Original cloth. £8.50

1149 **Read, Herbert** Staffordshire pottery figures *London, Duckworth 1929*
The first modern study of what were then considered 'rather lonely remnants of English peasant art'. Quarto. xvi + 24pp and 70 monochrome, 6 colour plates. Original cloth. £25

1150 **Reilly, Robin & George Savage** Wedgwood. The portrait medallions *London, Barrie & Jenkins 1973*
Illustrates all the medallion varieties known and gives biographical details of the subjects and references to Wedgwood's archives. Small folio. 380pp with many illustrations, and 16 colour plates. Original cloth. £17.50

1151 **Rhead, G. W.** and **F. A.** Staffordshire pots & potteries *London, Hutchinson 1906*
A general history of the Staffordshire industry, including interesting chapters on foreign designers employed by Staffordshire firms and on Minton's Art Pottery Studio in South Kensington. Large octavo. xvi + 383 + (1)pp and 4 coloured plates, 64 monochrome plates, many text illustrations. Original cloth. £40

1152 **Rice, D. G.** Rockingham ornamental porcelain *London, Adam 1966*
Quarto. 168pp including 142 illustrations (some coloured). Original cloth. £10

1153 **Rice, D. G.** The illustrated guide to Rockingham pottery and porcelain *London, Barrie & Jenkins 1971*
Octavo. xx + (2) + 194pp and 104pp of plates, 8 coloured plates. Original cloth. £6

1154 **Rose, Muriel** Artist potters in England. Second edition *London, Faber 1970*
Octavo. 64pp and 118pp of plates, 6 colour plates. Original cloth. £6.50

1155 (Rothschild collection) **Charleston, R. J. & John Ayers** The James A. de Rothschild collection at Waddesdon Manor. Meissen and other European porcelain (by) R. J. Charleston. Oriental porcelain (by) John Ayers *Fribourg, Office du Livre 1971*
Scholarly catalogue publishing Meissen, Strasbourg-Frankenthal, Doccia and Chelsea

porcelain, as well as a number of Chinese and Japanese pieces. *Octavo. 316pp with many illustrations (some coloured). Original cloth.* £26.50

1156 (Rothschild collection) **Eriksen, Svend** The James A. de Rothschild collection at Waddesdon Manor. Sèvres porcelain *Fribourg, Office du Livre 1968*
Splendid collection of soft-paste Sèvres porcelain, well catalogued by Eriksen. *Octavo. 340pp with many illustrations (some coloured). Original cloth.* £26.50

1157 **Rush, James** The ingenious Beilbys *London, Barrie & Jenkins 1973*
History of the Beilby family of glass painters and of glass manufacture in Newcastle upon Tyne. *Octavo. 168pp with many illustrations. Original cloth.* £5.50

1158 **Sandon, Henry** The illustrated guide to Worcester porcelain. 1751-1793 *New York, Praeger 1970*
Octavo. xvii + (1) + 96pp and 96pp of plates, 8 colour plates. Original cloth. £5

1159 **Sandon, Henry** Royal Worcester Porcelain from 1862 to the present day *London, Barrie & Jenkins 1973*
Octavo. xxix + (1) + 265 + (1)pp and 112pp of plates, 20pp of colour plates. Original cloth. £15

1160 **Sarre, Friedrich** Die Keramik im Euphrat- und Tigris-Gebiet *Berlin, Reimer 1921*
Folio. 30pp and 15 photo plates. Original cloth. £7

1161 **Savage, George** 18th-century English porcelain *London, Rockliff 1952*
Octavo. xx + 435 + (1)pp, colour frontispiece and 112pp of plates. Original cloth. £15

1162 **Savage, George & Harold Newman** An illustrated dictionary of ceramics *London, Thames & Hudson 1974*
A dictionary of terms dealing with the objects of pottery. Over 3000 definitions relating to wares, materials, processes, types, shapes, patterns and styles, together with a list of the European modellers and decorators, the main factories and their marks. *Large octavo. 320pp with over 600 text illustrations, and 14 coloured plates. Publisher's cloth.* £6.50

1163 **Scheurleer, D. F. Lunsingh** Chinese export porcelain. Chine de commande *London, Faber 1974*
Octavo. 256pp, 8 colour plates and 84pp of monochrome plates. Original cloth. £15

1164 **(Schreiber)** Victoria and Albert Museum. Department of Ceramics. Catalogue of English porcelain earthenware enamels and glass collected by Charles Schreiber ... and the Lady Charlotte Elizabeth Schreiber *London, 1924-30*
Complete set of the Schreiber catalogue (see also items below for separate parts). *Quarto. 3 vols. xviii + 226pp and 96 plates; xii + 140pp and 86 plates; (8) + 96pp and 48 plates. Original wrappers.* £40

1164a (Schreiber collection) **Rackham, Bernard** Victoria and Albert Museum. Department of Ceramics. Catalogue of English porcelain earthenware enamels and glass collected by Charles Schreiber ... and the Lady Charlotte Elizabeth Schreiber and presented to the Museum in 1884. Volume 1. Porcelain *London, Board of Education 1928*
Catalogues 825 items. *Octavo. xviii + 226pp and 96pp of plates. Original cloth.* £14

1164b (Schreiber) **Rackham, Bernard** Victoria and Albert Museum. Department of Ceramics. Catalogue of English porcelain earthenware enamels and glass collected by Charles ... and Lady Charlotte Elizabeth Schreiber ... volume III. Enamels and glass *London, Board of Education 1924*
The glass and enamels only – but they are very good. *Quarto. (8) + 102 + (2)pp and 48pp of plates. Original cloth.* £12

1165 **Shaw, Simeon** History of the Staffordshire potteries; and the rise and progress of the manufacture of pottery and porcelain; with references to genuine specimens, and notices of eminent potters *Hanley, for the author 1829*
The first book on the Staffordshire pottery industry, based on local knowledge and the recollections of many leading potters, and dedicated to Josiah Spode. Still a fundamental source for the history of Staffordshire pottery and porcelain; the Wedgwood firm receives generous treatment and Shaw gives interesting details of the products and history of many lesser manufacturers. *Octavo. viii + 244pp. Original boards, cloth spine.* £42

1166 **Shaw, Simeon** History of the Staffordshire potteries *Hanley, 1829 (David & Charles reprint 1970)*
Octavo. viii + 244pp. Original cloth. £2.75

1167 **Shinn, Charles & Dorrie** The illustrated guide to Victorian Parian china *London, Barrie & Jenkins 1971*
Octavo. xiv + (2) + 125 + (1)pp and 96pp of plates, 3 colour plates. Original cloth. £6

1168 **Smith, Alan** The illustrated guide to Liverpool Herculaneum pottery. 1796-1840 *London, Barrie & Jenkins 1970*
Octavo. xvi + 142pp and 96pp of plates, 7 colour plates. Original cloth. £6

1169 **Solon, M. L.** The art of the old English potter *London, Bemrose 1885*
Second edition, with appendix on foreign imitations of English earthenware. *Octavo. xxiv + 269 + (1)pp with 55 text illustrations. Original cloth.* **Illustration below.** £20

1169a **Solon, M. L.** The art of the old English potter *1883 (EP reprint, 1973)*
A critical study which still reads well and which records fine early pottery in Solon's own collection. *Octavo. xx + 210pp and 50 plates. Original cloth.* **Illustration below.** £3.50

1169-1169a

1170 **Solon, M. L.** Pâte sur pâte on coloured Minton porcelain vases 1885-1893 *London 1894 (Ceramic Book Co reprint 1972)*
Quarto. *(12)pp and 10 photo plates. Original wrappers.* £6.50

1171 **Solon, M. L.** A brief history of old English porcelain and its manufactories; with an artistic, industrial, and critical appreciation of their productions *London, Bemrose 1903*
In fact quite a substantial contribution to ceramic literature, not so much for the factual information it provides (though it is well organized and illustrated), but because its author, Marc Louis Solon, was for a long period Minton's principal designer – and before that an employee at Sèvres – and the aesthetic and critical judgements that he expresses are those that ruled late Victorian taste. *Octavo. xvi + 255 + (3)pp and 20 colour plates, 50 monochrome plates. Original decorated cloth, uncut. Limited edition.* £17

1172 **Solon, M. L.** Ceramic literature: an analytical index to the works published in all languages on the history and the technology of ceramic art *London, Charles Griffin 1910*
Extensive bibliography, useful for the full collations it provides and for Solon's critical and very opinionated remarks on the various items. A section at the end indexes the material by subject and adds lists of printed pattern books and sale catalogues. *Large octavo. xviii + (2) + 660pp. Cloth.* £38

1173 **Spelman, W. W. R.** Lowestoft china *London, Jarrold 1905*
Publishes the results of finds on the site of the Lowestoft pottery when excavated in 1902. An early application of archaeological techniques to problems of pottery history. *Octavo. (6) + 78 + (2)pp, frontispiece and 97 plates (some coloured). Original cloth. Limited edition of 500 copies.* £40

1174 (Stepney Pottery, Newcastle-upon-Tyne) **Wood, J(ohn)** Original engraved copper of a willow pattern design and a chinese design *Newcastle-upon-Tyne (c 1875)*
The copper-plate bears the willow pattern design on one side with a mark 'Willow' surrounded by the maker's name 'J. Wood Stepney Pottery Newcastle on Tyne', and has a Chinese design on the reverse side.
The plate is one used for transfer printing, a process which, for the production of blue-and-white earthenware, required the design to be engraved on a copper plate which was then warmed and the colour worked into its surface. A sheet of dampened tissue paper was applied to the plate and this assumed the character of the design. The transference of the tissue paper to the surface of the ware to be printed continued the operation which was completed when the ware had been fired. Few of the original copper plates which were used have survived.
The potter John Wood was in business at the Stepney Pottery from about 1872 to 1910. Bell 'Tyneside Pottery', 1971 pp 113-6, item 1007) mentions his business but does not record him as a manufacturer of willow pattern earthenware, so the copper makes an interesting addition to our knowledge. It seems likely that it belongs to an early date in Wood's production; other Newcastle makers of willow pattern were in operation well before 1870. *Original engraved copper. 400 × 310mm.* £120

1175 **Stoner, Frank** Chelsea Bow and Derby porcelain figures their distinguishing characteristics *Newport, Ceramic Book Co 1955*
Useful for its illustrations of similar figures from different potteries. *Quarto. xvii + (1) + 33 + (1)pp and 5 colour plates, 112 monochrome illustrations. Original cloth.* £12.50

1176 **Thomas, John** The rise of the Staffordshire potteries *Bath, Adams & Dart 1971*
The history of the pottery trade in the late 18th century, with much information on manufacturing, mechanization, working conditions and labour organizations. *Octavo. xii + 228pp with illustrations. Original cloth.* £8

1177 **Tilley, Frank** Teapots and tea *Newport, Ceramic Book Co 1957*
Teapots in pottery and porcelain, with an important and unexpected section on the metallic composition of British porcelains. *Quarto. xiv+(2)+135+(1)pp and 10 colour plates, 67 monochrome plates. Original cloth.* £12

1178 **Towner, Donald C.** English cream-coloured earthenware *London, Faber 1957*
Octavo. xv+(1)+107+(5)pp and 96pp of plates. Original cloth. £3.90

1179 **Wakefield, Hugh** Victorian pottery *London, Barrie & Jenkins 1970*
Octavo. 280pp with illustrations. Original cloth. £2.50

1180 **Wanner-Brandt, Otto** (editor) Album der Erzeugnisse der ehemaliger Wurttembergischen Manufaktur Alt-Ludwigsburg *Stuttgart, 1906*
The Ludwigsburg factory operated from 1758 to 1824, and this very comprehensive catalogue of its porcelain provides descriptions and photographic illustrations of over 1300 different items, as well as a short history of the factory and of others in South-West Germany. *Oblong folio. (8)+72pp and 122 photo plates illustrating over 1320 objects. Original cloth, gilt edges.* £90

1181 **Waring, J. B.** Ceramic art in remote ages; with essays on the symbols of the circle, the cross and circle, the circle and ray ornament, the fylfot and the serpent, showing their relation to the primitive forms of solar and nature worship *London, John B. Day 1875*
Pottery of the Iron Age and the Bronze Age considered from the artistic point of view, with special reference to symbolism. Waring discounts wilder theories about a Phoenician origin for pottery ornamentation but relates its symbolism to a common Indo-European cultural tradition. *Folio. (6)+ii+127+(1)pp, chromolitho title and 55 litho plates. Original decorated cloth, gilt edges, covers dampstained but contents unaffected.* **Illustration below.**
£36

1181

1182 **Watney, Bernard** Longton Hall porcelain *London, Faber 1957*
Octavo. xvi+72pp and 80pp of plates, 4 colour plates. Original cloth. £4

1183 **Watney, Bernard** English blue and white porcelain of the eighteenth century. Second edition, revised *London, Faber 1973*
Octavo. xxii+145+(1)pp and 96pp of monochrome plates, 8 colour plates. Original cloth. £7.95

1186

1184 (Wedgwood, Josiah) **Meteyard, Eliza** The life of Josiah Wedgwood from his private correspondence and family papers ... with an introductory sketch of the art of pottery in England *London, Hurst & Blackett 1865*

Eliza Meteyard's biography of Wedgwood is, as R. W. Lightbown writes in an excellent introduction to the reprint (below), 'still the fullest single picture of the potter and his world', founded as it is on a wealth of documentation and Miss Meteyard's appreciation of the many-sidedness of Wedgwood's career. Of interest both to students of the fine arts and to those with a more general interest in the British Industrial Revolution. *Octavo. 2 vols. xxxv+(1)+504pp; xxiv+643+(1)pp. Contemporary gilt stamped calf.* £45

1185 (Wedgwood, Josiah) **Meteyard, Eliza** The life of Josiah Wedgwood *London, 1865 (Cornmarket reprint 1970)*

A good facsimile reprint with a new introduction by Lightbown. *Octavo. 2 vols. Original cloth.* £18

1186 (Wedgwood, Josiah) **Meteyard, Eliza** Wedgwood and his works. A selection of his plaques, cameos, medallions, vases, etc. from the designs of Flaxman and others. Reproduced in permanent photography by the autotype process. With a sketch of his life and progress of his fine-art manufactures *London, Bell and Daldy 1873*

Folio. viii+(2)+68pp, photo frontispiece and 28 photo plates (each with 2 or 3 photos) with accompanying unnumbered leaves of text. Original decorated cloth, spine repaired, gilt edges.
Illustration above. £65

1187 **Whiter, Leonard** Spode. A history of the family, factory and wares from 1733 to 1833 *London, Barrie & Jenkins 1970*

Comprehensive history of the firm and its products. *Quarto. xiii+(1)+246pp with plates and text illustrations. Original cloth.* £12

1188 **(Williamson, George C.)** Signed enamel miniatures of the XVIIth, XVIIIth & XIXth centuries *London, Nachemsohn (1926)*

Octavo. 44pp and 12 plates. Original cloth. £8

1189 **Ziegler, J.** Études céramiques. Recherche des principes du beau dans l'architecture l'art céramique et la forme en général. Théorie de la coloration des reliefs *Paris, Mathias 1850*

One of the few books to have been written on the theory of ceramics, discussing pottery in relation to architecture, proportion, colour theories, form and shape, ornament and nomenclature. This is the text volume only (there should be an accompanying Atlas Céramique), but it is still a desirable item. *Octavo. (2)+348pp with woodcuts in text. Contemporary quarter morocco, ex library.* £15

1190 **Fisher, Stanley W.** English blue and white porcelain of the 18th century *London, Batsford 1947*
Quarto. xvi + 190pp, including 45 plates (1 coloured). Original cloth. £20

1191 **Furnival, William J.** Researches on leadless glazes *Stone, the author (1898)*
Octavo. viii + (2) + 135 + (1)pp. Original cloth, gilt edges. £10

1192 **King, William** Chelsea porcelain *New York, Scribners 1922*
Good critical study with a reprint of the 1755 Chelsea Porcelain Factory sale catalogue. Quarto. xv + (1) + 134 + (2)pp, with colour frontispiece and 69 plates (5 coloured). Original cloth. £35

1193 **Miller, J. Jefferson** English yellow-glazed earthenware *London, Barrie & Jenkins 1974*
Octavo. xvii + (1) + 126pp and 64 coloured and 74 monochrome illustrations. Original cloth. £8.50

1194 **(Sarreguemines)** Fayenceries de Sarreguemines, Digoin & Vitry-le-François. Majolique et articles de fantaisie *Paris (c 1920s)*
Attractive trade catalogue of the firm's ceramic wares, illustrated by many colour plates. Octavo. (2)pp, 2 frontispieces and 81 plates (numbered 1-27, 32-51, 1-34). Original printed wrappers. £48

1195 **Schnorr von Carolsfeld, Ludwig** Porzellan der Europäischen Fabriken des 18 Jahrhunderts ... dritte durchgesehene und erweiterte Auflage *Berlin, Schmidt 1920*
Convenient guide to 18th century German porcelain (the rest of Europe is dismissed in 25 pages at the end). Octavo. viii + 296pp and 143 photo illustrations. Original cloth. £6

1196 **B. B. Collection** Kunstauktion. Porzellan des Klassizismus. Sammlung B.B. Wien *Vienna, KRrntnerstrasse 23-25 June 1941*
Fine collection of Vienna porcelain of around 1800. Quarto. viii + 44pp, with 52 photo plates. Original cloth. £20

1197 **Falke, Otto von** AltBerliner Fayencen *Berlin, Wasmuth 1923*
Histories of the porcelain factories of Gerhard Wolbeer, Cornelius Funcke, J. G. Menicus and others at Berlin, with illustrations of their products. *Folio. 44pp, with 60 photo illustrations on 30 plates. Quarter morocco. Slightly dampstained at one corner, not affecting text.* £60

1198 **Hofmann, Friedrich H.** Geschichte der Bayerischen Porzellan-Manufaktur Nymphenburg *Leipzig, Hiersemann 1921-3*
Folio. 3 vols, containing in all xiv + (4) + (4)pp prelims. 732pp and 24 mounted photo plates (12 coloured), with 472 text illustrations. Original gilt lettered boards, parchment spines and corners. £300

1104-6

Glass

1201b

1201 **Diderot, D. & J. L. d'Alembert** (Encyclopédie). Recueil de planches sur les sciences, les arts libéraux, et les arts méchaniques, avec leurs explication *Paris, Briasson, David, Le Breton & Durand 1762-72; Livorno 1772-79*

Extracts of the sections relating to the various glass processes. See the item 1701 in the catalogue for details of the main publication. *Each listed section is folio with plates of average size 360 × 225mm, in paper wallet or card folder.*

a **Verrerie** (Glassmaking)
A large section forming almost a complete volume in itself and containing four parts showing the various types of glass manufacture.
Part I concerns the making of small glass vessels and has 29 plates with 34 views, and illustrations of the various processes. These include double-page illustrations of the inside of the glass-house with the furnace and nine workmen carrying out various tasks, 2 double-page plates of plans and sections, 1 double-page illustration showing the construction of the oven and the different operations requiring to build it together with plates of the various operations of preparing and mixing the materials and making the melting pots.
Part II shows the manufacture of plate or sheet glass in 19 plates with 4 double-page plates showing interior and exterior views, plans, elevations and sections of the

glass-house, views of the processes of rolling, and blowing the glass into different shapes, making the sheets of plate glass, and inserting and extracting the pots of molten glass from the ovens.

Part III illustrates the making of glass bottles with 14 views of the processes involved and double-page plans and sections of the Royal glassworks at Sèvre.

Part IV illustrates the English type of glassworks which was conical in shape permitting the concentration of air currents in a single upward movement. This structure is singled out because it gave greater efficiency in the use of fuel. A very complete visual description of the techniques involved. *54 engraved plates of which 15 double-page (numbered I-XXII, I-XIX, I-X, I-III) with 168 illustrations, and 9 + (1 blank) pp of text.* £65

b **Manufacture des glaces** (Plate-glass manufacture)
A very complete description, including 24 workshop vignettes, of the technique of manufacturing plate-glass, a material in great demand for the manufacture of mirrors in the 18th century. The plates show the processes of cleaning and preparing the materials, plans, sections and elevations of the various furnaces, and detailed drawings of implements, machinery and apparatus.

Particular emphasis is laid on the processes of removing the melting crucible and casting and rolling the glass, inserting and extracting the sheets from the annealing chamber, and detailed illustrations of the equipment and tackle used. 6 plates illustrate the forming of glass sheets with thin-blown glass which could be used for some purposes and had the advantage of retaining its fire-polish. Some of the most visually exciting plates are contained in the section of 8 plates on the ways of polishing the glass, and these also include detailed drawings of an early polishing machine which was in used at San Idelfonse in Spain. *43 engraved plates of which 8 double-page with over 280 illustrations, and 9 + (1 blank)pp of text.* **Illustration at head of section.** £50

c **Vitrier** (Glazier)
Tools and view of a glaziers workshop showing the setting of window glass in lead frames. Workers can be seen measuring the plate glass, cleaning it with sand, cutting it to size with diamonds, smoothing the edges, passing the lead through the rolling mill, fixing the glass in the frames and protecting the panes with paper. The illustrations of the tools include a detailed drawing of the lead-rolling mill. *4 engraved plates with 44 illustrations, and (1 + 1 blank)pp of text.* £8

d **Lunettier** (Spectacle-maker)
The making and grinding of lenses principally for spectacles and other optical instruments. The detailed drawings show various types of lenses, tools and details of the machines used in cutting and grinding. *4 engraved plates with 94 illustrations, and 1 + (1 blank)pp text.* £12

1202 **Arnold, Hugh** Stained glass of the middle ages in England and France *London, Black 1913*
Illustrated by colour plates after drawings by Lawrence Saint. *Quarto. xvi + 269 + (1)pp and 50 colour plates. Original decorated cloth.* £9

1203 **Beck, Doreen** The book of bottle collecting *London, Hamlyn 1973*
Mostly concerned with 19th century bottles, but good, and informative on history and methods of manufacture. *Quarto. 96pp including 97 illustrations. Original cloth.* £3

1204 **Bickerton, L. M.** An illustrated guide to eighteenth-century English drinking glasses *London, Barrie & Jenkins 1971*
Contains a good bibliography of English glass. *Octavo. xii + 86 + (16)pp with many illustrations. Original cloth.* £12

1205 **Bolas, Thomas** Glass blowing and working for amateurs, experimentalists, and technicians *London, Dawbarn & Ward 1898*
Described by the author as 'technically educational in the real sense of the term; as leading towards an understanding why each particular thing is done, and as facilitating that interdrift of method from craft to craft which is so conducive to progress'. *Octavo. Coloured frontispiece. 212pp with 104 text illustrations. Original cloth.* £15

1206 **A booke of sundry draughtes,** principaly serving for glasiers: and not impertinent for plasterers, and gardiners: besides sundry other professions. Whereunto is annexed the manner how to anniel in glas:

and also the true forme of the fornace, and the secretes thereof
London, Walter Dight 1615 (facsimile reprint London, Leadenhall Press 1898)
Interesting collection of designs for leaded glass. *Quarto.* (26)+66+(2)+(37, numbered 67-103)+(11)pp. *Original full vellum, uncut.* £15

1207 **British Society of Master Glass-Painters** A directory of stained glass windows executed within the past twenty years *London 1949*
Octavo. 66pp. *Original printed wrappers.* £4

1208 (Burne-Jones, Edward) **Bell, Malcolm** Edward Burne-Jones. A record and review *London, Bell 1892.*
Contains a chapter on his decorative work and a list of his stained glass cartoons. *Folio* xii+130+(2)pp and 76 plates. *Original cloth. Limited edition.* £42

1209 (Burne-Jones, Edward) **Harrison, Martin & Bill Waters** Burne-Jones *London, Barrie & Jenkins 1973*
The most recent study, with a catalogue of his stained glass designs for the Morris company. *Quarto.* xiv+210pp with 280 illustrations (many coloured). *Original cloth.*
£12

1210 **Chance Brothers** Designs for coloured ornamental windows from the glass works of Chance Brothers & Co near Birmingham *(Birmingham) 1853*
Designs executed for Chance Brothers by the French architect and draughtsman Jean Étienne Frederic Giniez (1813-67). His range extends from mediaevalist Gothic to ornament in the manner of Dietterlin. *Octavo.* (8)pp and 28 chromolitho plates. *Original decorated cloth.* £45

1211 **Cox & Sons** Illustrated catalogue of designs for stained glass windows for churches and domestic use *London, Cox 1870 (but 1872)*
Contains a long list of Messrs Cox's recent commissions for stained glass windows, including work in Australia, Canada, India, Japan and the West Indies. *Quarto.* 28+(2)pp including 18pp of photolitho illustrations. *Original wrappers. Preserved in folder.* £38

1212 **Day, Lewis F.** Windows. A book about stained & painted glass Second edition *London, Batsford 1902*
Mediaeval and renaissance glass, with emphasis on design and the techniques of the stained glass worker. *Octavo.* xii+420pp with 257 illustrations, some full page. *Original cloth.* £20

1213 **(Duty on window glass)** A statement of the proceedings in Ireland in opposition to the imposed double duty on British crown window glass in a letter from Mr John Girgin, merchant, of Dublin, to Messrs Lucas, Pater, and Coathupe, glass-manufacturers of Bristol *Dublin 1791*
Illustrates the operation of protective duties imposed by the Irish Parliament to restrict the import of British glass. It mentions glass manufacturers in Belfast and Glasgow. *Folio.* 4pp. *Preserved in cloth folder.* £25

1214 **Eggert, Franz X.** Die Glasgemälde der neuerbauten Mariahilf-Kirche in der Vorstadt Au zu Munchen; ein Geschenk seiner Majestat des Königs Ludwig I von Bayern und auf Allerhöchstdessen Befehl in der königl. Glasmalerei-Anstalt in München, unter der Leitung des Professors Heinrich Hess, gefertigt *Munich, Schreiner 1845*
Nineteenth century stained glass executed for King Ludwig I of Bavaria by the Royal School of Glass Painting at Munich and given by him to the Mariahilf Kirche. *Folio. Title leaf (text in German and French), litho dedication leaf, 18 folding litho hand-coloured plates. Original portfolio, printed paper boards.* £55

1215 **Franks, (Sir) Augustus Wollaston** A book of ornamental glazing quarries, collected and arranged from ancient examples *London, Parker 1849*
Franks' first published work (see also item 1041). It illustrates on handcoloured engraved plates 112 mediaeval glazing quarries (lozenge shaped glass panes) carrying ornaments and emblems. Very much in the spirit of Charles Winston and dedicated by Franks to him. *Octavo. 31 + (3)pp and 112 handcoloured plates. Original decorated cloth.*
£30

1216 **Frothingham, Alice Wilson** Spanish glass *London, Faber 1964*
History of glassmaking in Spain until the end of the 18th century, with chapters on Catalan and Castilian glass and on the royal factory at La Granja. *Octavo. 96pp and 96pp of plates. Original cloth.*
£5

1217 **(Glass manufactories)** An act to incorporate certain persons therein named, and their successors, with proper powers for the purpose of establishing one or more glass manufactories within the Kingdom of Great Britain; and for the more effectually supporting and conducting the same upon an improved plan, in a peculiar manner, calculated for the casting of large plate glass *London 1773 (13 Geo. III XXXVIII)*
The Act recognizes the Governor and Company of British-cast Plate Glass Manufacturers as a corporate body and sets out its articles. The company, the first in Britain to make cast plate-glass, began operations in 1776 and after the removal of French competition following the French Revolution dominated the plate-glass market. The act lists its original proprietors. *Folio. (24)pp. Preserved in cloth folder.*
£35

1218 **Harden, D. B. (and others)** Masterpieces of Glass *London, British Museum 1968*
The catalogue of the British Museum's exhibition of outstanding pieces of glass from its collection on the occasion of the International Congress of Glass held in London in 1968. 269 items are described and illustrated and they include examples of all the principal periods of glass manufacture from the second millenium BC to the end of the eighteenth century AD. Individual objects exhibited are discussed in detail with full technical information, bibliographical references and commentary. *Quarto. 200pp with 269 photo illustrations and 4 colour plates. Original cloth.*
£5

1219 **Harrison, F.** The painted glass of York. An account of the medieval glass of the Minster and the parish churches *London, SPCK 1927*
Octavo. xvi + 254pp with 8 text illustrations and 32 plates. Original cloth.
£15

1220 **Hartshorne, Albert** Old English glasses. An account of glass drinking vessels in England, from early times to the end of the eighteenth century. With introductory notices, original documents, etc *London, Arnold 1897*
A massive historical survey still valuable for Hartshorne's mastery of the literature of the subject, some large chromolithograph plates and an appendix of unpublished documents. Necessary reading for the scholar if not the collector. *Quarto. xxiv + 490pp including 365 text illustrations, and 67 plates. Original quarter imitation vellum.* **Illustration at end of section.**
£62

1221 **Haynes, E. Barrington** Glass through the ages *Harmondsworth, Penguin 1970 (reprint of 1959 edition)*
Octavo. 320pp and 96pp of plates. Original wrappers.
£0.65

1222 **Hix, John** The glass house *London, Phaidon 1974*
Study of the evolution of glass architecture from the 17th century to the present day; few references to buildings outside Britain and the U.S.A. *Quarto. 208pp including 317 illustrations. Original cloth.*
£7

1223 **Holiday, Henry** Stained glass as an art *London, Macmillan 1896*
The opinions of a leading stained glass designer on questions of art and design; he draws his inspiration from the Pre-Raphaelites and not the Ecclesiologists. A chapter at the end is devoted to the work in stained glass of Burne Jones and W. B. Richmond. *Octavo. Coloured frontispiece, xx + 173 + (1)pp with text illustrations, and 20 collotype plates. Original cloth, uncut. Ex library.* £25

1224 **Honey, W. B.** Victoria and Albert Museum. Glass. A handbook for the study of glass vessels of all periods and countries & a guide to Museum collection *London, Ministry of Education 1946*
A good general survey of the subject. *Quarto. xii + 169 + (1)pp and 72pp of photo plates. Cloth.* £12

1225 **Hutchinson, F. E.** Medieval glass at All Souls College. A history and description, based upon the notes of the late G. M. Rushforth *London, Faber 1949*
Octavo. 67 + (1)pp, frontispiece and 32pp of plates. Original cloth. £6

1226 **(Irish Glass)** A bill to permit the exportation of glass, manufactured in Ireland, from thence to any place whatsoever, except Great Britain *1778*
The bill sought to lift an embargo on the export of glass made in Irish factories. See also item 1213. *Folio. (4)pp. Preserved in folder.* £15

1227 **Kenyon, G. H.** The glass industry of the Weald *Leicester, University Press 1967*
Glass making in Surrey and Sussex in the Elizabethan period, much of it by French Huguenot glassmakers. *Octavo. xxii + 231 + (1)pp and 22pp of plates. Original cloth.* £4

1228 **Knowles, John A.** Essays in the history of the York school of glass-painting *London, SPCK 1936*
A substantial critical study which complements Harrison's more descriptive survey (item 1219). *Octavo. xvi + 268pp with 79 text illustrations, and 63 plates. Original cloth.* £22

1229 **Korn, Arthur** Glas im Bau und als Gebrauchsgegenstand *Berlin, Pollak (1929)*
On the use of glass in building. It illustrates factories, shops, offices, etc., by Breuer, Le Corbusier, Gropius, Mies van der Rohe, Bruno Paul and others. *Quarto. 254pp with 187 illustrations. Original cloth.* £20

1230 **Korn, Arthur** Glass in modern architecture *London, Barrie & Jenkins 1967*
English translation of the preceding. *Quarto. 142 + (2)pp. Original cloth.* £5

1231 **Levieil, Pierre** (Description des arts et métiers). L'art de la peinture sur verre et de la vitrerie *Paris, Académie de Sciences 1774*
History, techniques, causes of decline of glass painting, discussed by a famous glass painter of the day, with a section on glazing and tracery. *Folio. xiv + 245 + (1)pp, 13 engraved plates. Quarter calf, cloth sides.* £65

1232 **McGrath, Raymond & A. C. Frost** Glass in architecture and decoration . . . with a section on the nature and properties of glass by H. E. Beckett *London, Architectural Press 1937*
First edition, juxtaposing the best modern work of the 1920s and 1930s with that of Robert Adam, Decimus Burton and Paxton in the same material. McGrath is himself a fine creative designer and the book is handsomely printed and illustrated. *Quarto. xi + (1) + 664pp including 371 illustrations. Original cloth.* **Illustration over page.** £35

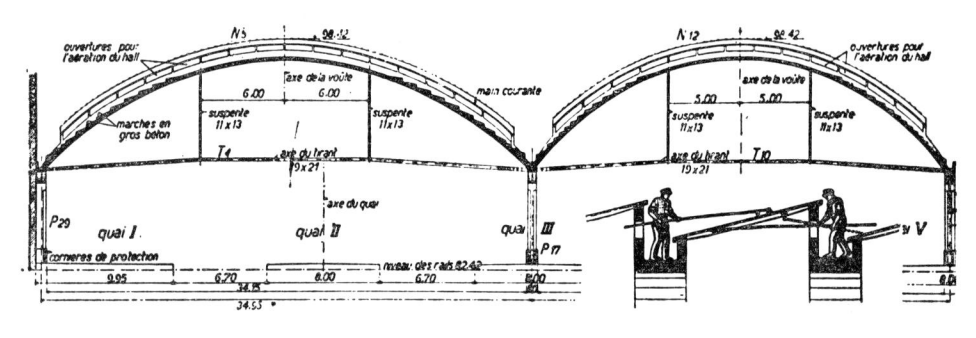

1232-3

1233 **McGrath, Raymond & A. C. Frost** Glass in architecture and decoration. New edition revised by Raymond McGrath. With a section on the nature and properties of glass . . . revised by H. E. Beckett *London, Architectural Press 1961*
Second edition, revised, enlarged, and with additional illustrations covering work of the 1940s and 1950s (which means that some of the illustrations in the first edition have been omitted). Quarto. 712pp including 418 photo illustrations and 82 text figs. Original cloth. **Illustration above.** £15

1234 **Middlemas, Keith** Continental coloured glass *London, Barrie & Jenkins 1971*
Quarto. 120pp with many coloured illustrations. £8

1235 **Nelson, Philip** Ancient painted glass in England 1170-1500 *London, Methuen 1913*
Includes useful lists of surviving glass arranged by county. Octavo. xviii+280pp with 34 text illustrations, frontispiece and 32 plates. Original cloth. £15

1236 **Pellatt, Apsley** Curiosities of glass making: with details of the processes and productions of ancient and modern ornamental glass manufacture *London, Bogue 1849 (reprint 1968)*
Excellent guide to the then current glass making processes. Octavo. viii+146+(2)pp with text illustrations and 6 colour plates. Original cloth. £8

1237 **Powell, Harry, J.** Glass-making in England *Cambridge, University Press 1923*
History of glass-making by the head of Messrs Powell, of the Whitefriars Works, London. Octavo. x+183+(1)pp including 106 illustrations. Original cloth. £18

1238 **Scheerbart, Paul** Glasarchitektur *Berlin, Verlag der Sturm 1914*
Scheerbart (1863-1915), 'best known as an eccentric writer of fantasticated novels' (Banham), was a friend of Bruno Taut, to whom this book is dedicated, and his faith in glass and contempt for conventional materials foreshadowed architectural developments of the 1920s. Important as part of the intellectual climate at the time that Taut and Gropius were emerging as major architects. Octavo. 125+(3)pp. Original wrappers. Preserved in folder. £55

1239 **Sewter, A. Charles** The stained glass of William Morris and his circle *New Haven, Yale University Press 1974*
A comprehensive history of the stained glass work of the Morris firm, full of information on Morris, Burne-Jones, Madox Brown and the other Pre-Raphaelites, and lavishly illustrated. A companion catalogue volume is announced. Quarto. xii+(2)+119+(3)pp with 16pp of colour illustrations and 232pp of plates carrying 665 monochrome illustrations. Original cloth. **Illustration opposite.** £20

1240 **Shaw, Henry** A book of sundry draughtes. Principaly serving for glasiers: and not impertinent for plasterers, and gardeners: besides sundry other professions *London, Pickering 1848*

Shaw explains in a preface that this is essentially copied from the 1615 'Book of Sundry Draughtes' (see item 1206), with the addition of a few designs by Thomas Willement and three plates showing window fastenings and stancheons. *Octavo. (8)pp and 117 plates. Original quarter cloth, printed paper boards.* £35

1241 **Sherrill, Charles Hitchcock** Stained glass tours in France *London, John Lane 1908*

Octavo. 298pp and 16 plates. Original cloth. £6

1242 **Sherill, Charles Hitchcock** Stained glass tours in England *London, John Lane 1909*

Octavo. xvi + 254pp and 16 plates, 5 maps. Original cloth. £6

1243 **Sherrill, Charles Hitchcock** A stained glass tour in Italy *London, John Lane 1913*

Octavo. xiv + 174pp and 33 plates, 1 folding map. Original cloth. £8

1244 **Sherrill, Charles Hitchcock** Stained glass tours in Germany, Austria and the Rhine Lands *London, John Lane 1927*

Octavo. xv + (3) + 304pp, colour frontispiece and 17 plates. Original cloth. £8

1245 **Sherrill, Charles Hitchcock** Stained glass tours in Spain and Flanders *London, John Lane 1924*

Octavo. 244pp, frontispiece and 16 plates. Original cloth. £8

1246 **Sowers, Robert** Stained glass: an architectural art *London, Zwemmer 1965*

Explores the relationship of glass and architecture and the viability of stained glass as an art form in modern secular society. *Quarto. 128pp including many illustrations, some coloured. Original cloth.* £5

1247 **Stannus, Mrs Graydon** Old Irish glass. New edition: revised and enlarged *London, The Connoisseur 1921*

Quarto. 16pp and 60 plates. Original cloth. £4

1239

1248 **Tarif du prix des glaces de la manufacture de Commentry** près Mon(t)luçon, département de l'Allier, dont le dépot est a Paris, Vieille Rue du Temple, No.126 *Paris, Gaultier-Laguionie (c 1810)*
Tables showing the cost in francs and centimes of plate glass in various sizes. Published just after decimalization, so measurements are given both in centimetres and inches. Octavo. (4) + 101 + (1)pp. Contemporary cloth. £25

1249 **Thorpe, W. A.** A history of English and Irish glass *London, Holland Press 1969 (reprint of 1929 edition)*
The classic history of English glassmaking. Quarto. xvi + 372pp and 168pp of plates. Limited edition. Original cloth. £18

1250 **Vavra, Jaroslav R.** 500 years of glass-making. The history of glass *Prague, Artia 1954*
English translation of a history of glass by a Czech scholar. It was written at an unpropitious period in the Cold War, but it is informative on Bohemian glass and politics are kept within bounds. Booksellers and librarians might even yearn to employ the Stakhanovite glass workers of Gusj, where 'norms are constantly being overfulfilled by two hundred and more percent'. Folio. 191 + (5)pp with 36pp index and 155 text illustrations, and 32 colour plates, 172pp of monochrome plates carrying 430 illustrations. Original cloth. £18

1251 **Warren, Phelps** Irish glass. The age of exuberance *London, Faber 1970*
Glass made in Ireland between 1780 and 1835. Octavo. Frontispiece 156pp and 102pp of plates. Original cloth. £6

1252 **Weale, John** (editor) Divers works of early masters in Christian decoration: with an introduction containing the biography, journal of travel, contemporaneous association in art, and a critical account of the works of Albert Durer; notices of his master Wohlgemuth and his friend Pirckheimer; Adam Krafft, and his sacrament-house at Nuremburg. With examples of ancient painted and stained glass, from York, West Wickham, Kent, and St. George's Chapel, Windsor; the ancient church and sacrament-house at Limbourg; the works of Dirk and Wouter Crabeth, &. Also a succinct account, with illustrations, of painted and stained glass at Gouda, in Holland, and the church of St Jacques at Liege *London, (Weale) 1846*
This ambitious publication stems from a visit by Weale to Holland during which he purchased from an architect at Utrecht a set of facsimile drawings of the windows of the church at Gouda. These are reproduced on chromolithograph plates made under the supervision of Owen Jones and John Waller. They are accompanied by a series of drawings by F. J. Rastrick of similar windows at St. Jacques, Liège; and by other more varied examples of stained glass from English sources. The text is made up by an account of the Durer circle composed by Weale from secondary sources; a section on the Crabeths translated from the Dutch by W. H. Leeds; and a short history of the Liège church and its windows. The significance of the publication was that it related English stained glass work to similar work on the European continent, and, through Durer, to the arts in a wider setting. Folio. 2 vols. Chromolitho frontispiece, litho half title, (2) + 52pp and 15 litho plates (1 coloured, 2 folding and 4 double-p); litho frontispiece, litho half title, title and 33 chromolitho plates (6 double-p). Original quarter morocco, gilt tooled spines with publisher's gilt device at foot. **Illustration opposite.** £140

1253 **Whall, C. W.** Stained glass works. A text-book for students and workers in glass . . . with diagrams by two of his apprentices and other illustrations *London, John Hogg 1905*
Octavo. xxviii + 390pp including 16 collotype plates and 73 text figs. Original cloth. £10

1254 **Wills, Geoffrey** English looking-glasses. A study of the glass, frames and makers (1670-1820) *London, Country Life 1965*
Quarto. 162pp including 164 illustrations. Original cloth. £8

1255

1255 **Winbolt, S. E.** Wealden glass. The Surrey-Sussex glass industry (A.D. 1226-1615) *Hove, Combridges 1933*
Octavo. *(10)+85+(1)pp with over 60 text illustrations. Original cloth.* £9

1256 **(Winston, Charles)** An inquiry into the difference of style observable in ancient glass paintings, especially in England: with hints on glass painting, by an amateur *Oxford, John Henry Parker 1847*
The first book to make a systematic classification by style of English mediaeval glass. Winston (1814-64), a barrister specializing in patent law, combined an exceptional technical grasp of stained glass processes with a keen critical eye, and in this first of his published works–issued as by an anonymous amateur–he established principles of classification which were fundamental to later research Curiously, he was not an advocate of strict mediaevalism for stained glass designs of his own time, and his view that it was improper to confine stained glass work 'to a mere system of servile and spiritless imitation' is a striking one for the 1840s. *Octavo. 2 vols. xiv+384pp; (2)+24pp and 75 litho plates of which some coloured. Original decorated cloth, spines repaired.*
£60

1257 **Winston, Charles** Memoirs illustrative of the art of glass-painting *London, John Murray 1865*
A collection of essays, published posthumously, with a biographical memoir and correspondence. *Octavo. Coloured frontispiece xiv + 362pp and 14 plates (12 coloured). Original cloth.* £40

1258 **Woodforde, Christopher** English stained and painted glass *Oxford, Clarendon Press 1954*
Octavo. Coloured frontispiece. xviii + 83 + (1)pp and 80 plates. Original cloth. £5

1259 **Patents for Inventions** Abridgments of Specifications. Class 56. Glass. 1897-1900, 1901-4, 1905-8, 1909-15, 1916-20, 1921-5, 1926-30 *London, HMSO 1903-32*
Run for 1897-1930 of specifications for glass, principally for improvements in the process of manufacture – the British Thomson-Houston Co., General Electric and Pilkingtons are prominent among the patentees. *Octavo. 7 vols bound in 2. Contemporary quarter morocco.* £70

1260 **Ashdown, Charles Henry** History of the Worshipful Company of Glaziers of the City of London, otherwise the Company of Glaziers and Painters of Glass *London, 1919*
Octavo. (8) + 163 + (1)pp and 6 photo plates 1 folding table. Original cloth. £10

1261 **Bles, Joseph** Rare English glasses of the XVII & XVIII centuries *London, Geoffrey Bles (c 1923)*
A substantial monograph based on the collections of the author and other private individuals. There are illustrations of 147 glasses, goblets, glass candlesticks, bowls, etc. A scarce work of reference. *Quarto. 269 + (3)pp including 100 plates carrying 147 mounted photo illustrations. Original cloth, uncut.* £54

1262 **Buckley, Francis** A history of old English glass *London, Benn 1925*
Includes much information drawn from 18th century newspapers and not available elsewhere, especially valuable for the cut glass trade. *Quarto. xxviii + 154 + (2)pp with 60 photo plates. Original cloth.* £48

1263 **Buckley, Wilfred** European glass. A brief outline of the history of glass making, with notes on various methods of glass decoration . . . with a foreword by Bernard Rackham . . . and with an essay on Dutch glass engravers by Dr Ferrand Hudig *London. Benn 1926*
Useful on the techniques of glass making and glass engraving. *Quarto. xxxvi + 96pp, with 110 photo plates. Original cloth.* £48

1264 **Arthur Churchill Ltd** A Coronation exhibition of royal, historical, political and social glasses commemorating eighteenth and nineteenth century events in English history *London, 1937*
A handsome, well illustrated trade catalogue. *Quarto. 44ff text, with 44 photo plates. Original cloth in slipcase.* £10

1265 **Fleming, Arnold** Scottish and Jacobite glass *Glasgow, Jackson 1938*
Strong on technology and on the place of glass in social history. *Quarto. xvi + 196pp, frontispiece and 56 plates. Original cloth.* £40

1266 **Hall, J. P.** Glass in modern architecture *(c 1937)*
Typescript thesis apparently written just before the publication of the first edition of McGrath's 'Glass in Architecture and Decoration' (item 000), but using many of the same illustrations and examples. *Quarto. (89)ff of typescript, with (111)ff of mounted photo illustrations. Cloth.* £15

1267 **Janneau, Guillaume** Modern glass *London, Studio 1931*
Illustrations of work by over 100 British, European and American designers of the period, with an introduction on Emile Gallé, Lalique and other prominent people and trends. *Quarto. viii + 184pp, including (128)pp of photo illustrations. Original cloth.* £24

1268 **Kazakova, L.** Gusj-Chrustalny *Moscow, Sovetskii Khudozhnik 1973*
A history of the Gusj glass factory, its content heavily weighted towards the period from 1959 onwards. The text is in Russian but there is a summary in rather poor English. *Quarto. 216pp with 153 photo illustrations (some coloured). Original boards.* £3

1269 **Lasteyrie, Ferdinand de** Histoire de la peinture sur verre, d'après ses monuments en France *(Paris, 1838 onwards)*
Lasteyrie's massive history of French stained glass was published in parts over a long period and seldom turns up in a complete state. This volume contains the portion of the text and plates that relates to the stained glass at Chartres, Bourges, Tours, Troyes and other cathedrals. The plates are drawn and lithographed by the author and printed by the firms of Lemercier Bénard, Letronne and Kaeppelin; all are hand-coloured, and they are very handsome. *Folio. Pages 1-160 (without prelims and text after p 160) and plates 1-80 (ex 110). Contemporary quarter morocco.* **Illustration below.** £65

1269

1270 **(Rackham, Bernard)** Victoria and Albert Museum. Department of Ceramics. A guide to the collections of stained glass *London, Board of Education 1936*
Octavo. x+(2)+138+(4)pp and 64pp of plates. £6

1271 **(Ramsey, William)** The Worshipful Company of Glass Sellers of London *London, for private circulation 1898*
A history of the Glass Sellers Company which prints correspondence with the Venetian glass maker Allesio Morrelli and other documents on the glass industry in the 17th century. *Octavo. 152+(4)pp with many illustrations. Original decorated cloth, gilt edges.* £12

1272 (Rowell, John) **Sidney M. Gold** A short account of the life and work of John Rowell *(Reading, privately published 1965)*
The first book to appear on an individual English glass painter of the eighteenth century. A painstaking and detailed account of the career of the Buckinghamshire artist John Rowell (1689-1756), cataloguing many hitherto undiscovered windows, including examples from All Souls and St John's Colleges, Oxford, Hartlebury Castle, Worcestershire, and The Vyne, Hampshire. *Octavo. (4) + 71 + (1)pp, frontispiece and 12 photo plates. Original cloth.*
£3

1273 **Westropp, M. S. Dudley** Irish glass. An account of glass-making in Ireland from the XVIth century to the present day *London, Herbert Jenkins (c 1920)*
Full of information on Irish glass factories and based on original documents, as well as extensively illustrated. *Quarto. 206pp with 40 plates illustrating 188 glass objects and 220 patterns and designs. Original cloth.*
£35

1274 **Whistler, Laurence** Engraved glass 1952-58 *London, Hart-Davis 1959*
A selection from Whistler's work as a glass engraver in the 1950s, including commissions for the Queen and Queen Mother and a glass designed to carry a poem by T. S. Eliot. As a commercial proposition for a publisher it can scarcely have been viable in the 1950s: but it is now long out of print and eminently collectable. *Octavo. 38pp, photo frontispiece and 88pp of photo illustrations. Publisher's decorated boards, from a design by the author.*
£34

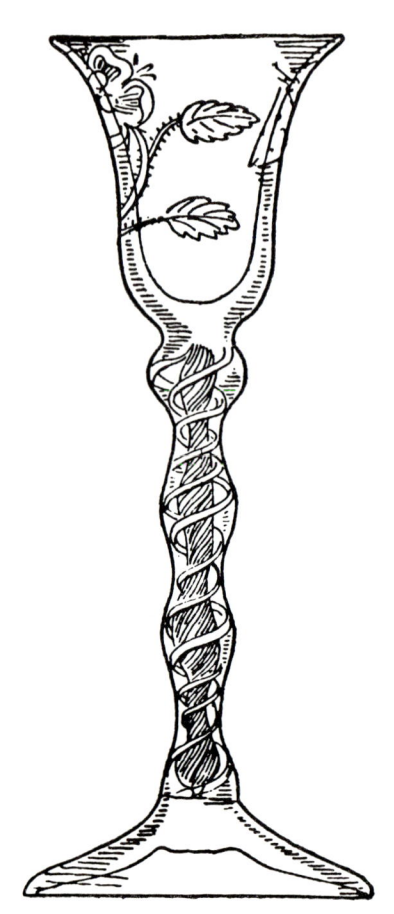

1220

Fabric and Textiles

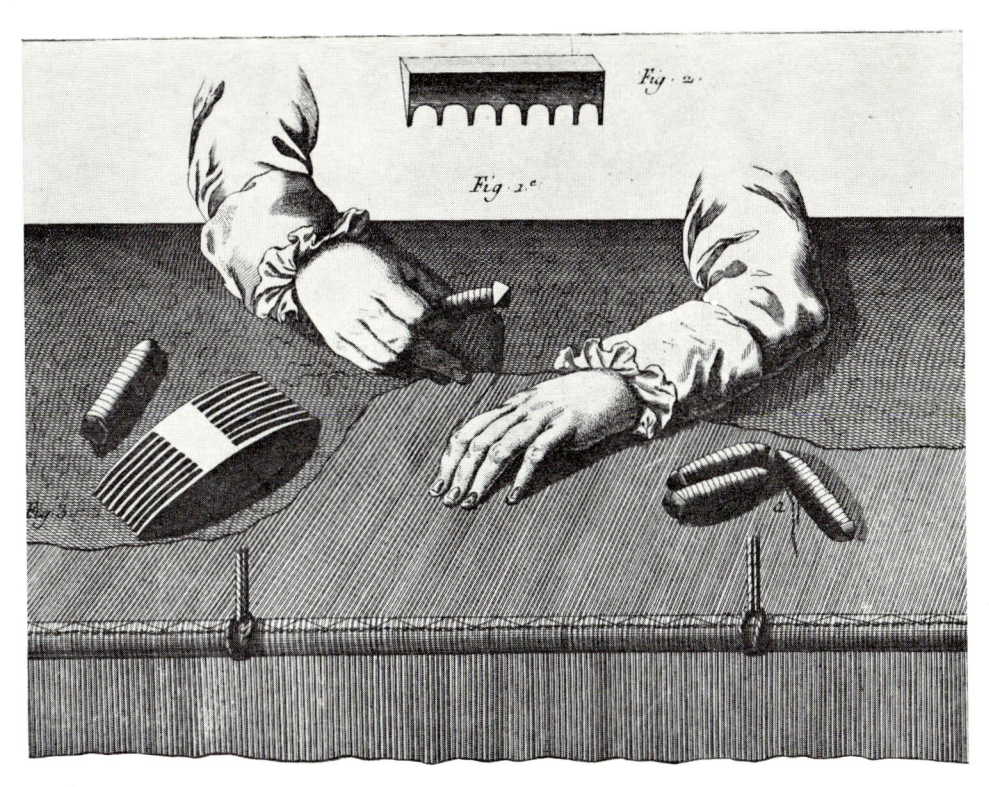

1301k

1301 **Diderot, D. & J. L. d'Alembert** (Encyclopédie). Recueil de planches sur les sciences, les arts libéraux, les arts méchaniques, avec leurs explication *Paris, Briasson, David, Le Breton & Durand 1762-72, Livorno 1772-6*

Extracts of the sections concerning the production of a wide variety of textiles and their dependant crafts. Diderot's particular interest in this industry and his fascination with the machinery in use is evident in the coverage he gives to the processes and the space he devotes to them. (See also item **1701**). *Each section listed is folio, the plates average is size 360 × 225mm and the suites are preserved in paper wallets.*

a **Draperie** (Cloth manufacture)
A suite showing all the processes of cloth manufacture and the relevant machinery, tools and equipment for washing stirring and rinsing, drying, sorting, beating and carding, teasing the fleece, spinning and reeling the thread, weaving, scoring, fulling, raising the nap, cropping, frising and pressing the wool cloth. The plates include two workshop views as well as other vignettes of workers carrying out the different tasks involved, a double-page plate of a loom, a full-page drawing of the fulling stock, and 2 plates illustrating the frising mill. *11 engraved plates of which 2 double-page with 50 illustrations, and 2pp of text.* £22

b **Fil et laine** (Spinning)
A suite dealing with the basic operations of spinning and preparing the thread for weaving. Five vignettes show the processes: as carried out in the home with women working a simple spinning-wheel with flyer, a hand spindle, a hand reel for winding into balls, a stick reel for winding into hanks; the workshop operation; and three views of various types of winding machines. The lower half of each plate gives working drawings of each piece of equipment with details of their parts. *Five engraved plates with 32 illustrations, and (1 + 1 blank)pp of text.* £15

c **Tisserand** (Weaver)
Full working drawings of a framed horizontal linen loom for making plain or tabby cloth, a double heddled loom with the shedding-mechanism operated by treadles. The illustrations include a double-page perspective view of the loom, plans and elevations from various angles and detailed drawings of the parts and pieces of the frame. Begins with view of a weaving shop. *Eight engraved plates of which 2 double-page, and 2pp text.* £12

d **Gazier** (Gauze loom)
Detailed drawings of a draw-loom for weaving gauze, with side and front views, details of the parts and ancilliary equipment, a large scale diagram showing the working of the warp threads and the achievement of the stages in the movement of the healds. *Four engraved plates with 21 illustrations, and (1 + 1 blank) pp text.* £10

e **Metier à faire du marli** (Marly loom)
Working drawings of the loom for weaving a fine cloth used in former times and known as marly. The plates include perspective view, plans, elevations, detailed drawings of each piece of the framework and the necessary attachments, and a final double-plate with a large scale diagram showing the interweaving of the threads for the pattern which made the marly weave. *Eight engraved plates of which 7 double-page, and (1 + 1 blank) pp of text.* £20

f **Faiseur de métier a bas, et faiseur de bas au métier** (Maker of stocking looms, & stocking weaver)
Illustrations of the earliest knitting machine, a hand stocking frame invented by the Reverend William Lee, curate of Calverton in Nottingham in 1589. The design is remarkable for the completeness and adaptability to its purpose and embodies all the principles used in most of the modern powered knitting machines. The plates show large drawings of the parts of its construction, and large scale diagrams of the various stages in the working of the hooked needles and the formation of the loops which produce the rows of stitches. The suite includes a workshop vignette of the frame being used in the home. *11 engraved plates numbered I-VII and I-IV of which 8 double-page with 95 illustrations, and 3 + (1 blank) pp.* £24

g **Soierie** (Silk manufacture)
The largest of the sections on the 'arts méchaniques' and the one in which Diderot took the greatest interest. The section is divided into 5 parts. I: Deals with the preparation of the silk before it is employed in making the fabric. It shows the various methods of reeling the silk beginning with a hand-turned crank-wheel, and shows various types of throwing machinery including Vauconson's winder, the Spanish winder, the Strasin's throwing machine, the Lyons machine and the type used traditionally in the Piedmont.
II: Concerns the weaving of plain and smooth silks, and has working drawings of the loom, illustrations of the settings of the warp threads, details of intricate parts of the machinery, patterns of the cording and healds, and the weave patterns in large scale diagrams for a wide variety of plain silk fabrics such as taffetas, gros de Tours, siamese silk, etc.
III: Shows the mechanics of the manufacture of brocades, damasks and figures silks, with working drawings of the loom, and the patterns and weaves of drugget, satined, lustred, double-sided and shiny Persian, Lucchanese, Gros de Tours etc, and for furnishing damasks, figured grosgrain, and Florentine damasks.
IV: Illustrates the techniques of velvet and velours with diagrams of the very intricate cut-velvet loom, and the setting and patterning for frised velours, English and Dutch velvets, cut velvets and details of the cop mill.
V: Concentrates on finishing processes showing the ways of shadowing certain kinds of materials, the knots used in the manufacture, ways of setting the heddles, lustering and watering silks, ways of folding the material which is to be moired, and gives large drawings of the calender machinery and the rollers. *135 engraved plates of which 23 double-page and 39 + (1) pp text.* £100

h **Teinturier en soie ou teinturier de rivière** (Silk dyer)
A very interesting series showing the dyeing of silk thread, with illustrations of the various types of coppers and other utensils, the special processes in the preparation of indigo and saffron dyes, rinsing the dyed threads in the river, and finally the drying process. The suite contains 5 workshop views of the various techniques and includes a large double-page view of the inside of a dyeing shed. *Eight engraved plates of which 1 double-page with 56 illustrations, and 2pp text.* £25

i **Découpeur et gaufreur d'étoffes** (Cutter and embosser)
The craft of cutting and embossing materials such as velours and paper, etc. with the tools and machinery involved. The illustrations include three vignettes showing a workshop where the materials are embossed by hand with stamping tools and by a hand-worked press using engraved plates, a workshop with a cylindrical roller press and a large hand-press, and a loft where the latest type of machinery had been installed. *Three engraved plates with 30 illustrations, and (1 + 1 blank) pp text.* £10

FABRIC AND TEXTILES 201

k **Tapisserie de haute-lisse des Gobelins – Tapisserie de basse-lisse des Gobelins – Teinture des Gobelins** (Gobelins factory high-warp and low-warp tapestry weaving – Dyeing at the Gobelins)
A complete set of the parts devoted to the weaving and dyeing of tapestries as practised in the Manufacture Royale des Gobelins on both the vertical high-warp looms and the horizontal low-warp looms. The illustrations include large double-plate workshop views, details of the constructions of the different types of looms and their parts, including the improvements made by Vaucanson, the setting of the warp threads, the position of the weavers when working, drawings of actions such as tracing the design, passing the shuttles, tightening the threads, winding the tapestry, and sewing and knotting together the different colours. The section on dyeing includes large pictures of the horse-powered wheel for drawing water, details of the pumps and cisterns, as well as the dyeing processes. *13 engraved plates of which 2 double-page, with 44 illustrations, and 2pp text; 18 engraved plates of which 5 double-page with 43 illustrations and 3 + (1 blank)pp text; 11 engraved plates of which 3 double-page, with 45 illustrations, and 2pp text. (Together 42 plates of which 10 double-page).* **Illustration at head of section.** £100

l **L'art de faire des tapis de pié façon de Turquie** (The making of oriental carpets)
Includes large workshop view, details of the loom and the tools, the making of the warp chains, the application of the pattern and diagrams showing the knotting and cutting of the threads to make the velvet pile. A fascinating vignette shows the means of spotlighting the work with a lamp in a tin holder hung round the weaver's neck. *Eight engraved plates of which 2 folding, with 43 illustrations and 2pp text.* £25

m **Rubanier** (Ribbon loom)
Detailed drawings showing the working parts and the construction of the frame and equipment of a loom for producing five lengths of ribbon at the same time. *10 double-page engraved plates with over 200 illustrations and 3 + (1 blank)pp text.* £15

n **Passementier** (Trimming maker)
The manufacture of various types of trimmings showing details of a cording-frame, a twisting wheel and loom, a braiding loom with point paper diagrams of the various patterns which can be made, and illustrations of the finished effects. The machinery and methods are shown for the making of galoons, figured ribbons, for mounting and rolling the ribbon, the process of fumigation, fringe-making, for producing low-warp tapestry and fancy ribbons, and for making simple tapestry on a square-framed hand loom. A fascinating suite with 13 vignettes of the craftsmen performing these various tasks in the workshops. *29 engraved plates of which 3 double-page with 470 illustrations, and 6pp of text.* £35

o **Brodeur** (Embroiderer)
Embroidery on frames or on tambourines with details of the different tools used and the stitches employed as well as illustrations showing the fixing on of sequins, palets and beads, with some of the designs used. *Two engraved plates with 29 illustrations, and 2pp text.* £6

p **Dentelle et façon du point** (Lace and its stitches)
An informative and decorative suite with a vignette of workers producing pillow-made lace and pricking out the pattern in vellum, while large drawings show the details of the lacemaking cushion, the pins and bobbins, 1 plate shows the stages in lacing a double set of two-thread plaiting, and the final plate gives pricked patterns and the finished lacing of Point d'Angleterre, four pinned pattern, square point, and a design for a lace flounce with a mesh background and closeworked flowers. *Three engraved plates with 20 illustrations, and 1 + (1 blank)pp text.* £10

1302 **Ackermann, R(ichard)** Repository of Arts &c: Needlework designs *London, R. Ackermann, Nov 1811-Dec 1820*

Designs for embroidery, needlework and lace, including borders, floral designs, flounces, muslin patterns and designs in a rectangular framework, a border and pattern for a veil, a chinese design, and a pattern for the cover of an ottoman for the King of Persia. *Octavo. 52 designs in etching and aquatint, woodcut and lithograph on 30 loose sheets; average size 145 × 230mm. Preserved in paper wallet.* £20

1303 **Ackermann, R(ichard)** Repository of Arts &c: Textile samples *London, R. Ackermann, July 1809-Nov 1811*

Samples of printed and woven textiles including printed cotton, linen, muslin, piqué, chintz, marly, damask, and silk, showing the latest materials which were being produced and sold in the fashionable shops. The samples, designed to be set 3 or 4 to a sheet are set within allegorical woodcuts of two different formats. *Octavo. 33 (of 64 samples) on 17 sheets. Samples sizes either 25 × 48mm or 43 × 50mm. Preserved in paper wallet.* £18

1304 **Asphaltum** Aspen-Ville Art Wallpapers. Season 1895 *London, Asphaltum, 1895*

A wallpaper pattern-book, of the type still familiar, showing a full range of inexpensive machine-made wall coverings in prices ranging from 3d to 3 shillings a piece. The samples begin with 3 qualities of lining-paper and progress through sanitary (i.e. washable), varnished and tile papers, wood-grains, examples particularly suitable for ceilings and staircases, to embossed, gilt-printed and satinette papers. A few groups are of particular interest: a series of four very dark papers advertised as 'French', a group of distempered papers with pleasant visual effects but a disagreeable texture, and a large series of papers showing co-ordinate patterns for dado, upper wall, frieze and ceiling. The patterns are predominately floral and those appealing most to the modern eye are often at the lower end of the price range with the most attractive in what is designated as 'art colouring'. London readers who have some experience of home decorating will be familiar with some of the patterns which they will probably have seen in resisting fragments, and will know that what the paper lacked in quality the hanger made up in the adhesive. Other patterns can still be seen in the more retrospective of the designs on sale today. Nothing has been discovered of the firm of Asphaltum. It may have been one of the London branches of the firm of Lightbown, Aspinall & Co. Several of the more attractive designs in this pattern-book are in the style of William Silver who was among the finer designers employed by that firm and made his greatest contributions in the 1890s. *Oblong folio. Over 500 samples of coloured papers and matching friezes. Original decorative lettered cloth.*   £225

1305 **Clouzot, Henri & Frances Morris** The Metropolitan Museum of Art. Painted and printed fabrics. The history of the manufactory at Jouy and other ateliers in France 1760-1815 by Henri Clouzot. Notes on the history of cotton printing especially in England and America by Frances Morris *New York, Metropolitan Museum of Art 1927*

Octavo. xvii+(1)+108+(2)pp, colour frontispiece and 92pp of plates. Original decorative cloth. Presentation copy from Frances Morris.   £22

1306 (**Coptic tapestries**) Étoffes et tapisseries Coptes. Influence Antique Byzantine Sassanide. 1e série. 2e série *Paris, Hessling (c 1920)*

Small folio. 2 sets of 8 plates each. Original wrappers.   £9

1307 **Damase, Jacques** Sonia Delaunay. Rhythms and colours *London, Thames & Hudson 1972*

Fully illustrated study, which includes designs for clothes and textiles. Quarto. 412pp with many illustrations (some coloured). Original cloth.   £14

1308 **Dufy, Raoul** Gazette du Bon Ton. No 8. Toiles de Tournon, lampas, brocarts et brocatelles *Paris, Editions Lucien Vogel & Bon Ton (1920)*

Designs for furnishing fabrics by the famous artist for the firm of Bianchini & Férier. They include two linen designs 'Le Tennis' and 'Les Arums', two brocades 'Longchamps' and the beautiful blue and gold 'Pégase', a brocatelle 'Les Fruits' and a richly coloured chinese silk 'La Jungle'. *Four coloured litho plates numbered XXXVIII-XL, with monochrome plates on inside of the publisher's printed wrappers.*   £8

1309 **Dupont-Auberville** L'art, la décoration et l'ornement des étoffes et des tissus chez les anciens et chez les modernes... Recueil historique, practique et technique de décoration polychromes *Paris, (Bachelin-Deflorenne, c 1875)*

A historical encyclopedia of fabrics of all kinds: silks, satins, velvets, brocades, damasks, wool fabrics, woven materials, textiles, tapestries, carpets, embroidery and trimmings from all periods, places and styles, with illustrations of over 600 examples taken from various museums and specialist collections. One of the earliest pictorial surveys of its kind to concentrate on historical fabrics. *Large quarto. 4 parts in 1. (12)+37+(3)pp and 100 chromolitho plates with 100 unnumbered ff of descriptive text. Buckram portfolio with original printed boards preserved.* **Illustration opposite.**   £140

1310 **Dupont-Auberville** Sammlung von Decorationen Stickereien und Stoffmustern aus der Bluthezeit der Renaissance. 38 Tafeln in Farbendruck mit begleitenden Erlauterungen... Deutsche Ausgabe von Rob. Reinhardt *Stuttgart, Paul Neff 1881*

Chromolithographic illustrations of 16th century European silk and damask patterns. This is a German translation using the plates of the original French edition. *Folio. Litho title, 3ff text and 38 chromolitho plates each with accompanying leaf of text. Original decorated cloth, rebacked.* £40

1311 **Eberl, Bruno** Mustersammlung orientischer Teppiche *Vienna, (the author, c 1900)*

Illustrations of every type of oriental carpet with a short description on each plate providing the relevant information for each example. *Octavo. 20 coloured and 126 monochrome plates. Publisher's printed cloth portfolio.* £15

1312 **Entwisle, E. A.** A literary history of wallpaper *London, Batsford 1960*

Combines a bibliography of literature on wallpaper with an anthology of literary references to it. *Octavo. 211 + (1)pp, coloured frontispiece and 102pp of plates. Original cloth.* £8

1313 **Fischbach, Friedrich** Ornamente der Gewebe. Gezeichnet und herausgegeben von Friedrich Fischbach *Hanau, G. M. Alberti 1874-80*

Textile designs from Egyptian times to the 18th century (but chiefly of the late Middle Ages), reproduced in colour from Fischbach's skilful drawings. A useful collection of precedents for the 19th century designer. *Folio. (2) + x pp and 159 (ex 160) coloured plates. Cloth portfolio, with original chromolitho front wrapper preserved inside.* £140

1314 **Gerspach, M.** Les tapisseries Coptes *Paris, Quantin 1890*

Octavo. (4) + 8pp and (196)pp of illustrations of tapestries, several coloured. Original cloth. £15

1315 **Godden, Geoffrey A.** Stevengraphs and other Victorian silk-work pictures *London, Barrie & Jenkins 1971*

Godden lists 1061 different items made by the Coventry firm of Thomas Stevens and its competitors. *Quarto. 492pp with 309 illustrations. Original cloth.* £10

1316 **Godon, Julien** Painted tapestry and its application to interior decoration. Practical lessons in tapestry painting with liquid colour *London, Lechertier Barbe & Co, 1879*
Octavo. xviii + 89 + (1)pp and 6 plates (of which 5 coloured); 26pp of adverts for paints, brushes, etc. Original cloth, partly unopened. £9

1317 **Guérinet, Armand** Étoffes Byzantines, Coptes, Romaines, etc. du IVe au Xe siècle *Paris (c 1920)*
Folio. Title leaf, 16 plates (of which 12 coloured). Original marbled paper boards, cloth spine. £25

1318 **Guerinet, Armand** Indiennes, toiles de Jouy, tapis orientaux, etc. 6e série *Paris (c 1920)*
Folio. Title leaf and 32 plates. Original marbled paper boards, cloth spine. £25

1319 **Hooper, Luther** Hand-loom weaving plain & ornamental ... with line drawings by the author & Noel Rooke *London, John Hogg 1910*
A volume in Lethaby's 'Artistic Crafts' series. Octavo. xxiv + 338 + (2)pp with 125 text figures, and 18 collotype plates. Original cloth. £9

1320 **Huetson, T. L.** Lace and bobbins. A history and collector's guide *Newton Abbot, David & Charles 1973*
Octavo. 188pp and 16pp of plates. Original cloth. £3.95

1321 **Hughes, Therle** English domestic needlework. 1660-1860 *London, Abbey Fine Arts, 1974*
Octavo. Coloured frontispiece, 256pp and 51 photographic plates (of which 3 coloured). Publisher's cloth. £2.50

1322 **Hulst, Roger A. d'** Tapisseries flamandes du XIVe au XVIIIe siècle ... deuxième édition *Brussels, Arcade, 1966*
Pictorial history of Flemish tapestries. Quarto. xxxiii + (1) + 315 + (3)pp with many illustrations, some coloured. Original cloth. £15

1323 **Jackson, Mrs F. Nevill** A history of hand-made lace ... with supplementary information by Ernesto Jesurum *London & New York, Gill, Scribner 1900*
Deals with the origin of lace, the growth of the great lace centres, modes of manufacture, methods of distinguishing various types, and the care of lace. The subject is well covered and illustrated with plates which illustrate the fashion of wearing the material as shown in contemporary portraits. It includes a good bibliography and a comprehensive dictionary of terms. Quarto. xii + 245 + (3)pp including 200 text illustrations, and 18 plates. Publisher's decorated cloth. £24

1324 **Jacobs, Bertram** The story of British carpets. Second edition *London, Carpet Review 1972*
Octavo. (6) + 212pp with text illustrations. Original cloth. £2

1325 **Jacoby, Heinrich** Eine Sammlung orientalischer Teppiche. Beitrag zur Geschichte des orientalischen Teppichs an Hand von 47 durch die Persische- Teppichs-Gesellschaft gesammelten Knupfarbeiten der letzten 4 Jahrhunderte *Berlin, Frisch 1937*
Quarto. x + (2) + 140pp and 51 plates, of which 4 coloured, 99 text illustrations. Original cloth. £18

1326 **(Japanese textile printing)** Yuzen stencil sheets *Japan (c 1875)*
A group of stencils of the kind which formed the main working tool for the traditional Japanese printer of textiles; the dye being applied over the stencils with a large soft brush

to prevent damage. The sheets in the group are mainly small repeat patterns of which several are formed by small punched holes. Some are intended to have a bolder design printed over them. Others have the network of fine hairs or silk threads forming a strengthening mesh to hold the pattern together. It was these types which formed the forerunners of silk screen printing as we know it today. This type of printing method takes its name from the man to whom the invention is attributed: a 17th century Shinto priest named Someya Yuzen. The sheets are in good condition. Some have been used for printing but many are in a pristine state. *34 cut stencil sheets on brown oiled paper. Pattern sizes vary from 351 × 115mm to 350 × 210mm on sheets of sizes from 405 × 240mm to 420 × 317mm. Each sheet preserved in stiff paper folder. In drop-back box.* **Illustration below.** £85

1326

1327 **Jones, M. W.** The history and manufacture of floorcloth and linoleum. A paper read before the Bristol section of the Society of Chemical Industry at the University *(Bristol 1920)*
Octavo. 42pp. Original cloth, unopened. £8

1328 **Kendrick, A. F.** Victoria and Albert Museum. Department of textiles. Catalogue of tapestries *London, Board of Education 1924*
Octavo. viii + 102pp and 36pp of plates. Original cloth. £10

1329 **Lenoir, G. Félix** Practical and theoretical treatise on decorative hangings or guide to upholstery... compiled with the assistance of head cutters of the leading Paris houses. Translated by C. J. Cassirer *Brussels, Lyon-Claesen (1890s)*
Plates only. The curtains and heavy classical draperies illustrated admit no breath of the Art Nouveau or even of the fashions of the Nineties, but Lenoir's publication must date from the last decade of the century. *Folio. 80 tinted litho plates (lacking plate 48). Original printed portfolio, repaired.* £22

1330 **Lewis, Frank** English chintz from earliest times until the present day *Benfleet, F. Lewis 1935*
A history of the manufacture of chintz and printed textiles generally, illustrated by over 150 examples of printed fabrics dating between 1769 and 1935. *Thick quarto. 36pp, frontispiece and 152 plates each with facing page of text. No 206 of a limited edition of 500 copies. Original cloth.* £45

1331 **London Carpet Company Ltd.** Catalogue *London (c 1930)*
Coloured illustrations of their range of carpets. *Oblong quarto. 16pp, illustrations. Original wrappers.* £4

1332 **(Maple & Co.)** Concerning carpets and art decoration of floors *London, (Maple & Co.) 1884*

Both a guide to carpets generally and an advertisement for Maple & Co.; 'Messrs. Maple & Co. feel that their extensive practical knowledge and experience enable them to offer to those about to furnish suggestions and advice of real value' – and they naturally advise the purchase of their own carpets. *Octavo. (2) + 99 + (1)pp. Original decorated cloth.* £12

1333 **Marillier, H. C.** English tapestries of the eighteenth century. A handbook to the post-Mortlake productions of English weavers *London, Medici Society 1930*

Octavo. xxiii + (1) + 128 + (4)pp and 48 plates. Original cloth. £15

1334 **Modern drapery and allied trades wholesale and retail** By leading specialists in every department under the editiorship of William S. Murphy *London, Gresham Publishing Co. 1914*

Review of the drapery trade in its entirety (materials, manufacture, shops, sales, finance), with a guide to technical terms and other useful information. *Octavo. 4 vols. Original cloth.*
Illustration below. £36

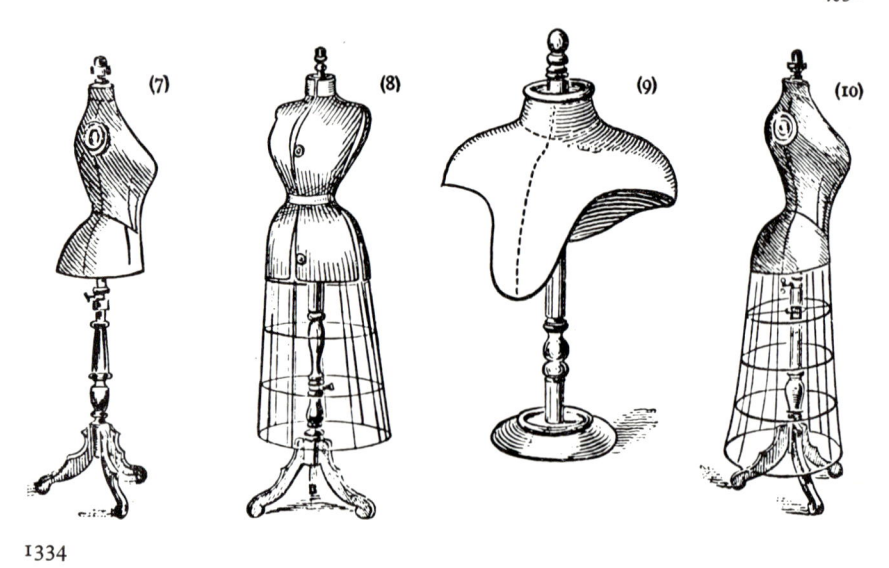

1334

1335 **Modern French tapestries** From original cartoons especially designed by the following contemporary artists: Braque, Raoul Dufy, Leger, Lurcat, Henri-Matisse, Picasso, Rouault *London, Lefevre Galleries 1937*

An exhibition catalogue. *Quarto. 24pp and 7 photo illustrations. Original wrappers.* £9

1336 **Morton, Jocelyn** Three generations in a family textile firm *London, Routledge 1971*

A history of Morton Sundour Fabrics Ltd and of the Morton family, including much information on the textile trade and textile designers; Voysey did much work for the firm and it had a long-standing interest in up-to-date designing. *Octavo. xxii + 480 + (2)pp, frontispiece and 34pp of plates. Original cloth.* £15

1337 **Patents for Inventions** Abridgments of specifications relating to sewing and embroidering. AD 1755-1866 *London, 1871*

Octavo. xxii + (2) + 384pp. Original wrappers. £10

1338

1338 **Pine, John** The tapestry hangings of the House of Lords: representing the several engagements between the English and Spanish fleets, in the ever memorable year MDLXXXVIII, with the portraits of the lord High-Admiral, and the other noble commanders, taken from the life. To which are added ... ten charts of the sea-coasts of England and a general one ... shewing the places of action between the two fleets; ornamented with medals struck upon that occasion, and other suitable devices. Also an historical account of each day's action, collected from the most authentic manuscripts and writers *London, the author 1739*

These important tapestries were commissioned around 1600 from the Dutch painter of seascapes, Hendrik Cornelisz Vroom (1566-1640), by Lord Howard of Effingham, who had commanded the British fleet at the time of the Armada. In Pine's day the tapestries hung in part in the Royal Wardrobe and in part in the House of Lords, and Pine gives as a reason for publishing engravings of them the danger that 'Time, or Accident, or Moths may deface these valuable shadows'. Those in the House of Lords were in fact destroyed in the fire that devastated the Palace of Westminster in 1834 and **Pine's is the only record of them.** The plates of the tapestries were engraved by Pine from drawings by C. Lemprière. The historical text, based on original documents, was written for Pine by Philip Morant, the historian of Essex. *Folio and oblong folio. 2 vols. Engraved title, (4) + 23 + (1)pp; 18 large engraved plates, of which 15 are printed in blue and black. Contemporary marbled paper boards.* **Illustration above.** £850

1339 **Raphael Sanzio da Urbino** The seven cartoons of Raphael, formerly at Hampton-Court now, for their better preservation, in the Queen's Palace, engraved in the Academy of Arts in the University of Glasgow, by James Mitchell, and the late ingenious William Buchanan, educated there *Glasgow, Robert & Andrew Foulis 1773*

A little-known set of engravings made either after Dorigny's drawings or his set of engravings, and probably the largest engraved suite produced in Glasgow up to that time. *Letterpress title and 7 engraved plates, sizes varying from 510:520 × 605:765mm, with wide margins. Preserved in cloth portfolio.* £65

1344

1340 **Robinson, Stuart** A history of dyed textiles. Dyes, fibres, painted bark, batik, starch-resist, discharge, tie-dye, further sources for research *London, Studio Vista 1969*

Octavo. 112pp and 24pp of plates. Original cloth. £5

1341 **Robinson, Stuart** A history of printed textiles. Block, roller, screen design, dyes, fibres, discharge, resist, further sources for research *London, Studio Vista 1969*

Octavo. 152pp and 40pp of plates. Original cloth. £5

1342 **Rock, Daniel** South Kensington Museum. Textile fabrics; a descriptive catalogue of the collection of church-vestments, dresses, silk-stuffs, needlework and tapestries, forming that section of the Museum *London, Chapman & Hall 1870*

A substantial collection, particularly rich in Continental vestments of the mediaeval period; the bulk of it was given to the museum by Dr Bock, a canon of Aachen, strongly influenced by Pugin, whose designs for vestments became known in Germany after the 1851 Exhibition. Daniel Rock was himself a close friend and admirer of Pugin. *Octavo. clxviii + 356pp and 20 chromolitho plates. Original cloth, rebacked.* £40

1343 **(Silks and velvets)** An act for encouraging the silk manufactures of this kingdom, and for securing the duties payable upon the importation of velvets, wrought silks, and silks mixed with other materials, not manufactured in Great Britain *London 1753*

Imposes strict controls on the import of silks and velvets. *Folio. (8)pp.* £7

1344 **Sugden, Alan Victor & John Ludlam Edmondson** A history of English wallpaper 1509-1914 *London, Batsford 1925*

Splendidly produced and very comprehensive history of wallpaper manufacture in England, based on thorough research and documentation and revealing the major role of designers – whether actively engaged in the trade like William Morris and Shand Kydd, or working from outside like Voysey, Lewis Day, Walter Crane, Talbert, Godwin and Dresser – in the development of the industry. There are histories of all important firms of wallpaper printers and a separate section on Lincrusta, Tynecastle and other varieties of raised wall covering. *Quarto. xiii +(1) + 281 +(1)pp, with 70 coloured illustrations tipped in on thick grey paper and 188 monochrome illustrations. Text printed on cream paper with wide margins. Original full gilt stamped vellum. No 22 of a limited autographed edition.*
Illustration above. £140

1345 **Swain, Margaret H.** Historical needlework. A study of influences in Scotland and Northern England *London, Barrie & Jenkins 1970*
A study based on signed or well-documented pieces. *Octavo. xii + 140pp and 68 photo plates (of which 10 coloured) on 26ff. Publisher's cloth.* £4

1346 **Tattersall, C. E. C.** A history of British carpets from the introduction of the craft until the present day *Benfleet, Lewis 1934*
The first history of carpet manufacture in Britain, with full technical information on early carpets, many large colour plates and short histories of firms. *Large quarto. Frontispiece, 182pp and 116pp of plates (many coloured). Original cloth. Dampstained at one corner but a scarce book.* £58

1347 **Thomson, W. G.** A history of tapestry from the earliest times until the present day *London, Hodder & Stoughton 1906*
First edition. The only comprehensive study of the subject in English. *Quarto. xvi+(2)+506pp, with 4 colour and 75 monochrome plates. Contemporary quarter vellum, patterned paper sides.* £18

1348 **Thomson, W. G.** A history of tapestry... third edition with revisions edited by F. P. & E. S. Thomson *Wakefield, EP 1973*
This includes a biographical sketch of the author by his son. *Quarto. xxiv+596pp, with over 100 photo plates (some coloured). Original cloth.* £10

1349 **Thornton, Peter** Baroque and rococo silks *London, Faber 1965*
Study of silks and silk patterns of the 17th and 18th centuries, based on wide research and the collections of the major museums. *Quarto. 209+(3)pp and 120pp of plates. Original cloth.* £9

1350 **Thurstan, Violetta** A short history of ancient decorative textiles *London, Favil Press 1954*
Second edition, revised. *Octavo. 96pp and 20 plates. Original cloth.* £6

1351 **Townsend, W. G. Paulson** Modern decorative art in England its development & characteristics. Volume 1. Woven & printed fabrics, wallpapers, lace & embroidery *London, Batsford 1922*
Contains illustrations of fabric designs by William Morris, Walter Crane, Voysey, Shand Kydd and others; the accompanying text identifies the main trends in design and is informative on the relationship of artist and manufacturer. No further volumes were issued. *Folio. xiii+(1)+149+(1)pp including 174 illustrations, many coloured. Original cloth.* £20

1352 **Wardle, Patricia** Victorian Lace *London, Herbert Jenkins 1968*
Octavo. 286pp including 12 text figures, and 64pp of plates. Original cloth. **Illustration below.** £3

1352

1353 **Waring & Gillow Ltd** Carpets of quality *London (c 1920)*
Lavish catalogue, with colour illustrations and printed in red and black with decorated initials. *Folio. 64pp with 42 mounted colour illustrations. Original printed wrappers.* £14

1354 **Warner, Sir Frank** The silk industry of the United Kingdom. Its origin and development *London, Drane (c 1915)*
Full of information on silk manufacture in Britain since the 16th century – at Norwich, Spitalfields, Macclesfield and elsewhere – and quoting from many original documents. *Octavo. 664pp and 54 plates. Original cloth. Ex library.* £17

1355 **Weibel, Adele Coulin** Two thousand years of textiles. The figured textiles of Europe and the Near East *New York, Pantheon 1952*
Excellent on textile history and techniques, with illustrations drawn entirely from American collections, many unfamiliar to the European scholar. *Quarto. xii+169+(3)pp with 332 illustrations. Original cloth in slipcase.* £40

1356 **Alford, Lady M.** Needlework as art *London, 1886 (EP reprint 1975)*
A history of needlework approached through style, design, colour, pattern, and materials with separate chapters on stitches and the different forms used for each type of end product. *Octavo. xxiv+(2)+422+(2 blank)pp including 29 text figures, and 85 plates (of which 2 double-page, the rest full-page). Publisher's cloth.* £8

Ornament

1401

1401 **Ackermann, R.** A selection of ornaments in forty pages. For the use of sculptors, painters, carvers, modellers, chasers, embossers &c. Part Ist (– Part III) *London, R. Ackermann's Lithographic Press, 1st November 1817, 1st June 1818, 1st Jan 1819*

This first work of decoration to be printed in the lithographic process provides an almost complete inventory of every classical type of motif capable of ornamental use. Friezes, mouldings, arabesques, scrolls, animals, figures and figure groups from antique vases, putti, satyrs, trophies, busts, and statues are interspersed, several on a page, with furniture designs, fountains, tripods, urns, casks, sarcophagi, candelabra, vases and other ornaments with all the appendages to provide easily followed patterns for small craftsmen to copy when giving a fashionable neo-classical appearance to interiors and objects.
Small folio. 3 parts in two. 40+40+40 lithographic plates including 3 titles. Part I in original paper boards, rebacked, with publisher's printed part-title wrapper pasted on front cover; Parts II and III in 1 volume, quarter green morocco. **Illustration above.** £150

1402 **Antonelli, Giuseppe** (editor) Collezione de'migliori ornamenti antichi sparsi nella citta di Venezia coll'aggiunta di alcuni frammenti di gotica architettura e di varie invenzioni di un giovane alunno di questa Imp. Reg. Accademia. Seconda edizione *Venice, G. Antonelli 1843*

An ornamental pattern book for artists and craftsmen with examples of ornamental reliefs and painted decorations on cornices, friezes, pilasters, capitals, statue bases, ceilings and sarcophogae, primarily from Venetian buildings. Although the work concentrates on renaissance and classical type examples of arabesques and scroll work the last two parts venture away from the Veneto to illustrate gothic work at Nuremberg, Strasbourg, Reims, Orleans, and even as far as Batalha and Lavenham. The first edition of the work had been issued in 1831. *Oblong quarto. 12 parts. (34)pp and 120 etched plates; each part with 2pp and 10 plates, and 10pp introduction. Publisher's printed wrappers, untrimmed, in board cover.*
£55

1403 **Audsley, W. & G.** Outlines of ornament in the leading styles. Selected from executed ancient and modern works. A book of reference for the architect, sculptor, decorative artist, and practical painter *London, Sampson Low 1881*

In this book the Audsleys discuss 'form' alone, 'divested of the fascination of gold and colour', and ornaments are arranged under type – fret ornament, interlaced ornament, and so on – rather than by date and style. There is however a useful range of Japanese designs. *Folio. (8)+14+(2)pp and 59 photolitho plates. Original cloth.* £45

1404 **Audsley, W. & G.** Polychromatic decoration as applied to buildings in the mediaeval styles *London, Sotheran 1882*

A 'practical and suggestive guide' for architects and decorators; the authors' intention is to combine in their designs new trends in polychromatic decoration and features of mediaeval ornament as shown by surviving fragments. *Folio. vi+(2)+32pp and 36 chromolitho plates (printed by Didot) with 33ff of descriptive text. Original cloth.* £50

1405 **(Audsley, W. & G.)** The Sermon on the Mount *London, Day & Son 1861*

'Illuminated by W. & G. Audsley architects, Liverpool. Illustrated by Charles Rolt Chromolithographed by W. R. Tymms'. A major example of mid Victorian chromolithography. See McLean:'Victorian Book Design and Colour Printing' p 133. *Large folio. 17 chromolitho plates. Original gilt decorated cloth with gilt stamped crosses and foliage patterns on covers.* £160

1406 **B. Bros.** (and others) Three trade catalogues of ornamental mouldings *London (c 1890)*

Of these, one, issued by B. Bros., is for 'Oval, Chippendale, swept and emblematic frames'; one is for 'Best washable gilt Alhambra and ornamental picture frame mouldings' (and is slightly defective); and the other carries no title. *2 vols quarto and 1 vol oblong folio. Original wrappers in cloth folder.* £45

1407 **Barnard, Julian** The decorative tradition *London, Architectural Press 1973*

On the Victorians' use of exterior ornament (sculpture, metalwork, terracotta, tiles, mosaic) on houses and public buildings. *Octavo. 144pp and 150 photo illustrations. Original cloth.* £5

1408 **Beauvallet, P. N.** Fragmens d'architecture, sculpture et peinture, dans le style antique; composés ou recueillis, et gravés au trait, par P. N. Beauvallet, statuaire ... ouvrage ... dedié à M. David, peinture (etc) *Paris, Joubert 1804*

The first six of twenty-four suites of plates issued under this or a similar title from 1804 onwards. The designs, some by Beauvallet and some by Cecile Beauvallet, are decidedly neo-classical but also show the influence of Egyptian art; they cover statuary, vases, furniture, garden ornaments and treillage. They are prefaced by an essay on decorative art by F. E. Joubert. *Folio. 8pp and 36 engraved plates. Contemporary quarter calf, spine repaired.* £36

1409 **Bedford, F. & I. C. Robinson** The treasury of ornamental art. Illustrations of objects of art and vertu. Photographed from the originals and drawn on stone by F. Bedford. With descriptive notices by I. C. Robinson *London, Day & Son (1856)*

Objects from the collection then housed at Marlborough House and later to be the core of the Victoria & Albert Museum's holdings in this field. The chromolitho illustrations of metalwork and textiles are particularly striking. (See McLean: 'Victorian Book Design' pp 126-8). *Quarto. 72ff, title and 70 chromolitho plates. Original gilt decorated cloth, rebacked.* £35

1410 **Berain, Jean** (Oeuvres) *Paris, the author (c 1670-1705)*
One of the most influential decorative designers whose work best represents the final period of the Louis XIV style. As 'Dessinateur du Cabinet du Roi' he was responsible for producing a wide range of decorative designs for the royal household. He developed a linear arabesque style of decoration which became very popular, and at the turn of the century hardly any designer was free from the domination of his forms. His suites were reissued in many parts of Europe, and in France it was remarked by Mariette that 'on ne faisait rien, en quelque genre que ce fût, sans que ce soit dans sa manière, ou qu'il en eût donné les desseins'. The following suites are the original issues published by Berain himself soon after his designs were made. Berlin Cat 343, Destailleur Notices pp 162-4, Guilmard pp 89-90. See also R. A. Weigert: 'Jean Berain'.
a **Suite B. Panneaux et corniches d'interieurs.**
Arabesque panels, pilasters, cornices, two plates of candlesticks and a design for a temple (probably for a fête). As 'Dessinateur du Roi' Berain was responsible for producing the designs for all the royal festivities and functions. *An untitled suite of 6 engraved plates on 5 leaves, average size 345 × 270mm, with large margins. In paper wallet.* £40
b **Suite C. Grand panneaux d'arabesques.**
Typical Berain arabesques: light in feeling, with slender forms, and motifs of canopies, sphinxes, satyrs, 'singeries', etc, mixed with narrow strap-ornament. *Untitled suite of 5 engraved plates, average size 320 × 245mm, with large margins. In paper wallet.* £50
c **Suite D. Grand panneaux d'arabesques en hauteur.**
Bolder and heavier designs more dependant on strapwork and providing studies in variations on the use of terms. *Untitled suite of 5 engraved plates, average size 325 × 255mm, with large margins. In paper wallet.* £55
d **Suite E. Panneaux des saisons.**
Each season is shown as a central personification flanked by three roundels with symbolic figures and is surrounded by arabesque decoration using appropriate motifs. A fifth plate shows Apollo with his chariot surmounted by a royal crown. *Untitled suite of 5 engraved plates; sizes 260 × 330mm and 315 × 245mm, with wide margins. In paper wallet.* £48

1410b

e **Suite F. Panneaux et montants.**
Three large panels and two designs in the form of three pilaster strips. The designs are here lighter and gayer, the forms more attenuated. *Untitled suite of 5 engraved plates with sizes varying from 243 × 193mm to 343 × 268mm, with large margins. In paper wallet.* £50

f **Suite G. Arabesques.**
Four large vertical panels, and a design for a sedan chair showing the decoration of the back and sides. Berain-type ornament gradually appeared on almost every sort of decorated object. *Untitled suite of 5 engraved plates with sizes varying from 313 × 213mm to 330 × 360mm; wide margins. In paper wallet.* £45

g **Suite L. Panneaux et plafonds.**
Arabesque designs of the artist's late period, invented after 1700 and influenced by Audran's work at the Château de la Ménagerie. *Untitled suite of 7 engraved plates on 5ff, with good margins. In paper wallet.* £54

h **Suite P. Cartels, vases, trophées et candelabres.**
A mixed collection of designs for 65 small objects including clock-cases, vases, salt cellars, plaques, ewers, a fine plate of trophy components and a last plate of 15 candelabra designs. *Untitled suite of 5 engraved plates, average size 360 × 245mm with wide margins. In paper wallet.* £45

i **Ornemens.**
A collection of mixed designs showing the range of Berain's invention: four magnificent candelabra, a plate of wall lights, fine panels for the side and rear of a carriage, and a group of courtiers in a stately dance (probably for a masque). *Title and 6 unnumbered engraved plates on 5ff, with sizes varying from 290 × 180mm to 105 × 230mm. Title plate cut to plate mark and mounted on large sheet to make it uniform, otherwise wide margins. In paper wallet.* £38

k **Chapiteaux**
Fifty-nine designs for ornate capitals using almost every type of motif favoured by Berain. *Untitled suite of 5 numbered engraved plates, average size 265 × 375mm. In paper wallet.* £35

1411 Bianconi, Carlo Esemplare di alcuni ornamenti per la gioventu amante del disegno *Bologna, Longhi (1780)*

An architectural and ornamental pattern book with examples drawn from a wide range of objects and countries. The plates include designs for moulding decoration, friezes, capitals, cartouches, masks, vases, candelabra, trophies, plants and flowers. The samples are interpretations of other pattern books, with the choice mainly of classical examples. Bianconi was permanent secretary of the Accademia della Brera in Milan for many years. *Oblong folio. Decorative engraved title and 24 numbered engraved plates. Paper boards.* £65

1412 Boucher, Franç(ois), père (Suite) 126 (Cartouches) *A(ugsburg), Joh. Georg Hertel (c 1750)*

Four plates copied from Boucher's 'Livre de cartouches' originally published in Paris by Huquier. The plates show allegorical cartouches with figures and objects and have the centres left blank. Hertel produced a large collection of about 500 suites of ornamental engravings after various European designers. Berlin Cat 416. *Four engraved plates, average size 300 × 200mm with good margins. In paper wallet.* £36

1413 Bourgoin, J. Théorie de l'ornement *Paris, A. Levy 1873*

Bourgoin, a specialist on Islamic art, the author of 'Les arts arabes' (1870) and 'Traité sur entrelacs' (on Islamic decoration) here makes a remarkable attempt to analyse the structural basis of pattern and provides one of the earliest and most interesting attempts to systematize its geometrical permutations. A very important book in the structural analysis of pattern. *Large octavo. (4)+xi+(1 blank)+366+(2)pp including 284 text illustrations, and 24 steel engraved plates with 330 ornamental motifs. Publisher's cloth, gilt.* £60

1414 Brunetti, Gaetano Sixty different sorts of ornaments invented by Gaetano Brunetti, Italian painter. Very usefull to painters, sculptors, stone-carvers, wood-carvers, silversmiths, etc. *(London), 25 June 1736*

The earliest series of engravings of rocaille ornament to be printed in England with the first furniture designs which display rococo tendencies to be found here. Brunetti was an obscure Italian decorative painter and it is not certain that he actually visited England though it has been established that he was working in Paris in 1730. The etchings of his designs, made by H. Fletcher and J. Rocque, played an important part in introducing the rococo style to English designers. The designs consist of all forms of cartouches, motifs for coach panels,

1414

wall panelling, fountains, overmantles, doorheads, mirror frames and picture frames. Six plates show furniture of a late Italian style. Much of the ornament is composed of amorphous leaf scrolls and shellwork twisted into the asymmetrical shapes characteristic of the high Rococo fashion. Berlin Cat 578. Guilmard p 331. *Octavo. 62 etched plates including decorative title and decorative subscription form, interleaved. Eighteenth century marbled-paper boards, quarter calf.* **Illustration above.** £190

1415 Bry, Theodor de Grotisch fur alle Kunstler. Grotis pour tous artisien *(Frankfurt, the author, c 1585)*

Frieze designs with grotesque decoration. Two forming a pair from the title suite have decoration contained with a line border, a central oval medallion and flanking half ovals. One is the title plate with lettering in centre and a signature in the side ovals, the other has a religious picture in the centre. The two other plates may not belong to the title suite. They are livelier in decoration, more metallic in appearance with ornament extending beyond the borders on lively grotesque motifs; one on a black ground, the other with beautifully devised patterns of insects, and flowers. This latter has the signature in reverse, the others are signed in the usual fashion. Berlin Cat 25. *Four engraved plates. Sizes 68 × 147mm (two plates), 95 × 181mm, 107 × 223mm. Two plates repaired for tear one affecting engraved suface. Tipped on handmade paper, in paper wallet.* £70

1416 Bry, Jo. Theodor de Figurative friezes with columns of soldiers *(Frankfurt, the author, c 1610)*

Etchings after designs by Hans Sebald Beham. The first shows a train of soldiers with horsemen, waggons and pike bearers, a camel in the centre and Death on horseback with his attendants bringing up the rear. The second shows a baggage train with camp followers led by a captain on horseback pointing behind himself; the monogram HSB on the waggon at the rear. The third frieze shows soldiers with pikes and muskets and a standard bearer in the centre flourishing his flag. All are signed. *Three etched plates, sizes 55:65 × 233:267mm; first plate repaired for small tears. In paper wallet.* £110

1417 **(Cahier, Charles & Arthur Martin)** Suite aux mélanges d'archéologie redigés ou recueillis par les auteurs des vitraux de Bourges. Première série. Carrelages et tissus *Paris, Morel 1868*

Extensive collection of tile and fabric designs, intended for the historian of ornament. The authors were Jesuits. *Folio. 2 vols in one. xii pp and 125 litho plates; (4)pp and 125 litho plates numbered 126-250. Original cloth.*
£45

1418 **Charpentier, R(ené)** Premier (Second) livre de differents trophées *Paris, Huquier (c 1730)*

Suspended trophies (etched by Huquier and J. F. Blondel) of arms, the arts, and with pastoral or religious attributes. The trophies are very similar in style to those carried out by Charpentier on the staircase and in the vestibule of the Hôtel de Vrillière, Paris, completed in 1715. Berlin Cat 404. Guilmard p 191. *Large quarto. 24 etched plates including two titles, in two suites lettered A & B, each numbered 1-12. Average size 280 × 130mm. Fine impressions with very large margins, untrimmed. In paper wallet.*
£130

1419 **Child, Heather & Dorothy Colles** Christian symbols ancient & modern. A handbook for students *London, Bell 1971*

Octavo. xxii + 270pp and 33 plates, with many line drawings in text. Original cloth. £6.50

1420 **Cipriani, Gio. Batt(ista)** Scelta di ornati antichi e moderni. — I cinque ordini dell'architettura di Andrea Palladio illustrati e ridotti a metodo facile *Rome, (Salomini for the author) 1801*

250 examples of the type of ornament predominantly used in architecture and interiors, of which the majority form frieze decoration. (Berlin Cat 600). The work is bound with a more important architectural publication which deserved a wider recognition than it appears to have received. This rare work simplifies Palladio's scheme of the orders, reducing them to a clear and logical system of proportions. Cipriani, a Sienese architect (1766-1839), who worked mainly in Rome, had originally produced the drawings illustrated in the book for his own personal use. He admired Palladio's system more than that of Vignola who was preferred by beginners for his clarity and lucidity. Cipriani believed that his own codification of Palladio's orders would make the method of the great architect more available and popular with students and beginners in architecture. This work is not in Berlin Cat or Fowler and is not recorded in any of the major collections. *Quarto. 2 works in 1. Etched title and 61 unnumbered etched plates; etched title, (4) + 24pp and 26 etched plates, numbered I-XXIV and 2 unnumbered. Nineteenth century embossed-paper boards, quarter straight grained morocco, rebacked; gilt stamped coat-of-arms on boards. A fine, clean untrimmed copy from the library of the Comte D. Bourtoulin with his bookplate.*
£175

1421 **Claesen, Charles** Recueil d'ornements et de sujets pour être appliqués a l'ornementation des armes d'après les dessins des principaux artistes. Gravé et publié par Charles Claesen *Liege, Claesen (c 1856)*

Illustrations of ornamentation appropriate for the barrels, stocks and working parts of guns and pistols. *Folio. Litho title and 37 litho plates (numbered 1-40 with 3 double page plates taking 2 nos each). Original quarter cloth portfolio.*
£40

1422 **Colling, James Kellaway** Examples of English mediaeval foliage and coloured decoration, taken from buildings of the twelfth to the fifteenth century *London, the author 1874*

Here Colling classifies examples of foliate ornament according to period. *Quarto. vii + (1) + 72pp with 79 text illustrations, and 76 litho plates. Original decorated cloth.*
£20

1423 **Colling, James Kellaway** Art foliage, for sculpture and decoration; with an analysis of geometric form. Second edition, revised *London, the author 1878*

A very complete manual on foliated ornament of all types and periods. Colling acknowledges the help of his pupil Owen Davis (see item 723). *Quarto. xii + 84pp with 116 text illustrations, and 80 litho plates. Original decorated cloth.*
£20

1424 **Crace, John D.** The art of colour decoration. Being an explanation of the purposes to be kept in view and the means of attaining them *London, Batsford 1912*

Crace's interest in decoration was hereditary – his father had been a partner of Pugin and the family owned a successful decorating firm – and he writes with the benefit of experience. His decorative ideals are however not Gothic or Art Nouveau but Italian Renaissance. *Quarto. Frontispiece, xiv+89+(1)pp with 16 text figures and 20 plates. Original decorated cloth.* £16

1425 **Crane, Walter** The claims of decorative art *London, Lawrence & Bullen 1892*

Octavo. vi+(2)+191+(1)pp with 8 text figures, and 16 headpieces at beginning of chapters. No 8 of a limited edition of 110 copies. Original decorated cloth, uncut. £60

1426 **Cutler, Thomas W.** A grammar of Japanese ornament and design with introductory, analytical, and descriptive text *London, Batsford 1880*

Cutler dates British interest in Japanese art as commencing in 1862 and in this book, published at the height of Japanese influence on the arts of the day, he identifies the main principles and idioms of the Japanese style. He acknowledges the help of W. Anderson, of Sir Augustus Franks (see item 1041), and of his publisher Bradley Batsford – to whom belongs much of the credit for a very handsome book. *Folio. Decorative title page, xi+(1)+31+(1)pp and 7 plates lettered A-G, 58 photolitho plates by C. F. Kell. Original gilt and blind decorated cloth. Author's presentation copy to Anderson.* £80

1427 **Darly, Matthias** The ornamental architect, or young artists instructor, consisting of the five orders drawn by aliquot parts, with their embellishments & ... by various masters *London, the author (1770)*

An extensive collection of designs, starting with studies of the orders but incorporating many examples of ornamental detail in a late rococo manner. Darly was a well-known ornamental engraver who had been responsible for the plates of Chippendale's Director (see item 34) and later produced 'Darly's Comic Prints of Characters' (a collection of caricatures dedicated to David Garrick). *Folio. 102 engraved plates including title leaf, dedication leaf and index leaf. Contemporary full calf, rebacked.* £260

1428 **Day, Lewis F.** The anatomy of pattern *London, Batsford 1898*
Octavo. xii+56pp and 41 plates. Original cloth. £4

1429 **Delafosse, J(ean)-C(harles)** Premier (– septième) livre de trophées *Paris, Chereau (c 1771)*

From Delafosse's 'Nouvelle Iconologie Historique' showing pendant trophies with attributes of the church, war, military might, rural life, hunting, music, the sciences, the arts and the virtues. Delafosse (1734-1789) was an architect, decorator, and assistant professor at the Academy whom Blondel described as 'homme de génie, mais peu consequent'. Yet his designs occupy an important and influential place in the history of French neo-classicism and the Louis XVI style. However, the decorative forms in these suites are somewhat outdated lacking the heavy rectilinear forms, rope-like swags, and Greek frets which characterise most of the designs of Delafosse. They hark back to the forms of thirty years previously and even show the influence of Le Pautre's designs of a century earlier. *Oblong folio. Seven parts in one. 35 engraved plates including 5 part titles, numbered NN-TT 1-5. Eighteenth century marbled-paper boards, quarter morocco.* £70

1430 **Delafosse, Jean Charles** Algemeen kunstenaars handboek; of schatkamer voor alle beoefenaaren van kunsten en handwerken *Amsterdam, Jan Willem Smit (c 1787)*

A selection of the plates from the 'Nouvelle Iconologie' copied by Jan de Witt for the Dutch market and produced in a reduced format with the designs in reverse and achieving a more formal effect than the exuberant originals. The plates were issued in two parts with title-pages reading 'Recueil des fontaines, frontispieces ...' and 'Recueil des portes, cheminées ...'. Both are without a date but bear the imprint of C. S. Roos, Amsterdam. Smit may have been responsible for the text which appears in two columns – French and Dutch – and was specially prepared for this edition. *Folio. 2 parts in one. (4)+39+(1)pp, 2 engraved titles and 103 engraved plates. Marbled-paper boards, calf spine.* £85

1431 **Delafosse, (Jean Charles)** L'oeuvre de Delafosse *Paris, Guèrinet (c 1890)*
Reprint of a selection of Delafosse's plates. 82 plates are reprinted from the previous item and keep their original numbering, the remaining plates are from later cahiers. *Small folio. 2 photolitho titles and 100 photolitho plates miscellaneously numbered. Publisher's printed-paper portfolio, cloth spine.* £35

1432 **Della Bella, Stefano** Raccolta de varii capricii et noue inventioni di cartelle et ornamenti posti in luce dal S.r Steffano Della Bella pittor fiorention, et da lui dissegnate et intagliate in Parigi appresso F. Linglese detto il Ciartres con privilegio . . . Recueil de divers caprices . . . par le mesme autheur *Paris, Pierre Mariette le fils 1646 (but later)*
Cartouches held and framed by animals (leopards, bulls, dogs, horses, lions) and human or semi-human figures. This suite was designed during Della Bella's stay in Paris in the 1640s and originally published by François Langlois, called Ciartres, whose imprint and publication date is retained on the plates. Although the suite retains the state of the title page of the Mariette reissue the paper suggests that the prints are later impressions, probably late eighteenth century. *Oblong quarto. 12 numbered etched plates including title and dedication. Average size 235 × 190mm. In buckram binding.* £40

1433 **Della Bella, Stefano** Libro de diverse cartelle e scudi d'armi disegnate da Stefano della Bella *Rome, Giovan Domenico Rossi, (c 1655)*
An Italian adaptation of the 'Raccolta di vari cappriaci' (see previous item) cut in reverse and with the addition of a new title and 2 extra plates. The engravings are cruder in line than the French versions which had been etched by Della Bella himself, but the impressions are sharp and remain in fine condition. *Small folio. 15 etched plates including decorative title, unnumbered. Average size 245 × 185mm. In early nineteenth century paper boards, calf spine.* £60

1434 **Dietterlin, Wendel** Architectura de quinque columnarum simmetrica distributione et variis eorundem ornamentis. Liber I. Per Vuindelinum Dieterlin pictorem Argentinensem. – Architectura de postium seu portalium ornatu uario. Liber II *Strasbourg, heirs of Bernhard Jobin, 1593 (on title of book one, but not issued before 1594), 1595*
First edition, second issue with text in Latin and French. Dietterlin's extravagantly imaginative work shows the exuberant flights of Mannerist fantasy which had such a marked effect on the craftsmen of the Low Countries and England. In this country the book provided an important source of decorative detail for many Jacobean builders although the only known direct quotation which still survives is on the west entrance to Charlton House in Kent. The importance of Dietterlin's designs has only been fully appreciated in recent years with the increased understanding of the development of Northern Mannerism. *Small folio. 2 vols in 1. Etched title, (8)ff of letterpress text, colophon leaf, and 38 etched plates numbered 1-34, 1 unnumbered (35), and 38-40 (36 and 37 were apparently never issued, as is corroborated in the second extended edition where the original plates 26-35 and 38-40 are incorporated as 176-188, numbered without a break). Plate 2 has a duplicate printing on the verso of the leaf, and plate 40 is attached to plate 39 to make one large illustration. Etched title, (3)ff of text (including the first half-page plate) and 56 etched plates numbered 2-55, 57-58. Plate 56 is a photostat facsimile. Contemporary full vellum, repaired; preserved in quarter oasis drop-back box.* **Illustration opposite.** £480

1435 **Dietterlin, Wendel** Architectura de constitutione, symmetria, ac proportione quinq; columarum; ac omnis, inde promanantis structurae artificiosae; utpote fenestrarum, caminorum postium seu portalium, pontium, alq; epitaphiorum . . . *Nuremberg, Balthasar Caymox, 1598 (but 1599 as the portrait records Dietterlin's death in that year)*
The second, enlarged edition of the work with the text in Latin and French.
This is, to all intents and purposes, a new work re-using the plates of the earlier edition and expanding them with the addition of ninety new designs for doors, windows, fireplaces, tombs and fountains, arranged so that each of the five orders forms a separate book. Only the suite of fountains attains the imaginative inventiveness of the earlier plates suggesting that Dietterlin's fantasies lost their force as he neared the end of his life.

ORNAMENT 219

1434-6

He died early in 1599 while the work was still in press. Berlin Cat 1942. *Folio. 5 parts in one. 209ff (miscellaneously numbered) including etched portrait frontispiece, 5 etched titles, 9ff of text and 194 etched plates. The main title with the lettering printed in black and red letterpress has had the cancel removed from the imprint over the name of Hubert Caymox, and the cancels have also been largely removed from the part titles of Books IV and V. Seventeenth century full calf, gilt. From the libraries of the Chevalier Gougnon d'Argenson, the 17th century French genealogist (probably his arms stamped in gilt on front board), and the architect, Jeanson; with their signatures.* **Illustration above.** £1050

1436 Dietterlin, Wendel Le livre d'architecture. Recueil de planches donnant la division, symetrie et proportion des cinq ordres *Liège, Claesen 1862*

Good litho reprint (and the only reprint known to us) of Dietterlin's 'Architectura'. It is made from the 1598-9 Nuremberg edition. *Folio. (2) + 210ff of plates. Contained in cloth portfolio, original covers enclosed.* **Illustration above.** £75

1437 **Dumont, J(acques)** Livre de nouveaux trophez *Paris, Huquier (c 1730)*

Dumont, who was principally a painter, was given the title 'le Romain' and these trophies attest to his knowledge of Roman sixteenth and seventeenth century decoration thus taking on a rather backward-looking form towards the style of Louis XIV. However, Dumont was also one of the artists painting the trophies of the Hôtel de Vrillière, Paris in 1716. Berlin Cat 396. Guilmard p 168. *Large quarto. 7 numbered etched plates including title (designed by Oppenord) with two designs to a plate. Average size 275 × 215mm. Fine impressions with wide margins, untrimmed; preserved in cloth wallet.* £60

1438 **Durant, Stuart** Victorian ornamental design *London, Academy Editions 1972*

Useful guide to Victorian designers from George Phillips and Pugin to Voysey. It includes a bibliography. *Small folio. 104pp including 96 illustrations (8 coloured). Original cloth.* £5

1439 **Eickhout, G(erbrandt) van (den)** Eenige ordonnantie van verscheide aerdige kindertjens *Amsterdam, Justus Danckerts (c 1650)*

A rare suite of engravings by a pupil of Rembrandt. The format for the designs which are of children playing games stems from the playing putti motifs of Raphael and his studio in the Vatican decorations, but the children here, unlike their Roman models, are quite revolting. *Title and 3 unnumbered engraved plates, average size 150 × 197mm. Tipped on hand-made paper. In paper wallet.* £40

1440 **(Die Gewerbehalle)** The Workshop. A monthly journal devoted to progress of the useful arts. Edited by Prof. W. Baumer, I. Schnorr and others. Vol 1 *London, Hagger (c 1865)*

English edition of the German periodical 'Die Gewerbehalle', issued 1863 onwards and devoted to furniture, ornament, ironwork and objets d'arts. Bound at the end is 'The Workshop Album', which illustrates 259 decorative objects. *Folio. iv + 384pp text and (4)pp + 92pp of illustrations. Quarter morocco, title leaf repaired.* £25

1441 **(Die Gewerbehalle)** The Workshop. New Series *London, Hagger (c 1865)*

Folio. 400pp with text illustrations. Original cloth, spine repaired. £25

1442 **Gibbs, John** Designs for Gothic ornaments & furniture, after the ancient manner, for ecclesiastical and domestic purposes, for the use of architects, and workers in metal, stone, wood, & &. Vol 1 *London, Bell 1853*

The author's intention was 'to raise more noble minds to a pure and refined taste, so that the architecture and furniture of ecclesiastical and domestic buildings may be in the ancient style and beauty of English architecture'; he was, in short, at this time a strict Gothicist of the school of Pugin. The designs in this volume – no second volume was published – are for furniture, metalwork and stonework; his Gothic chairs (plate 1) are peculiarly grotesque. *Octavo. 14pp and 48 litho plates. Cloth.* £45

1443 **Gibbs, John** Domestic architecture and ornament in detail: being a series of designs for windows, doorways, doors, capitals . . . furniture, and sundry ornaments, developed after the manner of the Romanesque – English and foreign, the Gothic, and other styles of architecture: for the use of architects, builders, sculptors, carvers, masons, cabinet-makers, workers in metal, and for art students generally, with descriptive letter-press *Oxford, for the author 1868*

By 1868 Gibbs was developing his own style which he considered had 'neither the rigidity of the Classic nor the severity of the Gothic'; one might add that his spiky sub-Ruskinian doors and windows and his coarse sculptural detail make a peculiarly unpleasing ensemble. Its interest is that it is a collection of designs for the cheap, but art-conscious, end of the market and shows the devices by which architects could reduce costs, e.g. by using bolder but less detailed stone moulding. *Folio. 8pp and (1) + 20 lithograph plates (of which 8 partly coloured). Contemporary quarter morocco, cloth boards.* £130

1444 **(Gibbs, John)** Capitals, foliage, doorways, arches, overmantels, etc *(c 1855)*

Plates signed 'JG' and their authorship is not otherwise indicated, but an attribution to Gibbs is plausible. The designs are predominantly Venetian Gothic, reflecting the influence of Ruskin, but other sources are involved, the overmantels, for example, echoing Grinling Gibbons. *Quarto. 24 litho plates. Contemporary quarter morocco, gilt tooled spine.*
£45

1445 **Götz, (Gottfried Bernhard)** (Muschlwerk. Sockel) *(Nuremberg, J. S. Negges (c 1770))*

Plinths with solid basic shapes given a complexity of outline by organic masses of sprouting leaves of all varieties, fronds, tendrils, and seaweed-like forms which twist and curl into scrolls and hide small putti. Typical German rococo decoration in the profusion and mixture of forms. Berlin Cat 126 1(3). Guilmard p 436. *Suite of 4 numbered plates, average size 187 × 110mm. In paper wallet.*
£25

1446 **Gribelin, Samuel** A new book of ornaments useful to all artists. Dedicated to the honourable Colonel Parsons *(London, the author) 1704*

Some of the earliest designs for gold and silver work to be published in England although they were made by an artist of European origin. The suite has two different types of design. Seven plates show compositions for panel-work of foliated scrolls and garlands with a central medallion of mythological motifs or portraits (one of Colonel Parsons). The remaining four plates are composed of several small designs in the shape of ovals, roundels or friezes. These were, no doubt, jeweller's designs for watch caps or backs, snuff boxes, mirror backs, straps, etc, on a black ground. The work would seem to be a later, amalgamated edition of earlier publications. The title states that 'These XVI plates are now made into one book of XII leaves', while a variant title of the same suite in the Berlin Catalogue (752) goes on to explain that 'the 8 small ones are thus printed to make the whole more regular'. The small jewelry designs probably stem from 'A book of ornament useful to jewellers, watch-makers and all other artists' (1697) while the ornamental panels come from another work of Gribelin 'A book of severall ornaments' (1682). Parsons was a friend of Gribelin (see item 1510). Berlin Cat 752. Guilmard p 107. *12 numbered engraved plates including title, of which 4 have two coppers to each plate. Sizes vary from 128:203 × 155:207mm. Several plates cut to plate mark, one plate has the two coppers separated; mounted on old paper and hinged on grey hand-made paper. Preserved in quarter morocco portfolio.*
£125

1447 **Gruner, Lewis & Emil Braun** Specimens of ornamental art selected from the best models of the classical epoches. Illustrated by eighty plates... With descriptive text by Emil Braun *London, Thomas M'Lean 1853*

One of the most impressive works of colour printing of the mid-Victorian period and the finest chromolithographic book to be published to that time, Gruner's 'Specimens' came into being as a result of the needs of industry for ornamental patterns. Most of the examples illustrated are taken from works in Italy and range from Pompeian frescoes to 16th century book bindings, with the works of artists such as Raphael, Giotto, Luni, Giulio Romano, and include the infrequently illustrated paintings from the bathroom of Cardinal Bibiena in the Vatican. The very fine plates include several in monochrome and some in only two colours while the excellent polychromatic examples show big, bold flower and fruit details, friezes and wall paintings, Early Christian mosaics, ceilings and floors. The fine drawings for these plates were made by Gruner but it is not known who carried out the lithography, and the printers though not mentioned on the plates are believed to be Winkelmann & Sons of Berlin. Nevertheless, whoever carried out the work required great skills of craftsmanship and a high standard of technique. *Large broadsheet atlas, quarto text. 3ff and 80 litho plates of which 48 chromolitho, 7 tinted litho; viii + 36pp and 7 litho plates. Contemporary marbled paper boards, quarter red morocco; matching end-papers.*
£285

1448 **Halfpenny, Joseph** Gothic ornaments in the cathedral church of York *York, Todd 1795*

Halfpenny (1748-1811) made his drawings for the 175 specimens of Gothic ornament illustrated when employed as Clerk of the Works to the architect John Carr, who carried out restoration work in the cathedral. Halfpenny was his own engraver and the plates are 'exceedingly careful and delicate in execution, but wanting in spirit . . . and far too smooth and neat to be characteristic of ancient art' (Eastlake). Halfpenny's book is, none the less, the first to deal specifically with Gothic sculptural detail and ornament, and an important precursor to the works of Carter, Britton, and Pugin. *Quarto. Engraved title (50)pp and 105 engraved plates. Contemporary full panelled calf, gilt tooled spine. A fine copy specially bound for the antiquary Sir Richard Colt Hoare (1758-1838), with his crest and arms on the spine; ex Colt Hoare sale (1883) lot 609.* £85

1449 **Halfpenny, Joseph** Gothic ornaments in the cathedral church of York *York, Todd 1795*

Another copy of the previous item. *Quarto. Engraved title, 50pp and 105 engraved plates. Marbled-paper boards, quarter calf.* £45

1450 **Hay, D. R.** Original geometrical diaper designs, accompanied by an attempt to develope and elucidate the true principles of ornamental design, as applied to the decorative arts *London, Bogue 1844*

Hay's aim in this collection of designs was to get away from conventional ornament to the geometry that lay beneath it. The results are decidedly Spartan but if they lack commercial appeal they are well adapted to the requirements of the student of a school of design, and that must be seen as Hay's achievement – and no other writer at this period matched Hay's grasp of the geometrical basis of design. *Oblong folio. (2) + 44pp and 24 plates numbered 1-24, 33 plates together at end numbered 1-33. Contemporary cloth.* £45

1451 **(Hertel, Johann Georg)** Suite No. 284. (Kartuschen) *Augsburg, J. G. Hertel (c 1760)*

Typical rococo cartouches with spiky outlines, scrolls and a multiple of C shaped curves or inverted C curves. The plates bear no designers signature and the suite forms part of the collection of ornament issued by Hertel. *4 numbered engraved plates, average size 220 × 182mm. In paper wallet.* £40

1452 **Hoppus, E.** The gentleman's and builder's repository: or, architecture display'd (etc) *London, Hodges 1737 (Gregg reprint 1969)*

The illustrations include 'such variety of ceiling-pieces, shields, compartments, and other curious and uncommon decorations, as must needs render it acceptable to all gentlemen, artificers, and others'. *Quarto. (4) + 101 + (1)pp, frontispiece and 84 plates. Original cloth.*
£9

1453 **Huquier, (Gabriel)** Nouveau livre de trophées de fleurs et fruits étrangers *Paris, Huquier (c 1740)*

Drop terminal groups of strange and unidentifiable fruits and flowers. One of the few suites of designs invented by Huquier who was renowned more for his engraving and etching of the works of others (see no 1418). Guilmard p 168. *Large quarto. 12 numbered etched plates including title, average size 195 × 155mm. Fine impressions with wide margins, untrimmed. In paper wallet.* £72

1454 **Hulme, F. Edward** Principles of ornamental art *London, Cassell (c 1875)*

A utilitarian, but certainly useful, guide to ornament and symbolism based on the author's wide studies. There is a good opening chapter on the relationship of ornament and design with comments on floor coverings and ceramics. *Quarto. xiv + 138pp and 32 litho plates. Original decorated cloth, gilt and blind stamped.* £20

1455 **Hulme, F. Edward** Suggestions in floral design *London, Cassell (c 1880)*

A series of full-page coloured plates of floral ornament, suitable for copying by student, designer or manufacturer. The plates are chromolithographed by Dupuy et fils of Paris, and Hulme provides a commentary on them. *Large quarto. 52pp and 52 chromolitho plates. Original stamped cloth.* £45

1456 **Jackson, Frank G.** Decorative design. An elementary text book of principles and practice *London, Chapman & Hall 1888*
first edition of a widely used manual of design and ornament. *Octavo. xii+174pp, including decorated title and 34 litho plates. Original cloth.* £7

1457 **Johnson, Tho(ma)s** A new book of ornaments ... design'd for tablets & frizes for chimney-pieces; useful for youth to draw after *London, the author 28th August 1762*

The only known copy of an unrecorded work by this woodcarver and designer who introduced and sustained the final phase of English rococo decoration. This suite should not be confused with the 'New Book of Ornaments' of 1760 of which only the title page and one other plate are extant, but of which seven plates are known from one of Weale's 19th century reprints (see item 1561). The former suite was previously believed to have been Johnson's last publication before concentrating on his work as a woodcarver. This present suite has a completely different format, shows quite another type of ornament and is not executed in the same process.

The designs are not at all like the richly curving frameworks edged with sharp, spiky forms familiar to those who know Johnson's earlier inventions. The compositions fall into two groups. Three plates (2, 4 & 6) consist of single, foliated, arabesque scrolls, developing with each plate from a simple leaf and flower tendril to include birds, beasts and a fish, to the final scroll where a dragon's head begins one end transforming into a cornucopia of flowers at the tail. The other group which includes the title, is made up of rustic scenes (a pair of swans, dogs attacking a bull, a herdsman with his sheep and goats at a water pump) set within fluid frames made from confronting and inverse C scrolls intertwined with leaves, flowers and eventually including a beast.

Each plate is signed 'T. Johnson invent & delin', and bears the imprint: Sold at ye Golden Boy in Grafton street St Anns Soho London, (or a variation thereof). *Small oblong folio. Six numbered plates including title, etched and engraved in the crayon manner. Sizes 201 × 347mm, 183 × 368mm & 202 × 350mm. Cut close to plate mark along some edges, carefully repaired for small tears along right sides of some plates but not affecting engraved surfaces. Preserved in cloth wallet.* **Illustration below.** £240

1457

1458 **(Johnson, Thomas) Hayward, Helena** Thomas Johnson and English Rococo *London, Tiranti 1964*
The first monograph on this much underrated and previously neglected master of English rococo ornament which reproduces all the previously known surviving designs and assesses their place in the development of eighteenth century taste. *Quarto. viii+46pp and 191 illustrations on 106 plates. Publishers cloth.* £8

1459 **(Jones, Owen)** Ancient Spanish ballads; historical and romantic. Translated, with notes, by J. G. Lockhart . . . a new edition, revised . . . the borders and ornamental vignettes by Owen Jones, architect *London, John Murray 1842*

Owen Jones was responsible for four chromolitho titles in Moorish style and for borders, ornamental letters and vignettes on nearly every page. 'The book as a whole is a splendid achievement both of illustration and printing' (McLean: 'Victorian Book Design' p 80). *Small quarto. (232)pp, 4 chromolitho titles and 6 litho plates. Contemporary full brown morocco, gilt tooled.* £40

1460 **Jones, Owen** The Sermon on the Mount. Illuminated by Owen Jones Arct. with a design by W. Boxall *London, Longman 1844*

An early Owen Jones illuminated book which makes interesting comparison with the Audsleys' mighty folio illustrating the same text (item 1405). *Small octavo. 32 coloured litho plates. Original full decorated morocco by Hayday, gilt edges.* £45

1461 **Jones, Owen** The Preacher *London, Longman 1849*

The text is taken from Ecclesiastes and illuminated by Owen Jones. *Small folio. (36)pp of coloured litho plates. Bound in full panelled gilt morocco, gilt edges, by Zaehnsdorf.* £85

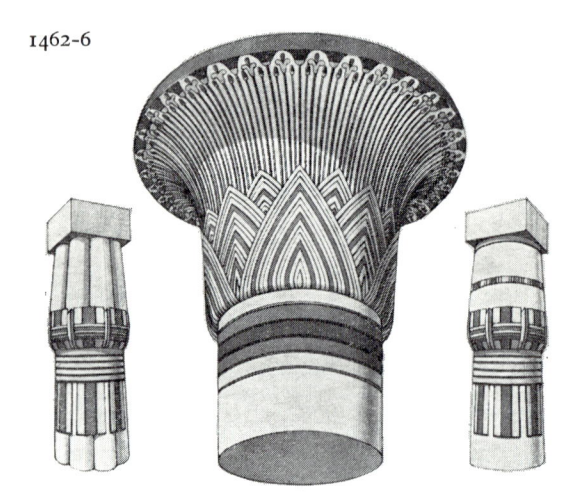

1462-6

1462 **Jones, Owen** The grammar of ornament *London, Day & Son 1856*

Jones's masterpiece, 'a horn-book of the angels', produced as a result of the impact of the Great Exhibition, was a prophetic work which was to mark a major change in aesthetic considerations and to herald the move towards non-representational art. The 3000 illustrations provided, for designers and manufacturers, a pictorial museum of motifs taken from an extensive range of subjects and sources. Among the large selection of Arabic, Persian, Indian, Chinese and Far Eastern ornament were the first illustrations of primitive art which showed it for its design content rather than presenting it in an anthropological sense. The text was an affirmation of Jones's own philosophy and an extension of that propounded by Piranesi (see item 459), of intelligent and imaginative eclecticism. The 37 Propositions on the decorative arts, formed practical guides which were followed by the most important designers of the time. The book was an early work to suggest nature as a basic source and Jones designated the largest section of the plates to illustrate this proposition; these included the first published design by the young Christopher Dresser. The book was also a major printing achievement. It was the first great compendium of historical styles, in an original format, where a global range of ornament was juxtaposed in coloured reproductions. The illustrations for the work were drawn by Jones's pupils and chromolithographed by Francis Bedford assisted by Fielding, Tymms and Sedgfield. The work first appeared in parts. *Large folio. Chromolitho title, letterpress title, 6+(2)+4+6+4 +4+2+4+4+4+2+4+2+2+8+6+16+4+14+4pp and 100 chromolitho plates. Publishers' half morocco, with spine and label designed by Owen Jones.* **Illustration above.**
£520

1463 **Jones, Owen** The grammar of ornament *London, Day & Son (1865)*
The 'New and Universal' edition published in a smaller format with the plates redrawn so that several required their illustrations to be set out on two plates instead of one. Compared to the original the drawings of this edition do not have the same care in execution while the colours are rather harsher and the tones less subtle. *Small folio. (2) + 157 + (1 blank)pp with numerous text illustrations and 112 chromolitho plates including decorative title. Full red morocco, gilt extras; signed binding of A. & J. Bolt of Bristol.* **Illustration opposite.** £135

1464 **Jones, Owen** The grammar of ornament *London, Day & Son (1865)*
Another copy of the previous item. *Small folio. (2) + 157 + (1 blank)pp and 112 chromolitho plates including decorative title. Publisher's gilt-decorated cloth.* **Illustration opposite.** £85

1465 **Jones, Owen** The grammar of ornament *London, 1865 (Van Nostrand Reinhold reprint 1972)*
A very good reprint of the 1865 edition. *Small folio. (2) + 157 + (1)pp with numerous text illustrations, and 112 coloured photolitho plates. Publisher's gilt decorated cloth. Dust wrappers.* **Illustration opposite.** £15

1466 **Jones, Owen** The grammar of ornament *London, Quaritch 1910*
One of the minor bookselling coups of Bernard Quaritch's successful career was the purchase of the remainder stock of the Day edition of the 'Grammar of Ornament'. After his death the firm brought out this reprint of it with a new title page. (It was again reissued with the same title page in 1928). *Small folio. Chromolitho title, title, 157 + (1)pp and 112 chromolitho plates. Original cloth.* **Illustration opposite.** £120

1467 **Jones, Owen** The psalms of David illustrated by Owen Jones *(London, 1861)*
The chromolithograph plates carry the text of the psalms surrounded by foliage designs in red, blue and gold. *Folio. (4) + 100pp of chromolitho plates. Original relievo leather binding designed by Owen Jones, with title 'The Victoria Psalter' on upper cover; spine repaired. (McLean: 'Victorian Bookbindings' p 103).* £120

1468 **Jones, Owen** One thousand and one initial letters *London & Leipsig, Day & Son and Ludwig Denicke 1864*
One of Jones's late publications the designs of which were taken mainly from the 'Victoria Psalter' (see previous item) and were much copied by amateurs. The popularity of Jones's illuminated works is testified to by the fact that this is a German edition, with the letterpress title in German. *Folio. Decorative chromolitho title, letterpress title, and 27 chromolitho plates. Original gilt lettered cloth boards, some foxing.* £78

1469 **(Jones, Owen & Henry Warren)** The history of Joseph and his brethren Genesis chapters XXXVII, XXXVIII and XL *London, Day & Son (c 1865)*
The final page of this book names Owen Jones and Henry Warren as 'illuminators' and A. Warren as lithographer. (See McLean: 'Victorian Book Design and Colour Printing' p 128). *Small folio. 52pp of chromolitho plates. Original decorated cloth.* £65

1470 **Jones, Owen** Examples of Chinese ornament selected from objects in the South Kensington Museum and other collections *London, S & T Gilbert 1867*
This work is the result of Jones's study of the Chinese art introduced into the West following the Anglo-Chinese Wars and the Ti-ping rebellion. It is a repudiation of his ideas on Chinese ornament of which he had stated in the 'Grammar' that 'its characteristic feature is oddness . . . unimaginative . . . and wanting in the highest grace of art, – the ideal'. He now finds that the new works of art he has studied do follow certain of the Propositions which he had laid down earlier. A very scarce and a very beautiful book. *Folio. 15 + (1)pp and 100 chromolitho plates including a decorative title. Two text leaves in facsimile. Contemporary quarter morocco.* £280

1471 **Jones, Owen** The leading principles in composition of ornament of every period . . . being a reprint from a paper read by him before the Royal Society of British Architects December 15, 1856 *London, Society for the Encouragement of Arts (1894)*

Quarto. (4) + 54 + (2)pp. Original full red gilt stamped morocco, gilt edges. Specially bound by Zaehnsdorf as the Owen Jones Prize of the Society for the Encouragement of Arts. £25

1472 **Klimsch, Karl** Ornaments *London, Asher (c 1870)*

Scroll, panel and ceiling ornament in a rather heavy Germanic manner – and in fact the English edition of an ornament collection published at Frankfurt am Main in 1868. *Folio. Title and 102 litho plates. Quarter morocco.* £30

1473 **Knight, (Frederick)** Knight's new book of seven hundred & fifty eight plain ornamented & reversed cyphers. Engraved by Nathaniel Gill & J. H. Whiteman *London, Knight 1832*

Octavo. Engr. title, 54 engraved plates of cyphers, (2)pp adverts. Original cloth with printed label on upper cover. First few plates damp stained. £30

1474 **Knight, (Frederick)** Knight's scroll ornaments, designed for the use of silversmiths, chasers, die sinkers, modellers, &c. *London, William, Griffiths, Ackerman & Co (c 1840)*

Leaf and scrollwork patterns and jewelry designs copied from a variety of earlier sources including Gribelin, Le Pautre, Meissonier, Cuvillier, etc. Knight produced a number of similar pattern books dealing with crests, gems, cyphers, alphabets, etc. *Quarto. 50 steel engraved plates including decorative title. Publisher's embossed cloth boards, rebacked.* £45

1475 **Kolb & Högg** Vorbilder fur das Ornamentenzeichnen. Eine Sammlung kunstgewerblicher Vorlagen fur den Unterricht im Freihand- & Sachzeichnen an Real- & gewerbl: Fortbildungs-Schulen. *Stuttgart, W. Effenberger (c 1890)*

Second edition. Designs for copying by students of craft schools. *Folio. 30 chromolitho plates. Preserved in ornamental cloth portfolio.* £16

1476 **Krammer, Gabriel** Architectura von den funf Seulen sambt iren Ornamenten und Zierden . . . *Prague, Marco Sadeler 1606*

Krammer (active 1598 to 1606) began his career as a piper in the Swiss Guards at Prague (according to the title-page) and eventually became a cabinet-maker and engraver. This book of the five orders consists of his own engravings of lively designs for fantastic cornices, cabinets, arches, altars, and other ornamental pieces in a typical northern mannerist style similar to that of Dietterlin and probably very much influenced by his designs.

The collection was first published in 1599 (some of the plates bear this date) and seems to have been well received since it ran to five reprints before the end of 1610. This is the third edition. (Berlin Cat 1944 for second edition). *Folio. Engraved title and 28 engraved plates numbered 1-26 and 2 unnumbered. Lacks text. Nineteenth century paper boards. One plate remargined; some designs have been pricked through, at an early time, possibly for needlework patterns.* £185

1477 **La Joue, (Jacques) de** Recueil nouveau de differens cartouches. – Second (Troisième) livre de cartouches *Paris, Huquier (c 1730-1735)*

Designs which begin by being regular in shape and with balancing motifs gradually take on irregular forms and develop contrasting lines. The culmination is reached in the final plate with a cartouche in the form of a great shell which takes on an amorphous shape suggesting, at the same time: a ship, a snail, and a chariot, ridden by two chinese figures. Other designs in this third suite (which can be dated to before December 1736) have attributes of The Sea, The Arts, etc, where the cartouche proper is conceived in forms which correspond, so that a design for Painting has its principal shape in the form of a palette, The Sea has a great shell, and Architecture a broken dome. Berlin Cat 400 (1). Guilmard p 152. *Large quarto. 36 etched plates including three decorative titles, in suites lettered A-C, each numbered 1-12. Average sizes 200 × 230mm and 220 × 185mm. Fine impressions with large margins, untrimmed. Preserved in cloth wallet.* **Illustration opposite.** £215

1477

1478 **La Joue, (Jacques) de** Neu inventierte Schilde funffter Theil. Cinquième livre de cartouches *Augsberg, Joh. Georg Merz (c 1750)*

Excellent German reversed copies of plates 1-4, 12 & 10 of 'Recueil nouveau de differens cartouches' (see previous item). The first four designs are given the addition of seasonal titles since their motifs are appropriate. The plates, engraved by Benedict Winckler, stand up well to the originals in the quality of their engraving. The suite bears the publisher's number 6 on the title and the letter E on each plate. *Six numbered engraved plates including decorative title, average size 182 × 225mm, with good margins. Tipped on green Ingres paper. Preserved in paper wallet.* £30

1479 **La Joue, J(acques) de** Livre de cartouches de guerre dédié a Monseigneur le Duc de Mortemart *Paris, Huquier, (c 1735)*

La Joue, who had worked for some time with Watteau, to whom he was greatly indebted, and later with Boucher, was named by Blondel as one of the 'trois premiers inventeurs du genre pittoresque', a genre abundantly evident in these etchings. La Joue designed a great number of undated ornamental suites but many of them can be attributed a publication date of between 1734 and 1736. Berlin Cat 400:(4). Guilmard p 152. *Large quarto. 7 numbered etched plates including title, average size 260 × 195mm. Fine impressions with wide margins, untrimmed; preserved in paper wallet.* £55

1480 **Langlois, N(icolas)** Dessins de divers ornemens et moulures antiques et modernes *Paris, N. Langlois (c 1690)*

A pattern book of small ornaments for all kinds of craftsmen including architects, metal workers, embroiderers, woodworkers and jewellers. The 190 examples of flowers and leaf scrolls, floret ornament, gadroons, interlacing, key patterns, bosses and rosettes, are complete with their appropriate name to provide a small glossary of ornamental terms. *Large quarto. Engraved title and 6 engraved plates lettered A-F; average size of plate 265 × 185mm, wide margins. Stitched in marbled-paper boards.* £70

1481 **(Langlois, Nicholas)** (Nouveaux desseins de cartouches) *Paris, Langlois (c 1690)*

Very pleasant and unusual cartouches with central strap-work shaped spaces surrounded by acanthus scroll and mask decoration, surmounted by pairs of facing putti and supported by satyrs, griffons, tritons, sphinxes and mermaids. The original coppers have had their centres cut out to leave the spaces for the cartouches and the suite is without title, though three plates bear the Langlois imprint. A title and imprint have been added in ink, in an old hand, in the lower part of the first plate. Special pulls of an unusual and rare suite. *Six unnumbered engraved plates, average size 160 × 247mm (numbers added in ink). Good impressions; in paper wallet.* £70

1482 **Langlois, N. (Collected by John James)** L'architecture à la mode ou sont les nouveau dessins pour la décoration des bâtimens et jardins *Paris, N. Langlois (c 1700-1716)*
A collection of engravings important in English architectural history and for an understanding of the architect who owned the designs. John James (c 1672-1746), Assistant Surveyor at St Paul's under Christopher Wren, and later to follow after the master as Surveyor of the fabric of St Paul's and joint Clerk of the Works at Greenwich, had a high regard for French architects, designers and their works, which culminated in his translations and publication of the written works of Claude Perrault and Le Blond. Nicholas Langlois' 'L'architecture à la mode' was a collection of suites of designs, by various ornamental engravers of the second half of the 17th century, which included ideas of all aspects of interior features and their decoration as well as drawings for gardens and their ornaments. When Langlois died in 1703 his stock was bought up by a fellow printseller and relation by marriage, Jean Mariette. Mariette reissued the work about 1720 in a collected version extending the publication to almost double the original size by including more up-to-date designs by the then fashionable decorators.
There would appear to be no definitive collation for these publications; all recorded copies vary as to the number of suites included, and to their content. It would seem that the title-page was issued with a group of designs of the customers own choice which might also be sold as separate suites. Mariette appears to have issued the Langlois title-page and plates, with the latter's imprint, while stocks of the sheets lasted, and sold them together with plates on which the imprint had been changed to his own when the old stocks ran out, and also with new designs as they appeared from the engraver's burin. The present collection is a typical mixed example apparently made about 1716. Only seven suites still bear Langlois' imprint, the remainder are Mariette issues. See Berlin Cat 359. Guilmard pp 113-4 & pp 128-131. Destailleur Sale Cat 1895 pp 105-6. The present volume collected and owned by John James adds to our evidence of his interest in French building and decoration. The collection consists of the following suites:
Blondel: Desseins d'un cabinet et d'une chambre à coucher *6 plates* **Briseville:** Diverses pièces de serruriers *16 plates* **Bullet:** Livre nouveau de cheminées *6 plates*
Cottar: Nouveaux dessins de lambris de menuiserie à panneaux de glaces *6 plates*
Francard: Portes cochères de menuiserie *6 plates* **Gabriel:** Maison de Varanjeville *3 plates*
Lassurance: Hôtel de Maison: *3 double-plates* Hôtel d'Auvergne *3 double-plates*
Lassurance & Dorby: Hôtel Desmarests *3 double-plates* **Le Blond:** Dessins d'une maison particulière *4 plates* Dessins d'une autre maison particulière *10 plates* Hôtel de Clermont *3 double-plates* **Le Blond, Mansart, Cottar:** Portes cochères *7 plates*
J. le Pautre: Portes cochères *6 plates* Alcoves à la françois *6 plates* Nouveaux desseins de plafons *6 plates* Termes, supports et ornements pour embellir les maisons et jardins *6 plates*
P. le Pautre: Cheminées nouvelles à la mansarde *6 plates* Cheminées et lambris à la mode *6 plates* Cheminées à la Royalle à grand miroir et tablette *6 plates* Portes à placard et lambris dessinez par le Sr Mansard et nouvellement executez dans quelques maisons roiales &c *6 plates* **Leroux:** Divers desseins de cheminées *6 plates* Nouveaux lambris et galeries, chambres, et cabinets *6 plates* Buffets *6 plates* **A. Loire:** Nouveaux dessins de gueridons *6 plates* **Mansar:** Hôtel de Lorge *7 double-plates* Château d'Issy *8 double-plates* Desseins d'une maison à batir à Paris *7 plates* Desseins de l'amphitheatre de la salle des machines du Château des Tuileries *6 double-plates* **Oppenord:** Desseins de couronemens et amortissemens convenable pour dessus de portes, coussures, croisées, niches, &c. *4 plates*
(unknown): Vases et bordures de miroirs *12 plates*
Quarto. 31 suites with 192 engraved plates in all. Eighteenth century full calf, gilt. John James's signature on title-page, with date and price on the fly leaf. Contemporary full calf, gilt. Preserved in quarter roan drop-backed box. **Illustration opposite.** £740

1483 **Lasinio, Carlo** Ornati presi da graffiti, a pitture antiche esistenti in Firenze *Florence, Niccoli Pagni & Gius. Bardi 1789*
A collection recording the decorative work in the sixteenth century antique style which existed in Florence. The etchings show charming grotesque and arabesque designs in the style of Raphael's Loggie decorations. Among the illustrations are compositions by the great exponents of grotesque work, Giovanni da Udine, Andrea di Cosimo Feltrini, and Bernadino Poccetti. Designs were taken from interior murals and ceiling work in the Palazzo Uguccioni, the Palazzo Pitti, with a series from the Laurenziana Library, while others show the ornamental designs and stucco decoration of typical Mannerist facades from buildings such as the House of Bianca Cappello in Via Maggio, the Palazzo Corboli, the Certosa, and the Palazzo Tamirez di Moltavo. (See also item 645). Berlin Cat 598 records and incomplete copy. *Folio. Etched title and 40 numbered etched plates. Contemporary hand-printed paper boards, a very large untrimmed copy.* £240

1482

1484 **Lavallée-Poussin, (Étienne de) & others** Nouvelle collection d'arabesques, propres a la décoration des appartemens; dessinées à Rome par Lavallée Poussin et autres célèbres artistes modernes, et gravées par Guyot. Precedée d'une notice historique sur le genre arabesque et d'une explication raisonée des planches de la collection par M. Alexandre le Noir *Paris & Strasbourg, Treuttel & Wiirte (1810)*

The first issues of this work in separate suites by the Guyot brothers about 1785 were amongst the earliest examples of the type of decoration made popular by Clérisseau and Belanger, and were inspired by the preceding excavations of the ancient Roman palaces and villas, the antiquities of Herculaneum (see items 1706), and the grotesques of Raphael and his studio. Only five of the ten parts are by Lavallée Poussin himself; these were drawn during his fifteen year stay in Rome and published soon after his return to Paris. The remaining suites were drawn by Voisin, Le Clerc, Berthelot, de Claire and L. Janneret. Janneret's final suite shows designs for 'Fonds d'appartements' and illustrates the use which could be made of the arabesques in the interior decoration of rooms. The introduction is by Alexandre le Noir, director of the Musée des Monuments Français. Berlin Cat 506, Guilmard p 261. *Quarto. 10 cahiers. 12pp and 40 unnumbered etched and aquatinted plates (4 to each cahier). Marbled-paper boards, quarter morocco.* £140

1485 **Leighton, John** Suggestions in design being a comprehensive series of original sketches in various styles of ornament. Arranged for application in the decorative and constructive arts ... with descriptive and historical letterpress by James K. Colling *London, Blackie (1880)*

Designs in all styles for use by artists and art-workmen. Leighton had published a smaller collection of them under the pseudonym 'Luke Limner' in 1852-3 – and he appears to have been the first English designer to borrow from Japanese models. *Quarto. Litho frontispiece, (2) +xii+176pp and 101 litho plates of Leighton's designs, and many text illustrations. Contemporary quarter calf.* £45

1486 **Leith, Samuel - Ballantine, James** The tradesmans book of ornamental designs. – Essay on ornamental art as applicable to trade and manufacture *Manchester, Ainsworth (c 1847) London, Orr 1847*

A four-page preface to Ballantine's 'Essay on Ornamental Art' serves as a preface to Leith's work also, and it is apparent that they were intended as the two parts of a single publication. As a compendium of designs the 'Tradesmans Book' is unusual for its date in the variety of artefacts for which designs are provided – the cabinet-maker, the damask weaver and the bookbinder are among those catered for – and Leith's eclectic designs include 'Louis Quatorze', 'Alhambra' and 'Egyptian' patterns. Ballantine's contribution reviews the chief decorative styles of the day. In an interesting passage inspired by Stephens and Catherwood's recent publication of the Maya remains he compares Maya and Elizabethan architecture and suggests that Elizabethan ornament 'so full of wild and irregular fancies' may be based on the drawings of adventurers returning from the Americas. *Folio. 42 litho plates (including title and dedication); 4 + 36pp with text figures. Original cloth.* £45

1487 Le Pautre, Jean Trophées d'armes à la romaine *Paris, Pierre Mariette (c 1657)*

Trophies of arms were a favourite type of ornament in French decoration and became a major motif of painting and sculpture in Lebrun's schemes. The culmination of their use is seen in his decoration of the Escalier du Roi at Versailles (see item 622) (Oeuvres suite 110). Destailleur Notices p 104. Guilmard p 74. *Six numbered plates, average size 147 × 213mm. In paper wallet.* £30

1488 Le Pautre, Jean Frises feuillages et autres ornemens à l'italiene *Paris, Pierre Mariette (c 1660)*

Hunting scenes, bacchanalian compositions, nymphs and playing putti intertwine among foliated scrolls set here and there with framed landscape compositions. (Oeuvres suite 2). Destailleur Notices p 95. *Six numbered plates with two panels to each plate. Average size 220 × 322mm, with wide margins. In paper wallet.* £40

1489 Le Pautre, J(ean) Grotesques et moresques *Paris, P. Mariette (c 1657)*

Designs inspired by the grotesques in Raphael's Vatican Loggie, but here interpreted in a more rich fashion, densely packed with figures and motifs. (Oeuvres suite 6). Destailleur Notices p 96. Guilmard p 70. *Six numbered engraved plates with three columns to each plate. Average size 228 × 158mm, with good margins. In paper wallet.* £30

1490 Le Pautre, J(ean) Rinceaux de frises, et feuillages nouvellement inventéz et gravéz *Paris, N. Langlois (c 1700)*

Foliated scrolls with putti: one large design to a plate and small inventions beneath. (Oeuvres suite 21). Destailleur Notices p 103. Guilmard p 70. *Six numbered plates, average size 145 × 210mm, with good margins. In paper wallet.* £24

1491 Le Pautre, Jean Livre de frise et ornemens nouvellement inventé et gravé *Paris, the author (c 1645)*

Foliated scrolls with putti and male nudes. Four plates each with two designs, two plates with four designs. Berlin Cat 314. Destailleur p 95. *Six numbered engraved plates, average size 152 × 223mm. Good margins. In paper wallet.* £30

1492 Le Pautre, J(ean) Termes de 4 saisons de l'année. Termes, supports, et ornemens, pour embellir les maisons et jardins *Paris, N. Langlois, (c 1700)*

Terms were a favourite supporting ornament for mantels, chimney-pieces, cornices, and friezes. More than twenty-four designs of different types are shown in this suite. From Langlois' edition of 'L'Architecture à la Mode'. Destailleur Notices p 104. Guilmard p 114. *Six numbered engraved plates, average size 166 × 253mm, with good margins. In paper wallet.* £55

1493 Le Pautre, (Jean) (Ruines romaines) *(Paris), le Blond, (c 1645)*

A little known and uncatalogued suite of Le Pautre's invention, probably made soon after his return from Italy, and reflecting the influence of Poussin and his followers. *Six unnumbered etched plates, average size 190 × 135mm. Fine impressions with wide margins. In paper wallet.* £48

1494 **Le Pautre, (Jean)** (Quatre pièces tirées de la mythologie) *Paris, N. Langlois (c 1695)*
A rare suite of four compositions in circular frames, representing Acteon, Orpheus, Pomona and the Burning of Troy. Each is accompanied by an explanatory verse and proverbs or morals forming part of the borders and illustrating the main composition. An unrecorded suite. *Four unnumbered engraved plates, average diameter 253mm. Cut to plate marks and mounted on old paper. In paper wallet.* £60

1495 **Le Pautre, (Jean)** (Suite de diverse sujets ou paysages encadrés de magnifique bordures.) *(Paris), le Blond (c 1650)*
Typical compositions for the overmantels of fireplaces which were frequently decorated with paintings in highly ornamental frames. This suite was not reproduced in the collected works. Destailleur Notices p 100. *Six unnumbered engraved plates, average size 300 × 235mm, with good margins. In paper wallet.* £48

1496 **Le Pautre, (Jean)** (Riches encadrements) *(Paris, le Blond c 1650)*
Oval designs in richly sculptured borders of irregular outline. The fitting together in these engravings of two half designs suggests a possible source for the asymmetrical inventions of the following century. This suite was not reproduced in the collected works. *Six unnumbered plates, average size 300 × 220mm, with good margins. In paper wallet.* £60

1497 **(Lock, Matthias)** A collection of ornamental designs, applicable to furniture, frames & the decoration of rooms, in the style of Louis 14th – on 24 plates, chiefly after Thos Chippendale *(London, John Weale c 1834)*
A collection of tables, mirrors, chimney-pieces, cartouches and 'morceaux de fantaisie' which again (see item 1561) does not stem from Chippendale's 'Director' as one might suppose. Four plates still retain the signature of Matthew Lock, and the work is, in fact, a reproduction of his suite of 'Six Tables' and plates from 'A New Drawing Book of Ornaments, Shields, Compartments, Masks.' The lively designs illustrate the effortless talent of this first English designer to master the conventions of French high rococo. The publication is one of a series of books of English rococo designs issued by Weale in between 1830 and 1860. *Quarto. 24 engraved plates including title. Publishers embossed cloth boards.* £85

1498 **Lockington, J(ohn)** Book of ornamented crests, engraved on twelve copper-plates, as a cabinet for the gentlemen and curious fancy worker; or pattern-book for the coach painter, engraver, jeweller, sadler, plater, embroiderer, modeller, &c. *London, Laurie & Whittle 1st Jan. 1812*
A highly decorative pattern book which was first published in 1791. The motifs are mainly birds and beasts with a certain charming naïvety and unfrighteningly fierce expressions. One plate shows horse and rider vignettes and the last plate departs from the series to show religious subjects in gothic-revival aediculae. *Twelve numbered engraved plates including title, average size 200 × 253mm. Stitched in contemporary blue-paper wrappers. Preserved in buckram folder.* £110

1499 **Loire, N(icolas)** Nouueaux desseins d'ornemens pour lembelissement des carosses, paneaux, lambris &c. Nouuellement inventez par N. Loire et grauez par A Loire *Paris, P. Mariette (c 1670)*
Lively designs for carriages and decorative panels capable of being executed in a variety of media from stucco to metal. The designs consist of painted panels enclosed by strapwork and leaf-scroll ornament with putti and mythical figures. The elder Loire (1624-1679) was active mainly in the field of painting and decorative work executing the decorations in Parisian hotels and royal châteaux while his younger brother, Alex (1640-1713) who engraved the plates was a renowned gold and silversmith. Destailleur Notices p 227. *Six numbered engraved plates including title with sizes varying from 160 × 200mm to 180 × 270mm, with good margins. Tipped on grey Ingres paper. In paper wallet.* £42

1500 **Marillier, (Clement Pierre)** Nouveaux trophées ou cartouches representant les arts et les sciences composées avec les atributs qui les caractérisent *Paris, Mondhare (c 1770)*

Marillier (1740-1808) one of the foremost book illustrators of his time, here produces a suite of decorative designs dedicated to his master Morlot. The classically composed plates for the different Arts and Sciences (Agriculture, Theology, Architecture, Music, War, Poetry, etc.) each include a busy putto and a medallion with the portrait of a famous practitioner of the art: Bossuet, Mansart, Lulle, Voltaire, Descartes, etc; each has a wide shaded border and an uplifting motto. Berlin Cat 461. Guilmard p 234. *Title and 12 unnumbered plates, average size 300 × 225mm. Stitched in marble-paper wrappers.* £65

1501 **Middleton, G. A. T. & R. W. Carden** Ornamental details of the Italian renaissance *London, Batsford 1900*

Folio. 10+(2)pp and 50 photolitho plates. Original cloth, ex library. £8

1502 **Meissonier, Juste Aurèle** Oeuvres *Paris, Huquier (c 1750)*

The complete and definitive edition of the works of Meissonier which constitutes the most important collection of rococo designs, originally published from the late 1720s onwards, and which were to become widely influential in Germany. The nineteen suites show an astonishing variety of items: architectural fantasies and executed projects, ceilings, cartouches, church ornament and fittings, clocks, interiors, furniture, fountains, mirrors, monstrances, ink stands, scissors, a sleigh, table-ware, tobacco and snuff boxes, tombs, and watch cases, all displaying the artist's brilliant ingenuity and skill of design. This work of great stylistic importance and visual beauty is now exceedingly rare. Berlin Cat 375. Destailleur Notices pp 226-233. Guilmard pp 155-8. *Folio. Engraved title, engraved portrait and 118 engraved plates on 74ff (in 19 suites lettered A-R and two unlettered) with continuous numbering 1-26, 28-116, 118 (numbers 27 and 117 were not issued) and 2 unnumbered plates belonging to suite A. Plates loose in quarter calf drop-back box, morocco label.* **Illustration below.** £1850

1503 **Meissonier, J(uste) A(urèle)** (Oeuvres) *Paris, Huquet (c 1750)*

Meissonier's compositions epitomize the generally accepted ideal of rococo design in the impulse towards asymmetry, the contrasting shapes, the organic nature of the forms whose plastic tendencies are the only backward-looking signs (and perhaps the only acknowledgement of the artist's italian origins). Complete copies of the collected works are excessively rare and the following are the ornamental suites which appeared in the collection. Berlin Cat 378. Destailleur Notices pp 226-232, Guilmard pp 155-7.

1502-4

a **Livre de legumes. Suite C.**
Culinary designs probably made in the early 1730s, and the first compositions of their kind in France. Four plates show shell palmettes surmounted either by bouquets of a wide variety of vegetables, or, with fish and water plants. The two remaining plates are trophy-like one with an oak spray bearing game birds, the other crossed sticks of celery supporting a hare. *Seven engraved plates including title, numbered 13-19, lettered C. Average size 158 × 102mm, some plates cut into plate mark at top and bottom but not affecting inner border. Tipped on hand-made grey paper, in matching wallet.* £42

b **Livre d'ornemens. Suite D.**
Meissonier's expression of the cartouche, with plastic frames, broken scrolls and energetic lines enclosing forms which were to become widely influential as 'morceaux de caprice' or 'morceaux de fantaisie' for their visionary edifices, sharp perspectives and airy fantasies. One of the most characteristic forms of rococo decoration. *Seven engraved plates including title, numbered 20-26, lettered D. Average size 105 × 205mm, occasionally cut close to one plate mark. Tipped on grey hand-made paper, in matching wrappers.* **Illustration opposite.** £50

c **Sixième livre. Suite F.**
Ornaments for the chronological map made for the King in 1733 and designs for the frame of the King's portrait. The designs are characterized by disjointed scrolls, shell motifs and asymmetrical trophies and cartouches. *Seven engraved plates numbered 35-41, lettered F. Sizes vary from 215:378 × 125:222mm. Tipped on grey hand-made paper and preserved in paper wallet.* £48

1504 **Meissonier, Juste Aurèle** Oeuvre de Juste Aurèle Meissonier *Paris, 1750 (Blom reprint 1969)*
Reproduction of the complete suites of the artist's designs with a reduction of some of the plates. Preceded by a full and scholarly introduction with a discussion of Meissonier's work by Dorothea Nyberg. *Folio. 46pp and 118 plates on 44ff. Original cloth.* **Illustration opposite.** £12

1505 **Mondon, (Jean)** Neu inventierte Vorstellungen von Stein und Muschel Werck mit Chinesischen Figuren verziert Dritter-Theil. Troisieme livre de formes rocailles et cartels ornés de figures chinois *Augsberg, Joh. Georg Merz (c 1750)*
German copies of designs first published in Paris in 1736 by one of the earliest followers of the three great innovators of the picturesque who was also the first to use the word 'rocaille' to describe this particular type of ornament. The designs show the rococo cartouche in a late phase of its development where it has become almost a picture in its own right rather than a decorative arrangement of motifs. Vegetable forms combine with masonry bent to conform to the fluid, curving rhythms of the style, and the constructions are enlivened by chinesified figures in the traditional shape of courtiers and wily orientals. *Seven numbered engraved plates including title, suite lettered N, size 230 × 173mm. Small defect in edge of title plate. Hinged on old paper. Preserved in marbled-paper wallet.* £35

1506 **Nicolai, Herrmann Georg** Das Ornament der Italienischen Kunst des XV Jahrhunderts. Eine Sammlung der hervorragendsten Motive *Dresden, 1882*
Details of architectural ornament taken from buildings in Venice, Vicenza, Brescia, Mantua and Pavia. The photo plates are very good for their date. *Folio. (4)pp and 100 photo plates. Original cloth portfolio.* £17

1507 **Nilson, J(ohann) E(saias)** Suite No. XI (Kartuschen) *Augsburg, the author (c 1755)*
Cartouches with emblems and rhyming couplets representing Religion, Military Bravery, Science and Agriculture. Berlin Cat 146:XI. Guilmard p 444. *Two engraved plates with four designs; sizes 190 × 286mm. In paper wallet.* £8

1508 **Oakeshott, George J.** Detail and ornament of the Italian Renaissance drawn by George J. Oakeshott architect *London, Batsford 1888*
Examples of ornament taken from buildings in Florence and Northern Italy. *Folio. (2)+6pp and 40 litho plates (including 5 double-p plates taking 2 nos each). Original cloth, recased.* £15

1509 **Oppenord, G(illes) M(arie)** Livres de differents morceaux à l'usage de tous ceux qui s'applique aux beaux arts *Paris, Huquier (c 1748)*

Giles Marie Oppenord (1672-1742), son of an 'Ebeniste du Roi', was one of the leading designers of the French Regency and probably the most fertile in invention, though many of his engraved ornamental designs were ideal creations which he never had the opportunity to execute. This present group of suites comes from the series familiarly known as the 'Moyen Oppenard' which were probably invented in the early 1730s. They include some designs which can be considered picturesque because of their asymmetry and the fusion of cartouche motifs with naturalistic elements, though the majority follow Oppenord's more usual plastic style derived from the Italian Baroque. Suites from the original issue. Berlin Cat 383, Guilmard p 141-2.

a **Premier livre de differents morceaux a l'usage de tous ceux qui s'appliquet aux beaux arts.**
Oppenord's most rococo inventions based on the cartouche. *Six numbered engraved plates including title, suite lettered A. Average size 325 × 228mm. In paper wallet.* £45

b **Troisième livre contenant des frises ou paneaux en longeur.**
It is difficult to understand quite how these very light and pleasant designs accord with the title. The inventions (three to a plate) are more in keeping with designs for overdoors, panel heads or panel centres than for friezes or strip panels. *Six numbered engraved plates including title, suite lettered C. Average size 320 × 212mm. In paper wallet.* £60

c **Quatrième livre contenant des montans ou pilastres.**
Designs based on renaissance examples of grotesques with their typical mixture of figures, plants, trophies and masks. *Six numbered engraved plates including title, suite lettered D. Average size 315 × 197mm. In paper wallet.* £55

d **Cinquième livre contenant des cartouches.**
Small asymmetrical designs, three to a plate. *Six numbered engraved plates including title, suite lettered E. Average size 313 × 327mm. In paper wallet.* £60

e **Septième livre contenant des fontaines pour la decoration des jard(in)s et places publiques.**
Several of the designs are difficult to distinguish in style from the cartouches in the Premier Livre. *Six numbered engraved plates including title, suite lettered F. Average size 315 × 225mm. In paper wallet.* £45

f **Dixième livres des oeuvres... contenant des guaismes.**
Twenty-nine classical designs showing half profiles. *Six numbered engraved plates including title, suite lettered K. Average size 312 × 205mm. In paper wallet.* £18

1510 **Parsons, Colonel (William)** A new book of cyphers; more compleat and regular than any yet extant. Wherein the whole alphabet (twice over) consisting of 600, is variously changed, interwoven, and reversed; with the coronets of England, by allowance of the Earl Marshall. As likewise some examples for the ready composition of any cypher consisting of 3, 4 or more letters: with ornaments suitable to most occasions ... The whole (with the English translated into French) engraven on 56 copper-plates *London, the author 1704*

Elegantly interlaced initials of combinations from AA to ZZ and including certain reversed letters. The cyphers were designed in circles in order to discipline their proportions in such a way that they could easily be used in ovals or squares. In the former shape they were popular for use on watch-backs but were also frequently found, inscribed in a variety of shapes on plates, snuff boxes, carriages, etc. The penultimate plate shows a method of using the designs to compose combinations of more than two letters, while a final plate illustrates the way to express in line the seven colours of heraldry by a variation of hatching. Parsons, a Buckinghamshire squire, designed and drew the plates which were variously engraved by Joseph Nutting who executed the script, Simon Gribelin II who carried out the first and final plates, and M. Tavel who engraved all the cyphers. Parsons and Gribelin were old friends and the latter was involved in the engraving of all the former's other works and dedicated his own 'New book of ornaments' to Colonel Parsons. The title-page/dedication of this publication is an extra tipped in the front of the present work. *Oblong quarto. 56 engraved plates numbered I-IV (i.e. dedication, half title, title, 2ff advertisements in English and French), (A)^4-M^4 and I-IV. Early nineteenth century marbled-paper boards, and half red morocco, gilt.* £475

1511 **Péquégnot, (Auguste)** Vases céramique et orfèvrerie... meubles de tout style... cheminées plafonds architecture décorations intérieures *Paris,(c 1850)*

Faithful copies of engravings taken from Du Cerceau, Le Pautre, Delafosse, Berain, Blondel, etc. Not at all the same as having the originals but many artists are represented and the collection gives a broad cross-section of the engraved material produced in France in the 16th-18th centuries. *Quarto. 3 vols, each with engraved title, containing about 528 engraved plates in all. Contemporary quarter red morocco, marbled-paper boards, uncut.* £65

1512-13

1512 **Pergolesi, Michel Angelo** (Designs for various ornaments) *(London, the artist) 1 May 1777 through to 1801*

Designs for ornamental panels, ceilings, furniture decoration, cornices, pilasters and fireplaces, doorways, friezes, urns, candelabra, complete wall schemes and interiors, decorative scrolls, leafwork and rosettes, all in imitation of the Adam style. Pergolesi was one of the group of Italian artists and painters who came to London under the auspices of James Adam and worked with Robert Adam's decorative team. Although he is thought to have been one of Adam's principal decorators his only recorded work is in the Long Gallery at Sion House and on some other minor work in the same building. The designs appeared first in 12 small suites of 5 plates each with an interval of six years before the next suites appeared while the final 4 plates were published posthumously in 1801 by Dulauchamp who calls himself 'successor to the late Signor Pergolesi'. The work includes the two dedication leaves to the Duke of Northumberland (his patron at Syon) and the Duchess of Buccleuch. Owing to the extended time between the appearance of the first and last suites (almost 25 years) complete sets are of excessive rarity. Berlin Cat 593 records only 61 plates. *Large folio. 72 engraved plates, some unnumbered, average height 460mm by varying widths of about 240-290mm. Printed in black, dark sepia and bistre. Marbled-paper boards, quarter calf.* **Illustration above.** £425

1513 **Pergolesi, Michel Angelo** (Designs for various ornaments) *(London, the artist) 1 May 1777 through to 1 April 1791*

Another copy of the previous item in a smaller run as is more usually found. In this slightly later issue, all the plates are numbered. *Folio. 60 engraved plates including the dedication 56 (bis) but lacking plate 42. Printed in black, dark sepia or bistre. Marbled-paper boards, quarter calf.* **Illustration above.** £215

1514 **Perkins, John** Floral designs for the table *London, Wyman 1877*
A unique little work by the head gardener at Thornham Hall, Suffolk, showing patterns for decorating with leaves, flowers and fruit, a dinner table serving from eight to one hundred guests. The majority of the designs are based on an arrangement of garlands and wreaths around vases, standard plants, lamps, bowls of fruit and dishes of confectionery. Special arrangements are included for wedding breakfasts, a home coming, harvest home dinners, a hunt breakfast and cricket luncheons. *Oblong small folio. 36pp and 24 coloured litho plates. Publisher's decorated paper boards.* £35

1515 **Pierretz, A(ntoine)** Recherche de plusieur beaux morceaux d'ornemens antiques et modernes, comme trophées, frises, masques, feuillages, et autres *Paris, Pierre Mariette fils, (c 1747)*
A pattern book of Louis XIV architecture and interior ornament with key patterns, plant and fruit garlands, swags, and motifs, frieze decoration, trophies, masks and arabesques. Eighteenth century impressions of plates which first appeared in 1648 (see Berlin Cat 318). *25 numbered etched plates including title. Average size 160 × 105mm, and with wide margins. The impressions remain good. In paper wallet.* £50

1516 **Pillement, J(ean)** A pair of Chinese figures *(London), 1st March 1759*
A pair of highly decorative figures engraved by Canot but invented by the talented French decorative artist and landscape painter who specialized in 'chinoiserie' designs, Jean Pillement (1728-1808). Pillement was a native of Lyon and his work was perhaps influenced by designs of the silk industry in that town. He worked in Paris, Poland, Austria and Portugal as well as spending some time in London where he exhibited regularly between 1760 and 1780. The present designs with their English copyright seem to stem from the beginning of his stay in London and his very decorative designs must have had a considerable influence on English artists and craftsmen with inclinations towards the rococo style: men such as Chippendale and Lock. The prints are in a large format and show a male dancer with a mask, and a girl holding ornamental birds; each is within a rococo framework of rustic motifs and is set against a Chinese landscape. *Two engraved plates each 415 × 274mm; cut to plate mark. Preserved in paper wallet.* £200

1517 **Pillement, Jean** Chinese figures in a landscape *London, 1 March 1759*
A suite of plates without title, slightly larger than Pillement's usual designs, showing three or more Chinese figures in the foreground by the side of a temporary shelter in a water landscape. One plate has a man exercising tethered cranes, another shows figures in a small boat, a third illustrates men making obeisance to a monkey on a pedestal, while the final plate delineates women with baskets of fruit. The plates are engraved by J. C. Canot and all bear the copyright 'London, Published accord^g, to Act of Parl^t, March 1st, 1759'. The third plate also bears the imprint 'A Paris chez C. Leviez rue St André des Arts vis a vis de l'Hôtel Château Vieux'. The suite would seem to correspond to that in Berlin Cat 449 Band 1 Canot (3). *Four engraved plates, each 277 × 430mm. Preserved in paper wallet.* £225

1518 **Pillement, (Jean, & others)** The ladies amusement; or, the whole art of japanning made easy. Illustrated in upwards of fifteen-hundred different designs, on two hundred copper plates; consisting of flowers, shells ... &c all adapted in the best manner ... To which is added, ... the most approved methods of japanning ... with directions for the due choice of composition, colours, &c. The second edition *London, Robert Sayer 1762 (Ceramic Book Co reprint 1966)*
A facsimile reprint from the only complete surviving copy of the original work with over 1500 drawings and designs of chinoiserie figures, motifs, and ornaments for gilding. The book was essentially a workshop manual and the original sheets were frequently used as transfers, which is why so few copies are still extant. Many of the designs which are included have been traced on Georgian furniture, tea-caddies, enamels, textiles, japanned ware and ceramics. *Oblong quarto. (4) + 6 + (2)pp and 200 photolitho plates. Publisher's cloth.* £10.50

1519 **Pillement, Jean** The fantastic original designs and chinoiseries of Jean Pillement *Newport, Ceramic Book Company (reprint) 1969*
Reproductions of 150 Pillement designs from more than 23 suites of designs of flowers, birds, and chinoiserie, intended for silks, embroidery and other applied arts. The plates, originally engraved by a variety of artists and watercoloured in a contemporary hand are reproduced about one third original size and set on an average of 4 to a plate. *Folio. 40 colotype plates. Preserved in card wallet.* £10.50

1520 **Poterlet, L. Henry** Mes petites compositions *(Paris), A. Guerinet, (c 1886)*
A series of charming rectangular compositions somehow reminiscent of perfumed cards. Based on flower designs the compositions seem to be composed of a mixture of 19th century naturalism, rococo scrollwork with a hint of art nouveau stylization, but the resulting effect is not nearly so heterogeneous as this sounds. *Quarto. 35 etched plates including decorative title, with miscellaneous numbering. 19th century quarter red morocco. Library stamp on verso of plates.* £22

1521 **Pugin, A. Welby** (Ornaments of the 15th and 16th centuries) *London, Ackermann 1835-7 (but issued in this form a little later)*
Collected edition of four suites of Gothic designs; 'Gothic furniture in the style of the 15th century' (see item 155); 'Designs for iron & brass work in the style of the XV and XVI centuries'; 'Designs for gold and silversmiths'; and 'Details of antient timber houses of the 15th & 16th centuries'. *Quarto. 4 parts in 1 vol. Coloured title and 24 etched plates; coloured title and 25 etched plates; coloured title, tinted title and 26 etched plates; coloured title and 22 etched plates. Original quarter calf, marbled paper sides.* £40

1522 **Pugin, A. Welby** (Ornaments of the 15th and 16th centuries) *Edinburgh, (c 1895)*
Lithographic reprint. The book enjoyed renewed popularity with the arrival of the Arts and Crafts movement. *Quarto. 4 parts in 1 vol. Collation as last but title pages and final plate in chromolitho adaptations. Original cloth.* £15

1523 **Pugin, A. Welby** Fifteenth and sixteenth century ornaments *Edinburgh, John Grant 1904*
Another lithographic reprint of item 1521, with a new title page and the contents bound in chronological order. *Quarto. 4 parts in 1 vol. Collation effectively as last, but with ivpp prelims. Original cloth.* £12

1524 **Pugin, A. Welby** Glossary of ecclesiastical ornament and costume, compiled and illustrated from antient authorities and examples...with extracts...faithfully translated by the Rev. Bernard Smith *London, Bohn 1844*
An important ornament book which Pugin used to emphasize the tradition of Catholic art 'and aid the restoration of that truly beautiful furniture and decoration that antiently adorned every Christian church'. The chromolithograph plates are by Michael Hanhart, a successful rival of Owen Jones. *Quarto. xiv+(2)+222pp and 73+(1) chromolitho plates. Original quarter red morocco, gilt stamped, spine repaired.* £135

1525 **Pugin, A. Welby** Glossary of ecclesiastical ornament and costume ...a second edition enlarged and revised by the Rev. Bernard Smith *London, Bohn 1846*
Quarto. xvi+245+(1)pp and 74 chromolitho plates numbered 1-73 and 29 bis. Original quarter red morocco, gilt stamped. £110

1526 **Pugin, A. Welby** Floriated ornament: a series of thirty-one designs *London, Bohn 1849*
A collection of designs published to illustrate Pugin's thesis that the best Gothic ornament, ancient and modern, is derived directly from nature. Two of the plates illustrate the use of floriated ornament in mediaeval churches and the rest portray original designs by Pugin based on the botanical illustrations in Jacobus Theodorus's 'Eicones Plantarum' of 1590. In basing ornamental patterns on plant features Pugin was anticipating the design theory of

Christopher Dresser. *Quarto. (8)pp and 31 chromolitho plates including title and frontispiece. Original quarter red morocco, gilt stamped.* £60

1527 **Pugin, A. Welby** Floriated ornament *London, Chatto & Windus 1875*

Reprinted from the original stones. *Quarto. viii pp and 31 chromolitho plates. Original quarter red morocco, gilt stamped.* £45

1528 **Richardson, Charles James** Studies of ornamental design *London, John Weale for the author 1851*

Richardson (1806-71), a pupil of Soane and a teacher at the Government School of Design at Somerset House, published a number of books on architecture, decoration and ornament, including the first serious studies of Elizabethan and Jacobean buildings and their furnishings. In this handsome folio he selects examples of ornament from very varied sources – the Italian renaissance, mediaeval embroidery, Roman glass, designs by Thomas Stothard, and Persian textiles – and illustrates them on large chromolithograph plates by Day & Son. The book was issued in two parts dedicated respectively to Prince Albert and Lord Granville, and the plates carry dates between October 1847 and October 1850. *Large folio. 2 parts in one. Title page, dedication leaf, (5)ff text and 8 plates (of which 6 are chromolitho); frontispiece, title page, dedication leaf, (2)ff text and 6 chromolitho plates, with 1 extra plate not called for in text. Original quarter red morocco, cloth sides.* £75

1529 **Rumley & Co.** Collection of ornaments *London, C. Tilt (& Rumley & Co) 1838*

Designs for chased and engraved metalwork in a variety of styles dependant upon earlier engraved plates from several sources. *Quarto. Decorative engraved title and 20 steel engraved plates miscellaneously numbered. Average size 220 × 165mm. Publisher's embossed cloth, spine rehinged.* £40

1530 **Sambin, Hugues** Oeuvre de la diversité des termes, dont on use en architecture, reduict en ordre *Lyon, (Jean Marcorelle for) Jean Durant 1572*

Sambin, architect, surveyor, cabinet-maker and joiner, displays the fantastic range of his invention and the width of his imagination in this work on columnular figures, which were popular mannerist features. Although his designs owe much to the previous works of Vredeman de Vries and Du Cerceau, Sambin outstrips both in the fertility of his imagination and the power of his inventions. His figures are in the Burgundian sculptural tradition of plastic forms and would continue in copies on Burgundian carved cabinets and buffets until the late 17th century. Some of the designs may have been used in the decorations of the town of Dijon for the entry of Charles IX in 1564. The doors of the Palais de Justice in this, Sambin's native city, carry a typical term figure, while the balusters of the screen in the chapel of the Palais are a modified version of the 6th figure in the book. The designs, generally rich and abundant in decoration, begin with reasonable restraint (though the first pair, which have insects and reptiles crawling in the nooks and crannies of the rustic masses from which they emerge, should prepare one for what is to come). Gradually the figures become more decorative and detailed and receive a number of attributes and appendages. One developes into a 'siamese twin'; on another the legs become satyrs or centaurs, the stomachs turn into viewing panels through which further pictures can be seen, or into door-knockers; small figures attach themselves to the larger, increase in numbers until the main figure becomes almost a complete Bacchanalian revelry in itself with massed forms of satyrs, goats and putti intermingled with heavy fruit and flower garlands and neo-classical motifs of masks, rams heads, acanthus leaves lions' heads, birds, and finally sublimates to the Three Graces. The whole presents a picture of rich, sensual fecundity and a powerful, pantheistic vision of the 'Dieu Terme'. The present copy retains the mispelling of Sambin's given name as 'Huges' on the title-page, but has the final word on p 32 corrected (from 'L'Agriculture' in some copies) to 'L'Architecture', and the final blank leaf (frequently missing) is here present, but, like the colophon leaf and one or two other empty pages it is covered with drawings of architectural details: mouldings, cornices, panels, terms, brackets, consoles, ceiling decoration, and chain-mail patterns etc, finely drawn, in an early hand. Berlin Cat 3920, Fairfax Murray Cat (French) 500, Fowler 285, Harvard Cat French 16th Century Books 481. *Folio. 76+(1+3 blank)pp (including decorative woodblock title border, 36 full-p woodblock terminal figures arranged in pairs, a decorative woodblock initial, 18pp of text each with a woodblock headpiece and tailpiece using 4 different headpiece designs and 3 tailpiece designs, and colophon). Seventeenth century full calf, gilt.* **Illustration opposite.** £1250

ORNAMENT 239

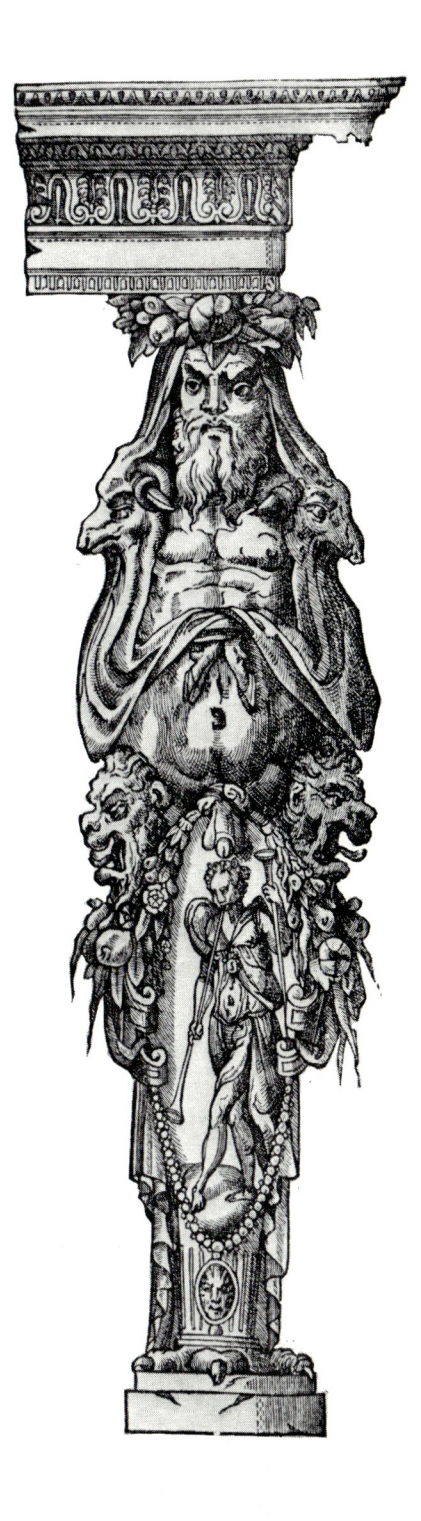

1530

1531 **Scott, William Bell** The Ornamentist, or Artisan's Manual in the various branches of ornamental art : being a series of designs selected from the works of Dietterlin, Berain, Blondell, Meisonier, Le Pautre, Zahn, Boetticher, and the best French and German ornamentalists with an introductory essay on ornamental art, by W. B. Scott *London, Fullarton 1845*

A selection of material from the classic ornament collections. William Bell Scott (1811-90) was at that time a master in the Government School of Design at Newcastle-upon-Tyne and this publication is aimed at the requirements of the industrial designer. *Folio. Litho title, 21+(1)pp, with 21 text figures and 77 litho plates (1 folding). Contemporary quarter calf, marbled paper boards.* £28

1532 **Seddon, John P.** Progress in art and architecture, with precedents for ornament *London, David Bogue 1852*

For Seddon, a follower of Ruskin who out-Ruskined his master in dislike of classical architecture, precedents for ornament are Gothic precedents and Venetian Gothic precedents for choice. His observations on contemporary trends are partisan but a vivid reflection of the influence of Ruskin at this early date. The plates show details of capitals and are lithographed by Vincent Brooks, Cyrus Mason and Leighton Bros. *Quarto. vi+(2)+60pp and 12 litho plates. Contemporary cloth.* £22

1533 **Shaw, Henry** Illuminated ornaments selected from manuscripts and early printed books from the sixth to the seventeenth centuries ... With descriptions by Sir Frederick Madden *London, William Pickering 1833*

A work which presented for the first time a variety of examples of rare manuscripts of exceptional beauty. A diversity of stylistic types and schools are shown from 6th century Greek script on gold ground, through Saxon capitals from the Lindisfarne Gospels, a complete alphabet from the Coblentz School of the 12th century and Flemish 15th century realistic scenes, to the courtly international gothic of the French and north Italian schools represented, with very renaissance motifs, by Milan and Florence. Particular attention was paid to ornamental work as exemplified by borders, arabesques and initials. The work is rendered of permanent value by the knowledge and taste displayed in the selection of examples and by the careful drawing and colouring of the plates. The scholarly catalogue descriptions were provided by Sir Frederick Madden, Assistant Keeper of the Manuscripts in the British Museum, who also wrote as an introduction the brief history of manuscripts pointing out the stylistic changes which took place. *Quarto. Title in red and black, decorative title, 18pp and 40+(3)ff and 59 stone-etched or lithographed plates highly finished by hand in opaque water colour heightened with gold leaf. Large paper copy from Alton Towers (see item 1742) with book label of Earl of Shrewsbury. Varnished paper boards, red morocco spine, preserved in cloth slipcase.* £220

1534 **Shaw, Henry** The encyclopedia of ornament *London, William Pickering 1842*

A forerunner of the numerous coloured pattern books of historical ornament which appeared after 1851. Besides stained glass and carved ornament in wood and stone, Shaw illustrates ironwork from Nôtre Dame, English painted tiles, 17th century needlework, lace and velvet, Holbein's jewelry designs for Henry VIII and surprising choices like the decorative borders of Israel van Meckenem and three Grolier bindings from the British Museum.

The plates were produced in a variety of media and include hand coloured copperplate line engravings, aquatints, a zincograph, and several printed in colour from wood blocks. The title page is printed from wood blocks in five colours and one plate is in black and six colours. *Quarto. 6pp and 60 plates including decorative title (of which 48 coloured or tinted). Large paper copy in a very fine 19th century gilt tooled red morocco binding.* £120

1535 **Shaw, Henry** The encyclopedia of ornament

Another large paper copy. *Quarto. 6pp and 60 plates, some coloured. Quarter morocco.* £70

1536 **Shaw, Henry** The encyclopedia of ornament

A standard copy. *Quarto. 6pp and 60 plates, some coloured. Quarter morocco.* £55

1537 **Shaw, Henry** The encyclopaedia of ornament. 1842 *Edinburgh, John Grant 1898*

Lithographic reprint, uniform with the undated Edinburgh reprint of Pugin's 'Ornaments' (see item 1522). *Quarto. vipp and 59 litho plates. Original cloth.* £15

1538 **Shaw, Henry** Alphabets, numerals and devices of the Middle Ages *London, William Pickering 1845*

Large paper copy of the first edition of one of Shaw's last multicoloured decorative books of fundamental importance in the study of typography, lettering and the art of the book. The examples are taken from wood and stone carvings, monumental brasses, early prints, and incunabula, with several pages of initials from old illuminated manuscripts, here printed in four colours, with some illustrations heightened in gold and a few hand tinted. *Imperial quarto. (8)pp and 48 plates of various media of which 26 coloured. Full morocco, gilt, gilt edges and revers. The copy from the Huth Collection.* **Illustration below.** £125

1538

1539 **Shaw, Henry** The handbook of mediaeval alphabets and devices *London, Quaritch 1853*

The most widely circulated of Shaw's ornament books, intended for architects, decorators and students of ornamental design. *Octavo. (10)pp including title in red and black, and 36+(1) coloured plates. Original blind-stamped cloth.* £18

1540 **Tatham, Charles Heathcote** Etchings, representing the best examples of ancient ornamental architecture; drawn from the originals in Rome, and other parts of Italy, during the years 1794, 1795, and 1796 *London, for the author 1799*

First edition. Tatham worked in Henry Holland's office and through Holland's assistance went to Italy for three years. During his stay there he was closely associated with Canova, Asprucci, Angelica Kauffman, Sir William Hamilton and Lord Carlisle, who became his patron. The materials and drawings which he brought back and form the basis of the present volume are in the Soane Museum. His work proved a particularly desirable source for designers of furniture and silver in neo-classical styles, and it ran to several editions. This edition has a list of the original subscribers who include Asprucci, Beckford, Bonomi, Brettingham, Canova, S. P. Cockerell, Dance, Flaxman, J. M. Gandy, Thomas Hope, Henry Holland, Soane and James Wyatt. *Folio. 12pp and (102) etched plates. Quarter calf, original marbled paper boards.* **Illustration on next page.** £150

1541 **Tatham, Charles Heathcote** Etchings... third edition *London, Gardiner 1810*

Folio. 8pp and 102 etched plates (numbered 1-100, 102, 47*; no plate 101 was issued). Quarter calf, marbled paper boards. **Illustration on next page.** £70

1540-1, 1543

1542 **Tatham, Charles Heathcote** Etchings, representing fragments of antique Grecian and Roman architectural ornament; chiefly collected in Italy, before the late revolutions in that country, and drawn from the originals *London, T. Gardiner 1806*

A second series of etchings of classical sculptural ornament. *Folio. (4)+3+(1)pp and 24 etched plates. Quarter calf, marbled paper sides.* £48

1543 **Tatham, Charles Heathcote** Etchings, representing the best examples of Grecian and Roman architectural ornament; drawn from the originals, and chiefly collected in Italy, before the late revolutions in that country *London, Priestley & Weale 1826*

Reissue of Tatham's two series of 'Etchings', with the second series numbered consecutively from 103 onwards. *Folio. 8+3+(1)pp and 126 etched plates numbered 1-100, 102-26, 47*. Quarter calf, marbled paper boards.* **Illustration above.** £85

1544 **Testelin, (Louis)** Les vertus innocentes, ou leurs symboles sous les figures d'enfans *Paris, J. van Merle 1671*

Louis Testelin (1615-1655), noted for his imitation bas reliefs and cameos in grisailles designed several suites based on putti forms. This particular one, advertised as 'necessaires aux amateurs de la muette poesie & de la pinture parlante', is based on bas-reliefs by Gerard van Opstal, a Brussels-born sculptor (1595-1668) who worked in Paris. The engraver is Louis Ferdinand (1612-1689), and the suite first appeared in 1654 just before Testelin's death. Berlin Cat 4008:(4) records first state. Guilmard p 55. *Folio. 8 engraved plates including title, average size 250 × 210mm. Plates trimmed to borders and hinged into marbled-paper boards. Lacks one plate: La Félicité. Preserved in cloth case.* £70

1545 **Turbayne, A. A.** Monograms & ciphers designed and drawn by A. A. Turbayne and other members of the Carlton Studio *London, Jack (1906)*

Quarto. xxi+(7)pp and 135 plates with more than a thousand monograms & ciphers. Contemporary quarter green morocco, gilt tooled spine. £32

1546 **Valentine, Lucia N.** Ornament in mediaeval manuscripts. A glossary *London, Faber 1965*

Designed as 'a tool for the iconographer' and useful for sculptural and architectural ornament too. *Octavo. 108pp, with many text illustrations. Original cloth.* £3

1547 **Vardy, John** Some designs of Mr. Inigo Jones and Mr. Wm. Kent *London, 1744*

Vardy (d. 1765) was a colleague and close associate of Kent and this collection of designs comprises 17 by Jones, nearly all for chimneypieces, and 36 by Kent for gold and silver plate, vases, candelabra, furniture and summerhouses. This is the only contemporary engraved record of Kent's non-architectural design work. *Folio. Engraved title, 2 engraved contents leaves and 53 engraved plates. Contemporary mottled calf, neatly rebacked with gilt tooled spine.* £375

1548 **Vulliamy, Lewis** Examples of ornamental sculpture in architecture. Drawn from the originals of bronze marble and terracotta in Greece, Asia Minor and Italy by Lewis Vulliamy archt in the years 1818, 1819, 1820, 18(21) and engraved by Henry Moses *London, the author (1823)*

Issued in eight monthly parts each with 5 engraved plates; parts 1 and 4-8 illustrate Greek ornament, part 2: Roman ornament and part 3: Italian cinquecentro ornament. Vulliamy (1791-1871) later developed a very successful architectural practice, working in Gothic, Italian renaissance and Jacobean styles. *Folio. Engraved title and 40 engraved plates. Contemporary boards, cloth spine.* £65

1549 **Vulliamy, Lewis - (Redman, D. J.)** Examples of ornamental sculpture in architecture – Ornaments from the antique, lithographed in twenty-one leaves *London, Vulliamy 1823, J. Taylor (1820)*

The Vulliamy work (see preceding item) has seven of the original front wrappers of the separate parts bound in and also 8 of the original notices describing the plates. Redman reproduces Roman and High Renaissance Italian ornament on lithographic plates signed 'Redman lith. Aprilis 1820'. Redman was the first English lithographic printer. He had worked for Philipp André and G. J. Vollweiler when they had been in England, and had set up on his own in 1813. This example of his work is not recorded in Twyman's recent 'English Lithography 1800-1850'. *Folio. Engraved title, 40 engraved plates; 21 litho plates including decorated title-page; original printed wrapper pasted on an extra folio leaf. Contemporary half calf, gilt tooled spine on raised bands with sunflower motifs, repaired at joints.* £120

1550 **Ward, James** The principles of ornament. Edited by George Aitchison. New and enlarged edition *London, Chapman & Hall 1896*

Octavo. xx + 208pp with many illustrations. Original decorated cloth. £4

1551 **Waring, J. B.** The arts connected with architecture illustrated by examples in Central Italy from the 13th to the 15th century *London, Vincent Brooks 1858*

'Examples of stained glass, fresco ornament, marble and enamel inlay, and wood inlay' (described thus on the printed title), drawn from churches in Florence, Siena and Pisa. The plates illustrating the stained glass and frescoes are particularly impressive. *Folio. Litho title, (2) + iv + 29 + (1)pp and 41 litho plates (all but 5 coloured). Original quarter morocco, cloth sides.* £55

1552 **Waring, J. B.** Stone monuments, tumuli and ornament of remote ages; with remarks on the early architecture of Ireland and Scotland *London, Day 1870*

Strictly an archaeological work, dealing with 'Keltic' civilisation in Britain and Western Europe and illustrating extant sites and remains; but it also shows Waring's preoccupation with ornament and symbolism and his continuing reliance on handsome lithographic illustration. *Folio. x + 96pp and 108 litho plates. Original blind and gilt stamped cloth, spine repaired.* £45

1553 **Watt, James Cromar** Examples of Greek and Pompeian decorative work *London, Batsford 1897*

Measured drawings of ornament taken from classical remains in Athens, Sicily and Southern Italy. *Folio. (8)pp, litho title and 60 litho plates. Original cloth.* £12

1554 **Watteau, A(ntoine)** Livre nouveau de differente trophées *Paris, Huquier & la v.ve Chereau, (c 1730)*

Pendant trophies of pastoral, festive and artistic attributes whose apparent simplicity disguises the profound originality of subject and treatment. The engravings were made from drawings after the death (in 1725) of the artist whose work is the embodiment of French Regency decoration. Berlin Cat 376. Guilmard p 146. *Large quarto. 12 etched plates including title, average size 245 × 180mm. Very fine impressions with large margins, untrimmed; preserved in paper wallet.* £165

1555 **Weisbrod, (C. W.), Adelaide Allou,** (etc.) Recueil d'antiquités Romaines ou voyage d'Italie, composé de 66 planches; dans lequel on trouve divers vases, autels, trepieds, arabesques, et autres sujets gravés d'après les dessins que differens artistes ont faits pendant leur séjour en Italie; gravés par Weisbrod, Adélaïde Allou, et autres *Paris, Basan (1769)*

The 66 plates fall into nine suites containing from 4 to 12 engravings; most are of vases, tripods, lamps, bas reliefs, arabesques, etc. The final suite is engraved by Adelaide Allou after Hubert Robert and consists of views of classical ruins. An interesting collection of material calculated to appeal to collectors and artists. Berlin Cat 478 records a copy lacking text. *Folio. Title leaf, 3+(1)pp and 60+(6) engraved plates. Contemporary paper covered boards, uncut. Dawson Turner's copy, with his name on the front endpaper and the date 1814.* **Illustration below.** £75

1555

1556 **Whittick, Arnold** Symbols for designers. A handbook on the application of symbols and symbolism to design *London, Crosby Lockwood 1935*

Octavo. Frontispiece, xvi+168pp with text illustrations and 15 plates. Original cloth. £4

1557 **Wilkinson, J. Gardner** On colour and on the necessity for a general diffusion of taste among all classes. With remarks on laying out dressed or geometrical gardens. Examples of good and bad taste illustrated by woodcuts and coloured plates in contrast *London, Murray 1858*

Includes a long discussion of taste in ornamental design. *Octavo. xvi+408pp with 62 woodcut text figures, and 8 colour plates. Quarter morocco.* £32

1558 **Wilkinson Heywood & Clark Ltd.** Painted arms, coronets, insignia and lettering *London (c 1910)*

Trade catalogue. *Quarto. (22)pp with several hundred coloured illustrations on plates. Original gilt-stamped cloth.* £18

1559 **Wind, Ludwig** Münchener Muster-Sammlung *Munich, Braum & Schneider, (c 1862)*
A manual of historic ornament and decorative details to be found in the buildings and objects of Munich and representing examples from Byzantine times to the mid 19th century. The illustrations include examples from plasterwork, friezes, supports, doors and windows, knobs, finials, feet, frames, hinges and ironwork grills. *Quarto. Title and 80 lithographed plates. Contemporary cloth boards, quarter oasis.* £18

1560 **Wornum, Ralph N.** Analysis of ornament. The characteristics of styles: an introduction to the study of the history of ornamental art *London, Chapman & Hall 1860*
Second edition of a basic ornament textbook giving the substance of lectures delivered by the author at various schools of design in the years 1848-50. *Octavo. Frontispiece, 112pp, with text figures and plates. Original decorated cloth. Ex library.* £5

1561 **(Johnson, Thomas)** Chippendale's one hundred and thirty three designs of interior decorations in the old French and antique styles for carvers, cabinet makers, ornamental painters, brass workers, modellers, chasers, silver smiths, general designers and architects *London, John Weale 1834*
A collection of mirrors, chimney-pieces, picture frames, candlesticks, clock-cases, brackets, girandoles and tables. The designs are not the invention of Chippendale as the title suggests but are the work of Thomas Johnson (see items 1457-8) and are restrikes of Johnson's plates which had first appeared in 1758 without a title but dedicated to Lord Blakeney, and were later issued, in 1761, under the title 'One hundred and fifty new designs' with the plates renumbered. The present plates are restrikes of all but five of the originals with Johnson's signature removed and Chippendale's added in its place. The designs which are mainly for carving work are all in Johnson's exuberant rococo style, with sharp, spiky decoration interspersed with chinoiserie motifs and hints of 'gothick' in some of the forms. In their original issues it was these designs which has such a marked influence on other contemporary designers and carvers, and, in particular, caused a change in Chippendale's style which is noticeable in the new designs for the third edition of the 'Director'. Between 1830 and 1860 Weale produced a series of publications reprinting English rococo designs, principally by Johnson and Lock, which were issued under the umbrella of Chippendale's name. (See also item 1497). *Quarto. Decorative engraved title and 49 numbered engraved plates. One plate remargined on right side. Contemporary paper-boards, quarter calf, rebacked.* £150

1562 **Panvinio, Onofrio** Amplissimi ornatissimiq(ue). triumphi uti L. Paulus de rege Macedonum Perse capto ... Imperatores Romani, triumpharunt ex antiquissimus lapidum ... accuratissima descriptio ... *Rome, Gio. Giacomo de Rossi (c 1660)*
Panorama of a triumphal procession in ancient Rome as shown on the stones, coins and as described in various ancient authors. The engravings were first published in Antwerp by Plantin about 1570; this edition was added by Gian Giacomo de Rossi to his issue of the large du Perac plan of Rome and was intended to form a decorative frieze to that publication. It seems to have been issued as a separate work on its own at about the same period. Abbey Life: Panoramas 451 (the Abbey copy lacks the last two plates). *12 numbered engraved plates on 4ff. Sizes vary from 155: 158 × 335: 366mm. Wide margins, untrimmed. Preserved in cloth folder.* £125

1563 **Seguy, E. A.** Insectes *Paris, Du Chartre & Van Buggenhoudt (c 1930)*
Some stunning plates by Seguy who here turns his eye to the less obvious field of the rare insects from the remote parts of the world to discover a juxtaposition of colours rarely found elsewhere. The drawings are artistically conceived yet scientifically accurate with four plates of interpretive patterns which have been included to illustrate the design possibilities inherent in these natural forms. The stencil colouring has made possible the reproduction of the freshness and intensity of the hues and tones of the insects themselves. *Folio. 20 collotype plates in full stencil colouring of watercolour and gouache, with 80 insect drawings and 15 decorative designs. Original portfolio with printed and stencil-coloured label.*
£250

1564 Seguy, E. A. Papillons *Paris, Tolmer (c 1928)*

Illustrations of exotic and highly colourful butterflies from India, New Guinea, S. America, the Himalayas, Africa, South-East Asia, and China, usually enlarged in size, sometimes as much as 10 or 15 times, but reproduced faithfully in form and colour combinations in a mixture of media: a colotype base with stencil in watercolour or gouache. Seguy, an entomologist, eventually became Director of the Laboratory for General and Applied Entomology at the Museum of Natural History in Paris, and although a dedicated scientist, here shows an artistic flair and sensitivity to the beauty of natural forms and a remarkable understanding of their application in the field of design. The positioning of the examples on the plates (which show 5 species to each plate) displays a feeling for colour, form, and spacial relationships, while their colour reproduction and deliniation remain scientifically accurate. At the same time the four plates at the end of the work, which illustrate the application of the examples from the previous pages to produce abstract designs, reveal a gifted pattern designer of high merit. *Folio. 20 collotype plates in full stencil colouring of watercolour and gouache with 80 butterfly drawings and 16 decorative compositions. Original portfolio with decorative printed and stencil-coloured boards.* **Illustration below.** £300

Vases

1602

1601 **Allou, Adelaide & P. Nicolet** Cinquième suite de vases composée de 12 feuilles *Paris, Bassin (1771)*
Typical neo-classical inventions with a diversity of form and ornamentation. Nicholet's designs display rather more fantasy of invention than Adelaide Allou's more regular, yet imaginative, designs. *Twelve etched plates, with sizes varying from 193:225 × 127:160mm. Wide margins. In paper wallet.* £65

1602 **Aquila, Francesco** Raccolta di vasi diversi formati da illustri artefici antichi e di varie targhe soppraposte alle fabbriche piu insigni di Roma da celebri architetti moderni *Rome, Domenico de Rossi 1713*
A pattern book of vases and armorial shields. The first part which consists of 32 vases in pairs on 16 plates, comprises half antique examples and half renaissance and baroque models designed after the manner of the ancients. Among the former are types from the Villas Borghese, Giustiniana, and Lante, the neo-Attic crater by Salpion of Athens once used as a baptismal font in Gaeta cathedral, and the cantharos in the forecourt of Santa Cecilia in Trastevere. The most important group among the modern vases are designs of ten by Polidoro da Caravaggio from the frieze of the Palazzo Milesi, four by Lanfranco from his ceiling decoration of the loggia of the Villa Borghese, and designs by Pietro da Cortona and Ciro Ferri. Aquila (who worked between 1690 and 1738 as chief engraver to the de Rossi family) dramatises the vases by placing them in the immediate foreground of diminutive Campagna-type landscapes so that each piece is magnified against the sky while a romantic countryside, deserted, with ruins, or, enhanced by a remote farmhouse, recedes behind the base and stem. Turning to the armorial shields we move directly from classical antiquity to Roman High Baroque. Here the 35 plates illustrate the varied manner in which Papal armorial shields were used on a diverse number of monuments: on church and palace façades, on the keystones and spandrels of arches, as overdoor decoration, on

tombs, balconies, and fountains. The buildings on which they are to be found were nearly all initiated between 1623 and 1667 during the reigns of the Popes Urban VIII Barbarini (1623-44), Innocent X Pamphili (1644-55) and Alexander VII Chigi (1655-67), and it is the arms of these popes which appear on the majority of the shields with the Chigi arms being the most widely represented in 17 examples. The architects responsible were mainly Bernini (with 21 elaborate sculptural creations) Borromini, and Pietro da Cortona. Much importance was attached by the Popes and their families to the display of these armorial shields as demonstrations of their princely munificense and power. Their artistic importance has yet to be explored. Berlin Cat 1140. Cicognara 3862. (We are indebted to Mr John Bury for the information on this item). *Oblong folio. 51 engraved plates including title and dedication leaves. Contemporary full vellum.* **Illustration at head of section.** £385

1603 **Arias, Paolo E.** Mille anni di ceramica Greca. Fotografie di M. Hirmer *Florence, Sansoni 1960*

A selection of the finest Greek vases, discussed and catalogued by Arias and illustrated by especially handsome photographs. *Quarto. 166+(2)pp, 240pp of plates and 52 coloured plates. Original cloth.* £25

1605

1604 **Bouchardon, Edmé** Premier (Second) livre de vases *Paris, Huquier (c 1735)*

Urns (etched by G. Huquier) of relatively simple basic shape usually with one complex, amorphous piece of decoration which adds a very plastic quality to the designs. Bouchardon was a friend of the Comte de Caylus and was distinguished by being the only artist praised by Le Blanc in his famous letter to Caylus criticising the bad taste in decoration and the too free range of Rococo ornamentation. But, according to Le Blanc, Bouchardon in his invention of ornamental forms 'n'en imagine que de nobles, & les distribues avec intelligence'. Berlin Cat 1060. Guilmard p 161. *Large quarto. 24 etched plates including two titles, in two suites lettered A & B each numbered 1-12. Average size 195 × 135mm. Fine impressions with very large margins, untrimmed. In paper wallet.* **Illustration above.** £150

1605 **Boucher, (Juste-Francois), fils** Nouveau livre de vases *Paris, la veuve de F. Chereau (c 1765)*

Vases and urns in the 'goût antique' with putti, wreaths, and heads as decoration and lion-head handles. Only one departs from the classical restraint by displaying a grotesque form and a menacing mask-head handle. Guilmard p 232. *Title and 7 unnumbered etched plates. Average size 130 × 95mm. Two plates trimmed very close, all others with good margins. Hinged on buff paper, in paper wallet.* £36

1606 **Christie, James** Disquisitions upon the painted Greek vases, and their probable connection with the shows of the Eleusinian and other

mysteries. – An essay upon that earliest species of idolatry, the worship of the elements *London, Longman 1825; Norwich, Stevenson 1814*
Two works by the younger James Christie (1773-1831), second of the Christie dynasty of auctioneers. The 'Disquisitions' were first published in 1806 under the stimulus of Christie's friendship with the collector Charles Townley, and they develop the theme of the connection between the subjects of Greek vase paintings and the Mysteries that had first been enunciated by Hamilton and d'Hancarville (see item 1609). The 1825 edition contains a new appendix classifying vases by form and colour (and explaining their various shapes as based on the buds of different varieties of water lily). The 'Essay' shows Christie's wide knowledge of comparative mythology and its two coloured plates illustrate symbolic representations on Chinese porcelain. *Quarto. xii+146pp including engraved vignette on half title and 6 headpieces, errata leaf and 16 engraved plates (of which 2 folding); (2)+iv+26pp and 2 folding coloured plates. Contemporary quarter calf, marbled paper boards.* £55

1607 **Fröhner, W.** Choix de vases Grecs inédits de la collection de son altesse impériale le Prince Napoléon. – Deux peintures de vases Grecs de la nécropole de Kameiros *Paris, Claye 1867; Baur & Détaille 1871*
These are two scarce and handsomely produced monographs by the Conservateur-Adjoint of the Musée des Antiques, Paris. *Folio. 2 works in 1. (6)+48+(2)pp and 7 chromolitho plates; 18+(2)pp with 1 text figure, and 2 chromolitho plate, 1 photoplate. Contemporary half red morocco, original printed wrappers bound in. Small stain on corner of first leaves.* £30

1608 **Gardner, Ernest Arthur** A catalogue of the Greek vases in the Fitzwilliam Museum Cambridge *Cambridge, University Press 1897*
Scholarly and fully illustrated catalogue. *Octavo. (2)+xxi+(1)+95+(1)pp and 41 photo plates. Original cloth.* £12

1609 **Hamilton, Sir William** Collection of engravings from ancient vases mostly of pure Greek workmanship discovered in sepulchres in the Kingdom of the Two Sicilies but chiefly in the neighbourhood of Naples during the course of the years MDCCLXXXIX and MDCCLXXXX. Now in the possession of Sir Wm. Hamilton . . . with remarks on each vase by the collector *Naples, W. Tischbein (for the author) 1791-5*
Sir William Hamilton sold an important collection of vases from Southern Italy and Sicily to the British Museum in 1772 and the 'Portland Vase' to the Duchess of Portland in 1784. He began a new collection in 1789 and published it in these fine volumes with the aid of Wilhelm Tischbein, Director of the Royal Academy of Painting at Naples, who was

1609-10

responsible for the engraved plates. The collection was later offered to the King of Prussia, who declined it; it was shipped to England in 1798 and the bulk was eventually sold to Thomas Hope for his country house at Deepdene. *Folio. 3 vols. Two engraved titles, engraved frontispiece, 159+(3)pp and 62 plates numbered P2, P3, 1-60; two engraved titles, 104pp and 4+62 numbered plates (with 61 and 62 on 1 page); two engraved titles, (6)+ 97+(1)pp and 67 plates numbered A-G (with D-F on one page) and 1-60. Quarter calf, gilt tooled spines, marbled paper boards. Some slight staining at lower margins.* **Illustration on previous page.**
£175

1610 **Hamilton, Sir William** Collection of engravings from ancient vases *Naples, W. Tischbein (for the author) 1791-2*
Folio. Vols 1 and 2 only. Quarter calf, gilt tooled spine. **Illustration on previous page.**
£95

1611 **Le Pautre, (Jean)** (Vases et cartouches inventé de nouveau) *Paris, le Blond (c 1645)*
First issue of this small untitled suite of vases set within richly decorated frames. (Oeuvres 104). Destailleur Notices p 105. Guilmard p 74. *Octavo. 6 numbered plates, average size 225 × 150mm. In paper wallet.*
£32

1612 **Le Pautre, (Jean)** (Grand livre de vases) *(Paris), le Blond (c 1650)*
Second issue of these ewer designs which are set against architectural or landscape backgrounds and enclosed within richly decorated frames. One plate still retains the imprint of the original publisher, le Cany. (Oeuvres 98). Destailleurs Notices p 105, Guilmard p 74. *Folio. 6 unnumbered engraved plates, average size 324 × 232mm, with good margins. In paper wallet.*
£45

1613 **Le Pautre, J(ean)** Vases à la moderne *Paris, Pierre Mariette 1659*
Vases and ewers with putti, animal and figure decoration. (Oeuvres 102). Destailleur Notices p 84. Guilmard p 74. *Octavo. 6 numbered engraved plates including title, average size 200 × 150mm, with wide margins. In paper wallet.*
£25

1614 **Le Pautre, J(ean)** Vases à l'antique *Paris, Pierre Mariette 1661*
Complicated designs with profuse fruit and plant ornamentation and figures in high relief. (Oeuvres suite 101). Destailleur Notices p 85. Guilmard p 74. *Six numbered plates including title, average size 225 × 155mm, with wide margins. In paper wallet.*
£36

1615 **Marot, J(ean)** Vases *(Paris), P. Mariette le fils (c 1740)*
A rare suite of vases by the elder Marot, richly decorated with garlands, masks, horns, putti, cornucopiae, birds, beasts, and plant ornament. Four plates are signed by Marot. This is the second issue of the plates which first appeared c 1670. Berlin Cat 1045:5 records only 5 of the plates. *24 numbered plates including title, etched and engraved. Sizes vary from 137:192 × 74:100mm. In fine condition with good wide margins. Preserved in paper wallet.*
£65

1616 **Moses, Henry** A collection of antique vases, altars, paterae, tripods, candelabra, sarcophagi, & from various museums and collections. Engraved on 170 plates by Henry Moses. With historical essays *London, Bohn (1814)*
Moses's collection of vase designs – drawn from the collections of the British Museum, Thomas Hope, C. H. Tatham, Sir John Soane and elsewhere – was more convenient for the student and pattern designer than Hamilton's massive folios, and it was widely used at the time. See also item 1617. *Quarto. xii+61+(1)pp (including engraved title and 18 engraved head and tailpieces) and 151 engraved plates (numbered 1-150 with 115 used twice), of which 10 are hand-coloured. Original cloth, spine repaired.*
£32

1617 **Moses, Henry** Vases from the collection of Sir Henry Englefield, Bart. drawn and engraved by H. Moses *London, Rodwell & Martin (1819)*
Engravings by Moses of vases in the collection of Sir Henry Englefield, for long the secretary and dominant personality of the Society of Dilettanti. The text is printed both in English and French and details are given of the provenance of some important pieces. *Quarto. Engraved portrait frontispiece, engraved title, 60+(4)pp and 39 engraved plates. Large paper copy. Contemporary straight grained quarter morocco, gilt tooled spine, marbled paper boards.*
£45

1618 **Moses, Henry** Vases from the collection of Sir Henry Englefield *London, Priestley & Weale (1848)*
Reissue of the first edition. *Octavo. Engraved title, engraved portrait, 60+(4)pp and 39 engraved plates (1 hand-coloured). Contemporary quarter morocco.* £15

1619 **Murray, A. S. & A. H. Smith** White Athenian vases in the British Museum *London, British Museum 1896*
'The vase-designs in the present publication ... have been reproduced from negatives taken by means of the cyclograph, an apparatus invented ... with the view of obtaining absolutely correct photographic copies of the paintings on vases of a cylindrical shape'. *Folio. 10pp and 27 photogravure plates each with facing leaf of text. Original quarter cloth.*
£20

1620 **Noble, Joseph Veach** The techniques of painted Attic pottery *London, Faber 1966*
Quarto. xvi+217+(1)pp, including 261 illustrations. Original cloth. £7.50

1621 **Percenet, (L-N)** (Suite de vases) *Paris, Demarteau (c 1765)*
A fine group of classical vases with leaf and garland decoration and handles in the form of lions-heads, swans, and dolphins. Berlin Cat 1078. Guilmard p 254. *Four plates engraved in the crayon manner and printed in red; numbered 441-444 (it is not known to what the numbers refer). Average size 270 × 195mm. In paper wallet.* £48

1622 **Petitot, (Ennemond-Alexandre)** Suite de vases *(Parma), Benigno Bossi (1764)*
Highly imaginative vase designs with double handles in the shape of lions' heads, nude figures, rams' heads, snakes, leaf tendrils, locusts, cockerels, elephants' trunks, and shell volutes, further decorated with garlands, putti, satyrs, leaf and mask ornamentation. The amorphous quality which many of the designs display holds them to a rococo past, as does the slight suggestion of asymmetry which is found on some of the designs, though their general effect is neoclassical. Petitot (1727-1801) was an architect, trained under Soufflot, who displayed Neo-classical tendencies. In 1753, at the suggestion of the Comte de Caylus, he became the official architect to the Prince of Parma. The first three vases in the suite were actually executed and placed in the gardens of the Prince's palace at Parma. Petitot dedicates the drawings to him while the engraver Bossi dedicates the book to M. de Tillot, the Marquis de Felino. The present copy agrees with that in the Foulc collection (but not in the Foulc Catalogue) as recorded in Guilmard p 225. Berlin Cat 1080. *Quarto. Decorative engraved title, 2 plates of engraved text, and 31 numbered engraved plates including decorative dedication plate. Title skilfully repaired. Contemporary full vellum.*
Illustration below. £110

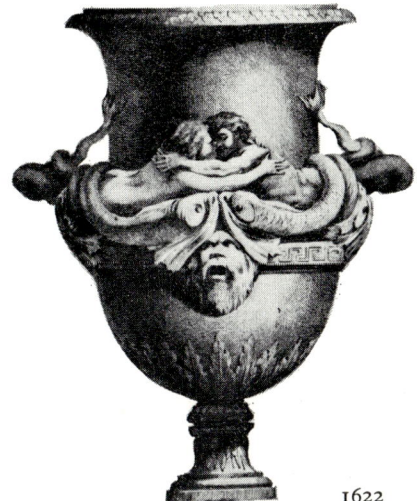

1622

1623 **Piranesi, Gio(vanni) Batt(ist)a** Vasi, candelabri, cippi, sarcofagi, tripodi, lucerne ed ornamenti antichi disegn(i) ed(iti) inc(esi) dal Cav. Gio. Batta. Piranesi. Tomo primo (... secundo) *Rome, the author (1778)*

These plates which represent Piranesi's etching skill and imaginative processes at their highest level are among the most underestimated works of the artist's genius. Furthermore they provide important evidence of his considerable influence upon the formation of later neo-classical designers both in England and France.

The plates belong to the final phase of Piranesi's career at a time when he was becoming increasingly dependent upon his foreign contacts, especially the patronage of British 'milordi' art collectors. By the late 1760s his activities as a 'vedutista', archaeologist and architect were combined with a profitable art-dealing business. A considerable proportion of the works illustrated here were originally restored and displayed in his showrooms, or 'museo' in the Palazzo Tomati, close to the Piazza di Spagna, the English quarter in Rome.

Nearly all the plates were enterprisingly dedicated to clients or prospective purchasers, and among the fifty Britons concerned were celebrated collectors such as Sir William Hamilton, William Weddell, Henry Blundell and Charles Townley. Other plates were connected with Piranesi's British associates in Rome, either as dedicatees such as James Byres, or as owners like Thomas Jenkins, Richard Hayward, Collin Morison and Matthew Nulty, most of whom acted as dealers or 'ciceroni' in addition to being artists.

As characteristic of Piranesi's didacticism, the detailed inscriptions he supplied to these illustrations provide much useful information about the original discovery and contemporary location of the objects concerned. The inscriptions indicate, for example: some 35 objects from over 25 British collections, ranging from modest cinerary urns and ornamental lamps to the magnificent 'Warwick Vase', bought by Hamilton and given to the Earl of Warwick in 1774. Other spectacular pieces include the fine marble crater with bacchic reliefs (then belonging to John Boyd and now in the Orangery of Kensington Palace), and two elaborate candelabra (presented by Sir Roger Newdigate to Oxford University in 1775 and now in the Ashmolean). These latter objects, as well as many others shown in the 'Vasi', came from the profitable excavations undertaken by the painter-dealer Gavin Hamilton in the Pantanello area of the Villa Adriana about 1769. Their final form, however, together with their memorable images, owe substantially to Piranesi's outstanding powers of creative reconstruction. Since the early 1760s when he became embroiled in the Graeco-Roman controversy Piranesi's roles as antiquarian and designer had become inextricably bound up with his polemic standpoint. Although he began in 1761 with a defense of the functional austerity of Italian civilization by 1765 he had changed his position radically. By this time he was praising the decorative variety and imaginative richness of Roman design, justifying the artist's freedom to transcend restrictive rules and conventions as established by Vitruvius and as imposed upon antiquity by later ages.

Further more, in the 'apologia' to the 'Camini' (see item 459) he urged the modern artist to emulate the creative fertility of Rome by combining varied motifs from antiquity to achieve works of striking originality. For Piranesi the restoration of antique fragments was equally amenable to this procedure and it is in this context that we must see the elaborately fabricated objects featured in many plates of the 'Vasi'. For instance, where a particular vase lacked its pedestal, Piranesi provided an appropriate one from another source, scrupulously indicating his artistic licence by means of letters in the illustration as well as by a reference in the accompanying inscription. In his more ambitious confections, however, Piranesi's baroque imagination carried him to unparalleled degrees of ingenuity where such explanations became superfluous. While these antiquarian fantasies inevitably earned him harsh criticism from his older contemporaries, they were to produce both a liberating and catalytic effect upon the imagination of those younger designers, inhibited by the austere message of Winckelmann and the orthodox Greek Revival.

The 110 sheets of the 'Vasi', were originally issued separately between 1768 and 1778 and only finally gathered together in two folio volumes each with its own title-frontispiece, in 1778, the year of Piranesi's death. Since they were not originally numbered there appears to be little consistency in the sequence of plates from one copy to another, (the order supplied in Focillon's 'Catalogue raisonné' nos 601-653, 654-718, cannot be relied upon). Moreover the editions after 1778 such as the Parisian one of Firmin-Didot in 1836, include additional plates by Francesco Piranesi, executed sometime between 1779 and 1780 while he was carrying on the family establishment. This present copy is the original issue, before any numbering of the plates. (We are indebted to John Wilton-Ely for this description).

Large folio. 2 vols. 58 unnumbered double-p etched plates on 56ff including large folding title made from two plates and 2 plates on one leaf; 69 unnumbered double-p etched plates on 55ff including large folding title made from 2 plates. Contemporary mottled calf, gilt; morocco label. One vol rehinged. **Illustration opposite.** £2250

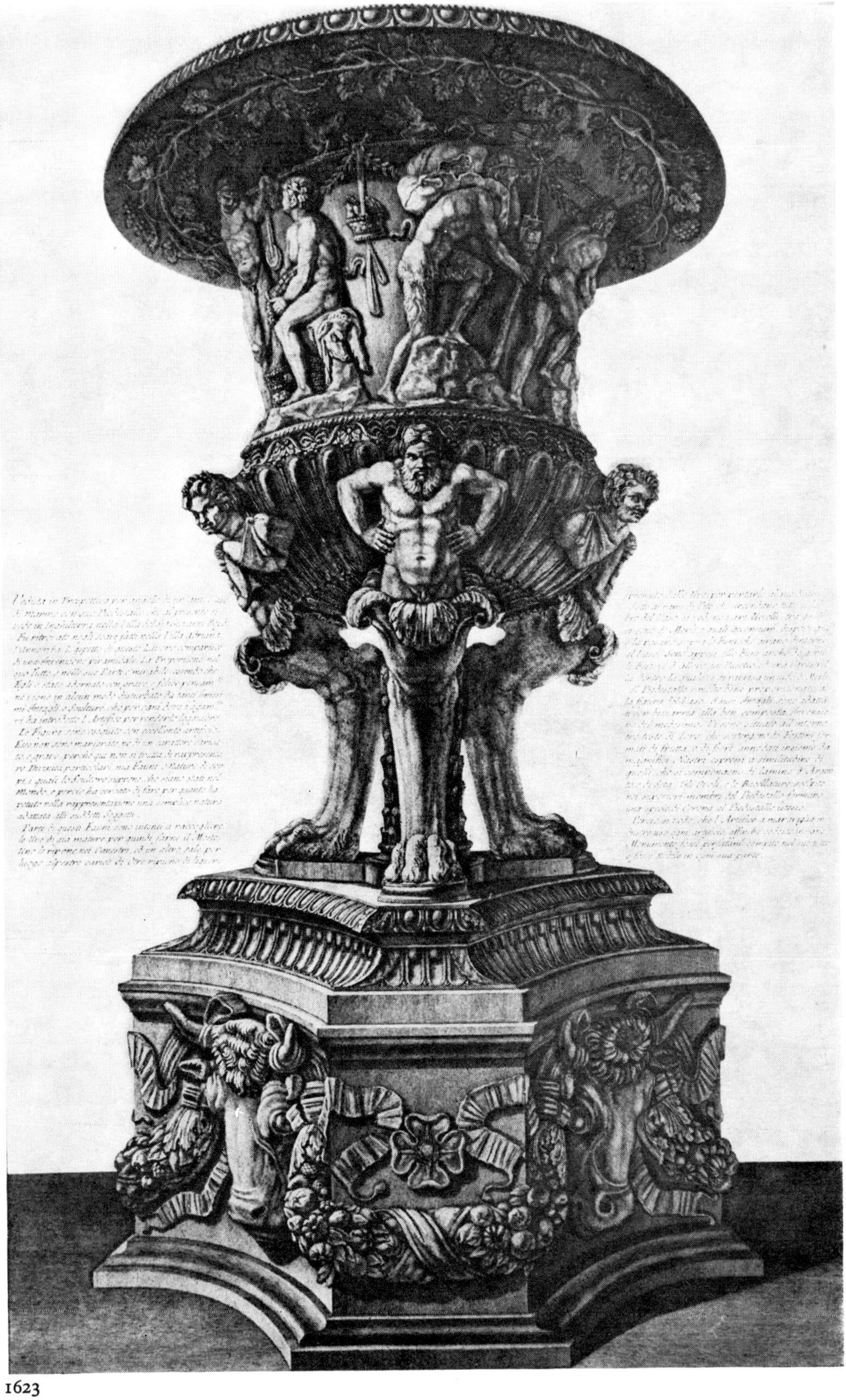

1623

1626

1624 **Polidoro (Caldara) da Caravaggio** Vasa a Polydoro Caravagino pictore antiquitatisq. imitatore presantiss. inventa Cherubinus Albertus in aes incidit atq. edidit Romae anno CIↃ DLXXXII *Rome, heirs of Cherubino Alberti 1628*

'Golden vases invented with such bizarre imagination that mortal eye could not conceive others more beautiful or more novel' is how Vasari refers to these famous designs from the frieze over the first floor of the Palazzo Milesi in Rome, here engraved by Cherubino Alberti. It is interesting to compare these large impressions of the urns with those by Aquila (see item 1602). Cherubino transcribes them from a low viewpoint, fills them full of life and movement, and colours them with dramatic highlights and shadows. Berlin Cat 1130. Guilmard p 286. *Eight engraved plates (of a suite of 10) numbered 1-3, 6-10, average size 250 × 160mm. Tipped on laid paper. In paper wallet.* £75

1625 **Polidoro (Caldara da Caravaggio)** (Vasi antichi) *(Amsterdam), F. de Widt (c 1650)*

Dutch engravings of the mannerist designs of Polidoro whose fantastic vase inventions would have a certain sympathy with the mannerist forms of the Netherlands. The present suite which illustrates quite different designs from the previous entries appears to be uncatalogued. *12 numbered engraved plates, average size 190 × 112mm, with wide margins. In paper wallet.* £55

1626 **Polidoro (Caldara) da Caravaggio** (Vases and trophies) *Rome, Gio. Batta Gelestruzzi 1660*

One of the most beautiful of the series of Caravaggio plates etched by Galestruzzi. Each plate bears two highly decorated mannerist vases flanking a trophy or bust. The final plate which bears the imprint and date shows the standing figures of two prophets and a Roman. The designs were taken from the facade decorations of the Palazzo Cesi in Via del Maschera d'Oro in Rome (see also item 633). Berlin Cat 538 (2). Bartsch XXI:63 nos 47-52. *Six numbered etched plates with an average height of 117mm and widths varying from 153 to 191mm. Very fine impressions with wide margins. Tipped on green Ingres paper. In paper wallet.* **Illustration above.** £50

1627 **Stockbauer, Jacob & Heinrich Otto** Die antiken Thongefässe in ihrer Bedeutung für die moderne Gefässindustrie *Nurnberg, F. Korn 1876-8*
Folio. *5 parts in 1. (6)pp and 30 coloured litho plates each with accompanying text leaf. Cloth portfolio enclosing the separate parts in their original printed wrappers.* £30

1628 **Thoms, P. P.** A dissertation on the ancient Chinese vases of the Shang dynasty, from 1743 to 1496, B.C. *London, the author 1851*
A selection of material from a famous Chinese manual on the vases of the Shang, Chow and Han dynasties; the illustrations 'were engraved, or rather cut, expressly for the translator, by A-Lae, a native of Canton, after the manner that blocks are cut for printing Chinese books'. *Octavo. 64pp including decorative title page and 43 text illustrations. Original wrappers.* **Illustration below.** £40

1628

1629 **Vico, Eneas** Sic Romae antiqui sculptores ex aere et marmore faciebant *Rome, 1543*
An impressive group of urns, ewers and vases by one of the most inventive of the sixteenth century Italian decorative engravers who was a protegé of Cosimo de Medici. The designs are very much in the mannerist tradition, heavily dependant on classical examples but enlivened by the original use of imaginative motifs. The group lacks three plates from the middle of the suite, and these have been replaced (probably at some time in the 18th century) by candelabra designs in much the same decorative vein, one of which is dated 1552. Berlin Cat 1125, 1126. *13 engraved plates from two suites, numbered I-IIII, VIII-XIII (of which only the first plate bears the quoted title, the others with Vico's monogram and the legend 'Romae ab antiqui repertum M.D.XXXXIII') and 3 unnumbered plates. Sizes vary from 240 × 178mm to 280 × 200mm. In paper wallet.* £225

1630 **Windus, Thomas** A new elucidation of the subjects on the celebrated Portland Vase, formerly called the Barberini: and the sarcophagus, in which it was discovered *London, for the author 1845*

Notes by Windus on the interpretation of the subjects represented in the cameo reliefs of the vase. He suggests that the vase was the funerary urn of Galen the physician, and that the scenes represent his most famous diagnosis: of the dangerously ill lady whose disorder was discovered to be her love for a rope dancer. A postscript reports the smashing of the vase 'into innumerable fragments' by 'an individual morbid with the organ of destructiveness' (a drunk with a walking stick) in February of the year of publication. The plates include four superb illustrations of the vase, with the fond in a deep blue representing the blue-black opaque glass of the original. *Large oblong quarto. (2+27)ff the latter numbered in 106 columns and with 19 text illustrations, and 10 lithographed plates of which 4 coloured. Publisher's embossed cloth boards, gilt, morocco spine; uncut.* **Illustration below.**   £38

1631 **Winter, Franz** Die jungeren Attischen Vasen und ihr Verhältnis zur grossen Kunst *Berlin, Spemann 1885*

Quarto. vi+72pp. Contemporary half morocco. Neat underlining in text.   £12

1630

'Frustum'

1702e

General

1701 Diderot, D. & J. L. d'Alembert Encyclopédie, ou Dictionnaire raisonné des sciences, des arts et des métiers, par une société de gens de lettres.–Nouveau dictionnaire pour servir de supplément aux dictionnaires des sciences, des arts et des métiers.–Suite de recueil de planches sur les sciences, les arts libéraux, et les arts méchaniques, avec leur explication.–Table analytique et raisonnée des matières contenues dans les XXXIII volumes in-folio du Dictionnaire des sciences, des arts et des métiers et dans son supplément *Paris, Briasson, David l'aîné, Le Breton, Durand 1751-57; Neufchastel, S. Faylche & Cie 1765 (false imprint); Paris, Briasson, David, Le Breton, Durand 1762-72; Paris & Amsterdam, Pancoucke, Stoupe, Brunet, & M. M. Rey 1776-77, 1777*

This celebrated work was probably the most influential publication of the 18th century and one of the greatest achievements of its kind. The rational and humanist spirit of its articles led to the French clergy opposing its publication and eventually to its censorship. The disruptive effect of its writings on orthodox philosophy was an important contribution to the controversies which preceded the French Revolution. Not least in this effect was the importance it placed on science and technology.

The space which was devoted to the applied arts and the technological processes is of particular interest to us. On the eve of the Industrial Revolution when technology was in a state of transition the volumes of engraved plates provide a record of great clarity and practical, detailed information on the way that technical processes had been carried out for the past several centuries.

Diderot, himself, took particular charge of the 'arts méchaniques'. He studied them, not theoretically from his study, but in a practical manner, spending whole days in workshops. His method was to begin by following the sequence of processes of the particular craft he was studying, then closely examining, in turn, each machine or piece of equipment used, and having the various parts and their workings explained to him. This was followed by a period in which he observed the machines being dismantled, and after an examination of the parts, reassembled. Then he would watch carefully while the worker operated the machine, and finally, he would take the worker's place and carry out the mechanical processes involved. In this way Diderot made himself familiar with some very complicated pieces of machinery such as the cut-velvet loom and the hosery knitting machine. In fact, he eventually became something of an expert on the textile crafts, an interest which is reflected in the resulting pictorial descriptions of these subjects, and the underlying understanding which they reveal.

Complete sets of the 'Encyclopédie', which ran to 35 volumes and was published over a period of 30 years are very costly and not often offered for sale. We are, however, able to offer the following set. *Folio. 35 volumes. Consisting of 17 vols of text, 11 vols of plates (with 269, 233, 201, 299, 248, 294, 259, 254, 253, 337, 239 plates respectively), 4 vols of Supplément with 244 plates, and 2 vols of the Table analytique. Contemporary tree calf.* £3850

1702 Diderot, D. & J. L. d'Alembert (Encyclopédie). Recueil de planches sur les sciences, les arts libéraux, et les arts méchaniques, avec leurs explication *Paris, Briasson, David, Le Breton & Durand, 1762-72; Livorno, 1772-9*

Miscellaneous suites from the previous item dealing with a wide variety of decorative crafts, and supplying some of the most unusual engravings of the series. *Each section listed is folio with single plates averaging 360 × 225mm, and is preserved in a paper wallet.*

a **Boutonnier.** (Buttonmaker)
Over 100 illustrations with three workshop views illustrating the making of different types of buttons: wooden buttons also used as bases or forms; metal buttons; and braided ones. The most interesting illustration is perhaps the braided button workshop which shows a worker covering a button with silk, another sewing on embroidery and ornaments, and two others making cords or straps for watches, garters and frogging. A final plate shows 16 different button designs and some decorative laminated strips of foil. *Six engraved plates and 2pp text.* £15

b **Cartier.** (Playing-card maker)
A fascinating suite showing the processes of making playing cards with all the equipment and the wood blocks for printing the picture outlines, the pattern pieces for adding the colours and printing the number cards. The text is more extended than usual and includes a glossary of paper terms, gives details of the amount of work a good employee can manage in a day, outlines the statutory hours of work in the city of Paris, and the means of assuring that the laws governing the sale of playing cards are carried out. *Six engraved plates with 60 illustrations, and 5 + (1 blank)pp text.* £18

c **Évantailliste.** (Fan-maker)
An attractive section which shows that fan-making was very much a female craft. The suite includes three workshop views showing sizing and preparation of the paper which includes stretching and drying on semi-circular racks, painting the paper, marking and folding the pieces and mounting on the wooden ribs. Two plates give detailed diagrams of the stages in the folding and mounting process. *Four engraved plates with 37 illustrations, and 2pp text.*

d **Formier.** (Last-maker) £12
The trade of making boot and shoe trees or forms shows a workshop view, 7 different operations in making a shoe tree, patterns for 13 women's forms and 5 men's forms, boot blocks and a plate of tools. *Four engraved plates with 63 illustrations and 1 + (1 blank)pp descriptive text.* £12

e **Fleuriste artificiel.** (Artificial flower-maker)
Lovely workshop scene with a crowd of men, women and children occupied in the various tasks of making the artificial flowers including preparing the paper and vellum or fabric, cutting and assembling the shapes and arranging the completed flowers. The suite includes 100 illustrations of templates of the punches for cutting leaves and flowers of anemones, ranunculi, carnations, lilac blossom, jasmine, stocks, wallflowers, marigolds, scabious,

oleander and many other plants. 2 plates (50 illustrations) show the tools of the trade. A final double-plate shows an elaborate table setting for fruits, sweets and desserts where the flowers are used as decoration. *Eight engraved plates of which 1 double-page with 160 illustrations, and 2pp descriptive text.* **Illustration at head of section.** £16

f **Lutherie.** (Musical instruments)
The first part of this suite on the making of musical instruments illustrates the organ with all its various parts while the second section concerns other instruments. The illustrations include fine decorative plates showing ancient and foreign instruments, 2 plates of instruments worked by a wheel, several plates of wind instruments including ancient types, and the tools used to make them, a group of plates showing stringed instruments and their tools, several diagrams of the harpsichord and its parts, and a group showing details of the harp. A beautiful workshop vignette shows a variety of instruments and their frames scattered around the shop, hanging from the walls and ceiling, and littered over the floor. The view shows the workers planing instrument boards, making the console of a harp, finishing off a violin and varnishing the frame of the harp. A final double-page plate forms a table which compares the ranges of the voice and other musical instruments with that of the harpsichord. *34 engraved plates (numbered I-XI, I-XXII, and X bis, of which 1 double-page) with over 350 illustrations and 7 + (1 blank) pp text.* £42

g **Marbreur de papier.** (Paper-marbler)
Details of the equipment and two busy workshop scenes showing the marbling of paper for books including views of mixing the gum solution, preparing the pigment, sprinkling the colours on the solution, putting the solution on the paper and combing in the pattern. Another vignette shows glazing, waxing, and folding paper, and marbling the edges of books. *Two engraved plates with 34 illustrations, and (1 + 1 blank) pp of descriptive text.* £9

h **Tabletier. – Tabletier cornetier.** (Chess-board maker)
Two unusual suites illustrating the work of the maker of chess-boards, chess-men, backgammon boards and pieces, tortoise-shell snuff boxes, combs and fancy articles of ivory, ebony and bone. Besides a workshop scene the illustrations include details of the preparation of the ivory, drawings of the drilling machines and the various presses employed, other tools as well as examples of the finished articles. *Two suites in one. 16 engraved plates with 275 illustrations and 3 + (1 blank) pp text; 4 engraved plates with 77 illustrations and 1 + (1 blank) pp text.* £24

1703 **Le dictionnaire universel des arts et des sciences de M.D.C. de l'Académie Françoise** Nouvelle édition révue, corrigée & augmentée par M*** de l'Académie Royale des Sciences *Paris, P. G. Le Mercier fils 1732*
Revised edition of a dictionary of terms used in the arts and sciences, compiled by Thomas Corneille (1625-1709), half brother of the dramatist, and first published in 1694 as a supplement to the Académie Francaise's dictionary of the French language. *Folio. 2 vols. (10) + (676)pp (numbered to 678 with 297-8 and 323-4 omitted and 325-6 repeated); (4) + 645 + (1)pp (numbers 555-6 omitted and 559-60 repeated). Contemporary full mottled calf, gilt tooled spines.* £85

1704 **(Dyche, Thomas)** Nouveau dictionnaire universel des arts et des sciences, François, Latin et Anglois ... traduit de l'Anglois de Thomas Dyche *Avignon, Francois Girard 1753*
The translator explains in an interesting preface that he found existing French dictionaries unsatisfactory – fortunate for him that at Avignon he was out of reach of Parisian literati – and preferred to base himself on Dyche. He goes on to say that his translation is not really a translation at all since he has freely adapted the original and has copied Dyche's method more than his text. (Dyche was a London schoolmaster who wrote several lexicographical works between 1708 and 1735). *Quarto. 2 vols. (4) + iv + vi + (2) + 603 + (1)pp; (4) + 575 + (1)pp. Contemporary full mottled calf, gilt tooled spines.* £68

1705 **Dictionnaire portatif des arts et metiers** Contenant en abrégé l'histoire, la description & la police des arts et métiers, des fabriques et manufactures de France & des pays étrangères *Paris, Lacombe 1766*
Useful portable dictionary, partly abridged from the large 'Description des Arts et Metiers', partly based on original material from a number of named contributors, e.g. Varenne de Beost on artificial pearls, Baumé on glass and Du Moustier on acoustics. *Octavo. 2 volumes. xxiii + (1) + 588pp; (4) + 723 + (1)pp (numbered to 715 with 53-60 repeated). Contemporary full mottled calf, gilt tooled spines.* £46

1706

1706 (**Le Antichita di Ercolano**) Le pitture antiche d'Ercolano e contorni incise con qualche spiegazione (5 vols) De' bronzi di Ercolano e contorni incisi con qualche spiegazione (2 vols : vol 1, Busti; vol 2, Statue). Le lucerne ed i candelabri d'Ercolano e contorni incise con qualche spiegazione (1 vol). Catalogo degli antichi monumenti dissotterata dalla discoperta citta di Ercolano ... composto e steso da Monsignor Ottavio Antonio Bayardi (1 vol) *Naples, Regia Stamperia 1757, 1760, 1762, 1765, 1779; 1767, 1771; 1792; 1755*

Complete set of this attempt at a definitive catalogue of the buildings and works of art excavated at Herculaneum during the 18th century under the patronage of the King of the Two Sicilies. Publication of the volumes took nearly forty years and they had an influence on the development of the decorative arts throughout Europe, affecting painters (Batoni, Mengs, Vien) as much as they did architects (Adam, Wyatt, Soane). They were produced by the Accademia Ercolanese, a semi-official body charged with the supervision of the excavations, and copies were distributed to dilettanti and collectors by royal favour rather than through the book trade. *Folio. 9 vols, containing in all 3530 pages, pagination including over 600 engraved plates and hundreds of text vignettes, headpieces and tailpieces. Vols 1-7 bound in contemporary quarter straight grain morocco, original marbled-paper boards; vols 8 and 9 in modern binding to match.* **Illustration above.** £1200

1707 **Army & Navy Co-operative Society Ltd** A complete set of the 'General Price Lists' of the Army and Navy Stores for the years 1925-38 *London, 1925-38*

The Army & Navy Co-operative Society, founded in 1871 to provide goods and services at reduced prices to officers and their families, ran (and still runs) an enormous store in Victoria Street, Westminster. Its price-lists, issued biennially, chronicle the articles despatched to ships, regiments, garrisons, and officers' wives wherever the British flag flew – and the price lists duly note 'Union Jacks only kept in stock. Other flags to order'. They are a lasting record of British taste in everything from abdominal belts to oil paintings. Each price list is extensively illustrated with pictures of furniture, china, plate, handbags, overcoats, unshrinkable underwear, tombstones, and trophies ('Members will oblige, when giving orders for hoofs to be mounted as inkstands, by stating whether they require them with or without pen-rack'). *Quarto. 8 vols (for the years 1925/6, 1927/8, 1928/9, 1929/30, 1931/2, 1933/4, 1935/6, 1937/8), each containing over 1150pp and illustrated throughout. Original cloth.* £85

1708 **Aslin, Elizabeth** The aesthetic movement. Prelude to Art Nouveau *London, Elek 1969*
Discussion of taste in England from the 1850s to the late 1880s, informative on neglected figures like Nesfield and E. W. Godwin, and dealing at length with Japanese influences on English design. *Quarto. 192pp including many illustrations (some coloured). Original cloth.*
£5

1709 **Bossert, H. Th.** Ornamente der Volkskunst. Neue Folge. Keramik. Holz. Metall u.a. *Tubingen, Wasmuth 1952*
Folio. 22+(2)pp and 48 coloured plates. Original cloth.
£6

1710 **Chase, Judith Wragg** Afro-American art and craft *New York, Van Nostrand 1971*
Quarto. 142pp, many illustrations. Original cloth.
£8

1711 **Creswell, K. A. C.** Early Muslim architecture. Umayyads A.D. 622-750 *Oxford, Clarendon Press 1969*
New edition of the first part of Creswell's history of Muslim architecture up to 935, which entirely supersedes the earlier edition published in 1932. It contains definitive accounts of the architecture and decoration of the Dome of the Rock at Jerusalem, the Great Mosque at Damascus and other Umayyad buildings, and discusses at length domes, minarets and distinctive Islamic innovations in architecture. *Large folio. 2 vols. Colour frontispiece, xl+372pp and 63 plates; vi+312 (numbered 373-684)pp and 80 plates. Original cloth.* £120

1712 **De La Nezière, J.** Les monuments mauresques du Maroc *Paris, Levy (1921)*
An excellent photographic record of Moroccan architecture and ornament, with many examples of sculpture and interior details; probably the best publication on the Islamic architecture of the area. *Folio. xvi+27+(1)pp, with 100 photogravure plates (4 hand-coloured). Original printed board portfolio.*
£75

1713 **Edwards, Paul** English garden ornament *London, Bell 1965*
Garden buildings, garden furniture, garden sculpture, topiary, well-heads, gates are all covered in this well-written study. *Octavo. 168pp with 73 text illustrations and 32pp of plates. Original cloth.*
£1

1714 **Eriksen, Svend** Early Neo-classicism in France. The creation of the Louis Seize Style in architectural decoration, furniture and ormulu, gold and silver, and Sèvres porcelaine in the mid-eighteenth century... translated... and edited by Peter Thornton *London, Faber & Faber 1974*
An in-depth survey of the developments, beginning in the field of architecture and moving on to the decorative arts. A much needed study which provides a clear perspective of the origins and progress of neo-classical decoration in France. The book is invaluable for its biographical section which covers the majority of artists who played any part in the movement, for making available documentary material not otherwise accessible, and for its detailed commentaries on the works illustrated. *Quarto. 432pp, 7 part titles, and 270 monochrome plates with 499 photographic illustrations, 8 colour plates.*
£35

1715 **Ewerbeck, Franz** Die Renaissance in Belgien und Holland... zweite unveranderte Auflage *Leipzig, Seemann 1891*
A very extensive selection of illustrations of Renaissance architecture, ornamental details, sculpture, woodwork and metalwork. Issued in 16 parts each containing 24 plates. *Folio. 2 vols containing 384 photolitho plates, (6)pp prelims and (64)pp of text. Contemporary quarter morocco, marbled-paper boards.*
£42

1716 (Gibbons, Grinling) **Bullock, Albert E.** Grinling Gibbons and his compeers. Illustrated by sixty phototypes of the principal carvings in the churches of Saint James's, Piccadilly and Saint Paul's Cathedral *London, Tiranti 1914*
A very useful record of carvings by or attributed to Gibbons – and one of the earliest

publications of the Tiranti firm. *Folio. (8)pp, with 61 photo illustrations on 52 plates. Original portfolio.* £20

1717 (Gibbons, Grinling) **Tipping, H. Avray** Grinling Gibbons and the woodwork of his age (1648-1720) *London, Country Life 1914*
Still the fullest study of Gibbons as carver and of the school of wood carving associated with him. *Folio. xi+(1)+259+(1)pp including portrait frontispiece and 234 text illustrations. Original quarter cloth.* £45

1718 **Hillier, Bevis** Art Deco of the 20s and 30s *London, Studio Vista 1970*
Octavo. 168pp with many illustrations. Original wrappers. £1.25

1719 **Hillier, Bevis** The world of Art Deco ... an exhibition organized by the Minneapolis Institute of Arts July-September 1971 *London, Studio Vista 1973*
The 1441 objects described in this exhibition catalogue illustrate every facet of Art Deco and there is also a good bibliography of the subject. *Quarto. 224pp including many illustrations. Original cloth.* £5.50

1720 **Jourdain, Margaret & R. Soame Jenyns** Chinese export art in the eighteenth century *London, Country Life 1950*
Quarto. 152pp including 144 illustrations. Original cloth. £15

1721 **Kalnein, Wend Graf & Michael Levey** Art and architecture of the eighteenth century in France. The Pelican History of Art *Harmondsworth, Penguin 1972*
The architectural part has useful sections dealing with interior decoration and surveys in turn the various decorative styles from the final Louis XIV style to the transition from Classicism to Romanticism. *Large octavo. xxvi+420pp, coloured frontispiece and 304 photographic plates. Publisher's cloth.* £12

1722 **(Leighton, John)** Contrasts & conceits for contemplation. By Luke Limner *London, Ackermann (c 1847)*
A very pleasing collection of caricatures by the redoubtable Leighton, a fine and imaginative draughtsman, a prolific designer of bookbindings and, as a press cutting pasted inside this book reveals, a practising transvestite. See also item 1485. *Oblong octavo. 20 handcoloured engraved plates. Contemporary full panelled calf gilt, by Rivière, gilt inner dentelles. Original printed wrappers bound in. Bookplate of Lord Queenborough.* £52

1723 **Lenning, Henry F.** The Art Nouveau *The Hague, Nijhoff 1951*
Valuable for its coverage of Henry Van de Velde, with an admirable chapter on exhibitions and another on interiors and furnishings. *Octavo. (14)+142+(2)pp, including frontispiece and 54 text illustrations. Original cloth.* £10

1724 **Lethaby, W. R.** Home and country arts *London, Home and Country 1923*
Octavo. (8)+118+(2)pp. Original wrappers. £4

1725 **Migeon, Gaston** Manuel d'art musulman. Arts plastiques et industriels. Deuxième édition, révue et augmentée *Paris, Picard 1927*
Islamic painting, sculpture, coinage, carving, metalwork, glass, pottery, textiles and carpets are all dealt with and illustrated in this convenient two-volume guide. *Octavo. 2 vols. 440pp; 460pp; with 462 text illustrations. Original wrappers.* £16

1726 **Morris, William** Some hints on pattern designing. A lecture delivered ... at the Working Men's College, London, on December 10, 1881 *London, Longmans 1899 (Printed at the Chiswick Press with the*

Golden type designed by William Morris for the Kelmscott Press)
Small quarto. (2) + 45 + (1)pp. Original boards. £45

1727 Muséographie Architecture et aménagement des musées d'art. Conférence internationale d'études Madrid 1934 *Société de Nations, Office International des Musées (1934)*
A complete survey of the problems of museum display. Volume 1 begins with museum buildings and then discusses lighting, heating and exhibitions; volume 2 deals with the special problems of exhibiting sculpture, objects of decorative art, coins, drawings, prehistoric implements, etc. Required reading for the museum curator and for the student of interior design and display in the 1930s. *Quarto. 2 vols. 526pp in all and very many illustrations. Original cloth.* £40

1728 Perrot, Georges & Charles Chipiez Histoire de l'art dans l'antiquité. Egypte – Assyrie – Perse – Asie Mineure – Grèce – Etrurie – Rome *Paris, Hachette 1882-98*
The first seven volumes of this influential history of ancient art (10 were published). Its wealth of illustration – there are thousands of woodcut text figures and many chromolitho plates – made it a convenient guide to the architecture, sculpture and particularly ornament of classical antiquity. *Octavo. 7 vols, each with many illustrations. Contemporary quarter vellum, marbled-paper boards.* £42

1729 Prisse d'Avennes L'art Arabe d'après les monuments du Kaire depuis le VIIe siècle jusqu'a la fin du XVIIIe *Paris, Morel 1869-77 (reprint Dordrecht 1974)*
Covers architecture, ornament, murals and mosaics, ceilings, doors, faience, glass, fabrics, furniture; the illustrations include 120 chromolithograph plates of high quality. *Folio. 4 vols, containing viii + 296pp and 214 plates (120 chromolitho), with 77 other illustrations. Limited edition bound in full calf. Expensive for a reprint but the original is even more expensive and in any case almost unobtainable.* **Illustration below.** £360

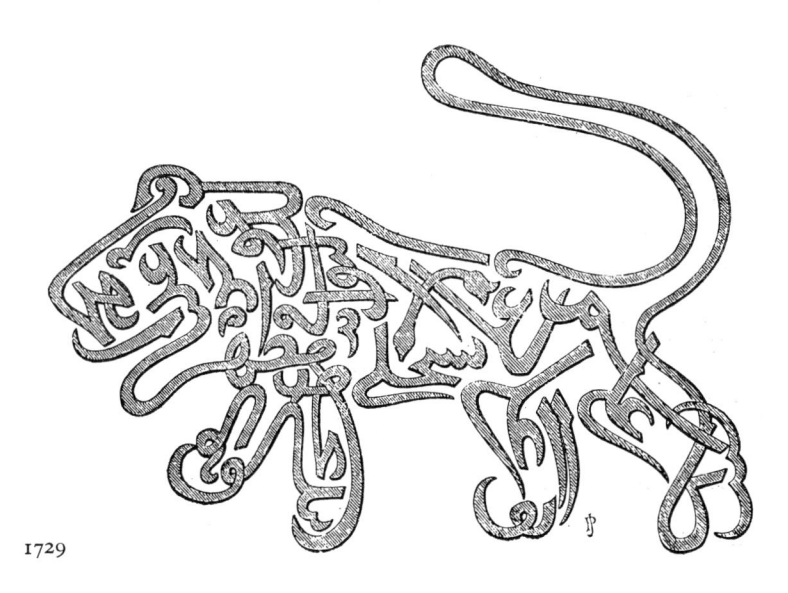

1729

1730 Read, Herbert Art and industry. The principles of industrial design *London, Faber 1966*
Fifth edition, with an extensive new preface. *Octavo. 212pp including many photo illustrations. Original cloth.* £2

1731 **Reitlinger, Gerald** The economics of taste. Volume I: The rise and fall of picture prices 1760-1960. Volume II: The rise and fall of objets d'art prices since 1750. Volume III: The art markets in the 1960s *London, Barrie & Rockliff 1961, 1963; Barrie & Jenkins 1970*

Reitlinger's trilogy is the only study of the European art market over the last two centuries and is a most useful work of reference – though the prices he records make melancholy reading for the collector of 1975. *Octavo. xvi + 518pp; xvi + 708pp; viii + 696pp. Original cloth.*

(a) Vol I £15
(b) Vol II £5
(c) Vol III £5

1732 **'Sable Plume'** Coffins and coffin making *London, Undertakers Journal nd (1920s?)*

The various styles of coffin; how to make them; and how to do so most cheaply. *Octavo. iv + 180pp with 338 text figures. Original cloth.* £15

1733 **Texier, Charles & R. Popplewell Pullan** Byzantine architecture; illustrated by examples of edifices erected in the East during the earliest ages of Christianity. With historical & archaeological descriptions *London, Day & Son 1864*

The first scholarly study of the architecture of the Byzantine period, with measured drawings of buildings and a careful descriptive text. The plates include 13 chromolitho illustrations of murals and mosaics at Thessalonica, Trebizond and elsewhere. *Folio. viii + (4) + 218pp and 71 plates (numbered I-LXX with LXa) of which 14 are chromolitho and remainder litho. Cloth, with original gilt decorated front wrapper pasted inside.* £150

1734 **Vallance, Aymer** Art in England during the Elizabethan and Stuart periods ... with a note on the first century of English engraving by Malcolm C. Salaman *London, The Studio 1908*

Small folio. x + 120pp, illustrations. Contemporary quarter calf. £9

1735 **Valuable secrets concerning arts and trades:** or approved directions from the best artists ... containing upwards of one thousand approved receipts relative to arts and trades *Dublin, James Williams 1778*

The Dublin edition of a work first published in England in 1775 in a translation from the original French. It offers its readers over a thousand hints and recipes for the processes of engraving, glassmaking, dyeing, painting on glass, gilding, casting, etc., and for such domestic pastimes as fishing, bird catching, wine making and the preparation of snuff. *Duodecimo. (8) + xxvii + (1) + 312pp. Contemporary full calf, rebacked.* £38

1736 **Weerth, E. Aus'm** Fundgruben der Kunst und Ikonographie in den Elfenbein-Arbeiten des christlichen Altertums und Mittelalters *Bonn, Hanstein 1912*

Folio. (8)pp, with 35 large tinted litho plates of ivories. Original cloth portfolio. £15

1737 **Williamson, G. C.** The book of ivory *London, Muller 1938*

History of the use of ivory in sculpture and decoration. *Octavo. xi + (1) + 247 + (1)pp and 16 plates. Original cloth.* £7

Sales and Collections

1741 **Alton Towers** Catalogue of the magnificent contents of Alton Towers, the princely seat of the Earls of Shrewsbury which ... will be sold by auction, by Messrs Christie & Manson, at the Towers, on Monday, July 6, and twenty-nine following days ... *(London, Christie 1857)*

The extensive sale of Alton Towers continued for nearly five weeks and disposed of almost four thousand items, among which were included the contents of the cellars – over 5000 bottles of wines and spirits – the stables and outhouses. The house was the home of the Earls of Shrewsbury and had been built for the 15th Earl by James Wyatt. It was sold after the death in 1852 of Bertram Arthur, the 16th Earl, a rich Catholic magnate, collector, and patron of the younger Pugin. Although the most important part of the sale was undoubtedly the 708 old master paintings, mainly of the seventeenth century, the larger part of the sale dealt with furniture, furnishings, porcelain, sculpture, bronzes, ornamental objects, majolica and early ware, silver and plate, china and glass, table and bed linen, and even kitchen utensils. The interest in the catalogue is increased by the addition of marginal annotations in a contemporary hand marking the price realised for each item. *Octavo. iv + 219 + (1)pp. Red cloth.* £45

1742 **Alton Towers** Catalogue of the extensive and valuable library of the late Right Honourable the Earl of Shrewsbury, removed from Alton Towers which ... will be sold by auction by Messrs S. Leigh Sotheby & John Wilkinson ... on Monday, the 22nd of June, 1857, and eleven following days ... *(London, Sotheby 1857)*

See the preceding item. Lord Shrewsbury's library was particularly strong in Roman Catholic literature and the decorative arts and Newman, Pugin and Cardinal Wiseman are among the authors best represented. The sale ran to 3804 lots; one book from it is listed in our present catalogue (item 1533). *Octavo. 20 + 5(1)pp. Priced throughout in a contemporary hand. Contemporary cloth.* £20

1743 **(Bing, S)** Collection S. Bing. Objets d'art et peintures du Japon et de la Chine *Paris, Durand-Ruel 7-12 May 1906*

Sale catalogue of the great collection of Chinese and Japanese sculptures, lacquer, porcelain, bronzes, netsuke and paintings formed by one of the most ardent promoters of the Art Nouveau. There were 951 lots and the most important pieces are illustrated and have their measurements given. *Folio. 6 parts. Original printed-paper wrappers contained in original cloth portfolio.* £85

1744 **(British Museum)** Museum Britannicum, being an exhibition of a great variety of antiquities and natural curiosities, belonging to that noble and magnificent cabinet, the British Museum. Illustrated with curious prints, engraved after the original designs, from nature, other objects; and with distinct explanations of each figure, by John and Andrew Van Rymsdyk, pictors *London, I. Moore for the authors 1778*

An enthusiastic and rather disorganized selection from the British Museum's holdings; to quote the elder Van Rymsdyk's preface, 'some things fine, others middling, and a few so so'. It portrays the Museum's collections when there was still no clear distinction between antiquities and curiosities, and classical rings and fibulae are oddly juxtaposed with birds' eggs and spiders' nests. *Folio. (4) + xvi + 84pp and 30 engraved plates, 1 engraved vignette. Original marbled paper boards, calf spine.* £45

1745 **Denison, Christopher Beckett** Catalogue of the valuable collection of pictures, works of art, and decorative objects, of Christopher Beckett Denison, Esq., deceased. Christie 6 June-15 July 1885 *London, 1885*

Beckett Denison (1825-84), a younger brother of Lord Grimthorpe, the architect, was a heavy buyer at the Hamilton Palace sale and other sales of the 1870s and 1880s, and this catalogue complements the Hamilton catalogue as a record of the taste of the period. *Octavo. 283 + (1)pp illustrated by 33 actual photographs of furniture, porcelain, etc. Original cloth.* £30

1746 **Grimwade, A. G.** (and others) Treasures of a London temple. A descriptive catalogue of the ritual plate mantles and furniture of the Spanish and Portuguese Jews' Synagogue in Bevis Marks *London, Taylors Foreign Press 1951*
Octavo. xii + 68 + (2) + v + (1)pp, frontispiece and 20 photo plates. Original cloth. £5

1747 **Hamilton, Duke of** Catalogue of the collection of pictures, works of art, and decorative objects, the property of His Grace the Duke of Hamilton ... which will be sold by auction, by Messrs Christie, Manson & Woods, on Saturday, June 17, and Monday, June 19, 1882 (etc). First (-fifth) portion
Sale catalogue of the Hamilton Palace collection, dispersed in seventeen days in June-July 1882 and critical for the study of the decorative arts because it incorporated the great collection formed by William Beckford (1759-1844). Octavo. 234pp with 78 photographic plates. Contemporary cloth. £35

1748 **Hamilton, Duke of** The Hamilton Palace Collection. Illustrated priced catalogue *London, Remington 1882*
Quarto reprint of the sale catalogue with names of buyers, prices, and some corrections; but illustrated by litho text illustrations only. Quarto. (8) + 244pp including text illustrations. Original cloth. £15

1749 **(Handley-Read)** Victorian and Edwardian decorative art. The Handley-Read collection *London, 1972*
Catalogue of the exhibition in March-April 1972 at the Royal Academy of the superb collection of Victorian decorative arts formed by the Handley-Reads. The range extends from Pugin to the Art Nouveau. Folio. 140pp with many photo illustrations. Original wrappers. £4

1750 **(Lansdowne House)** Illustrated catalogue of the loan exhibition of English decorative art at Lansdowne House, February 17th-28th, 1929 *London, The Collector (1929)*
16th-18th century objects, especially tapestry, needlework, furniture and plate. Quarto. xx + 112 + (2)pp and 102 plates (some coloured). Original cloth. Limited edition. £6

1751 **(Museé Bourbon)** Catalogue des statues en bronze, et des objets précieux du Musée Bourbon de S.M. le Roi des Deux Siciles *Naples, 1820*
The bronzes and jewellery and other items from Herculaneum and Pompeii. Octavo. 40 + 159 + (1)pp. Contemporary quarter calf, gilt tooled spine, marbled-paper boards. £12

1752 **Nevill Holt** A catalogue of superior and elegant furniture ... and valuable mélange of articles of taste and vertu, at the mansion of Nevill Holt, near to Market Harborough ... which will be sold at auction by Messrs Robins (13-21 September 1848) *London, 1848*
The contents of an old Roman Catholic family's Leicestershire country house (furniture, porcelain, paintings, a large library, the fittings of the family chapel, etc.). Quarto. 76pp.
£18

1753 **Robinson, J. C.** Catalogue of the Soulages collection; being a descriptive inventory of a collection of works of decorative art, formerly in the possession of M. Jules Soulages of Toulouse, now ... exhibited to the public at the Museum of Ornamental Art, Marlborough House *London, Chapman & Hall 1856*
The Soulages collection, formed by its owner in the decade 1830-40, was purchased by subscription in 1856 as an addition to the holdings of the Museum of Ornamental Art. It was particularly rich in maiolica and faience (and this part of the collection is particularly well catalogued), but also comprised glass, bronzes and furniture of the renaissance period.

The select list of subscribers (included in the volume) includes a cross-section of those who encouraged the arts at the time: the largest subscribers were the potters Minton and Wood of Burslem, and the industrialist Titus Salt, but they also included Owen Jones, Redgrave, Brunel, Scott, Crace and Elkington. *Octavo. xvi + 200pp with text illustrations. Original cloth.* £25

1754 **Robinson, J. C.** Catalogue of the various works of art forming the collection of Matthew Uzielli, Esq. of Hanover Lodge, Regent's Park, London *London, Clayton 1860*
Glass, maiolica, enamels, gems (a particularly good series), jewelry. *Octavo. vi + 304pp and 14 plates. Original cloth, gilt edges. Author's presentation copy.* **Illustration below.**
£15

1754

1755 **(Rothschild)** Catalogue of the magnificent contents of 148 Piccadilly, W.1, sold by order of Victor Rothschild, Esq. comprising... the valuable French XVIII century furniture (etc). Sotheby 19-22 April 1937 *London, 1937*
These were the contents of the town house of the senior English branch of the Rothschild family, furnished by Baron Lionel de Rothschild (1808-79) and almost unaltered since his death. The furniture is particularly splendid but there is a whole range of other decorative objects of the kind that appealed to mid-Victorian Rothschilds; even the few lots of books include publications by Digby Wyatt and Henry Shaw. *Octavo. iv + 172pp and 62 plates (2 folding). Original boards.* £15

1756 **Schreiber, Lady Charlotte** Lady Charlotte Schreiber's journals. Confidences of a collector of ceramics & antiques throughout Britain, France, Holland, Belgium, Spain, Portugal, Turkey, Austria & Germany from the year 1869 to 1885. Edited by her son Montague J. Guest with annotations by Egan Mew *London, John Lane 1911*
The diaries of a voracious and indefatigable collector of china, enamels, snuff boxes, fans, lace, watches and so on. It provides an unrivalled account of the European antique trade in the 1870s and 1880s (dealers, prices, availability of objects, contemporary taste) and a vivid picture of Lady Charlotte herself, attacked by the collecting passion in her fifties and trailing her submissive second husband all over the Continent to squire her and carry her purchases. *Octavo. 2 vols. xl + 502 + (2)pp; xiii + (3) + 541 + (1)pp, each with many plates. Original cloth.* £65

1757 **South Kensington Museum** Catalogue of the special loan exhibition of Spanish and Portuguese ornamental art, South Kensington Museum, 1881. Edited by J. C. Robinson *London, Chapman & Hall 1881. Large paper copy*

Quarto. 212pp. Original printed boards, morocco spine. £10

1758 (Stowe) **Forster, Henry Rumsey** The Stowe catalogue priced and annotated *London, Bogue 1848*

The Dukes of Buckingham, possessors of Stowe – the creation architecturally of a succession of major figures in house and landscape design (Vanbrugh, Bridgeman, Leoni, Kent, Gibbs, Adam, Capability Brown, etc.) – were in financial difficulties from early in the 19th century, and the bankruptcy of the second Duke brought about a gigantic sale of paintings, porcelain, plate, furniture, objets d'art and wine. It took place over forty days between 15 August and 7 October 1848 and Forster later produced this annotated edition of the catalogue for subscribers; it includes a historical introduction, notes on the important lots, and prices and names of buyers. *Quarto. xliii + (1) + 310pp with frontispiece and 16 plates. Contemporary blind stamped cloth.* £30

1759 **Stowe (Sale catalogue)** The Ducal estate and the contents of the mansion *4-28 July 1921*

The core of the Stowe estate remained intact until 1921, when the last Duke's daughter sold the house, the park and all associated property. The catalogue ran to 3955 lots and even the auctioneer writes in an introduction of the 'profound regret' with which he catalogues a sale 'which may destroy for ever the glories of historic Stowe'. The house, grounds and garden temples are described in full, with illustrations, and so are the still splendid furnishings and paintings, china, wine and books. *Folio. 232 + (2)pp with 47 illustrations and 5 plans. Cloth.* £45

1760 **Strawberry Hill** A catalogue of the classic contents of Strawberry Hill collected by Horace Walpole *London, Robins 1842*

Sale catalogue of the contents of Strawberry Hill, sold on the instructions of a descendant. A complete record of the books, coins, pictures, china, bronzes and furniture. *Quarto. xxiv + 250pp, litho frontispiece and text illustrations. Quarter morocco, original front label pasted inside front cover.* £25

1761 **Strawberry Hill** A description of the villa of Mr. Horace Walpole ... at Strawberry-Hill near Twickenham, Middlesex. With an inventory of the furniture, pictures, curiosities, &c. Strawberry Hill, Kirgate 1784 *(reprint London 1964)*

Quarto. Frontispiece, title, iv + 96pp and 26 plates, 2ff leaflet and folding plan loosely inserted. Original cloth. £10

1762 **Victoria and Albert Museum** An exhibition of works of art belonging to the livery companies of the City of London *London, Board of Education 1927*

Octavo. 81 + (3)pp and 80pp of plates. Original cloth. £7

1763 **Yamanaka & Co Inc** Oriental art. The entire stock of the New York store ... of Yamanaka & Co ... by order of the alien property custodian of the United States *New York, Parke-Bernet 1944*

Sale catalogue of the extensive stock of vases, bronzes, porcelain, etc; the firm went into liquidation in the United States after Pearl Harbour. *Octavo. 3 parts (and an additional catalogue of garden sculpture). 190pp; 120pp; 140pp; 8pp. Original printed wrappers.* £18

Collectable Objects

1771 **Andere, Mary** Old needlework boxes and tools. Their story and how to collect them *Newton Abbot, David & Charles 1971*
Octavo. 184pp including 18 text illustrations, and 16pp of plates. Original cloth. £3.50

1772 **Baker, Oliver** Black jacks and leather bottells. Being some account of leather drinking vessels in England and incidentally of other ancient vessels *Cheltenham, for W. J. Fieldhouse (1921).*
Folio. 190 + (8)pp including 72 text figures, and 24 plates (4 coloured). Original cloth uncut. No 392 of limited edition. £25

1773 **Baughan, Rosa** The leather work book: containing full instructions for making and ornamenting articles so as to successfully imitate carved oak; specially written for the use of amateurs *London, Bazaar Office (c 1870)*
The author's idea is that leather should be used to give plain wooden surfaces the appearance of being carved. This works well enough with photograph frames or blotters but her scheme for the leather decoration of a plain white deal sideboard from Oetzmanns (see item 114) is somewhat ambitious. *Octavo. 88pp including 32 text illustrations. Original decorated cloth.* £8

1774 **Bulau, Alwin E.** Footprints of assurance *New York, Macmillan 1953*
An excellent work of reference which catalogues and illustrates 1796 marks of fire insurance companies in America and Europe. *Quarto. xiii + (3) + 319 + (1)pp, with 8 colour plates and 1796 photo illustrations. Original cloth.* **Illustration below.** £25

1774

1775 **Clark, Erland Fenn** Truncheons their romance and reality *London, Jenkins 1935*
Truncheons, bludgeons and life preservers. *Octavo. 242pp, including many photo illustrations. Original cloth. Author's autograph on prelims.* £12

1776 **Epstein, Diana** Buttons *London, Studio Vista 1968*
Brief but well illustrated history of buttons in Europe and America. *Octavo. 84pp including 2 colour plates and many photo illustrations. Original cloth.* £3

1777 **Evan-Thomas, Owen** Domestic utensils of wood XVIth to XIXth century. A short history of wooden articles in domestic use from the

sixteenth to the middle of the nineteenth century *London, Evan-Thomas 1932*
Excellent photographic illustrations make this of continuing value, though its text has been in part superseded by Pinto's book on treen (item 1788). *Quarto. x + 178pp including frontispiece and 69 photo plates. Original cloth.* £32

1778 **Evan-Thomas, Owen** Domestic utensils of wood. XVI to XIXth century *London, 1932 (EP reprint 1972)*
Quarto. 190pp. Original cloth. £5

1779 **Field, June** Collecting Georgian and Victorian crafts *London, Heinemann 1973*
Guide to a variety of 18th and 19th century leisure pursuits and their products – cut paper flowers, sand pictures, patchwork and so on. Well illustrated. *Octavo. (8) + 162pp with 238 illustrations. Original cloth.* £4.50

1780 **Hipkins, A. J.** Musical instruments historic, rare and unique . . . illustrated by a series of fifty plates in colours drawn by William Gibb *Edinburgh, Black 1888*
Illustrations and descriptions of a number of most important and interesting musical instruments, largely based on the exhibits at a loan exhibition at the Albert Hall in 1885 not otherwise catalogued. Chromolitho plates by McLagan and Cumming, Edinburgh. *Folio. xix + (1) + 107 + (1)pp and 50 chromolitho plates. Half red morocco, gilt decorated.*
Illustration below. £110

1780

1781 **Launert, Edmund** Scent & scent bottles *London, Barrie & Jenkins 1974*
Bottles in glass, silver, porcelain and enamel, mainly 17th century or later. *Small folio. 176pp with 200 illustrations. Original cloth.* £10

1782 **Lenk, Torsten** Flintlaset dess upkomst och utveckling *Stockholm, Nordisk Rotogravyr 1939*
Important study of flintlock guns. *Small folio. 188pp and 130pp of photo plates. Half blue morocco.* £17

1783 **Longhurst, M. H.** English ivories *London, Putnam 1926*
Discussion and catalogue of extant English ivories, including several important mediaeval items. *Quarto. xviii + 171 + (1)pp, frontispiece, 57 plates. Original cloth.* £32

1784 **Matthews, Leslie G.** Antiques of the pharmacy *London, Bell 1971*
The first book to cover all the objects used by the apothecary and pharmacist – whether pottery, glass, metal, or wood – and helpful in the identification and dating of pharmaceutical antiques from the 16th century onwards. *Octavo. xiv + 120pp and 48pp of plates. Original cloth.* £5.50

1785 **McClinton, Katharine Morrison** Antiques in miniature *London, Barrie & Jenkins 1970*
Miniature furniture, pottery and porcelain, glass, silver, pewter, copper, brass and tin. *Quarto. x + 182pp including many illustrations. Original cloth.* £4

1786 **Neal, W. Keith & D. H. L. Back** The Mantons: gunmakers *London, Herbert Jenkins 1967*
Catalogue of the Manton's entire output. *Quarto. xvi + 300pp with plates. Original cloth.*
£10

1787 **Pinto, Edward H.** Wooden bygones of smoking and snuff taking *London, Hutchinson 1961*
Octavo. 96pp, frontispiece and 32pp of illustrations. Original cloth. £6

1788 **Pinto, Edward H.** Treen and other wooden bygones. An encyclopaedia and social history *London, Bell 1969*
The only recent work of reference on a vast range of wooden objects intended for use in the household and in the course of trade. The term treen is properly used of articles made by the turner, and Pinto's extensive collection (now owned by the Birmingham City Museum) has formed the basis for this comprehensive survey of the turner's products and their role in daily life. *Octavo. x + 458pp with 460 illustrations on plates. Original cloth.* £12.50

1789 **Pinto, Edward H. & Eva R.** Tunbridge and Scottish souvenir woodware. With chapters on bois durci and pyrography *London, Bell 1970*
Authoritative survey of decorative woodware (snuff boxes, cigar cases, jewel boxes, etc.), based on the Pintos' great collection and their extensive research. *Octavo. 149 + (1)pp with plates. Original cloth.* £4

1790 **Toller, Jane** Prisoners-of-war work 1756-1815 *Cambridge, Golden Head Press 1965*
Articles in straw, bone, wood, horn, etc., produced by French and Dutch prisoners of war in British gaols. *Octavo. (8) + 23 + (1)pp and 14pp of plates. Original cloth.* £2

1791 **White, Gwen** European and American dolls and their marks and patents *London, Batsford 1966*
A really admirable book which discusses all kinds of doll – wood, ceramic, wax, rag, rubber, talking, singing, walking, crawling, feeding, swimming – and illustrates 625 different makers' marks as well as 353 dolls. There are also details of all doll patents and a full list of manufacturers. *Quarto. 274pp, including frontispiece and 96pp of photo illustrations and many text figures. Original cloth.* £15

Clocks, Watches and Precision Instruments

1801 **Diderot, D. & J. L. d'Alembert** (Encyclopédie) Recueil de planches sur les sciences, les arts libéraux, et les arts méchaniques, avec leurs explication *Paris, Briasson, David, Le Breton & Durand, 1762-72; Livorno 1772-9*

Each section listed is folio with plates averaging in size 360 × 225mm for single plates; preserved in paper wallet, or in boards.

a **Horlogerie.** (Clock and watch-making)
An extensive section on the mechanisms of clocks and watches in two parts. Part I has 2 plates on an alarm clock, 5 plates showing a horizontal clock with details of its movements and striking mechanism. Other plates show spring-driven clocks, various types of equation movements, ordinary watches and their improvements, swing-wheel watches and their developments, different escapements, pendulum clocks, repeating clocks and their developments. It continues with various types of watches – alarm watches, equations watches marking months and quarter, different repeater watches. 6 plates of tools, various machines and instruments – for remounting, cutting the fusé chain, a demonstration of the movement of the cogs, mechanisms for making the wheels and their parts and a view of chiming mechanisms and clock wheels.
Part II was made under the direction of the Swiss horologist Jean Romilly who supervised the drawings and provided the text for the plates as well as the introduction to the whole section. It deals with a machine for rounding off the cogs (5 plates), another for experiments on the friction of the pins (5 plates), and finally one for equalising the swing-wheels. The descriptive text is extensive. *64 engraved plates with many duplicate numbers but lettered A-EEE, a-n, including over 400 illustrations, and 25 + (1 blank)pp descriptive text.*   £65

b **Balancier.** (Scale-maker)
A fine suite of plates showing the making of balance-scales with detailed drawings of the tools and utensils and illustrations of the different types of balance-arm, various patterns of weights, details of spring-balances and a plate devoted to the special scales used for determining the carat weight of diamonds. *Five engraved plates with 80 illustrations and 2pp text.*   £18

1802 **Bird, Anthony** English house clocks: 1600-1850. An historical survey and guide for collectors and dealers *Newton Abbot, David & Charles 1973*
Octavo. 314pp including 25 text figures, and 32pp of plates. Original cloth.   £5.95

1803 **Chapuis, Alfred & Eugene Jaquet** The history of the self-winding watch 1770-1931 *Neuchatel, Griffon 1956*
Documents the work of the Swiss watchmakers Perrelet, Breguet and Recordon, who pioneered the self-winding watch, and traces its later history. *Octavo. 246pp including colour frontispiece and 154 text figures. Original cloth.*   £15

1804 **Chapuis, Alfred & Edmond Droz** Automata. A historical and technological study. Translated by Alfred Reid *Neuchatel, Griffon 1958*
Fascinating account of automata of all kinds (clocks, toys, singing birds, mechanical spiders, automaton magicians and musicians, trick machinery, robots). *Quarto. 407 + (7)pp including 488 text figures, frontispiece and 17 plates. Original cloth.* **Illustration opposite.**   £35

1805 **Grimthorpe, Lord** A rudimentary treatise on clocks, watches, & bells for public purposes ... eighth edition ... with a new preface and new list of great bells, and an appendix of weathercocks *London, Crosby Lockwood 1903 (reprint EP 1974)*
Octavo. xvi + 404pp including 81 text illustrations. Original cloth.   £5

1806 **Mortensen, Otto** Jens Olsen's clock. A technical description *Copenhagen, Technological Institute 1957*
The astronomical clock in Copenhagen Town Hall designed by the Danish clockmaker Jens Olsen (1872-1945). *Small folio. 156 + (4)pp and 83 photo illustrations. Original cloth.*   £10

1807 **Oppenord, G(illes) M(arie)** Second livre contenant differens desseins de pendules *Paris, Huquier (c 1748)*
Oppenord's designs for clock cases are based on the form of the invention of cartouches. Suite from the 'Moyen Oppenord'. Berlin Cat 383. Guilmard p 141. *Six numbered engraved plates including title, suite lettered B. Average size 320 × 225mm. In paper wallet.*
£48

1808 (Wetherfield Collection) **Vernay, Arthur S.** The Wetherfield collection of English clocks. With an introduction and commentary text by Arthur S. Vernay *New York, Vernay 1928*
Quarto. 62 + (2)pp with 100 illustrations of clocks. Original cloth. £8

1804

Lamps and Lighting

1821 Bartoli, Pietro Santi Le antiche lucerne sepolcrali figurate raccolte dalle cave sotterranee, e grotte di Roma, nelle quali si contengono molte erudite memorie. Disegnate, ed intagliate nelle loro forme da Pietro Santi Bartoli . . . con l'osservazioni di Gio. Pietro Bellori *Rome, Antonio de' Rossi 1729*
Bartoli, a pupil of Poussin, was one of the leading exponents of late 17th century classical art in Rome and like his master exercised great influence in Britain about a century later, when his designs were a major influence on the decorative work of the Adam brothers and their followers. These plates of sculptured lamps provide motifs for panel and ceiling designs and precedents for pottery in classical styles. The text and notes are supplied by Bellori. *Quarto. 3 parts in 1. (8) + 16pp, engraved title and 37 engraved plates; 16pp engraved title and 46 engraved plates; 12pp, engraved title and 33 engraved plates. Quarter calf, marbled-paper boards. 19th century presentation inscription on front end paper includes an epitaph.* **Illustration below.** £55

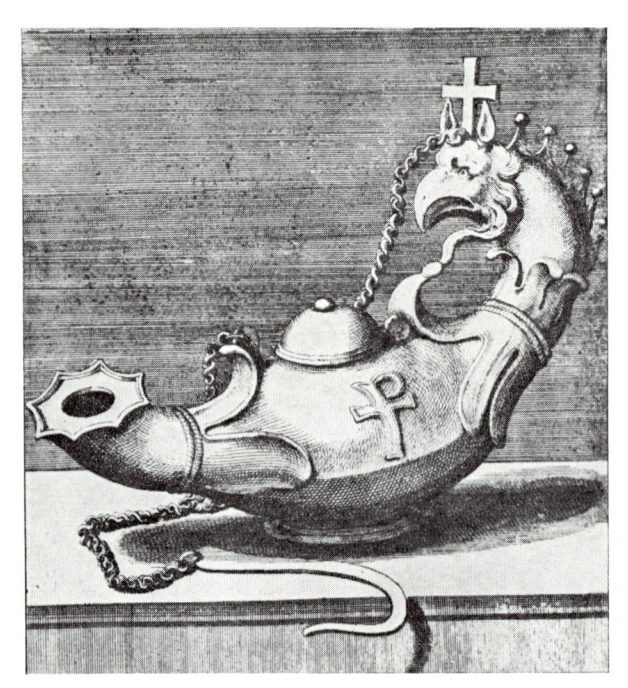

1821

1822 The Bland Light Syndicate, Ltd (Catalogue) *London, 1909*
Trade catalogue of a firm of gas light fitting manufacturers. *Octavo. 44pp including many illustrations. Original wrappers.* £4

1823 C.E. & Co (Catalogue). Lantern fittings
Octavo. 12pp with illustrations. Original wrappers. £4

1824 Deutsches Metallwarenwerk Katalog nr. 36. Standleuchter und Geräte *Berlin 1914-5*
Trade catalogue of standard lamps, table lamps and chandeliers. *Small folio. 40pp illustrated throughout, and 4pp price list. Original wrappers.* £22

1825 Kalff, L. C. Kunstlicht und architektur *Eindhoven, Philips 1943*
Study of the design of light fittings in relation to architecture and interior decoration. *Octavo. 300pp including 294 illustrations. Original cloth.* £12

1826 **Walter Macfarlane, & Co** Illustrated catalogue of Macfarlane's Castings. Electric-lighting and ventilation *Glasgow (c 1905)*
Mainly devoted to a vast range of 'electric light pillars' for arc and incandescent lighting. The designs illustrated include many that must have been in stock in the 1880s, if not the 1870s, and they provide an excellent view of late Victorian taste in lighting and lamp posts. *Folio. 156pp, illustrated throughout. Original cloth.* £55

1827 **Read, A. B.** Lighting the home *London, Country Life 1938*
Read was Director of Design at the Lighting Centre. *Octavo. 72pp and 40pp of plates. Original cloth.* £4

1828 **Robins, F. W.** The story of the lamp (and the candle) *London, OUP 1939*
A history of lighting and its appliances from the earliest times to the coming of electricity, with 'sidelights' on animal lamps, mine lamps, lighthouses, street lighting, and the symbolism of light. *Quarto. xiv + 156pp, frontispiece and 27 numbered plates. Publisher's cloth.* £16

1829 **Simmons, George Henry James** An album containing applications for patents, drawings, written specifications, manuscript descriptions, printed leaflets and other material, largely concerned with lighting 1866-75
The applications for patents include: improvements in lamps for burning hydrocarbon and other oils; the 'Alexandra Cabinet'; self-acting limelight for regulating and economizing oxygen gas for submarine and other uses; magnesium wire pocket lamp; flashing signal and whistle for locomotive engines; etc. *Small quarto. The album contains material dating from 1866 to 1875 and the applications for patents are illustrated by many of Simmons' own drawings. Gilt and blind stamped cloth.* **Illustration below.** £65

1830 **Stokvis, W. J.** (Catalogue of chandeliers) *(London c 1920)*
Trade catalogue of Stokvis's products – manufactured at the Royal Dutch Factory, Arnhem – which were based on 17th century Dutch models. This imaginative catalogue illustrates both the candelabra themselves and the paintings (by Dou, Metsu, Teniers, etc.), that show the 17th century originals. *Octavo. 56pp, mostly photo illustrations, with 8pp price list. Original wrappers.* £10

1902

1901 **Antoine Berjon** Designs for silk fabrics *Lyon c 1785*

Four original floral designs of leaf and flower sprays and bouquets in modes vary
degrees of naturalism and stylization, and including a corner motif for a large sq
Antoine Berjon (1754-1843) of Lyon, was a painter, draughtsman and designer
eventually became Professor at the École des Beaux Arts in his native town whe
specialised in the instruction of floral drawing and is considered as one of the fin
draughtsmen of the period in this field. However, he spent the greater part of
life as a commercial designer, first for a silk factory and later for an embroidery
*2 drawings in pencil and watercolour; sizes 248 × 221mm and 440 × 267mm: 1 dra
and postercolour 363 × 228mm; 1 drawing in pencil and postercolour 478 × 390mm.*
Illustration above.

1902 **G(eorge)-F(rançois) Blondel** Decorative designs of clas
architectural ruins in a landscape with figures *Rome c 1755-65*

A design probably dating from the 1750s or 1760s when the artist was in Rome
where he came under the influence of Robert Adam, or made immediately follo
return to Paris when the nostalgia for classical antiquity was still prevalent in h
George-François Blondel (c 1730-c 1791) was the son and pupil of Jean-Franç
and like his father was an architect, designer and engraver. After returning fro
worked for a time in Paris before moving, by way of Amsterdam (1762), to Lor
he settled in 1764. A similar design in pen and red chalk, dated 1760 or 1763, is
in the Kupferstichkabinett Berlin (n. 1888) and is illustrated in Berckenhagen
Französischen Zeichnungen der Kunstbibliothek Berlin', Berlin 1970, p 317 F
*Two pen, black ink and grey wash drawings forming a pair. Each 292 × 220mm m
contemporary card with green wash borders, gilt. Each signed in bottom left-hand
'G. F. Blondel'. On the reverse of one drawing a later hand has written in pencil '
les ruines. Blondel'.* **Illustration opposite.**

1903

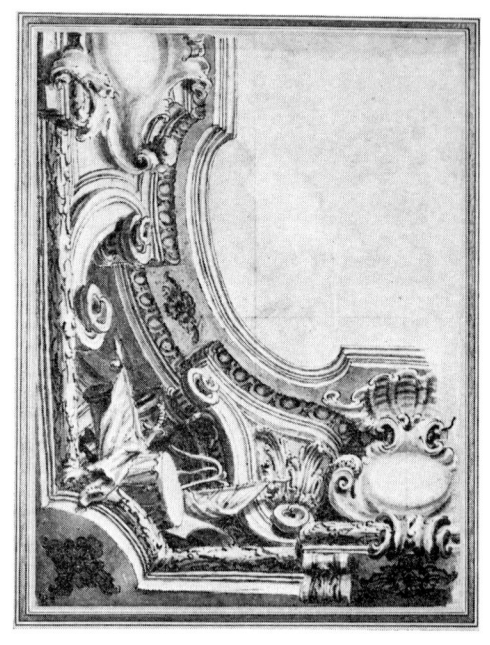

er design for a quadratura ceiling with
...century

gn for a painted ceiling in steep perspective depicting an illusionistic balcony with sters upheld by scrolled corner brackets and decorated with a cartouche in the middle ch side. The centre of the ceiling left plain. This drawing and the following two items e an interesting addition to the body of 17th and 18th century decoration from Bologna h has yet to be thoroughly studied and investigated so that the hands of Tesi, Colonna, ozzi and others can be distinguished. *Pen and brown ink with grey and ochre wash, es of brown watercolour. Hinged in card frame. From the Edward Fatio collection with the tor's mark. 275 × 215mm* **Illustration above.** £140

Bolognese School Quarter design for a quadratura ceiling with er trophy *Bologna 18th century*

nted illusionistic ceiling designed as a deeply coved cornice decorated with large nental brackets and central escutcheons. The corner trophy with the motifs of drum, sword, shield and cannon barrel, suggest a ceiling for a study or counsel chamber. In me hand as the previous item. *Pen and brown ink, with grey, blue and bistre washes. d in card frame. From the Edward Fatio collection with the collector's mark. 280 × 217mm* **ration above.** £125

Bolognese School Quarter design for an illusionistic ceiling *na 18th century*

her design in the same hand as the two previous items but with a more complicated ctive suggesting a double cornice, one below the other. Although the structure of the ctural elements—brackets, friezes, parapets, pediments—is more clearly defined ganised than in the previous items the design is enriched by the suggestion of y applied surface decoration and carved ornamentation, and by the infilling of the space with strapwork and scrolled leaves. *Pen and brown ink, with grey, yellow, nd blue-grey wash. Laid in card frame. From the Edward Fatio collection with the r's mark. 340 × 210mm* £160

1906 **Bonnar** Album of decorative designs *(Edinburgh) c 1875*
An album of designs, both originals and copies of early works, with particular emphasis on decorative items. The album was probably compiled by a member of a firm of decorative painters. One drawing is of a lamp designed for Jones & Willis Art Metal Manufacturers of Birmingham. Two designs are for Christmas cards from Mr & Mrs Bonnar, possibly related to William Bonnar (1800-1853) the decorative artist and painter. *An album of 55 pencil, pen and watercolour drawings, 25 photographs, and other miscellaneous items. Cloth.*
£30

1907 **Style of J. F. Boucher** Original designs for dado panelling and overdoors *France c 1775*
On one sheet is found a simple dado scheme of plain rectangular panels punctuated by pilaster units with delicate drop ornaments hanging from a ribbon bow; above this is a design for a matching overdoor with more details of the mouldings carved with egg-and-dart motifs, and acanthus leaves. The second sheet shows three varying designs for single dado panels with flanking pilasters. On two of the designs both pilasters and panels are decorated, the panels with a single ornament of leaf and blossom spray, or a garland. The third design concentrates its decoration on the pilasters and mouldings. The simple rectiliniar style of these designs with their discretely classical decoration is typical of the period 1765-1780. *Five pen and brown ink drawings on two sheets; 148 × 260mm and 274 × 155mm. Tipped on old paper with ink rule and gilt borders.* £45

1908 **Gille-Paul Cauvet** Designs for friezes *France c 1775*
Six designs for ornamental architectural mouldings being variations of acanthus leaf patterns. They include vertical leaves with turned back tips and fluting; trefoils with leaves and florets; alternating floral bud and leaf gadroons; palmettes with leaf scrolls and florets; vertical turned-back leaves alternating with leaf sprays; leaves and florets within egg-and-dart shapes; and leaf scrolls and leaf sprays. Cauvet (1731-1788) was a sculptor and architect as well as a decorator who is principally known for his ornamental designs. He held the position of sculptor to Monsieur, the King's brother, and worked for Marie Antoinette. For many years he was director of the Academy of St Luke. Many of his designs were engraved in ornamental collections published in 1777 as 'Recueil d'ornament à l'usage des jeunes artistes'. The present drawings are typical of some of those made by Cauvet for this work and were engraved in the stipple manner to imitate crayon, and printed in red ink. *Seven drawings in red crayon on three sheets; 207 × 301mm, 217 × 313mm, and 226 × 300mm. Tipped on old paper with brown ink rule and gilt borders.* £150
Illustration below.

1910   *1909* **Circle of Cellini** Ornamental decoration with shells and mask
c 1560
Pendant decoration intended for stucco or metalwork. There is an attribution in an old hand 'Del Marcellini cavati dall'Antico'. Carlo Marcellini (1646-1713) was a Florentine sculptor and architect whose works can be seen in Florence and at Pratolino. The present design appears to be much earlier and a later attribution to the circle of Benvenuto Cellini would seem more likely. *Pen and brown ink drawing with brown wash, over black chalk. Mounted on old paper and tipped in a card frame. 281 × 182mm* **Illustration opposite.**   £60

1910 **Claude-Aimé Chenavard** Receuil des dessins de tapis, tapisseries et autres objets d'ameublement ... *Paris c 1828*
Original drawing for the title page of item 31 together with a proof plate. The two items afford a fine comparison highlighting the contributions of a good etcher or engraver and illustrating the reversals which take place in the transfer from paper design to copperplate. The title is set within an architectural framework and is surrounded by tools and attributes of the weaving industry. In this particular case the title of the work has been altered in the interval from 'Recueil de dessins executés à la manufacture de tapis de S.A.R. Mr la Dauphine' to the above. Chenavard was, apparently, one of the favourite designers of Louis Philippe. *Black ink and brown-black was drawing on buff paper. Size 166 × 310mm. Etched and aquatinted plate printed on buff paper in brown-black ink. Size 212 × 355mm, cut to plate mark. Mounted on card.* **Illustration above.**

1911   £110

1911 **Stefano Della Bella** Design for an ornamental frieze *c 1645*

Detail of a typically classical-inspired frieze with leaf scrolls, medallion with portrait, and putti holding a garland. The design was probably intended as half of the complete frieze. Della Bella (1610-1664) was one of the most inventive and original designers of decorative motifs. His engraved suites were very popular and exercised a lasting influence especially in France where his long stay in Paris during the 1640's had made him a familiar figure (see also items 1432-3). *Drawing in black chalk, pen and brown ink, with sepia wash. Mounted on stiff paper with gilt border; in card frame. 108 × 278mm.* **Illustration opposite.** £220

1912 **Dutch School** Design for a stucco ceiling *c 1775*

Stucco ceiling with central oval attached to corner roundels containing putti holding baskets of flowers by curled shell designs and bell-flower drops. The spaces between the corners decorated with crossed olive branches. A design in transitional style where neo-classical restraint and antique motifs are beginning to be included. *Pen and black ink with grey wash. Tipped on old laid paper with ink and gilt border rule. 235 × 240mm.* £55

1913 **Style of Charles Eisen** Design for a fountain *Paris c 1750*

A rocaille cascade with tritons, dolphin, swan and waving fronds. The drawing is in the fluid style of Eisen depicting the forms in soft and rounded masses. An old attribution gives the drawing to Oppenord but this is unlikely. *Pen and bistre ink, grey wash over black pencil. Tipped on thick laid paper with gilt and ink ruled border. 240 × 150mm on sheet 263 × 180mm.* **Illustration below.** £65

1914 **English School** Designs for a pair of weather vanes *1747*

Two designs for wrought iron weather vanes with letters of the cardinal points (W & E shown), swallow-tailed guidons with waved points, and scrollwork decorated stems set on spheres. One design, 7½ft high rises from a spire, has the guidon pierced with the date 1747, a wavy arrow-head pointer, and terminates in a ball and cross finial. A second design, 9ft high, rises from a cupola, has a guidon pierced with the letters GR, and is surmounted by a royal crown and cross. This design suggests a royal building and bears a striking resemblance to the vane of Chelsea Royal Hospital. *Pen and black ink, grey wash. Each 365 × 270mm.* £40

1909

1913

1915 **English School** Design for a wall panel *c 1780*
A design in the French style. The panel is set above a dado and decorated with a design composed of pastoral elements: the fragment of a pillar, a basket of flowers, leaf sprays and branches, grasses in a vase, a bird's nest with eggs. Small rosettes pinioning the border at the corners are echoed in the dado. *Pen and black ink over pencil, with purple watercolour. Tipped on old laid paper with ink and gilt ruled border. 282 × 192mm.* £45

1916 **English School** Two interior designs in the Regency manner *c 1825*
Two delicate designs lightly drawn and prettily rendered. One shows wall and ceiling decoration together; in this the spaces are divided into geometrical compartments and decorated with typical neo-classical motifs. A recent attribution suggests that Antonio Basoli was responsible for these designs as well as that of item 1948. A second drawing for a ceiling decoration depicts a wide cornice with acanthus leaves, winged chimeras and rosette paterae around a central rectangle with a painted open sky. *Pen and black ink with blue, grey and brown wash, various water-colours. Each 340 × 220mm.* £36
Illustration below.

1917 **English School** Painted screens and decorative panels *c 1925-30*
Original workshop drawings and sketches for painted screens, decorative panels and wall paintings. The drawings are from a commercial studio, several are inscribed with working notes while some still have their job numbers. Many of the drawings show the progress of the design from the tentative early sketches to the finished painted drawings for presenting to the client. There is a variety of designs showing decorative panels with birds and flowers, hunting scenes, landscapes, traditional English village scenes, historical pictures and portraits. One series of designs is concerned with the restoration of church screens at Ranworth, Norfolk, and Southwold, Suffolk. This latter was undertaken in 1930 under the direction of E. W. Tristram (1882-1952) the painter and art historian. It is accompanied by notes detailing the painted instructions for executing the work, suggesting that the present artist (all the drawings are in the same hand) may have been a pupil of Tristam. *95 original drawings of which 50 pencil or crayon, 15 pen and wash, 30 watercolour, and 3ff of pencil manuscript or typescript. Sizes vary from 95 × 75mm to 250 × 430mm to 310 × 300mm. In portfolio.* £35

1916

1918 **French School** Design for a table centre *c 1670*
A drawing for a gold or gilded table centrepiece in the shape of a winged cupid. The figure rests on a heavy base with leaf and gadroon ornamentation and bears an empty cornucopia in each hand which he holds aloft. The design is typical of those produced in the royal workshops for Louis XIV and is possibly from the Lebrun school. *Black chalk with yellow and sienna washes. Tipped on old laid paper with gilt and ink ruled border. 297 × 227mm.*
Illustration above. £85

1919 French School Design for a balcony *c 1710*

A wrought iron balcony balustrade for a royal building. The design has the royal arms of the Kings of France in the centre flanked by motifs which include an Apollo head surrounded by a sunburst and surmounted by a royal crown. This symbol was prevalent during the reign of Louis XIV for its connotations with the 'sun king' but it also persisted as a motif with royal connections for the first three-quarters of the 18th century. Thus certain parts of the design suggest an early 18th century style while other parts are in keeping with a later period, around mid-century. *Pen and grey ink with grey wash. Scale drawing with scale rule. Tipped on old paper with brown ink rule and gilt border. 148 × 340mm.*
Illustration above. £80

1920 French School Design for an overdoor decoration *c 1735*

Design for the decoration of an overdoor lunette for an ecclesiastical college. A cartouche formed by C scrolls and crinkled leaf fronds is flanked by cornucopiae from which spring leafy tendrils. The centre of the cartouche bears the inscription 'Seminarium Archiepiscopalis'. A fully symmetrical rococo design. *Pen and brown ink with grey watercolour. Tipped on old laid paper with gilt and ink ruled border. 182 × 312mm.* £40

1921 French School Designs for podia *France c 1750*

Two designs for a low, wide, projecting base (possibly for a statue group or a fountain basin) with a central shield cartouche. The principal design is decorated with large gadroons and leaf swags. In the mid-18th century altars frequently took on the form of the pieces in this design and were known as 'autels en balustre'. *Pen and grey ink, with grey wash, brush and watercolour. Crease marks necessitating some repairs. Laid on old paper and tipped on laid paper, with gilt and ink ruled border. 210 × 310mm.* £30

1922 French School Design for an ironwork gateway *France c 1765*

A design for a gateway and flanking railings of simple format. The plain spiked rails have small backing scroll decoration at the base and at waist height and are set in piers with intertwining ornament, which are crowned by alternating vases and putti. The simplicity of the design which excludes all extraneous matter suggest a date in the third quarter of the century. *Pen and brown ink with a very light grey wash. Carefully repaired for tears. Tipped on old paper with brown ink rule and gilt border. 223 × 347mm.* £30

1923 French School Design for a wall plaque *France c 1780*

An early neo-classical design with an oval space (possibly for a portrait) set within a flat rectilinear frame which is decorated with leaf sprays–on one side mistletoe, on the other oak. The oval is upheld like a mirror by a winged mask pinion flanked by swags and rosettes. This kind a design could have had a multitude of uses–as a sepulchral monument, as a stucco plaque on the exterior of a building, or as an interior panelling design. *Pen, black ink and grey wash. Tipped on laid paper with gilt and ink ruled border. 280 × 230mm.*
£38

1924 **French School** Design for a jewel cabinet *France c 1800-1810*
Delicately drawn design for a jewel cabinet. A small piece only 4ft high and 2ft wide with very slender supports (each side having an alternative arrangement). The square-shaped cupboard section has the front decorated with arabesque panels around a central circular plaque. A very delicate and decorative design, at one time attributed to Thomire but much more light and airy than the designs which issued from his workshop. *Pen and black ink. Tipped on laid paper, with gilt and ink ruled border. 293 × 152mm.* **Illustration above.**
£110

1925 **French School** Design for a wall decoration *c 1800*
A delicate and finely rendered drawing possibly the design for a dining room. The wall is articulated by pilasters with lotus leaf capitals set over a dado, the intervening panels decorated with borders of loaded vine stalks and central motifs of classical plinths bearing heaps of fruit. Putti playing with animals decorate the frieze while the door is ornamented with painted roundels depicting the classical Roman ruins. An interesting and pretty design. *Pen and black ink with pink, blue and grey-green wash, heightened with watercolour. 125 × 198mm on sheet 207 × 300mm.* £25

1926 **French School** Documents d'artistes *c 1885*
Two designer's scrapbooks, one containing 183 sheets with more than 1000 ornamental details of arabesques and grotesque designs, friezes, mouldings, plaques, and cartouches, etc, and 81 sheets of costumes, allegories, equestrian figures, coats of arms. The second volume is devoted to coats-of-arms and heraldic devices. Most of the designs would seem to be copies from engravings but with some examples copied on the spot from ornamental details or objects. One device is dated 1881. *Quarto. 2 vols, 46ff with 264 sheets of drawings tipped in; 31ff (of which 13 blank) with 200 sheets of drawings tipped in, and 20 printed examples. Quarter morocco.* £80

1927 **German School** Design for a cartouche *c 1715*
Leaf scrolls and interlaced tendrils form the delicate open framework of a cartouche design which is ornamented with leaf sprays that give the appearance of the feather forms of which the early German designers were so fond. There is a suggestion of wrought iron work in the execution of the design. *Pen and black ink with grey watercolour brush lines, on brown tinted paper. Some small waterstains on the left side only affect a small part of the drawing. Hinged on old paper with black ink rule and gilt border. 348 × 245mm.* £38

1928 **German rococo school** Original designs for trophies *c 1735*
Four designs for trophies with motifs of antique armour, helmets, and weapons, together with animal and birds' heads, flags, arrow sheaths, etc. Each trophy group is set on a low pedestal faced with an asymmetrical cartouche, and surmounted by a vertical architectural motif – column, pedestal, pilaster, obelisk, etc. A curious mixture reminiscent of the trophy groups of Charpentier (see item 1418) but clearly of German origin with notes in that language on the colours to be used. *Four designs in red chalk on one sheet (two designs on recto, two on verso). Tipped on old paper with brown ink rule and gilt borders. 212 × 330mm.*
Illustration below. £48

1928

1929

1929 **Giovanni Giardini** Design for a large candelabrum *Rome c 1710*
Full scale drawing for a candelabrum large enough to serve as a Paschal candelstick, being a good deal taller than the height of a man. The design should be compared with that on plate 33 of Giardini's published designs in 'Promptuarium artis argentariae' (items 928-9). The present design has the same component parts, differently ornamented, and is rather more decorative in its final effect. The motif of putti heads encircled by wings is on both designs but is repeated at various stages of the candlestick in the present drawing. The underdrawing shows signs of 'repenti'. *Black chalk, pen and brown ink, with grey and purple wash; on eight attached sheets. This and the following drawings are from the same album as those formerly in the Kaufman collection which were exhibited at Portsmouth in 1969, nos 96-8 in 'Fantastic and ornamental drawings'. 2200 × 7600mm.* **Illustration above.** £525

1930

1930 **Giovanni Giardini** Design for a candelabrum *Rome c 1720*
This and the following drawings are much superior in quality to Giardini's engraved works both in design and execution of the drawing. Although the forms of this design are strictly symmetrical and the ornamentation based on traditional classical motifs, the design is more rococo in feeling than any of the ten engraved designs for candelabra. The forms are rounder, the shape lacks the sharply faceted quality of those pieces, and the drawing is executed with marked bravura. In 1720 Giardini produced two candlesticks in silver and malachite for the private chapel of Cardinal Francesco Barberini, which are among the artist's most noted works. The colouring of this drawing suggests that the piece was intended to have been carried out in silver and silver-gilt. *Black chalk, pen and brown ink with blue and ochre wash, heightened with brown watercolour; on three attached sheets. The provenance as for the previous item. 1095 × 370mm.* **Illustration above.** £385

1931 Giovanni Giardini Design for a papal mace Rome c 1720

A highly decorative design with an intricate outline, richly ornamented with figures of putti, terms, animals and masks, together with leaf scrolls and garlands, shells and shields. The head of the mace is decorated with a dove flanked by figures of War and Peace, and is surmounted by the Papal Arms upheld by putti. The cartouche section of the arms is blank so it is not known for which Pope the design was intended. Giardini's principal patron was the Albani Pope Clement XI (1700-1721) though he also worked for Innocent XII who preceded Clement XI, and Innocent XIII who followed him. Two designs for papal maces appear in the engraved designs but neither are as elaborate or as fine as this drawing.
Black chalk, pen and brown ink with grey wash, on two attached sheets. Provenance as previous items. 1217 × 269mm. **Illustration below.** £485

1932 Giovanni Giardini Design for a civic mace Rome c 1710

Of all the designs in this group this is probably the closest in feeling to those engraved, and is formed with six facets. The decoration is, however, more strictly controlled within the main forms than is displayed in the published works, and is based mainly on strapwork with accompanying shields and ovals containing heads of saints. A silver-gilt processional mace by Giardini with the date mark 1698-1710 is now in the V & A Museum, London.
Black chalk, pen and brown ink with grey wash; on two attached sheets. Provenance as for the previous items. 822 × 282mm. **Illustration below.** £270

1933 **Giovanni Giardini** Design for a clock in the form of a baldacchino *Rome c 1700*

A design obviously inspired by Bernini's baldacchino of St Peter's. Bernini would still have been working as architect of the Fabbriccà when Giardini arrived in Rome and was still alive and active when the goldsmith was put in charge of the Papal Foundry in 1698. The decorated twisted columns with their corinthian capitals and high abacci, the part entablature, and the semi-dome with scroll columns surmounted by an openwork crown, are directly derived from Bernini's masterpiece. Giardini's modifications to form the clock design include setting the clock face against a second curved entablature, upheld by male nudes and set over an arched mirror. The clock face is surmounted by an hour-glass and a bell is suspended from the crown. Figures flank the columns at the base. The piece appears to have been intended to be made in coloured marbles and gilt bronze. It is much more spirited in form and line than the rather heavy, prosaic aedicule form of the clock which is illustrated in the engraved designs (plate 81). *Black chalk, pen and brown ink, brown, yellow and blue washes, brown, purple, yellow and blue watercolour; ink ruled border. In card frame. 421 × 281mm.* **Illustration above.** £380

1934 **Giovanni Giardini** Design for a dish with putti and a bacchus *Rome c 1700*
Since the motifs and iconography of this design allude to wine and drinking-more suitable to a chalice than to a dish – the drawing may well be one for a festive drinking bowl. A central roundel, intended to be carried out in gilt, shows a seated male figure being served wine in a bowl by a putto. The border of the bowl is formed by a medley of intertwined and tumbling putti drinking from jars, vases, chalices, bowls and hogskins, and falling into languorous, comatosed poses against wine barrels. The outer rim is decorated with twined vine stalks bearing leaves and grape bunches. Giardini did not include dishes in his published designs. *Pen and brown ink, grey and yellow wash, heightened with white. In card frame. Provenance as for previous items. 534 × 783mm.* **Illustration below.** £500

1935 **Giovanni Giardini** Design for a dish with putti playing and frolicking around a herm *Rome c 1700*
A very light-hearted and gay drawing delicately rendered, produced life size, with the central historiated section taking up the major part of the design. The inclusion in this central section of jars, barrels, a chalice, and two young satyrs with vine garlands around their heads suggests another dish for a festive occasion. The border designs here consist of leaf scrolls and facing C scrolls. *Pen and brown ink with grey wash over pencil. In card frame. Provenance as for previous items. 475mm diameter on sheet 532 × 780mm.* £600

1934

1936 **John Gilbert** The Throne Room of St James's Palace *London c 1840*
Drawing of the Throne Room showing details of the upper part of the room's decoration and the canopy of the throne together with sketched in figures at the lower left. The drawing was made at the investiture of a Knight of the Garter and was engraved by Melville for 'London Interiors' 1841. Gilbert worked for many years as an illustrator for the 'Illustrated London News'. *Pencil, pen and sepia ink. Tipped on laid paper and hinged in card frame. 170 × 146mm.* £18

1937 **A(ugus)te (Alexandre) Guillaumot** Vue à l'exterieur de la grille royale au Château de Marly-le-Roi *(Paris c 1863)*
Guillaumot's drawing of the wrought iron gates and railings at the main entrance of the château de Marly (destroyed in 1798) made for his monograph on the château which was produced from documents in the Bibliothèque Impériale, and published in 1865. The drawing shows an elevation and plan to a scale of 15mm to 1 metre. It bears the inscription 'Grille Royale' and is signed 'A.te Guillaumot père, Marly". *Drawing in pencil, pen and black ink with grey and brown washes; margined with ink and wash border. 245 × 421mm.*

£20

1938 **Heaton, Butler & Bayne** Preliminary designs for memorial windows *14 Garrick St London, c 1900-1905*
The stained glass firm of Heaton & Butler was founded in 1855 when Clement Heaton (1824-1882) joined forces with James Butler. In 1862 Robert Turnhill Bayne (1837-1915) was taken into partnership and at once took over as chief designer. This collection is typical of the later style of the firm which was outstandingly popular both in England and elsewhere, particularly in the USA; one of these designs (a memorial to John Smith Grey 1819-99) actually bears the stamp of the American branch of the Gorham Manufacturing Co. The designs are all for two-light windows and show varying scenes from the Life of Christ (particularly the Nativity and the Adoration) to images of the saints.
They include windows dedicated to Frederick Hamilton Temple Blackwood, 1st Marquis of Dufferin & Ava, and to Ann Ingham (1839-1903). *10 designs in pen, ink and watercolour on a scale of 1ins to 1 ft. Mounted on stiff card. Sizes vary from 200 × 125mm to 300 × 145mm.*
Illustration opposite.

£85

1939

1939 **P. S. Heijnines** Sketchbook *c 1840*
Architect's sketchbook of Italian buildings with many interiors and decorative details including illustrations of the baptistery and S Miniato in Florence, the wall decorations of Etruscan tombs, early Christian mosaics in Rome (including one exceptionally beautiful example of the ornament in one of the vaults in San Clemente), the wall paintings and decoration at Pompeii and fragments of polychromatic Graeco-Roman painted decoration to be found in Southern Italy. *Large folio. 5off with 112 sheets of which 14 pen and ink, 27 pen, ink and wash, 37 pen, ink and watercolour (some heightened in gold), 5 pen, ink and gouache, 29 pencil. Quarter calf.* **Illustration above.**

£140

1940 **Henry Holiday** Cartoons for the stained glass East Window of Wakefield Cathedral *London 1866*

Eleven life size cartoons, fully coloured depicting a crucified Christ and other scriptural figures (Abraham, Moses, Jacob, etc) for the east window of Wakefield Cathedral, executed in 1866. The window was destroyed in 1904 during the restoration by J. L. Pearson, so that these cartoons are all that survive of an important milestone in 19th century stained glass. Holiday combined with G. G. Scott on the design and with Lavers & Barraud on the execution. 8 are signed by Holiday and dated January and February 1866 and of the remaining three, one carries the name of Lavers & Barraud. Holiday had made his first designs for stained glass in 1863 for the firm of James Powell & Sons where he had succeeded his friend Burne-Jones as head designer. In the late 1860s and the 1870s Holiday also frequently made designs for Heaton, Butler & Bayne (see item 1938) collaborating only on a few occasions with Lavers & Barraud. The first occasion had been in 1864 when he took over from Millais the commission of William Burges to design the windows for Worcester College Chapel, Oxford. Then in 1865 Holiday designed the east window of Cobham Church, Surrey for G. G. Scott's rebuilding, a design made by Lavers & Barraud. Then followed the Wakefield commission. These cartoons show the strong influence which Morris and Burne-Jones had on Holiday's style at this date, and provide one more example which illustrates how these three artists, more than any other at this time, were gradually revolutionising stained glass design. *11 brush and watercolour drawings overlaid with varnish. Each approximately 3000 × 700mm.* £250

1941 **Henry Hughes (Ward & Hughes)** Preliminary designs for stained glass windows *Frith St London c 1860*

Henry Hughes (1822-1883) became a partner in the firm of Ward & Nixon (founded in the 1830s) in 1855 and soon became the dominant force in the output of the new company of Ward & Hughes. These designs are typical of his early work which was frequently carried out in collaboration with Charles Winston (see items 1256-7) and their windows, often signed, are to be found all over Britain. The present drawings show the design for a double light window depicting St John the Baptist and Christ as 'Salvator Mundi'. The second drawing is for a large round-headed window with a central compartment depicting the Ascension of Christ and 12 subsidiary scenes illustrating incidents from the Life of Christ. *Two pen, ink, and wash drawings 500 × 320mm and 580 × 330mm.* £60

1938

1942 **Italian School** Studies of designs for a wall bracket, an escutcheon, and other ornaments *Italy c 1615*
Designs with mask, scroll and vase ornament in the style of a follower of Stefano della Bella. The forms are fluid, the ornamentation based on grotesque masks. *Pen and brown ink, brown wash over black chalk. Mounted in card frame. 230 × 180mm.* £20

1943 **Italian School** Grotesque decoration *16th century*
Grotesque decoration in a light and fluid manner. A rectangular panel with birds, masks, winged chimera, dolphin heads, scrolls and terms. A second drawing shows a design for a vertical strip of the candelabra type, here illustrating only the left half of the design, and dominated by a winged chimera at the base. Decoration of this type became popular after about 1500 when holes began to appear in the underground vaults which had once formed the ground floor of the Golden House of Nero. These allowed the artists to enter the chambers and make sketches of the ceilings which had been painted and stuccoed with this type of fanciful design which then became an essential part of the vocabulary of European decoration. (See items 368 & 638). Raphael's adaptations of these designs, known as 'grotteschi' (items 642-645) are among the most famous adaptations of the genre. *Pen and brown ink over pencil. Tipped on old laid paper with gilt and ink ruled border. Foxed and repaired for tear in bottom left corner, not affecting the drawn surface. 290 × 218mm.* £150
Illustration below.

1943

1944 **Italian School** Frieze with antique motifs *Rome 16th century*
Drawing of a frieze in the fashion which was popular in 16th century Rome for the decoration of the façades of the palaces, and which was practised most successfully by Polidoro da Caravaggio and Maturino. The present drawing shows the familiar elements of some of the designs carried out by these artists, particularly on the façade of the Palazzo Cesi (items 633 & 1626). The motifs which form part of the composition include vases, trophies, shields, fasces and a seated figure bearing a roman toga. *Black crayon. Tipped on old laid paper with gilt and ink ruled border. 98 × 338mm.* **Illustration above.** £55

1945 **Italian School** Half design for decorated ceiling *17th century*
Design for a painted and stucco ceiling conceived as a border set round a central circular space. An inner border following the central circle is decorated with panels of sporting putti and tritons separated at the corners by lion's head paterae. Winged eagles decorate the corners infilling the circle and the square. Very similar designs were also widely produced in France in the mid-century. *Pen and brown ink with brown, green and pink wash, carmine watercolour. Hinged on card. 205 × 100mm.* £35

1946 **Italian School** Wall scheme for a salon *Rome c 1800*
Two designs showing the door and window walls of a room housing a pair of large landscape paintings in the style of Gaspare Duget. The walls above the mottled dado are covered in green damask figured in patterned stripes. An arabesque frieze and a plaque with classical scene fills the overdoors. Similar classical motifs are on the plaque above the windows (with masks and tritons) and eagle motifs decorate the spaces beneath the windows. The drawings were at one time attributed to Étienne Lavallée-Poussin (see item 1954) but are not in his style or hand. *Pen and brown ink over black chalk, with brown, yellow, blue and green watercolour. 185 × 265mm.* **Illustration below.** £45

1947 **Italian School** Wall scheme for a salon *Rome c 1800*
Two drawings originally on one sheet. In the same hand as the previous item and possibly intended for the same house. The drawings show part of the window and door walls of a room housing a pair of paintings of classical Roman ruins in the style of the late 17th or early 18th century. The paintings are set in walls divided into small geometrical compartments decorated with arabesques, medallions and classical scenes. At one time attributed to Lavallée-Poussin neither the designs nor the hand accord with his style (see item 1954). *Pen and brown ink over black chalk, with grey, brown and blue wash, yellow, green, brown and blue watercolour. Each 200 × 166 mm.* £40

1948 **Italian School** Design for a ceiling and upper wall *Rome early 19th century*
Design for a ceiling in the neo-classical tradition, composed of small square coffers with rosettes. The main decoration of the ceiling is formed by a large square centrally placed coffer painted with a group consisting of a madonna with children. This is flanked with octagonal coffers inset with roundels and decorated with classical figures in stucco relief. The central compartment of the upper wall has a panel matching these side decorations. The piece may be by the Bolognese designer Antonio Basoli. *Pen and dark brown ink, with grey wash, grey, blue, pink and brown, and red watercolour. 875 × 520mm.* £60
Illustration below.

1948

1949 **Italian School** Design for the ceiling of the chapel of the Society of Providence *Rome c 1840*
Design for a painted ceiling for a small chapel. The drawing shows a compartmentalised ceiling with the areas separated by leaf decorated ribs and the various sections painted with representations of the Virgin, and winged putti. The design is inscribed 'Progretto di Decorazione in Pittura per la Cappella della R. a Opera della Providenza' and has a signature which is only partly decipherable but appears to be P. Feaysard. The Conservatory of the Divine Providence, a women's charitable institution was founded in 1674 and was attached to the church of S Orosola a Ripetta. *Pen and black ink with touches of grey wash. Laid on old paper with ink rule and wash border. In card frame. 205 × 355mm.*
£30

ORIGINAL DRAWINGS 297

1950 **J.F.K. & Z.** Geschilderde winkel gordijnen *(Holland 1890s)*
A selection of shop-blind designs in an Aesthetic Movement or early Art Nouveau idiom. They are handpainted in a variety of colours and the motifs employed include lilies, ears of corn and irises. *Oblong octavo. 43ff of handpainted designs, with one additional leaf carrying 4 designs folded in at end. Original gilt stamped cloth.* **Illustration below.** £140

1950

1951

1951 **Charles Eamer Kempe** Surviving archives of Kempe and the Kempe firm of stained glass artist and church decorators *c 1850-1907*

After Morris, Charles Eamer Kempe (1837-1907) is the best-known figure in 19th century stained glass design. His distinctive, highly developed, finely painted, mature style soon became popular with the later Victorians and his was one of the most successful and prolific of all stained glass firms. His style was widely imitated and much English stained glass up until the second World War showed his influence which is notable in the work of Geoffrey & Christopher Webb, Ninian Comper, Hugh Easton, Archibald Nicholson, Geoffrey Smith, and F. C. Eden.

Kempe came from an old Sussex family which gave its name to the Kempe Town development in Brighton. He was destined for a career as a clergyman but a pronounced stammer decided him against taking orders and he found an outlet for his High Church convictions in the stained glass and decorative schemes for churches.

Kempe received his early training from Messrs Clayton & Bell, and the earliest of his designs documented here – a window for Gloucester Cathedral, dating from 1865 – was executed by that firm. In 1866 Kempe began working on his own account having his windows carried out, until 1868, by the London firm of Thomas Baillie. Outstanding among these commissions is the series of windows at the Kempe family church at Ovingdean (1867) and the chancel windows and decorations at Staplefield Church (1868). The strong influence of the architect G. F. Bodley and of the William Morris circle is apparent here in terms of both colour and design.

After setting up his own firm in 1869 one of Kempe's first major commissions was the decoration of the ceiling of the church at Tue Brook, Liverpool, designed by Bodley. The two were to collaborate frequently after this, Bodley designing the churches and Kempe the glass and furnishings. During the 1870s Kempe's mature style rapidly evolved; though no formal records of his work in the 1870s and 1880s are included in this collection (probably none survive) much of the firm's from this period can be traced through the sketchbooks, scrapbooks and photographs which are included.

From 1893 onwards there is a complete record of the firm's stained glass work. Kempe continued to direct the firm until his death in 1907 when he was succeeded by his nephew

Walter Ernest Tower (1873-1955), a pupil of Aston Webb, and who had joined the firm in the 1890s. The business finally closed down on Tower's retirement in 1934. The archives in the present collection appear to represent the entirety of the records passed from Kempe & Tower and preserved in the Tower family who had inherited both Kempe's interests in the firm and his house and papers. (We are indebted to Mr Martin Harrison for this description). *7 volumes describing over 3500 separate commissions for all the windows painted by the Kempe firm between February 1893 and its closure in 1934, with sketches, measurements, and notes on subjects and colouring; 12 sketchbooks dating from the 1850s and 1860s, with sketches of English and Continental architecture, decoration, stained glass, showing the main early influences on Kempe's imagery; 2 sketchbooks of architecture and furnishing by Walter Tower; an album of photographs of work carried out for Bodley & Garner; a book of plans of large glazing schemes for churches c 1903-1905; a large volume of newspaper cuttings relating to the firm's commissions between 1865 and 1907; a file of photographs connected with the repair, in 1915 of the war-damaged window by the Van Linges at Lincoln's Inn Chapel; postcards of churches and plans of complete glazing schemes, 1916; a volume of window inscriptions 1901-1907; an album of photographs of reredoses; 12 albums containing photographs of reproductions of architecture, painting, carving, metalwork, gardens, church screens etc in England and Europe from all periods including two watercolours of 1835 by William Turner of Oxford 'for C. E. Kempe's instruction'; a source book belonging to Tower illustrating 14th and 15th century stained glass; a box of correspondence relating to the later commissions; 4 volumes of material concerning the Kempe and Tower families, including the scrapbook of Kempe's mother, a family photograph album, and numerous cuttings; 5 volumes of cuttings, magazine articles, photographs, sale catalogues, and the Visitors' Book from 1883-1907, of material relating to Old Place, Lindfield, Sussex, the 16th century country house of C. E. Kempe which he refitted and greatly enlarged according to his own decorative principles.* **Illustration opposite and below.** £2250

1951

1952 **Style of Richard Lalonde** Original drawing for scrollwork frieze *France c 1770*

Frieze design with foliated scrolls around rosettes and punctured by a large fleur-de-lys motif. A clear and restrained design with hatched background. *Pen and black ink with grey wash. Tipped on old stiff paper with brown ink rule and gilt border. 88 × 334mm on sheet 128 × 348mm.* £45

1953 **Style of Richard Lalonde** Design for a mirror *France c 1770*

A traditional design incorporating a mixture of picturesque and neo-classical motifs. A flat, beaded, strapwork-like frame is surmounted by a roundel ornamented with three minute shields and topped by a ribbon bow. The top edge is draped with laurel leaf ropes and leaf sprays are intertwined around the inner framework. *Red chalk. Tipped on old laid paper with gilt and ink ruled border. 225 × 137mm on sheet 270 × 215mm.* £40

1954 **Étienne de Lavallée-Poussin** Design for a wall panel *(Rome, c 1770)*

Arabesque design for a vertical wall panel with leaf scrolls, garlands, cornucopiae, satyrs, human figures and a central portrait-type medallion. The fine, spirited style of execution and the line of the leaf scrolls, in a form radiating outward from rosettes, should be compared with the drawing in the University of Michigan Museum of Art (1960/2.25; published in R. Wunder: 'Architectural and Ornamental Drawings . . . in the Collection of the University of Michigan Museum of Art, 1965, no 54), rather than the engraved designs in item 1484 which deteriorate in their transfer to the copperplate. *Pen and black ink drawing with brown wash shadows. Tipped on thick paper with gilt and black border lines, mounted on thick card. Preserved in cloth wallet. 160 × 79mm.* **Illustration below.** £115

1954

1955 **Samuel Lysons & Robert Smirke** Original drawings made in preparation for Lysons' publication on the Romano-British antiquities of England, Reliquiae Britannico-Romanae, published *1813-17*

The drawings are of architectural details, inscribed tablets, sculptural reliefs, mosaic pavements, glass, pewter, earthenware and jewelry. 31 of them were used by Lysons for his book; the remainder were probably intended for further volumes of the Reliquiae series that were projected but never appeared. *57 drawings in pencil, pen and black ink with wash and watercolour, varying in sheet size from 356 × 390mm to 720 × 525mm. Tipped on thick paper. Preserved in quarter cloth portfolio with morocco label on upper cover.* £435

1956 **Mewès & Davis** Workbooks for hotel and apartment schemes
Paris c 1910
The books show complete schemes for the interior decorations and furniture of some Parisien hotels and apartments during the first part of the century. The names of the Hôtel Chatham, the Galerie Hôtel and the Hôtel Maurice are mentioned. The schemes are very conservative and are worked out in the eclectic and interpretive styles varying from Louis XIV to Louis XVI and the more marked features of each style smoothed out to conform to the requirements of a commercial concern and the comfort of the clients. The designs are fully comprehensive ranging from room plans with furniture arrangements and wall elevations, ceiling and wall decoration, individual items of furniture – beds, seats, cupboards, tables, drawers, and desks – through to the fitments, furnishing pieces, ornaments and fittings. The Anglo-French firm of Mewès & Davis was a successful partnership of two architects trained at the Beaux Arts; Charles Mewès (1858-1914) and Arthur J. Davis (1878-1951), and had offices both in Paris and London. The firm was responsible for the building and interiors of several hotels in both capitals, among which the most notable were the Hôtel Jules Ferry and the Ritz in Paris, and the Carlton Hotel and the Ritz in London. The firm was also responsible for the furniture and fitting out of several trans-atlantic liners: the Aquitania, the Lanconia, and the Franconia. The present collection provides a complete record of the fitting-up of hotels and private interiors of the period. *Eight volumes. Each 323 × 215mm. 825 drawings on 551ff of which 44ff loose. The majority of the drawings in pencil and watercolour, but a few in pencil and wash only. Green hard-backed folders with metal mounts.* **Illustration above and below.** £750

1956

1957 **William Eden Nesfield** Swillington-the half of wrought iron gate *May (18)60*

Original drawing with explanatory notes and measurement in manuscript. Scale 1½ins to 1ft. Inscribed 'The gate to move on gun metal centres and to have foot stops attached to stones. The whole to be of wrought iron and the several parts put together with clips and bolts as shown in the drawing'. The details show the side elevation of the standards, and include large drawings of details such as a sketch of the bottom bar, a sketch of the top bar, a plan of the foot, and a sketch of the latch. *Pen in black and brown ink on architect's paper, backed with tissue. Size 405 × 615mm.* £30

1958 **William Eden Nesfield** Design for a chimneypiece *London c 1870*

Chimneypiece design for a town house conceived in a fashion typical of the period using the classical elements in the surround and a picture-frame type of overmantel indicating that the latter could enclose either a painting or a mirror. The scale is given of ½ins to a foot and inscriptions on the verso show the drawing to be no 246 and suggest the client might have been W. John Lord of 37 Gt Portland St. *Pencil and grey wash. 232 × 165mm.* £20

1959 **H. Percival** Furniture designs *1902-1907*

Drawings by a London furniture designer and cabinet-maker at the turn of the century. The majority of the drawings are typical commercial designs in the debased 'art furniture' style favoured at that period, but a few are specially designed individual pieces. These latter include a group of three very decorative coloured drawings for a conversation-corner unit incorporating seating, cupboards, and bookshelves, and are enlivened by art-nouveau motifs. The rest show designs for music and china cabinets, bookcases, tables, dressers and bedroom suites. One drawing is fully signed, 4 are initialled and 4 are dated; various items bear the name of the firm or the customer, while one gives Percival's address in Canonbury Square, Islington. *Nine original drawings of which 5 in black lead pencil, 1 in black ink, 9 in pencil, ink, and coloured washes. Sizes vary from 190 × 105mm to 380 × 510mm.* **Illustration below.** £30

1959

1960

1960 **School of Nicholas Pineau** Original design for a boiserie scroll *France c 1730*
A typical piece of rococo scrollwork in the form of an 'S', enriched with curling leaves, crinkled-edged foliage, and vegetation merging into shells. The scroll is surmounted by a bending dragon with curly tail which is biting into one of the leaf tendrils. A fine decorative design. *Red chalk drawing. Light waterstain on lower half but not spoiling final effect. Hinged on old paper with brown ink rule and gilt border. 302 × 194mm.* £55
Illustration above.

1961 **G. W. Rhoades** Original designs for bedroom furniture *London c 1880*
A collection of trade designs mounted on card with each card showing a suite of bedroom furniture: wardrobe, dressing table, wash-stand, bedside table, clothes horse and chair. The designs are clearly intended for a manufacturer's catalogue and are numbered between 54 and 144 with some unnumbered designs and some duplication of drawings in a different medium and on a different type of paper. The firm of G. W. Rhoades labelled themselves 'Artistic & General Furniture Manufacturers'. They operated from 5 & 7 Laburnham Street, London E2. This area off the Kingsland Road in Shoreditch has been a principal area of furniture manufacture in London since the early 19th century.
58 drawings in pencil, pencil and wash, pen and black ink, on card, cartridge paper or tracing paper mounted on card. Average size 488 × 350mm. Preserved in portfolio. £65

1962 **Office of Anthony Salvin** Decorative designs for Greystoke, Cumberland *London c 1845*
Drawing for an armorial shield marked as No 12 and indicating the colours, and a sketch for a standard bearing lion shown in front and side view and indicated to be '¼ real size'.
Pen and black ink on tracing paper. 375 × 280mm. Black ink and brush. Lion 160 × 60mm and with standard 300 × 70mm on sheet 350 × 250mm. £10

1963 **Jas. Schoolbred & Co.** Original designs for trade catalogue *London c 1890*
Two designs for bedroom suites, two sideboard designs, a mirror and a Sheraton table; the latter in a different hand. One drawing numbered E165 and dated 1 Nov. 90. *Nine pencil and wash drawings on 3 sheets, 1 pen and wash, 1 pencil drawing. In paper wallet.* £15

1964 **W. Scott** Designs for gothic chairs *c 1835*
Designs for solidly gothic chairs with cushioned seats, turned front legs, splay-back back legs and the variety in the designs being mainly confined to a variation in the decoration of the chair back. Two designs are decorated with a ducal crest. The drawings would seem to be early designs in the gothic manner. It is not clear whether the inscription of 'W. Scott Esq' which is found on two of the drawings refers to the designer or to the client. *Eight designs on seven sheets. Tipped on sugar paper. In cloth wallet. Average size 250 × 180mm.*
£30

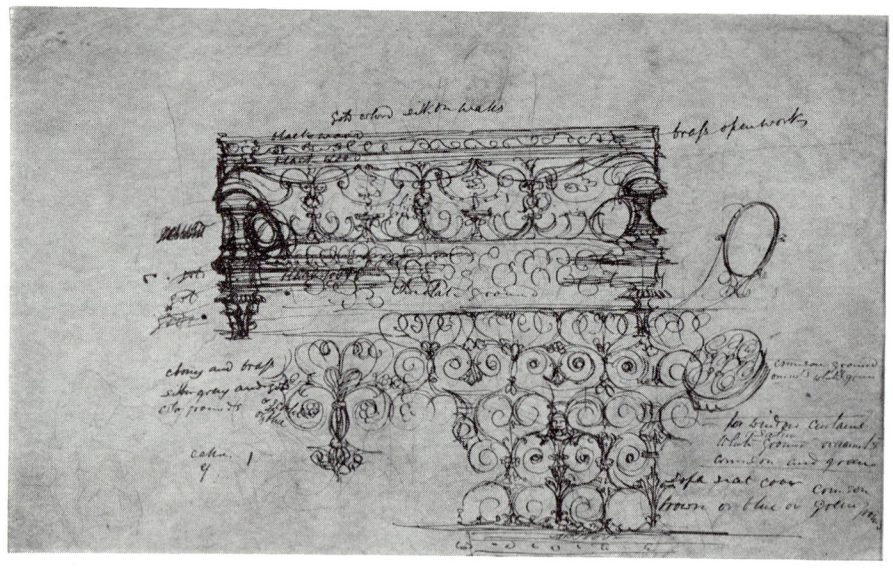

1966

1965 Mary Smirke Decorative wall panel *London c 1800*

A highly ornamented design with a central rectangular panel depicting a plinth on which two putti uphold a roundel containing a representation of the head of a young girl. Surrounding panels are richly decorated with ovals with figures of girls, leafs spray and garlands, scrolls and ribbons and swags. An inscription on the verso states that the panel was 'designed by Mary Smirk, enlarged for her father Robert Smirk RA'. Mary (1779-1853) was the second child of the artist Robert Smirke and sister of the architect. For several years she assisted her father in his studio squaring up and enlarging his small designs and transferring them to canvas. Later she was frequently employed as a copyist. *Pencil. 465 × 300mm.* £18

1966 Alfred Stevens Original design for a sofa *c 1860*

Design for a straight-backed sofa with upholstered ends over wood. The very free drawing includes details of the patterning of the seat-cover, the scrollwork of the back and ends of the roll-cushions. The piece was obviously intended for a particular interior setting since the inscription notes the details of the wall covering and the curtains, as well as the colour and material of the settee: 'black wood – brass openwork' and 'sofa seat cover brown or blue on crimson green ground' etc. *Pen and black ink drawing over pencil sketches of figures; verso: figure studies in red chalk and ornamental detail in pencil. Tipped on stiff paper, in card frame. Preserved in paper wallet. From the Drury Collection. 195 × 318mm.* £220
Illustration above.

1967 Jean-Marie-Victor Viel Ceiling design for the Villa Magnani *c 1855*

A ceiling design for a large room in the light and delicate manner of the early Pompeian style. Classical figures like those from Greek vases inscribed in squares, and signs of the zodiac in roundels, alternate with figures placed in domed and columned aedicules. All these motifs are connected with flower garlands and the intervening spaces are filled with cornucopiae, sphinxes, birds, sea-creatures and mythical animals. The designs stand out darkly from a light ochre ground. This first Pompeian style of decoration was part of the eclectic movement of the mid-century and became fashionable after the building of the Maison Pompéienne for Prince Jérôme Napoléon in Avenue Montaigne. Jean-Marie-Victor Viel (1796-1863) was a pupil of Vaydoyer and Lebas. He spent the greater part of his professional life as architect to the Préfecture de Police where he was its chief architect for the last three years of his life. His major work was producing the designs for the

Palais de l'Industrie which was erected 1853-5. *Pen and ink drawing coloured with ochre wash, and blue, green, ochre and black watercolour. Inscribed 'Villa Magnani' in a contemporary hand at the bottom left corner. With an inscription in the same hand retained from an old cover and mounted on the inside of the case; this reads 'Donne par Mon ami Viel Architecte. du palais de l'industrie. Bri . . .'. Repaired for small tears and surface cracks, preserved in cloth case. 866 × 436mm.* £65

1970

1968 **Edouard-August Villain** French 17th century interior *Paris 1856*
Drawing of a typical French interior for an ante-room in the French court style showing all the typical elements of decoration to be found in interiors of that period. An illustrative and instructive drawing carefully rendered. Villain (1829-1876) was a nephew of Charles Percier and became one of the municipal architects of Paris. *Pen and black ink. Tipped on cartridge paper. 330 × 245mm.* £18

1969 **Edouard-August Villain** Dado panelling from Pompei *c 1859*
Colourful and decorative panel with the motif of a bird eating fruit and with painted and ornamental bases of columns and pilasters. Villain travelled extensively in Italy in the late 1850s. *Pen and black ink over pencil. Black, purple and green gouache with watercolours. Tipped on sugar paper. 135 × 245mm on sheet 280 × 245mm.* £20

1970 **Monogramist V. V.** Design for a fountain *Netherlands c 1610*
Design for an octagonal fountain decorated with shells and plaques of classical figures. The piece is similar in style to designs in the work of Vredeman de Vries. The drawing bears the unidentified monogram V ... V. *Pen with sepia ink and wash. Tipped in card mount. 155 × 233mm on sheet 225 × 335mm.* **Illustration above.** £45

1971 **Harry Wimhurst** Measured drawings of tea boxes, late 18th and early 19th cents *London 1909*
Eight sets of full size measured drawings showing tea boxes in a variety of woods and tortoiseshell veneer with different inlays. The drawings show elevations, lids, sections, and a view of an interior with its fittings. *24 pencil and watercolour drawings laid on two sheets of card, each sheet 760 × 555mm.* £8

1972

1972 **Paul Vincent Woodroffe** Collection of drawings and photographs of stained glass including completed windows *Chipping Campden 1900-1945*
Woodroffe (1875-1945) was a book illustrator, heraldic artist and highly skilled stained glass designer working firmly in the Arts and Crafts tradition pioneered by Christopher Whall. This collection forms his own record of executed and unexecuted stained glass designs over forty years. A Roman Catholic, Woodroffe did a great deal of work for Catholic Churches, schools and Cathedrals; prominent amongst those recorded here are windows for Stonyhurst College (his old school) and Oscott College as well as Downside, and St Patrick's Cathedral in New York. After leaving Stonyhurst Woodroffe studied at the Slade where he took first prize for life drawing. He exhibited at the RA (from 1900), the New English Art Club, and most significantly, the Arts and Crafts Exhibition Society where, from 1899, he frequently showed his stained glass designs. He had a close association with Ashbee and was one of the first to follow him to Chipping Campden where Ashbee built Woodroffe's house and studio. Woodroffe provided many illustrations for Ashbee's Essex House Press as well as several for Laurence Housman's works. The collection forms an impressive record of the work of this leading stained glass artist of the first half of the century. The albums are arranged chronologically and provide photographs of the finished work together with 225 meticulously executed drawings in ink and wash. All are titled and in many instances Woodroffe has added on the verso information on the commissioning of the design and what he was paid for it. (We are indebted to Mr Martin Harrison for the information in this description.) *Quarto. 6 volumes. Three volumes bound in half morocco and three volumes in buckram.* **Illustration above and opposite.** £425

1973 **Matthew Digby Wyatt** Illuminated border designs *c 1845*
Four beautifully rich border designs consisting of a motif painted in a single colour and a three-colour edging painted over gold leaf. Three examples have two designs within the same framework while a fourth example is a single pattern. The repeat motifs include scrollwork, roundels, fleur-de-lys, and crosses. A fifth item shows part of a design for a book binding with painted strapwork border and a central strapwork motif on painted paper applied on gilt paper. *Four border designs painted in red, blue, white, black, and purple, over gold leaf. Tipped on stiff card. Each 61 × 125mm. Red, blue, green and black watercolour on paper with cream wash, applied on gilt paper. On stiff card. 165 × 107mm.* £60

1974 **Matthew Digby Wyatt** Designs for geometrical mosaics *London c 1846*
Four geometrical designs set within roundels. Two designs are variations of the same basic eight-pointed star pattern. Two are designed in red, black and gold, two others add white to those colours. One pair have the initials LP below and the other pair are marked by GP. *Four designs on one sheet. Each roundel measures 70mm diameter on a sheet 440 × 270mm.* £35

1975 **Matthew Digby Wyatt** Drawings of polychromatic ornament *c 1848*
A group of small drawings in typical Digby Wyatt vein of historical polychromatic ornament with details of ceilings, floors, borders and individual motifs and patterns from a variety of sources. One drawing is inscribed 'Ceiling deanery Worcester' with below 'Botolph Church Norfolk' while another declares itself to be the 'Chancel Screen Burlingham' and (St) 'Edmond's Norfolk' with, by the side 'Rafter diaper – Nave Aldenham Herts'. *12 designs on 10 sheets. Strong watercolour over pencil or pen and black ink. 3 designs heightened with gilt paint. Sizes vary from 9 × 34mm to 140 × 70mm, and 55 × 55mm to 105 × 100mm.* £42

1976 **Matthew Digby Wyatt** Early sketches for the decorative title of 'Metalwork and its artistic design' *London c 1851*
Small sketch of an alternative design to that finally used in the book. This already has the basic forms of the final design but with minor differences in the proportions of the component parts and some alterations to details of the patterning and ornamentation (see also item 979). *Pen and black ink on pale blue notepaper. Tipped on cream cartridge paper. 150 × 117mm.* £22

1977 **Matthew Digby Wyatt** Design for a medal for the Great Exhibition building *c 1851*
Design for a medal to commemorate the opening of the Crystal Palace and showing the eastern transept end façade. The surrounding inscription reads 'The Temple of Peace opened May 1st 1851'. Wyatt was Secretary to the Executive Committee of the Exhibition and designed several of the interior courts. *Terra-cotta wash and watercolour over pencil. 38mm diameter on sheet 97 × 140mm.* £35

1972

1978 **Matthew Digby Wyatt** Design for a letterbox with door knocker *London c 1860*

A vigorous and lively design showing M Digby Wyatt at his robust best in intimate details. The knocker is particularly flamboyant with frolicksome cupids reposing on the flanking ends of flowery scrolls. The drawing shows the front in great detail and includes sketches of the side and a section through the centre. *Pen and black ink on pale blue writing paper, tipped on cream woven paper. 185 × 225mm.* **Illustration above.** £40

1979 **Jacopo Zucchi** Design for the wall decoration of a room with a coved ceiling *Italy c 1580*

An interesting original design for the long wall of a room. The scheme shows an architectural framework with a central niche containing a classical statue of a huntsman and his dog, flanked by large rectangular panels for holding paintings, and terminated by a segmental headed window at each extreme. Each feature is separated by Ionic columns. Zucchi (1541-1589) was a pupil of Vasari, worked principally as a decorator, and undertook major schemes on his own account mainly in Rome. The attribution of this design to Zucchi is based upon a comparison with four definite Zucchi drawings in the RIBA Collection. *Pen and brown ink drawing with bistre and sepia washes. Margined to give a lined border in gilt and brown ink. Hinged in card frame. 200 × 425mm.* £320 **Illustration below.**

1979

Index

Items illustrated are printed in bold figures. Numbers in parentheses indicate an inferred reference.

A

Aalto, A. 93
Abbati, N. dell'. 661
Absolom, J. **753**
Ackermann, R. 2, 76, 1302, 1303, **1401**
Adam, R. 3, 30, 81, 139, 305, 441, 923, 963, **1511**, 1512
Adam, R. & J. 30, **302-304**, 311, 1511, 1512
Adam, W. 302
Adams, potters. 1130
Adams, M. 4, 306, 350, 384
Adnet, J. 525
Aesthetic Movement 1708, **1950**
Aikin, E. 94
Alberti, C. 1624
Alcock, Sir R. 702
Aldenham, Herts, (church). 1975
Alford, Lady M. 1356
Alison, F. 127
Allen, H. 1002
Allou, A. **1555**, 1601
Amsterdam
 Royal Palace **522**
 Town Hall **522**
Alton Towers 1741, 1742
American pottery 1021, 1107, **1111**
Andere, M. 1771
Anderson, L. L. 904
Anderson, W. 1426
Andirons or firedogs 444
Andrae, W. 1003
Andrews, E. D. 5
Antichità di Ercolano, Le **1706**
Antonelli, G. 1402
Aquila, F. 640, 646, **1602**
Aquila, P. **605**
Arabesques 1410a, **1410b**, 1410f, 1410g, 1483, 1484, 1525, 1555, **1954**
Arbeiten der Österreichischen Kunst-Industrie 701
Arias, P. E. 1603
Armour 801i, **854**
Armstrong, W. 782
Army & Navy Co-operative Society Ltd. 1707
Arrowsmith, H. W. & A. 307
Art Deco 314, 315, 436, **747**, 759, 1718, 1719
Art Journal, The 702-708
Artificial Flowers **1702e**, 1779
Art Nouveau 157, 463, **743**, 804, 1708, 1723, **1950**
Art Treasures Examiner 713
'Artistic Houses', American interiors 308
Arts & Crafts Exh Soc 709-711
Art & Decoration, periodical 436
Arts & Crafts movement 709-712, 714-716, 718-721, 765, 767, 788, **902, 903, 1972**
Arts décoratifs de Grande-Bretagne et d'Irlande 712

Arundell, F. V. J. **342**
Ashbee, C. R. 116, 472, 714, 715, 725, **902, 903**, 916, 936
Ashdown, C. H. 1260
Aslin, E. 6, 1708
Asphaltum 1304
Aspen, V. 21
Aspen-Ville Art Wallpapers 1304
Assay Offices, Parl Reports 905
Aston Hall 17
Atkinson, R. 384
Aubry-Le-Comte, H. L. V. J-B. 649
Audran, C. 654
Audsley, W. & G. 1403-1405
Aveline, P. **983**
Aviler, C. A. d' 309
Ayers, J. 1155
Ayrton, M. 802

B

Bacharach, E. 525
Bagge, E. 310, 365
Bagnaia, Villa Lante 618
Baillie Scott, M. H. 7, 382, 384, 472, 521, 716, 724, 725, 783
Baily, J. 467
Bainbridge, H. C. 926
Baker, O. 1772
Baldry, A. L. 763, 764
Ballantine, J. 1486
Ballantyne, A. R. 1060
Bankart, G. P. 311, 312, 395
Barbezat & Cie 803
Barley, M. W. 313
Barnard, Bishop & Barnards 804, 805
Barnard, J. 1004, 1407
Barnsley, S. & E. 163
Barrett, F. A. 1005, 1006
Barret, M. 525
Barry, C. 125, 979
Bartolozzi, F. 302
Bartoli, P. S. 634, 640, 647, 648, **1821**
Basoli, A. 1948
Battersby, M. 314, 315
Baughan, R. 1773
Bauhaus 779, **796**
Baumer, W. 1440
Bayardi, O. A. 1706
Bayerischer Porzellan-Manufaktur 1198
Bayonne, Maison de Brethous 432
Beard, T. **785**
Beardsley, A. 783
Beauvallet, C. 1408
Beauvallet, P. N. 1408
Beck, D. 1203
Beckett, H. E. 1232, 1233
Beckford, W. 475
Bedford, F. 797, 975, 979, 980, 1409, 1462

Beham, H. S. 1416
Behrens, P. 461, 469, 725, 729
Beilby, W. & M. 1157
Bell, M. 1208
Bell, R. C. 1007
Bellargue, G. de 166
Bellori, G. P. 650, **1821**
Belton House 857
Bemrose, W. 8, 9
Benn, J. W. 21
Bennett, W. J. 467
Bennet, R. 1008
Berain, C. 521, 906, 907
Berain, J. 10, 316-319, 521, 806, **1410, 1482**, 1531
Bercy, C. A. 654
Berendsen, A. 1009
Bergeron, L. E. 11
Berjon, A. 1901
Berlage, H. P. 12, 13, 717, 725
Berling, K. 1010
Bernini, G. L. 1602, **1933**
Ber(r)ettoni, N. 602
Berthelot 1484
Bertsch 402, 438
Beunat, J. **320, 321**
Bianchini & Férier 1308
Bianconi, C. 1411
Bickerton, L. M. 1204
Biedermeier furniture 88
Bielefeld, C. F. 322, 323
Bielenski, le Comte 434
Biennais, M-G. 73
Biet, J.-E. 324
Bing, S. 725, 743, 1743
Bird, A. 1802
Birmingham Brass Fittings **807**
Black, M. 325, 776
Blackburne, E. L. 603
Blacker, J. F. 1011
Blackwood, F. H. T. 1938
Bland Light Syndicate Ltd 1822
Bles, J. 1261
Blomfield, R. 709
Blondel, G.-F. **1902**
Blondel, J. F. 326-328, 1418, 1482, 1511, 1531
Blount, G. 718
Blue and white transfer ware 1029, 1030, 1109, 1174, 1190
Blunt, R. 1012
Böckel, J. Ch. 869
Bodley & Garner 1951
Boett(i)cher, H. 1531
Bolas, T. 1205
Bologna
 Palazzo Poggi 661
 San Michele in Bosco **610, 611**
Bolognese School drawings 1903-1905
Bonnar, (W). 1906
Bordeaux, R. 808
Borromini, F. 1602
Borsato, G. 329, 453
Bossert, H. T. 1709
Bossi, B. **1622**
Botolph Church, Norfolk 1975

Bottles 1203, 1772, 1781
Bouchardon, E. **1604**
Boucher, F. Senior 1412
Boucher, J. F. **14**, 330, 331, 1605, 1907
Bouchet, L. 365
Bouet, G. 808
Boulenger 908
Boulle, P. 10, 93, 147
Boulton, M. 923, 963
Bourges Cathedral 1269
Bourgoin, J. 1413
Bovingdon, J. 15
Bow porcelain 1078, 1122, 1175
Bowers, R. S. 15
Boys, S. 363
Brackett, O. 16, 106
Brandon, R. 494
Brandt, G. 516
Brangwyn, F. 382, 783
Braque, G. 1335
Braun, E. 1447
Braun, E. W. 984
Brawn, T. 909
Brayley, E. W. **440**
Brears, C. D. 1013
Brenna, V. 990
Breuer, P. 93, 1229
Breuhaus, F. A. 332, 402
Brewer, C. C. 728
Bridgens, R. 17, 18, **854**
Brighton, Royal Pavilion 440, 470, 483
Briseville, M. **1482**
Bristol porcelain 1078, 1136, 1137
British Decorators, Incorporated Institute of 446
Brocklesby House 491
Brongniart, A. **1014**
Brooks, V. 814
B. Bros 1406
Brown, G. M. 1239
Brown, R. 19
Brown, W. N. 1015
Bruant, L. 367
Bruckmann, P. & Co. 910
Brunetti, G. **1414**
Brunner, H. 911
Bry, J. Th. and T. de 912-915, 1415, 1416
Buchanan, W. 1339
Buckler, J. C. 180
Buckler, J. C. & C. A. 808
Bucklersbury, Roman pavement 664
Buckley, F. 1262
Buckley, W. 1263
Bulau, A. E. **1774**
Bullet, P. 334, 1482
Bullock, A. E. 1716
Bullock, G. 2
Bureau du Journal des Dames 136
Burges, W. 202, 335, 707, 797, 979, 980, 1940
Burlingham, Chancel screen 1975
Burlington Fine Arts Club 809, 1016-1018
Burlington, Lord 503
Burne-Jones, E. 1208, 1209, 1223, 1239
Burton, D. 822
Burton, W. 1019, 1020

Bury, J. B. M. 20, **810**
Bury, S. **903**
Bushnell, G. H. S. 1021
Butler, A. J. 1022
Buttons 1702a, 1776

C

Cabinet Maker and Art Furnisher 21
Caglieri, L. 915
Cahier, C. 1417
Cahiers de la céramique 1023
Caillouet 811
Cairo **1729**
Caldicott, J. W. 985
Cambridge Colleges 205, 857
Campbell, C. 503
Campbell, I. 402
Campen, J. van **522**
Camporesi, P. **642**
Canot, J. C. 1516, 1517
Capon, W. 658
Carlsson, D. 21a
Carlton Studio 1545
Carpets 1301l, 1311, 1324, 1325, 1331, 1332, 1346, 1353, **1950**
Carracci, A. **605**, 606-609, 650
Carracci, L. **610**, **611**
Carrick, E. 350
Carrington, N. 336, 337
Carron Co. 812
Carter, J. 30
Cartouches 1411, 1412-**1414**, 1432, 1433, 1451, **1477**, 1478, 1479, 1481, 1497, 1500, 1503b, 1505, 1507, 1509a, 1509d, 1927
Cassel, Westphalia 366
Cassell's Household Guide 338
Cassini, G. M. 990
Casson, H. 384
Castleford Pottery 1024
Castle Howard 492
Cattermole, R. 467
Caughley porcelain 1047
Cauvet, G. P. 1908
C. E. & Co. 1823
Ceilings 604-609, 615, 621, 623-626, 629, 631, 638, 639, 642-644, 646-649, **651**-653, 661, 666, 1482, **1903**-1905, 1912, **1916**, 1945, 1967
Celadon ware 1055, 1057
Cellini, B. 916, 917, **1909**
Cescinsky, H. 22-25, 235
Cesio, C. 606, 607
Chalk, L. 26
Chambers, W. **27**-**29**
Chamblin, B. de 339
Chamot, M. 1025
Champneys, B. 702
Chance Brothers 1210
Chantilly 613
Chantilly porcelain 1074
Chapuis, A. 1803, **1804**
Chareau, P. 525
Charles, R. 30
Charleston, R. J. 1155
Charleston, R. R. 1134
Charlton House 1434
Charpentier, R. 1418, **1928**
Chartres Cathedral 1269

Chase, J. W. 1710
Chater Collection 1131
Chauveau, F. 340
Chelsea porcelain 1116, 1117, 1175, 1192
Chenavard, C-A. 31, 32, **1910**
Chermayeff, S. 333, 756
Chiavistelli, J. 629
Child, H. 1419
Child & Child 183
Child, P. 33
Chimney pieces & fireplaces 205, 309, 316-319, 330a, 330d, 334, 341, 401, 411-414, 416, 418, 429, 456, 458, 459, 462, 464, 466, 476, 479, 503, 804, 858, 875, 1482, 1497, 1547, 1958
Chinese Armorial Porcelain 1075
Chinese pottery & porcelain 1008, 1017, 1026, 1036, 1084, 1095, 1163
Chinoiserie 23, **27-29**, 48, 86, 370-373, 1470, 1517-1519, 1720, 1743
Chippendale, T. 19, 34-38, 81, 93, 189, 1497, 1561
Chiswick House 503
Chrétien 649
Christie, J. 1606
Church, A. H. 786
Church, W. A. 1027
Arthur Churchill Ltd. 1264
Cipriani, G. B. 1420
Civil Service Supply Assn 131
Claesen, C. 1421
Claire, P. T. de 1484
Clark, E. F. 1775
Clarke, S. 709
Clarkson, D. A. 814
Clement d'Armont, L. 341
Clifford, A. 918
Clock and Watchmakers Petitions, Report 961
Clockcases 96, 165, 177d, 1807, 1933
Clouston, R. S. 38
Clouzot, H. 815, 1305
Coalport 1049, 1050, 1090
Coates, W. 63, 333
Cobden-Sanderson, T J. 709, 725
Cochin, C. N. 367
Cockerell, S. & D. 712, 736
Coffins 1732
Coignet 152
Coleridge, A. 36
Collection Catalogues 106, 137, 166, 486, 855, 1002, 1008, 1016, 1041, 1067, 1131, 1133, 1148, 1155, 1156, 1164, 1180, 1270, 1342, 1608, 1745, 1746, 1754
Colling, J. K. 1422, 1423, 1485
Commentry, France 1248
Committee of Master Carpenters 39
Compagnie des Arts Français 490
Compiègne, château 450
Comyn, Ching & Co. Ltd. 816
Condy, N. **342**
Conran, T. 343
Constantinople, Sultan's Palace 822
Contet, F. 817

Conway, M. D. 344
Cookworthy porcelain 1115
Cooper, R. G. 1028
Copeland porcelain 1050
Copenhagen, astronomical clock 1806
Coptic tapestries 1306, 1314
Corbin, P. & F. 818
Corneille, T. 1703
Cornforth, J. 364
Cortona, P. B. da 604, 1602
Cotchett, L. E. 40
Cothele House **342**
Cottar(t), P. 1482
Cotterell, H. H. 919
Cottingham, L. N. **819**
Courtauld Family 920
Courtin, L. 659
Cox & Sons 1211
Coypel, N. 367
Coysh, A. W. 1029, 1030
Crabeth, D. & W. 1252
Crace, J. D. 446, 1424
Crallan, F. A. 41
Crane, W. 709, 712, 719-722, 1344, 1351, 1425
Crawford, A. **902**
Creswell, K. A. C. 1711
Crivellari, B. 661
Croft-Murray, E. 612
Crouch & Butler 345
Crouch, Joseph 345
Crown jewels 982
Crystal Palace 785, 1977
Cunego, D. 302
Curle, A. O. 921
Curran, C. P. 346
Cushion, J. P. 1031
Cutler, T. W. 1426
Cuvillier, F. de 1474
Cyphers 906, 1473, 1510, 1545

D

Dalziel, W. F. 125
Daly, C. 347
Damase, J. 1307
Dan, H. 828
Danhauser, J. 88
Darcel, A. 922
Darly, M. 1427
Darty, P. 42
Davenport pottery & porcelain 1112
Davis, O. 21, 723, 1423
Davis Ltd. 820
Davison, T. 724
Dawber, G. 455
Dawe, G. 94
Day, L. F. 702, 804, 1212, 1344, 1428
Day, R. 233
Dean, W. 822
Decker, P. **348, 349**
Deepdene 94
Dekorative Kunst **725**
Delafosse, J-C. 1429-1431, 1511
De La Motte, P. 726
De La Nezière, J. 1712
Delaunay, S. 351, 1307
Delevoy, R. 789
Delieb, E. 923

Della Bella, S. 1432, 1433, **1911**, 1942
Demont 821
Denison, C. B. 1745
Dennis, R. 733, 1032, 1033
Derby Porcelain 1006, 1050, 1061, 1090, 1175
Derrington & Sons 727
Description des arts et metiers **167**, 1035
Deshairs, L. 436
Design and Industries Assn 728
Design Magazine 799
Deutscher Werkbund 517, 728, 729
Deutsches Metallwarenwerk 1824
Deville, J. 43
DeVoe, S. S. 352
Dibdin, C. 363
Dictionaries 67, 218, 219, 1703-1705
Dictionnaire universel des arts et des sciences 1703
Dictionnaire portatif des arts et metiers 1705
Diderot, D. & J. L. d'Alembert **1, 301, 601, 801, 901, 1001, 1201, 1301, 1701, 1702, 1801**
Dietterlin, W. **1434-1436**, 1531
Dijon **1530**
Dillon, F. 363
Djo-Bourgeois 525
Dohme, R. 44
Dolby, C. T. **753**
Dolls 1791
Donnelly, P. J. 1034
Doors 330c, 340, 443, 1482
Dorfles, G. 234
Dorigny, N. 639, 1339
Doulton stoneware 1032
Dowling, H. G. 731
Down, H. A. 353
Downing, A. J. 354, 355
Drapery Trade, Review 1334
Drayton House 857
Dresden china 1070
Dresser, C. 702, 732, **733**, 786, 1344, 1462
Drinking glasses 1204, **1220**, 1247, 1249, 1261, 1264, 1265
Drouet, S. 525
Droz, E. **1804**
Dublin Exhibition 1853; 706
Du Breuil, J. 103
Du Cerceau, J. A. 93, 103, 1511 1530
Dudley, R. C. 975
Dufferin & Ava 1938
Dufrène, M. 365
Dufy, R. 1308, 1335
Duget, G. 1946
Duhamel du Monceau, H-L. 1035
Dumont, J. 1437
Dupont-Auberville **1309**, 1310
Dupré-Lafon 525
Dupuy Frères 356
Durant, S. **1438**
Durbin, L. 736
Durer, A. 1252
Du Sartel, O. 1036
Dutch School drawings 1912
Duty on Window Glass 1213
Dyche, T. 1704

E

Eaglestone, A. A. 1037
Eames, C. 93
Eastlake, C. L. 45-47, 494, 495
Ebelmann, H. J. 103
Eberl, B. 1311
Eck, C. L. G. 823
Ecke, G. 48, 236, 237
Edelinck, G. 654
Edinburgh University 302
Edwards, F. jun 357
Edwards, P. 1713
Edwards, R. 49-51a, 85, 100, 186, 845
Edmondson, J. L. **1344**
Eggert, F. X. 1214
Eickhout, G. van den 1439
Eisen, C. 1913
Eisler, M. 734
Elder-Duncan, J. H. 358
Elsaesser, M. 381
Embroidery 13010, 1337, **1901**
Enamels 901m, 1015, 1016, 1025, 1041, 1077, 1124, 1135, 1147, 1188
Encyclopedias 338, 786, 1309, 1701
Engelhardt, K. von 735
Engelmann, G. 649
Englefield, Sir H., collections 1617, 1618
English armour **854**
English Ceramic Circle 1038
English Delftware 1044, 1148, 1190
English Interiors, prints **528**
English School drawings 1914, 1915, **1916**, 1917
Engraved gems 969, 970, **983**, 987-989, 1754
Entwistle, E. A. 1312
Epstein, D. 1776
Eriksen, S. 1156, 1714
Essex House Press **903**, 916, 1972
European decoration, prints 529
European Enamels 1016
Evan-Thomas, O. 1777, 1778
Evans, J. 924
Ewerbeck, F. 1715
Exhibition catalogues 239, 703-708, 712, 726, **733**, 741, 743, **747, 748, 749**, 750, 790, 809, 925, 1017, 1018, 1032, 1033, 1038, 1111, 1218, 1335, 1744, 1749-1751, 1753, 1762, (1780)

F

Fabergé, P. C. 925, 926
Facey, J. W. 359, 385
Fahrenkamp, E. 439
Falke, O. von 1196
Falkner, F. 1039
Fans 1702c
Fantetti, C. 646
Farleigh, J. 736-738
Farr, M. 739
Fastnedge, R. 53, 109, 187
Fatio, E. **1903**-1905

Faucci, R. 632
Fawkes, F. A. 54
Feltrini, A. de C. 1483
Ferdinand, L. 1544
Ferrari, G. 360, 824
Ferri, C. 1602
Festival of Britain 740
Feuchère, L. 361
Feulner, A. 55
Ffoulkes, C. 825
Field, J. 1779
Fife House 819
Firegrates and stoves 357, 471, 477, 479, 519, 804, 805, 812, 858, 873, 875, 882
Fischbach, F. 1313
Fisher, A. 1040
Fisher, J. 741
Fisher, S. W. 1190
Fizaine 927
Fleming, A. 1265
Fletcher, H. 1414
Flood, P. 790
Floors 627, 628, 630, 656, 657, 628, **662**, 664, 668, **1955**
Florence 1483
  S. Miniato 1939
  Uffizi Gallery **629**
Foley, E. 56
Follot, P. 365
Folnesics, J. 362
Fontainebleau 428, 450, 454, 613
Fonthill 475
Foot, J. & Sons Ltd 57
Ford, R. 363
Fordrin, L. 826, 877
Die Form ohne Ornament 730
Forster, H. R. 1758
Fournier Frères 827
Fowler, C. 797
Fowler, J. 364
Fowler, W. **662**
Fra by og Kirke 238
Francard, L. 1482
Franks, Sir A. W. 1041, 1215, 1426
Franque, F. 449
Fréchet, A. 365
Frederiksen, E. E. 735
French Ecclesiastical buildings 614
French Furniture 52
French Interior design, prints **527**
French School, drawings **1918-1926**
Frescoes 602, **610, 611**, 615, **618**, 619, 639-645, 650, 663
Frey, G. 58
Frezza, G. G. 602
Frogmore House 467
Fröhner, W. 1607
Frost, A. C. 1232, 1233
Frothingham, A. W. 1216
Fry, M. 63, 745
Fry, R. 441
Funcke, C. 1196
Furniture and Decoration 59
Furniture Gazette 131
Furniture History Society 60
Furniture Trades Organiser 61
Furnival, W. J. 1042, 1191

G

Gabriel, J. 1482
Galestruzzi, G. B. 633, 636, 1626
Garde-Meuble, Le 62
Garden furniture and ornament 229, 230, 232, 404, 419, 1713
Gardner, E. A. 1608
Gardner, J. S. 828-830, 853, 878
Garner, F. H. 1044
Garner, H. 1043
Gaunt, W. 1125
Gautier, P. **831**
Geddes, N. Bel 742
Geerlings, G. K. 832, 833
Geffroy, G. 743
Gélis-Didot, P. 613, 614
Gerente, H. 808
German procelain 1133, 1180
German School drawings 1927, **1928**
Gerspach, M. 1314
Die Gewerbehalle 1440, 1441
Giacomotti, J. 1045
Giardini, G. **928, 929, 1929-1935**
Gibb, W. **1780**
Gibbard, R. 233
Gibberd, F. 63, 776
Gibbons, G. 1716, 1717
Gibbs, J. 1442-1444
Gibbs, W. 494
Gilbert, C. 126
Gilbert, J. 1936
Gill, N. 1473
Gimson, E. 64, 163, 239
Giniez, J. E. F. 1210
Giovanni da Udine 618, 647, 1483
Giovannini, G. 610
Giulio Romano 368, 615, 616, 618, 639
Glaisher, J. W. L. 1018, 1146
Glass Manufactories 1217
Glass-Painters, British Society of Master 1207
Glass Sellers, Company of 1271
Glaziers, Company of 1260
Gloag, J. 65-68, 744-746, 834
Gloucester Cathedral 1951
Godden, G. A. 1046-1054, 1087, 1315
Godon, J. 1316
Godwin, E. W. 702, 1344
Gold, S. M. 1272
Goldfinger, E. 63, 69
Goldicutt, J. 617
Goldscheider **747**
Gomme E. Ltd 70
Gompertz, G. St. G. M. 1055-1057
Gooch Catalogue 131
Goodall, W. **753**
Goodhue, B. G. 813
Goodman, J. B. 95
Goodman, W. L. 71, 72
Gorham Manufacturing Co 1938
Gori, A. 629
Gori, A. F. 990
Gosse, E. 702
Gothic Furniture 45-47, 152-155, 202, 203, 213, 242, 1964
Gotz, G. B. 1445

Grande argenterie 930
Grandjean, S. 73
Grandjean de Montigny, A. 366
Granet, J. J. 367
Gray, J. M. 969, 970
Gray, M. 776, 780
Great Exhibition 1851 703-705, **748-753, 785,** 797, 798
  Medals 748
  Official Catalogue **748**-751
Greek Vases 1603, **1606,** 1607-1610, 1616-1620, 1627, 1631
Green, D. 1058
Greenwood, W. E. 368
Grey, J. S. 1938
Greystoke, Cumberland 1962
Gribelin, S. 1446, 1474
Griggs, F. L. 358
Griggs, W. 835
Grimthorpe, Lord 1805
Grimwade, A. G. 931, 1746
Gropius, W. 1727, 1229
Grotesques 1415, 1483, 1489, 1509c, **1943**
Groult, A. 365
Gruner, L. **618,** 619, 1447
Gucht, G. van der 965
Guérinet, A. 1317, 1318
Guest, M. J. 1756
Guild of Handicraft 714, 715, **902, 903,** 916
Guillaumot, A. A. 1937
Guilmard, D. **74,** 369
Guns 1782, 1786

H

Haberfeld, H. 754
Haddon Hall 205
Haghe, L. 752
Haghia Sophia, Trebizond 665
Hahm, K. 75
Haiger, E. 438
Halfpenny, J. 1448, 1449
Halfpenny, W. & J. **370-373**
Hall, H. B. 1059
Hall, J. P. 1266
Hamelin-Bergeron, P. 11
Hamilton, Duke of 1747, 1748
Hamilton, Sir W. **1609, 1610,** 1623
Hampton Court Palace 205, 467, 822, 877, 878
Hamptons 131
Hancock, R. 1060
Handley-Read, C. 79, 1749
Hanhart, M. 1524
Harden, D. B. 1218
Hardivillier, C. A. d' 649
Hardwick Hall 205
Harris, E. 3
Harris, J. 76, 836
Harris, M. & Sons 77
Harris & Sheldon Ltd. 837
Harrison, F. 1219
Harrison, M. 1209
Hartley, Greens & Co. 1104
Hartshorne, A. **1220**
Haslem, J. 1061
Hasluck, P. N. 78

INDEX

Hatfield House 205
Havell, D. 467
Haweis, Mrs. H. R. 374
Hay, D. R. 1450
Hayden, A. 1062
Haydon, B. R. 612
Haynes, E. B. 1221
Hayward, H. 79, 1458
Hayward, J. F. 932
Heal, Sir A. 80, 163, 382, 728, 743, 933
Heaton, Butler & Bayne 1938, **1940**
Heaton, J. A. 81, 375, 376, 377
Hefner-Altenek, J. H. von 82
Heidrich, M. 438
Heijnines, P. **1939**
Heiligenthal, J. J. **320, 321**
Hendley, T. H. **934**
Hepplewhite, A. & Co. 83, 84
Hepplewhite, G. 81, 85, 139
Herculaneum **1706**, 1751
Héré de Corny, E. 838
Heritage, R. 233
Hertel, G. L. **86**
Hertel, J. G. 1451
Hess, H. 1214
Hessling, E. 378
Hettwig, C. 87
Hevesi, L. 754
Hibon, A. 810
Higgins, R. A. 1063
Higgins, W. Mullingar 379
High Wycombe furniture 226
Hill, O. 384
Hillerin, J. de 460
Hillier, B. 1064, 1065, 1718, 1719
Hillyard, W. H. 494
Himmelheber, G. 88
Hinckley, F. L. 89
Hindley & Wilkinson Ltd 90
Hipkins, A. J. **1780**
Hirth, G. 380
Hittorff, A. 618
Hix, J. 1222
H. L., catalogue 91
Hobson, R. L. 1017, **1066**, 1067
Hodgkin, J. E. & E. 1068
Hoever, O. 839
Hoffmann, H. 381
Hoffmann, J. 116, 402, 438, 734, 754
Hofmann, F. H. 1197
Holbein, H. 1534
Holbourne Ltd 92
Holgate, D. 1069
Holiday, H. 1223, 1940
Holland, M. 935
Holland, H. 140
Holme, C. 382, 754, 755, 936
Holme, G. 756
Holmes, J. M. 383
Homes and Gardens 384
Honey, W. B. 1070-1074, 1224
Honour, H. 79, 93
Hoole, Henry E. & Co. 782, 873
Hooper, L. 1319
Hope, T. 76, 94, 140
Hopkinson, J. 95
Hoppenhaupt, J. M. **96**
Hoppus, E. 1452
Horder, P. M. 455
Horkstow mosaics 628
Houghton House 503

House Decorator and School of Design 385
Howard, D. S. 1075
Huber, A. 97
Huetson, T. L. 1320
Hugh, A. 1202
Hughes, G. B. 937, 1076, (1077)
Hughes, G. R. 938
Hughes, H. 1941
Hughes, T. 1321, (1077)
Huguet, B. 310
Hullmandel, C. J. 819
Hulme, F. E. 98, 1454, 1455
Hulst, R. A. d' 1322
Huquier, G. 1418, 1453, **1604**
Hurlbutt, F. 1078, 1079
Hurrell, J. W. 99
Hussey, C. 483
Hutchinson, F. E. 1225
Huth, H. 79, 162a
Hutton, E. 620
Hyde, J. A. 1080

I

Illustrations of Art Manufactures 757
Image, S. 382
Importation of earthenware 1081
Ince & Mayhew 30, 100
Indian Art & Industry, Journal 934
Industrial art 758
Industrial Design 169, 361, 771, 774-777, 787, 787a, 791, 797, 798, 1730
Intarsia 1b, 102, 1551
International Exhibition
 1862 707, 708, 791
 1925 759
Ionides, B. 386, 387, 455
Irish Glass 1226
Islamic pottery 1022, 1101
Issy, Château 1482
Italian School, Drawings 1942-1949
Ivories 1737, 1783

J

Jack, G. 101
Jackson, C. 939
Jackson, F. E. 728
Jackson, F. G. 1456
Jackson, F. H. 102
Jackson, Mrs. F. Nevill 1323
Jackson, George & Sons 388, 389, 506
Jacob, G. 147
Jacob-Desmalter, F-H-J. 73
Jacobs, B. 1324
Jacobson & Co. 390
Jacoby, H. 1325
Jacquemart, A. 1082
James, J. **1482**
Janneau, G. 1267
Janneret, L. 1484
Japanese Pottery 1083
Japanese textile printing **1326**

Japanning **198**, 1518
Jaquet, E. 1803
Jennings, A. S. 392
Jennings, H. J. 391
Jenyns, R. S. 1083, 1084, 1720
Jervis, S. 103
Jesurum, E. 1323
Jewelry 901g, 901h, 901i, 914, 918, 924, 926, **934**, 936, 941, 948, 966, 968, 973, 975, 978, 982, 1446, 1474, 1480, 1534-1536, 1751, 1754
Jewitt, L. 8, **1085-1087**
Jewson, N. 240
J. F. K. & Z. **1950**
Joel, D. 104
John, W. D. 1088-1092
Johnson, T. **1457**, 1458, 1561
Jones, B. 105
Jones, E. A. 920, 940
Jones, I. **503**, 836, 1547
Jones, J. 106
Jones, M. W. 1327
Jones, O. 1252, 1459-1461, 1462-1466, 1467-1471
Jones, T. E. 797
Jones & Willis 1906
Jonge, C. H. de 1093
Jonquet, A. 107
Joubert, F. E. 1408
Jourdain, F. 365, 393
Jourdain, M. 49, 50, 108-110, 164, 394-399, 1720
Jousse, M. 840
Jouvenet, J-B. 367
Jouy Manufactory 1305
Joy, E. T. 79
Julienne, E. 941
Jupe, R. 111, 112

K

Kahn 525
Kalff, L. C. 1825
Kalnein, W. G. 1721
Kambly, J. M. 44
Kampmann, H. **400**
Kaufman Collection 1929
Kazakova, L. 1268
Kelly, A. 401
Kempe, C. E. **1951**
Kendrick, A. F. 1328
Kent, W. 503, 1547
Kenyon, G. H. 1227
Kidson, J. R. & F. 1105
Kindts, E. J. 113
King, T. H. 942
King, W. 1094, 1192
Kirkerup, A. **400**
Klein Möbel-Tischler 114
Klimsch, K. 1472
Knight, C. 760
Knight, F. 1473, 1474
Knole 205
Knowles, J. A. 1228
Koch, A. 402
Kolb & Hogg 1475
Konody, P. G. 722
Korn, A. 1229, 1230
Kornwolf, J. D. 716
Koyama, F. 1095
Krafft, A. 1252

L

Krammer, G. 103, 1476
Krauth, T. 115, 116
Kunst und Kunsthandwerk am Bau 761

Lacroix, M. 341
Lace 1301p, 1320, 1323, **1352**
Laffillée, H. 614
La Fosse, C. de 367
La Joue, J. de **1477-1479**
Laking, G. F. 117
Lalique, R. 365
Lalonde, R. **118**, 1952, 1953
Lamb, E. 125
Lamerie, P. de 943
Lamour, J. **841, 842**
Lamprey, J. H. 758
Lancaster, H. B. 1096
Landhaus Andreae 332
Lane, A. 1097-1099, 1100, 1101
Lanfranco, G. di S. 1602
Langley, B. 403, 403a
Langley, T. 403
Langlois, N. 1480-**1482**
Lasinio, C. 645, 663, 1483
Lassurance 1482
Lasteyrie, F. de **1269**
Latham, B. 1102
Launert, E. 1781
Lavallée-Poussin, E. de 1484, 1946, 1947, **1954**
Lavers & Barraud 1940
Lawrence, F. 131
Lawrence, H. 1024
Leach, B. 736, 1103
Leaded glass 1206
Leather 1772, 1773
Lebas 1967
Le Blond, J. 404, 1482
Lebrun, C. 621, 622, **1918**
Le Clerc, P. T. 1484
Le Corbusier 461, 1229
Leeds Pottery **1104-1106**
Lefuel 473
Leger, F. 1335
Lehmann, H. 1107
Leighton, J. 1485, 1722
Leith, S. 1486
Lemprière, C. **1338**
Lenk, T. 1782
Le Noir, A. 1484
Lenoir, G. F. 1329
Le Nôtre, A. 404
Lenning, H. F. 1723
Lenygon, F. see also Jourdain, M. 108, 396
Le Pautre, J. **119, 405**, 406-415, 464, 487, 521, 623-626, 843, 944-947, 1474, 1482, 1487-1496, 1511, 1531, 1611-1614
Le Pautre, P. 416-419, 464, 521, 1482
Leroux, J. B. 420, 421, 1482
Lethaby, W. R. 64, 101, 702, 709, 711, 762, 844, 978, 1319, 1724
Levard 365
Levetus, A. S. 754
Levieil, P. 1231
Lewis, F. 1330

Lewis, M. D. S. 948
Lichtwark, P. 725
Liénard, M. 152, 422
Lightbown, R. W. 1185
Limner, L. 1722
Limpach, M. J. **928, 929**
Lindsay, J. S. 845
Liselund, Denmark **400**
Lister, R. 846, 847
Litchfield, F. 121, 1108
Litchfield & Co. 120
Little, W. L. 1109
Liverani, G. 1110
Liversidge, J. 122
Loar, P. A. **1111**
Lock, M. 1497
Lockett, T. A. 1112
Lockington, J. 1498
Loftie, W. J. 423
Loir, A. 654
Loire, A. 1482, 1499
Loire, N. 1499
London
  Adelphi 302
  Apsley House 363
  Bethnal Green Museum 1041
  British Museum 1218, 1619, 1744
  Broadcasting House 333
  Buckingham House/Palace 467, 619, 822
  Carlton Hotel 1956
  Carlton House 467, 483
  Chelsea Hospital 205, 822, 1914
  Cumberland Gates, Hyde Park 819
  Dorchester House 486, 782
  Greenwich 822
  Grocer's Hall 322
  Houses of Parliament 612
  House of Commons 170
  House of Lords 242, **1338**
  Kensington Palace 467
  Kenwood House **302, 303**
  Lansdowne House 302, 1750
  Palace of Westminster 658, **1338**
  Ritz Hotel 1956
  St. James's Church 1716
  St. James's Palace 467, 1936
  St. Paul's Cathedral 1716
  Somerset House 503
  South Kensington Museum 344, 781, 835, 1342, 1470, 1757
  Tower 940
  Victoria & Albert Museum 106, 217, 223, 487, 790, 1002, 1038, 1164, 1224, 1270, 1328, 1409, 1762, 1932
  Vintner's Hall 819
London Cabinet Makers 123
London Cabinet Maker's Union 124
London Carpet Co. Ltd. 1331
Longhurst, M. H. 1783
Longton Hall porcelain 1182
Loudon, J. 125
Loudon, J. C. 125, 126
Lossow & Kuhne 402
Loukomski, G-K. 424-426
Ludwigsburg porcelain 1180
Lurcat, J. 1335
Luthmer, F. 427
Luton Park 302, 303

Lutyens, Sir E. 163, 358, 455, 526, 879
Luxembourg Palace 654
Luxmoore, C. F. C. 1113
Lysons, S. 628, 1955
Lysons, S. & Robert Smirke 1955

M

Macfarlane, W. & Co 848-850, 1826
Macht, C. 1114
Mackenna, F. S. 1115-1117
Mackintosh, C. R. 93, 127, 382, 725
Macquoid, P. 51, 128, 129
Madden, Sir F. 1533
Magazines & Journals 59-61, 78, 136, 146, 350, 384, 385, 517, 702, **725**, 758, **783**, 784, 799, 1440, 1441
Magne, H. 428
Majolica 1110, 1143, 1144
Malavasia, C. C. 610
Malkin 1028
Mallet, J. V. G. 1012
Mallet, R. & W. 125
Mallett, W. E. 130
Malmaison, château 450
Manni, D. M. **629**
Manning, A. 1118
Mansart, J.-H. 367, 521, 1482
Mantons 1786
Mantovano, R. 616
Mantua
  Ducal Palace 618
  Palazzo del Té 615, 616, 618
Manufacturers' brochures 131
Manwaring, R. 132
Maple & Co. Ltd. 133, 134, 1332
Mare, A. 490
Marie, A. 460
Mariette, P.-J. 309, 339
Marillier, C. P. 1500
Marillier, H. C. 1333
Markham, C. A. 986
Marks, M. 1119
Marlier, C. B. 821
Marly, château de 1937
Marot, D. 429
Marot, J. 405, 464, 487, 1615
Marot, P. 851
Marquetry 1b, 102, (141), 1551
Marshall, H. G. H. 523
Marshall, H. R. 1120
Mason, J. H. 728
Masse, H. J. L. J. 949
Massé, J-B. 621
Masson, A. 430
Master Thomas of Durham 658
Master Walter of Durham 658
Master William of Westminster 658
Matthews, L. G. 1784
Matisse, H. 1335
Maturino, 1944
Maufe, E. 333
Mayall **785**
Meckenem, I. van 1534
Medici Tapestries 648
Medley, M. 1121

INDEX

Meissen Porcelain 1010, 1070, 1127, 1133
Meissonier, J.-A. 432, **433**, 434, 487, **952**-954, 1474, **1502-1504**, 1531
Menabuoni, G. 629
Menicus, J. G. 1196
Mennecy porcelain 1074
Merrill, Th. 439
Merton Abbey Ironworks 859
Meteyard, E. 1184-1186
Metman, L. 852
Meubles et objets de goût 136
Meudon, château 318
Mcw, E. 1122-1124, 1756
Mewès & Davis **1956**
Meyer, F. S. 116, 853
Meyrick, Sir S. R. 180, **854**
Michael, H. 116
Michaelis, R. F. 949
Middlemas, K. 1234
Middleton, G. A. T. 1501
Midland Furnishing 131
Migeon, G. 1725
Miller, F. 435
Miller, J. J. 1193
Minton pottery & porcelain, 1046, 1050, 1170
Mirrors 301b, 1254, 1953
Mitchell, J. 1339
Modern French decorative art 436
Modern French tapestries 1335
Moffatt, H. C. 137
Mollet, A-C. 437
Mondon, J. 1505
Monogramist, V. V. **1970**
Moorcroft, W. & W. 1033
Moore, A. 763, 764
Moorey, P. R. S. 855
Morant, P. 1338
Morell & Hughes 2
Morgan, T. 630
Morgan, W. de 1125, 1126
Morgan & Sanders 2
Morley-Fletcher, H. 1127
Morrell, J. B. 138
Morris, F. 1305
Morris, M. 711, 712
Morris, W. 709, 712, 765, 772, **1239**, 1727
William Morris & Co. Ltd. 765, 856, **1239**, 1344, 1351
Morris, W. & Co., (Ruskin House) 766
Morris Singer Co. 856
Mortensen, O. 1806
Morton, J. 1336
Morton Sundour Fabrics Ltd. 1336
Mosaics 601a, 617, 620, 627, 628, 656, 657, 662, 664, 667, 668, 1955, 1974
Moscow, the Kremlin 424
Moser, W. 754
Moses, H. 1548, 1616-1618
Mouldings 99, 135, 141, 193, 195, 309, 356, 503, 1411, 1480, 1908
Mountford, A. R. 1128
Muller, A. 469
Mulliner, H. H. 396, 524
Munich
    Marianhilfe Kirche 1214
    Royal School of Glass Painting 1214

Murals 603, 604, 616, 617, 621, 622, 632-637, 654, 658-661, 1483
Murbach, E. 631
Murphy, B. S. 857
Murphy, W. S. 1334
Murray, A. S. 1619
Musée Bourbon 1751
Muséographie 1726
Musgrave, C. 79, 139, 140
Musical instruments 1702f, **1780**
Muthesius, H. 438, 439, 521, 725, 729
Myer, V. 333

Mc

McClelland, N. 431
McClinton, K. M. 1785
McColl, D. S. 783
McGaw & Co 135
McGrath, R. 333, 441, **1232**, **1233**

N

Nahl, J. A. 44
Nancy 838, **841**
Nantgarw porcelain 1088, 1090
Nash, J. N. 752
Nash, J. 363, **440**, 819, 822
Nash, P. 350, 441
National Assn for Advancement of Art 787, 787a
Nattier, J. M. 654
Navarro, A. de 955
Naylor, G. 767
Neal, W. K. 1786
Needlework 1302, 1321, 1337, 1345, 1356, 1751
Nelson, P. 1235
Nesfield, W. E. 1957, 1958
Neurdenburg, E. 1129
Nevill Holt 1752
New Hall China Manufactory 1069
Nicholet, P. 1601
Nicholls, R. 1130
Nicholson, P. 141
Nicholson, P. and M. A. 76, 142, 143
Nicolai, H. G. 1506
Niemeyer, O. 402
Nilson, J. E. 1507
Noble, J. V. 1620
Nolhac, P. de 442
Nordhagen, P. J. 627
Normand, C. **810**
Nouveau livre d'porte d'la chambre 443
Nouveaux interieurs français 525
Nyberg, D. 1504
Nymphenburg, porcelain factory 1198

O

Oakeshott, G. J. 1508
O'Brien, Thomas & Co. 858
Oetzmann & Co. **144**, 145
Ogden, C. 508
Old Place, Lindfield, Sussex 1951
Olivier, J. J. **810**
Olsen, J. 1806
Oman, C. 956
Omega Workshops 441
Op Gen Oorth, J. 381
Oppenheim, Albert von, collection 1132
Oppenord, G. M. 444, 1482, 1509, 1807
Opstal, G. van 1544
L'Orange, H. P. 627
Orange, J. 1131
Orrefors glass 793, 794
Osmont 146
Ottaviani, D. **642**
Ouradou, M. 659
Overdoors 330e, 1907, 1920
Ovingdean Church, Sussex 1951
Oxford
    Colleges 205, 857, 1225
    Radcliffe Library 510, 512

P

Pabst, A. 1132
Packer, C. 147
Painted glass 510-512, 1207, 1210, 1212, 1219, 1228, 1231, 1235, 1252, 1256-1258, 1269
Pain, W. 30, 445
Palissy, B. 1118
Palladio, A. 1420
Palmer, T. W. & Co. 859
Panelled rooms 217
Panels & panelling 170, 205, 217, 330b, 406-408, 420, 457, 1410a, **1410b**, 1410c, 1410d, 1410e, 1410f, 1410g, 1482, 1509b, 1907, 1915-1917, 1923, **1954**, 1965
Pankok, B. 116
Panvinio, O. 1562
Papier-maché 320-323, 352, 388, 389
Papini, R. 768
Paris
    Élysée Palace 437
    Hôtel d'Auvergne 1482
    Hôtel Bielenski 434
    Hôtel Chatham 1956
    Hôtel de Clermont 1482
    Hôtel Desmarests 1482
    Hôtel d'Évreux 437
    Hôtel Galerie 1956
    Hôtel Jules Ferry 1956
    Hôtel de Lorge 1482
    Hôtel de Louvois 404
    Hôtel de Maison 1482
    Hôtel Maurice 1956
    Hôtel Ritz 1956
    Hôtel Roquelaure 421
    Hôtel de Vrillière 1418
    Les Invalides 367, 449
    Louvre 450, 613, 852

Maison de M. Dodun 339
Maison de Varanjeville 1482
Ministère des Travaux Publiques 421
Nôtre Dame Cathedral 659, 826, 1534
Petits-Augustins, Church of 324
Tuileries 340, 450, 473, 1482
Papworth, J. B. 467
Paris Exhibition
  1844 769
  1867 202, 778
  1878 770
  1900 743
  1925 793, 794
Parisian goldsmiths 957
Paris porcelain manufacturers 1134
Parker, B. 472
Parma. Camere di S. Paolo 618
Parsons, F. A. 447
Parsons, Col. W. 1510
Pasini, A. 958
Passe, C. de **148**
Pastorini, B. 302
Patents for inventions 149, 860-862, 959, 1259, 1337, **1829**
Patmore, D. 447, 526
Pattern books 215, 445, 1304
Paul, B. 438, 448, 469, 725, 729, 1229
Pauls-Eisenbeiss, E. 1133
Pavia, Certosa 618
Payson, W. F. 150
Peach, H. H. 728
Pearson, J. L. 1940
Pellat, A. 1236
Pellegrini, G. A. 612
Penrose, F. C. 979
Pequegnot, A. 1511
Pérau, G-L. C. 449
Percenet, L-N. 1621
Percier, C. and P. F. L. Fontaine 73, 450-453, 810
Percival, H. 1959
Pergolesi, M. A. 30, 81, **1512**, **1513**
Perkins, J. 1514
Periodicals 21, 350, 384, 385, 517, 526, 702, **725**, 758, **783**, 784, 799, 1440, 1441
Perrot, G. 1728
Perruzzi, B. 368, 618
Petitot, E-A. **1622**
Petit Trianon 454
Pevsner, N. 739, 771, 772, 780
Pfnor, R. 454
Phillips, G. 1438
Phillips, P. A. S. 943
Phillips, R. R. 455
Picasso, P. 1335
Picart, B. 654
Pierretz, A. 456, 1515
Pigeon, H. C. **753**
Pillement, J. 1516-1519
Pine, J. **1338**
Pineau, N. **457**, 458, 1960
Pinto, E. H. & E. R. 1787-1789
Pinturicchio, B. 618, 632
Pinxton pottery 1090
Piper, J. 350
Piranesi, G. B. 302, **459**, **1623**
Pirckheimer, W. 1252
Pisa, Campo Santo 663

Pitt-Rivers, H. A. L. F. 863
Pla(i)sterers, Company of 484
Plastering & plasterwork 99, 311, 312, 346, 356, 360, 390, 498, 506, 647
Platz, G. A. 461
Playing cards 1702b
Plinval de Guillebon 1134
Poccetti, B. 1483
Poelzig, H. 461
Poillerat, G. 864
Poilly, F. 462
Poiret, P. 365
Polidoro Caldara da Caravaggio 633-637, 944, **1602**, 1624-**1626**, **1944**
Pompeii 617, 1751, 1939, 1969
Ponce, N. 638
Ponti, G. & B. 964
Popelin, C. 1135
Popp, J. 448
Portefeuille des arts decoratifs 151
Portland vase **1630**
Poterlet, L. H. 1520
Potter, H. J. 873
Pountney, W. J. 1136, 1137
Powell, A. H. 64
Powell, H. J. 1237
Pozzi, S. 602
Praz, M. 463
Preece, J. 885
Price books 39, 123, 124, 181, 323, 859, 1248, 1707
Price, E. S. 1138
Price, J. E. 664
Pricke, R. 464, 465
Prignot, E. 152, 241
Primaticcio, F. 616
Pringuer, H. 21
Prisse d'Avennes, E. **1729**
Prodan, M. 1139
Prutscher, O. 438
Pugh, P. D. G. 1140-1142
Pugin, A. 2, 153, 154, **440**
Pugin, A. W. 93, 153, 155, 156, 242, 865, 960, 1438, 1521-1527
Pullan, R. P. 335, 1733
Pulawy, Poland **433**
Putnam, J. P. 466
Pye, D. 773
Pyne, W. H. 467

Q

Queensware **1104-1106**
Quellijn, A. 522
Quellinius, H. 522
Quennell, C. H. B. 384

R

Racinais, H. 468
Rackham, B. 1002, 1129, 1143-1146, 1164, 1270
Rainaldi, F. 645
Ramsey, W. 1271
Randau, P. 1147
Ranworth, Norfolk 1917
Raphael 368, 618, 639-641, **642**, **643**, 644-650, 1339

Rapin, H. 365
Rastrick, F. J. 1252
Raumkunst in Dresden 469
Ray, A. 1148
Raynal, G. 157
Read, A. B. 1827
Read, H. 774-776, 1149, 1730
Recollections of the Great Exhibition 753
Recueil de pierres gravées antiques 987
Redman, D. J. 1549
Reeve, R. 467
Reilly, R. 1150
Reitlinger, G. 1731
Reni, G. 611
Rhead, G. W. & F. A. 1151
Rhoades, G. W. 1961
Ricci, M. 612
Ricci, S. de 158
Rice, D. G. 1152, 1153
Rice, D. T. 665
Richards, C. R. 777
Richardson, C. J. 1528
Richardson, G. 81, **651**, **652**, 653
Richmond, W. B. 1223
Riemerschmid, R. 116, 439, 469
Roberts, H. D. 470
Roberts, J. 752
Robertson, E. G. 866, 867
Robertson, H. 756
Robins, F. W. 1828
Robinson, J. C. 1409, 1753, **1754**, 1757
Robinson, S. 1340, 1341
Rocher, G. M. 159
Rock, D. 1342
Rockingham pottery 1037, 1152, 1153
Rocque, J. 1414
Roe, F. 160, 161
Roentgen, A. & D. 93, 162, 162a
Roeper, A. 471, 868, 869
Rogers, J. C. 163, 164
Rohe, M. van der 1229
Rokewode, J. G. 658
Rolt, C. 1405
Roman pavements 656, 657, **662**, 668
Rome
  Baths of Livy 638
  Golden House of Nero 638, 1943
  Hadrian's Villa 638
  Opera della Providenza, chapel 1949
  Palazzo Cesi 633, 1626, 1944
  Palazzo Farnese **605**-609
  Palazzo Gaddi 634
  Palazzo Milesi 635, 1602, 1604
  Palazzo Pamphili 604
  Palazzo Ricci 637
  Palazzo Tomati 1623
  Sta Maria in Monte Santo 602
  Sta Maria del Popolo 602
  S. Orosola a Ripetta 1949
  St. Peter's 1933
  Vatican Loggie 618, **642**-649, 1489
  Vatican Stanze 640, 641, 650
  Villa Borghese 1602
  Villa Farnesina 618, 639, 650
  Villa Madama 368, 618, 638

Rooke, N. 1319
Roscher, G. M. 165
Rose, F. 110
Rose, M. 1154
Rossi, F. 962
Rothschild 166, 1155, 1156, 1755
Ross, J. W. 494, (495)
Rothery, G. C. 472, 666
Rouault, G. 1335
Roubo, M. **167**
Roux-Spitz 525
Rouyer, E. 473
Rowe Bros. & Co. 870
Rowe, E. 168
Rowe, R. 963
Rowell, J. 1272
Royal Parks 822
Rubens, P. P. 654
Rudd, J. H. 243
Ruhlmann, E-J. 365, 474
Rumley & Co. 1529
Rush, J. 1157
Rushforth, G. M. 1225
Russell, A. 220
Russell, G. 163, 169, 740, 745
Russell, R. D. 233, 350
Rutter, J. 475
Rymsdyk, J. & A. van 1744

S

Sabattini, L. 964
'Sable Plume' 1732
Saint Cloud, château 404, 450
Saint-Cloud porcelain 1074
Sadler, J. 1138
Sage, Fredk. & Co Ltd 170
Saint, L. 1202
Saint Denis, cathedral 324
Sala, G. A. 778
Salda 171
Sale Catalogues 1741-1743, 1747, 1748, 1752, 1755, 1758-1760, 1763
Salembier, H. 118
Saltglaze pottery 1113, 1128
Salverte, F. de 172
Salvetat, A. 1014
Salvin, A. 1962
Salzburg, Residenz 362
Sambin, H. **1530**
Sanders, W. B. 173
Sandon, H. 1158, 1159
Sarre, F. 1160
Sarreguemines 1194
Sarresbourg 320, **321**
Sartorinska, Princess **433**
Savage, G. 1161, 1162
Savorelli, G. 642
Saward, B. C. 655
Sceaux, château 404
Scent bottles 1781
Schachinger, F. 174
Schaefer, H. 79
Scheerbart, P. 1238
Scheidig, W. 779
Scheurleer, D. F. L. 79, 1163
Schinkel, K. F. 88
Schnorr, I. 1440
Schnorr von Carolsfeld, L. 1195
Schönthaler, F. & Söhne 175

Schoolbred, Jas. & Co 1963
Schottmüller, F. 176
Schreiber, Lady C. 1756
Schreiber Collection 1164
Schübler, J. J. **177**, 476-479
Schumacher, F. 725
Scott-Mitchell, F. 480
Scott, G. G. 1940
Scott, W. 1964
Scott, W. B. 178, 1531
Sedding, J. D. 709
Seddon, J. P. 202, 707, 1532
Seeley, J. 163
Seely & Paget 163, 384
Seguy, E. A. 1563, **1564**
Seidel, G. von 402
Serres, J. T. 481
Sèvres factory 31, 32, 753, 1014, 1074, 1123, 1156
Sewter, A. C. **1239**
Seymour, J. & T. 179
Shaftoe, W. 965
Shaker furniture 5
Shand Kydd 1344, 1351
Shaw, G. B. 702
Shaw, H. 17, 125, 180, 202, 836, 1240, 1533-1537, **1538**, 1539
Shaw, N. 461, 702, 707
Shaw, S. 1165, 1166
Shearer, T. 30, 181, 182
Shelton, E. 494,
Sheraton, T. 19, 30, 38, 76, 81, 93, 140, 183-187
Sherrill, C. H. 667, 1241-1245
Shinn, C. & D. 1167
Siddons, G. A. 188
Siena, Cathedral Library 632
Simmons, G. H. J. **1829**
Simon, C. 189
Simpson, R. 1028
Singers of Frome 856
Singleton, E. 190, 191
Sitwell, S. 925
Skinner, J. 656
Slipware 1028
Sluyterman, K. 482
Small, J. W. 192
Small, T. 193-195, 871, 872
Smirke, M. 1965
Smirke, R. 1955, 1965
Smirke, S. 494, 822
Smith, A. 1168
Smith, B. 1524, 1525
Smith, G. 2, 76, 140, **196**, 197
Smith, H. C. 483, 966
Smith, H. E. 657
Smith, H. T. 728
Snell of Albemarle St 2
Snuff boxes 901g, 907, 951
Soane, Sir J. 822
Sobotka, W. 381
Society of Antiquaries 658, 668
Society of Industrial Artists 780
Sognot, L. 365, 525
Soho Works, Birmingham 923
Solon, M. L. 1169-1172
Soulages, J. 1753
Southwold, Suffolk 1917
Sowers, R. 1246
Spelman, W. W. R. 1173
Spence, B. 384
Spielman, M. H. 787a
Spilsbury, J. 988
Spode porcelain 1062, 1187
Spriggs, W. 131

Spurling, P. 484
St. Edmond's, Norfolk 1975
Stabler, H. 728
Stafford, J. 2
Staffordshire pottery 1102, 1109, 1140, 1149, 1151, 1165, 1166, 1176
Stained glass 510-512, 662, 1202, 1207-1212, 1214, 1223, 1225, 1231, **1239**, 1241-1246, **1252**, 1253, 1258, **1269**, 1270, 1551, **1938**, 1940, 1941, **1948**, 1949, **1951**, **1972**
Stalker & Parker **198**
Stanislas of Poland 838
Stanley-Barrett, H. 199
Stannus, Mrs. G. 1247
Stanton, W. 857
Staplefield Church 1951
Statz, V. 967
Stella, A. B. 616
Stengle, W. 485
Stephanoff, J. P. 467
Stepney Pottery, Newcastle-upon-Tyne 1174
Stevengraphs (Thomas Stevens) 1315
Stevens, A. 486, 707, 782, 873, **1966**
Stevenson, R. 822
Stirling, A. M. W. 1126
Stockbauer, J. 1627
Stokes, J. 200
Stokvis, W. J. 1830
Stoneman, V. C. 179
Stoner, F. 1175
Stoneware 1032, **1111**, 1121, 1128
Stothard, C. 658
Stothard, T. 1528
Stowe 503, 1758, 1759
Strange, T. A. 244, 487
Stratton, A. 488
Strawberry Hill 1760, 1761
Streeter & Co. 968
Stritt, H. G. 489
Studio, The 755, **783**
Studio Yearbook of Decorative Art 784
Sturgis, R. 190
Subes, R. 864
Süe, E. 490
Süe & Mare 365, 490
Sugden, A. V. **1344**
Surugue, L. 622
Sutherland, T. 467
Swain, M. H. 1345
Swan, A. 30
Swansea porcelain 1089, 1090
Symonds, J. A. 917
Symonds, R. W. 37, 163, 201
Symonds and Yorke 63
Syon House 2, 302, 303a, **1511**

T

Talbert, B. 202-204, 1344
Talbot, W. H. Fox 748
Tallis, J. **785**
Talman, W. 857
Talor, W. 1028
Tang pottery 1139

Tanley, château 456
Tanner, H. 205
Tapestries 1301k, 1306, 1314, 1316, 1322, 1328, 1333, 1335, **1338**, 1339, 1347, 1348, 1751
Tassie, J. & W. 969, 970
Tatham, C. H. 491, 492, 971, **1540, 1541**, 1542, **1543**
Tattersall, C. E. C. 1346
Taut, B. 493
Tavenor-Perry, J. 874
Taylor, J. 2
Teale Fireplace Co. 875
Teale, T. P. 875
Technical Educator, The 786
Terms (herms) 610, 611, 1482, 1492, **1530**
Tesco, L. **642**
Testelin, L. 1544
Texier, C. 1733
Thessalonica 1733
Theunissen, A. 206
Thierry, J. **810**
Thiollet, F. 207, 876
Thomas, J. 1176
Thomas, W. 30
Thomassin, P. 641
Thomire, P-P. 1925
Thompson, F. B. **494, 495**
Thoms, P. P. **1628**
Thomson, P. 208, 209
Thomson, W. G. 1347, 1348
Thornton, P. 1349
Thorpe, W. A. 1249
Thurstan, V. 1350
Tibaldi, P. 661
Ticher, K. 972
Tiffany, L. C. 725
Tijou, J. **877, 878**
Tiles 1004, 1009, 1027, 1042, 1093
Tilley, F. 1177
Tingry, P. F. 496
Tinti, M. 245
Tipping, H. A. 210, 1717
Tischbein, W. **1609**
Toft, R. 1028
Toller, J. 211, 1790
Toms, W. **212**
Tools 1a-e, 71, 72, 167
Torksey pottery 1090
Tours Cathedral 1269
Towndrow, K. R. 486
Tower, W. 1951
Towner, D. 1106, 1178
Townsend, W. G. P. 1351
Trade Catalogues 4, 52, 54, 57, 70, 90-92, 120, 133-135, **144**, 145, 171, 174, 175, 222, 224, 229, 230, 231, **320**-323, 356, 376, 377, 388, 389, 390, 499, 715, 727, 766, 803-805, **807**, 812, 816, 818, 820, 827, 830, 837, 848-850, 856, 858, 859, 870, 875, 879, 882-884, 908-910, 927, 930, 968, 973, 1194, 1211, 1264, 1304, 1311, 1331, 1353, 1406, 1558, 1786, 1822-1824, 1826, 1830, 1961, 1963
Trafalgar House 2
Trebizond 1733
Treen 1777, 1778, 1787, 1788
Trianon 417
Triggs, O. L. 788

Tristram, E. W. 1917
Troost, P. L. 438
Trophies 1418, 1429, 1437, 1453, 1487, 1500, 1515, 1554, **1928**
Troyes Cathedral 1269
Trueb, A. 497
Truncheons 1775
Tsarskoie Selo 426
Tue Brook Church, Liverpool 1951
Turbayne, A. A. 1545
Turner, L. 498
Turner, W. 1130, 1951
Turners of Lane End 1064
Turning 11, 33, 194
Tymms, W. R. 791, 1405
Twopenny, W. 180
Tynecastle Co. 499
Tyneside pottery 1007, 1035, 1174

U

Ulivelli, C. 629
Ungewitter, G. G. 213
United Lumber & Veneer Co 131
Universal Decorator, The 494, 495
Unwin, W. C. 214
Upholstery 1e, 2, 43, 87
Uzielli, M. **1754**

V

Vacquier, J. 500
Valentine, L. N. 1546
Vallance, A. 936, 1734
Vanbrugh, Sir J. 822
Van de Velde, H. 116, 469, 725, 729, 789, 1723
Vanherman, T. H. 501
Van Linges 1951
Vardy, J. 1547
Vavra, J. R. 1250
Vaudoyer, L. 1967
Vennekool, J. 525
Venturini, G. F. 636
Verchère, J. 215
Verlet, P. 216
Vernay, A. S. 1808
Versailles 417, 428, 442, 468, 613, 621, 622, 1487
 Château de la Ménagerie 418, 1410g
Vico, E. 989, 1629
Victorian & Edwardian Decorative Arts 790
Viel, J-M-V. 1967
Villain, E-A. 1968, 1969
Villa Magnani 1967
Vincennes porcelain 1074
Viollet-le-Duc, E. **218, 219**, 502, 659
Voisin, F. 1484
Volpato, G. **642**
Voysey, C. F. A. 382, 725, 783, 724, 1344, 1351, 1438
Vredeman de Vries, J. 93, 103, 1530, **1970**
Vroom, H. C. **1338**
Vulliamy, L. 1548, 1549

W

Waals, P. 163, 220
Wagner, J. 661
Wagner, L. 660
Wagner, O. 725
Wainwright, J. J., & Co. 973
Wainwright & Waring Ltd. 879
Wakefield Cathedral, Yorks. 1940
Wakefield, H. 1179
Walker, E. 709, 712
Walker, W. 221
Wallace Collection 487
Wallace, W. & Co. 222
Waller, J. 1252
Wallpaper 1304, 1312, **1344**
Walmer Castle 363
Walpole, H. 1760, 1761
Walton, P. 1024
Wanner-Brandt, O. 1180
Ward & Hughes 1941
Ward, J. 1550
Ward-Jackson, P. 223
Ward & Nixon 1941
Wardle, P. 974, **1352**
Ware, I. **503**
Waring & Gillow 62, 131, 224, 391, 743, 1353
Waring, J. B. 791, 975, **1181**, 1552
Warner, Sir F. 1354
Warren, H. 1469
Warren, P. 1251
Warren, R. H. 1148
Watney, B. 1182, 1183
Watson, F. J. B. 225
Watson, R. M. 504
Watt, J. C. 1553
Watteau, A. 1554
Weale, J. **1252**
Weaver, Sir L. 226, 505, 506, 880, 881
Webb, J. 202
Weber, M. M. 649
Wedgwood, J. 1114, 1150, 1165, 1184-**1186**
Weerth, E. A. 1736
Wegert, F. 507
Weibel, A. C. **1355**
Weisbrod, C. W. **1555**
Welch, R. 792
Wellington, Duke of 363
Wellow, Roman pavement 656
Wells, P. A. 227, 228, 246
Wembley Exhibition 505
Westall, W. 467
Westmacott, R. 494, 495
Westropp, M. S. D. 1273
Wetherfield Collection 1808
Wettergren, E. 793, 794
Whall, C. W. 1253
Wharton, E. 508
Whistler, L. 1274
White, Gleeson 795
White, Gwen 1791
White, J. P. 7, 229, 230
Whitefriars Works 1237
William Whiteley Ltd. 231
Whiteman, G. W. 509
Whiteman, J. H. 1473
Whiter, L. 1187
Whittick, A. 1556
Whittock, N. **510-512**

Wild, C. 467
Wilde, O. 513
Wilkinson, Heywood & Clark Ltd. 1558
Wilkinson, J. G. 1557
Wilkinson, W. R. T. 976
Will, J. M. 977
Willement, T. 1240
Willett, R. 514
Williams-Ellis, C. 384, 455
Williamson, G. C. 1119, 1188, 1737
Wills, G. 1254
Wilson, H. 978
Wilson, J. 515
Wimhurst, H. 1971
Winbolt, S. E. 1255
Wind, L. 1559
Wind vanes 1914
Window Glass 1213
Windsor Castle 117, 467, 1252
Windus, T. **1630**
Wingler, H. M. **796**
Winkler, B. 1478
Winston, C. 1256, 1257, 1941
Winter, F. 1631
Woelfer, M. 232
Wohlgemuth, M. 1252
Wohnungskunst das bürgerliche Heim 517

Wolbeer, G. 1196
Wollin, N. G. 518
Woodbridge, C. 193-195, 871, 872
Woodcarving 8, 9, 20, 41, 82, 98, 99, 101, 141, 168, 173, 335
Wood Family 1039
Wood, J. 1174
Woodforde, C. 1258
Woodroffe, P. V. 1972
Woods 89
Worcester, deanery ceiling 1975
Worcester porcelain 1005, 1047, 1050, 1060, **1066**, 1067, 1090, 1120, 1158, **1159**
Workshop, The 1440, 1441
Wornum, R. N. 703, 1560
Wren, Sir C. 822
Wright, F. L. 756
Wright, G. & Co. 882
Wright, L. 519
Wrotham potters 1146
Wrought iron 802, 832, 846, 847, 871, 872, 1937, 1957
Wyatt, J. & S. 923
Wyatt, M. D. 723, 797, 975, 979, 980, 1973-**1978**
Wynn, Sir W. W. 303

Y

Yamanaka & Co. Inc. 1763
Yapp, G. W. 798, 981
Yates & Hamper **807**
Yerbury, F. R. 520
York Minster 138, 1219, 1252, 1448, 1449
Young, D. & B. 233
Young & Marten 883, 884
Younghusband, Sir G. 982
Yuzen Stencils **1326**

Z

Za(h)n, B. 1531
Zanotti, G. 661
Zanuso, M. 234
Ziegler, J. 1189
Zucchi, A. 302
Zucchi, J. **1979**
Zuiger, E. 649

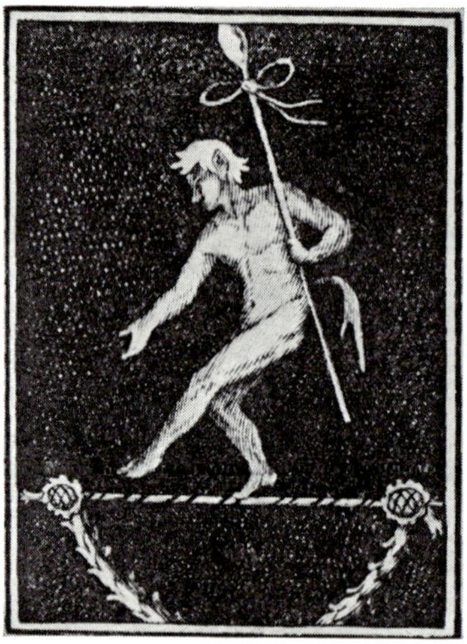